TWISTERS
DICK CATE

**ILLUSTRATED BY
CAROLINE BINCH**

YEARLING BOOKS

TWISTERS

A YEARLING BOOK 0 440 862132

Originally published in Great Britain by Victor Gollancz Ltd.

First publication in Great Britain

PRINTING HISTORY
Victor Gollancz edition published 1987
Yearling edition published 1989

This book is set in 12/13 pt Century Schoolbook

Yearling Books are published by Transworld Publishers Ltd.,
61–63 Uxbridge Road, Ealing, London W5 5SA, in Australia by
Transworld Publishers (Australia) Pty. Ltd., 15–23 Helles
Avenue, Moorebank, NSW 2170, and in New Zealand by
Transworld Publishers (N.Z.) Ltd., Cnr. Moselle and Waipareira
Avenues, Henderson, Auckland.

Made and printed in Great Britain by
The Guernsey Press Co. Ltd., Guernsey, Channel Islands.

TWISTERS

Chapter 1

Was that what he ought to be?

Billy was watching *Zed's Men*, and wondering if he ought to be the leader of a crime-busting squad.

Mrs Drury had told them all they had to think out what they would like to be when they grew up. That was last Friday. All weekend Billy had been scratting his brains looking for an idea, but so far he hadn't found a sausage in there, not even a mouldy one. Now it was Monday night – and they were supposed to write the essay tomorrow morning!

What he'd really like to do was play football for Sunderland. But he'd already told Mrs Drury that when they first came into her class, and she'd made a big joke of it.

'Is that all, Robinson?' she'd asked him. 'You're sure you wouldn't rather play for England?'

All her pets had laughed. Samantha Soskiss had nearly coughed her tonsils up. Pity she hadn't!

Billy wasn't going to have them all laughing at him again. He'd just have to think of something else.

His best mate, Elvis Potter, had known straight off what he wanted to be. Elvis had it all worked out even before they left the classroom. He didn't even bother to take the bit of paper that Mrs

Drury – or Mrs Dreary as Elvis called her – dished out for them to make their notes on. Elvis said notes only confused him. He was lucky that way.

And Elvis wouldn't tell anybody what his brilliant idea was, not even Billy; he said it was so brill that if anybody heard of it they'd pinch it straight away. Billy wondered what it was. Knowing Elvis, it was probably something barmy.

Billy often watched telly while he did his homework. He found it helped him to concentrate. It was just as well his mam and dad weren't in, though. They reckoned it was *impossible* to do your homework and watch telly at the same time. They were funny that way.

Also, they hated *Zed's Men*. If his dad saw *Zed's Men* was on, he always said, 'You're not watching that tosh again, Our Billy?' His mam didn't call it tosh; she called it rhubarb.

Zed Carroway – the leader of the crime-busting gang – was trussed up like a Christmas turkey, and half a dozen baddies were ringed round him. You could tell they were baddies, because it was the sort of series where all the baddies had bad teeth and big beer-bellies. They were itching to do Zed over, but Billy knew they'd probably have to wait till after the adverts before they were allowed to do that.

Not that Zed was worried. Zed was never worried. He was a neat, insignificant-looking guy. To look at him, you wouldn't have thought he could harm a fly. But in actual fact he had black belts in every single one of the martial arts. In last

8

week's episode he had paralysed a guy just by looking at him; he hadn't even lifted a finger!

Now, as the baddies prowled round him, threatening him with their crowbars and guns, he stared back at them with insolent blue eyes that looked about as nervous as a glacier.

Billy wouldn't have minded that – having insolent blue eyes that looked about as nervous as glaciers. They'd have been handy to stare back at people with. He would like to have stared back at Butch with eyes like that. Or Howells, say. Just lately, he was making Little Chuff's life a bit of a misery.

Trouble was, Billy's eyes weren't even blue.

So what! There were wine-lakes nowadays, weren't there, in the EEC? Butter-mountains. There must be a tiny heap of blue eyes lying around somewhere.

Billy was just beginning to explore one – the blue eyes were all squidgely, and kept leaping out between finger and thumb like greased frogs – when he heard his dad coming up Gordon fronts in the factory van. Billy knew it was his dad, because every time he changed gear the van groaned in agony, and because Dot leapt off the sofa to meet him.

A second later his dad came through the front door, did his usual poor imitation of wiping his feet on the doormat, nearly fell over poor Dot, and bombed through into the living room.

'How do,' he said, as he flew past. 'You're not watching that tosh again, Our Billy? Where's your mam?'

9

'Round next door, Dad.'

'Whatever for?' he shouted from the kitchen.

'No idea, Dad.'

She'd probably gone round there because he was late back from the factory again – Mr Murray, next door, also worked at the factory. This was the third or fourth time Billy's dad had been late back from work in a fortnight. It wasn't like him. 'I think he must've found himself a fancy woman!' Billy's mam had said to Mrs Murray over the backyard wall the other night. Of course that was only a joke.

'Get down, Dot!'

Billy's Dad usually took her for what he called a Jimmy Riddle the minute he got back from work, but tonight – especially as it was Monday – he wouldn't have the time.

'What's this your mother's got in the oven?'

He heard his dad open the oven door – smelt a whiff of hot cheese, heard his dad say 'Good God!' – and shut the door fast. Whatever was on the menu tonight, Billy wondered. Stewed head in cheese sauce?

'No idea, Dad.'

'And when's this stuff supposed to be ready?'

Ask me another, Billy thought.

'No idea, Dad,' he said.

'Get down or I'll murder you!' his dad said, probably speaking to the dog. 'And when exactly is she reckoning to come back?'

Couldn't tell you, Dad. I'm not a mind reader. Not yet.

'Don't know, Dad,' he said.

Meanwhile Toni Poloni and Emil were on their way to rescue Zed.

Toni Poloni was an eighteen-stone strong man in a circus. Last week he had held up a collapsing building with one arm, while he fought off three armed guards with the other.

At the moment he was driving their armour-plated wagon (disguised as a hamburger van) at ninety miles an hour over a ploughed field; Emil sat stonily beside him on the front bench-seat.

Emil had been shellshocked in the war and normally his face twitched all the time because he was so nervous. Only when he was in danger did he become calm, because he was the sort of chap who thrived on it. As Toni added the finishing touch to his driving performance by ramming straight through a brick wall, Emil allowed a faint smile to play over his lips; for the first time this week he began to look relaxed and happy.

'What time do you make it in there?'

'Nearly half-past six, Dad.'

'Half-past six! Half-past six! It can't be! I'm absolutely positive!' As his dad swept back through the living room, he said, 'You'll get square eyes watching this lot!'

It wasn't exactly the first time he'd cracked that one, either.

Then he clumped upstairs muttering the sort of remark under his breath that isn't usually allowed in decent books, nutty Dot pat-pattering at his heels, no doubt still hoping for her walk, poor daft, deluded animal.

11

Billy knew why he was in a panic. Monday night was Pool Night at the Club, and Billy's dad was always in big demand as a referee because he was fair-and-square and treated everybody even-handed.

He was a bit on the narky side tonight. But that was probably because he was worried about his job. There was some talk of the factory shutting down. It had only been open for about a year. But so had Northern Iron Castings next door to it, and they had closed down a month back.

Billy's dad said it was some fiddle. The firms got some money from the government, then after a bit shut up shop and moved somewhere else. Billy didn't understand it.

Zed had cut through the bonds that had bound him (he had used his nailfile!) and was now fighting his way out of the barn as well. He had already dealt with three of the beer-bellies and was now on his fourth. He took a sock on the jaw that sent him over a table, through a steel filing cabinet, and halfway through a wall. But he came out fighting, naturally, and knocked Beer-belly Number Four into the middle of next week.

Trouble was, it was just like Steven said. (Steven had married Billy's sister, Sandra, and when Belton pit had shut down they'd moved to Barnsley. They had a little girl called Alice Margaret Julie now.) Steven always reckoned that in all the fights in *Zed's Men* nobody had ever yet drawn blood. 'Where's the blinking tomato sauce?' he kept shouting every time he watched it (and he never missed it). 'Surely we can spare a

little blob!'

He seemed to be right. Number Five had just hit Zed over the napper with a steel drum. There was no sign of blood (tomato sauce), not the slightest smudge. Zed didn't even blink.

Of course, if Billy really *did* start off a crime-busting squad, he could make a start by finding out who'd been nicking all the money from the school porches since they'd started collecting for the Blind Dogs Appeal. The police had even been called in and the teachers kept having spot-checks at both gates at going-home time, but so far they hadn't caught anybody.

A lot of folks thought it was Elvis. But Billy knew it couldn't be. Elvis was a nut. He was always up to mischief, could lie like two gas meters when he wanted to, and his dad sold illegal copies of videotapes in Bishop Auckland market. But Elvis was no nicker. Of that Billy was absolutely certain.

Even the headmaster, Mr Starr, seemed to think it was Elvis. And *he* ought to have had more sense. He kept calling Elvis to his office and making him stand there through play-times. Elvis reckoned this was because he'd scratched the L off the sign for Peel Street, but everybody knew it couldn't be just for that.

After they'd cleared Elvis's name, the squad could move on to rounding up hijackers and solving bank robberies – that sort of thing. They might even get on the telly.

They could call themselves *Billy's Boys*. They could use an old TV detector-van to go round in.

That would be a good disguise. Also, everybody round where Billy lived would scatter indoors as soon as they saw it coming, because none of them had a TV licence (they couldn't even spell it!). Then *Billy's Boys* could get up to what they liked. What a great idea! Nobody would suspect it was them because they were all just school kids. They could get people to call out their names for them in registration, just like in a prison film Billy had seen. Elvis could be one of the gang. And Emma Ward. Emma was ace at gymnastics and scared of nothing. He could just imagine her abseiling off the school roof or climbing up the rusty drainpipe beside Miss Benfold's classroom. Of course, if Emma was in the gang he'd have to change its name.

Billy could just see it all in the local paper.

CRIME-BUSTING BILLY!

Belton Buildings schoolboy, Billy Robinson, yesterday brought to justice a gang of desperate ruffians whose burglaries and kidnappings have baffled the CIA, Scotland Yard, the FBI, Interpol, and the combined police forces of several counties over the last few years.

In an exclusive interview with this paper, and sixteen others, the young northern sleuth said, 'It was nothing, really. I put my success down to pure natural intelligence.'

Modesty indeed!

We have it on good authority that the Prime Minister herself is determined to reward this

14

youthful sleuth (it would probably be written as sluthful yewth; they made more mistakes than an England defence) *and on* THE WORLD AT TWO *yesterday she said, 'This is the kind of young person we are desperately in need of in our country today. Not a moaning minny, but someone willing to scramble to the top, at the expense of everybody else, and put the Crate back on Britain!'*

Here-hear, we say, Prim Mestinner.

It has further come to our ears that the Tyneside Tec may soon be flown, at government expense, to an undiscovered aisle in the Pacific Ocean for a well-earned rest free from school and other worries, including his mam and dad as the pear of them have recently been driving him up the—

'Who the devil's made all this mess on the carpet, Our Billy?'

That was his mother speaking. Did Toni Poloni have a mother? It seemed unlikely. Billy tried to imagine Toni as a baby. He imagined him in a high-chair, and the high-chair collapsed . . .

'Eh?'

'It's all over this carpet and all!'

She must have come through the back door like the Silent Menace From Outer Space and had now materialized just behind the sofa where Billy was sitting. She was holding aloft a dustpan and brush – her usual weapons of war.

'What mess, Mam?'

He craned his neck, pretending to be interested.

15

He knew if he didn't show a bit of sympathy, his mother might easily eliminate *Zed's Men* with a flick of her finger.

'This mess on the carpet! It's all over the shop!'

'Took me shoes off the minute I came in,' said Billy.

'Somebody must have done it,' said his mother, disappearing beneath the sofa back to do a mopping-up job on the enemy. A tick later she reappeared over the ramparts. 'Where's your father? Has he come in yet?'

'Upstairs.'

She went to the foot of the stairs and shouted up: 'Have you trailed this mess all through the house, Dick?'

'What mess?'

'Gritty stuff. It's all the way up the stairs and all.'

'Must've been summat I picked up on me boots.'

Brilliant! If Billy had said something like that, he'd have had his ears knocked off.

'Waste of time trying to keep this house clean.' Brush, brush, brush. 'You're getting worse than Our Billy, and that's saying something. Will you have time for a bite to eat before you rush off?'

'What time's it got to down there, lass?'

'Quarter to seven, Dad!' Billy shouted up.

'I'll have to get me skates on.'

That sounded a good idea to Billy. He'd like to see his dad coming downstairs on a pair of skates.

'I'll just scald the tea, then,' said Billy's mam. 'You're never watching that rhubarb again, Our

17

Billy?' she said, as she went through the room and into the kitchen. 'Time you were old enough to know better!'

Toni Poloni was holding the crooks' car high above his head now. Six of the gang were leaning out of the windows, shaking their fists at him. Toni just grinned back at them. He had wall-to-wall teeth, more teeth even than Billy's grandma (and she'd got three sets of falsies on the National Health in the days when they were still free).

'I thought you had some homework to do tonight?' his mam asked, as she came back into the room.

Emil was sixty feet up in the air, tightrope-walking along a high-voltage cable. A stick of dynamite was sizzling in his mouth (he needed his hands free to keep his balance), and he was hoping to drop it through a hole in the roof and rescue Zed. He had about three seconds before the dynamite exploded. He'd never looked calmer in his life.

'I've done it, Mam!'

'And what was it, exactly?'

Zed was covered by two shotguns. He was still filing his nails. He'd just persuaded the two dumbos who had him covered to step back right under the hole in the roof.

'Just had to think something out, Mam.'

'Answer me properly, young man, or off this rhubarb goes!'

'We just had to think out what we'd like to be when we grew up, that's all.'

Emil dropped the explosive, just in time. It blew

18

the roof off the barn. It also blew Emil off his tightrope (fortunately Toni Poloni caught him safely in his arms). Of course, Zed's eyes twinkled in merry amusement at all this stuff.

'Well? I'm waiting!'

'Eh? Oh – I thought I'd like to be a millionaire.'

It was the second thing that came into his head. The first was that if he told his mother he wanted to be the leader of a crime-busting gang, she'd have gone head-first through the ceiling.

'Humph!' His mother had the knack of looking like a dying camel when she wanted to. 'In that case you'd better start thinking about qualifications. Money doesn't grow on trees, you know. You haven't done a bat since you've been in that Mrs Drury's class.'

Billy's dad had been coming downstairs as she spoke, and he finished off the performance by apparently diving head-first down the last three feet. There was a bump noise, Billy's dad said about six words that wouldn't be allowed in a decent book, then Dot scattered past them into the kitchen, looking remarkably like a member of a newly-endangered species of wildlife.

'That dog'll have to go!' he said. 'It really will! It's just come down them stairs like a ton of bricks and nearly taken my legs from under me!' Then he turned to Billy. 'It's right what your mother says, Our Billy. You haven't done a bat since you went up last September. You'll have to mend your ways, my lad.'

'I blame that Potter lad,' said Billy's mam.

She only said that because Mrs Potter didn't

19

believe in killing herself with housework. People said her vacuum cleaner was under the stairs, still wrapped in the original package it came in twenty years ago, but that was probably a slight exaggeration.

'I don't know what he sees in the lad,' said Billy's dad. 'A proper liability. I wouldn't have anything to do with the Potters, me.'

It was just as well the kettle blew then, otherwise there might have been a yard-long lecture.

Billy watched the end of *Zed's Men* while his mam and dad had supper. In the end everything was all right. It always was. The poor people had their land back again, and all the baddies got ducked in the river, then ended up in the clink. Everybody was happy, except Toni Poloni, who was annoyed because now the danger was over Emil had started twitching again. It was the same every week. That was why Billy liked it. He couldn't wait till next Monday night.

Just before the adverts ended there was a knock at their back door.

It was blinking Samantha Soskiss collecting money for the Blind Dogs Appeal. Blinking cheek! And his mother gave her twenty pence. She'd only given Billy fifty!

He didn't say anything. He just sat on the sofa and sizzled, like Emil's stick of dynamite had sizzled a few moments before. Soskiss had already sold three miles more tickets than anybody else. She was bound to get the prize now. Life wasn't fair.

It wasn't fair for Dot, either, just at the moment. He heard his dad speak to her in a sharp way. Billy could imagine her face. She would be showing the whites of her eyes, looking all ashamed.

Billy waited till his dad had cleared off to the Club before he went in for his supper. Dot was sitting by the back door, wanting to be out for her walk. When he'd finished his supper he'd take her down to the Old Line for a sniff around. And maybe when he came back his mam might let him go to see Elvis.

'Mam, will me dad really get rid of Our Dot?' he asked, as he sat down at the table.

'Don't be soft, Our Billy,' she said. 'Your dad's only human, you know.'

Billy sometimes wondered.

Chapter 2

Billy often wondered if Howells was human as well.

He looked human. That was the tricky thing about Howells. He had big blue eyes, a bit like Zed's, only more innocent; more like a baby's than a glacier's. And he was always dressed neat and tidy. His shoes were always polished – his mam probably cleaned them for him every night. His mam and dad thought the world of Danny Howells. So did most of the teachers.

Even Mr Starr thought the world of him, and although he was a decrepit old dodderer (Elvis reckoned he'd started school the year before Noah), he still ought to have had more sense.

Because Danny Howells could be nasty.

Very nasty at times.

Like now, for instance.

Billy and his mates were having a kick-about before morning bell. Ossie Turnbull was fouling like mad, but nobody could say anything because it was his ball. Billy took the ball off Daz, avoided Ossie's attempt to scythe off his legs, then centred the ball to Elvis who missed – for some reason he didn't seem to have his mind on the job this morning – so Emma Ward took advantage and nodded it neatly past Joey White, who was supposed to be in goal. Joey was in line to get the top award in the Clown of the

22

Month competition, because although he was ace-plus at drawing and painting, that did not appear to help a fat lot, not when he was playing in goal.

It was just after Emma scored that Howells came out of the bogs and yelled out Chuffy's name.

Chuffy, who had been leaning against Miss Benfold's wall watching them play – he liked tapping the ball to Elvis whenever it came his way – went as white as a sheet.

To be honest, Chuffy – or Little Chuff as he was sometimes called – never exactly looked a picture of health. His big sister, Patricia, who was in Billy's class, was similarly pasty-faced. There was always something up with her. Even on a good day she always looked like she'd just been put through the mangle backwards. She burst into tears every time Old Ma Drury did her world-famous imitation of a fire-eating dragon.

Chuffy's face went whiter than white when Howells called him again: 'Over here, dummy!'

That was a good one and all, coming from Howells: he was pretty high up in the Bonehead League himself.

Except at football, that is. Even Billy had to admit that. Howells was a genius at football. He was so good that Miss Benfold didn't put him in the school team unless they were losing something like 9–0 at half-time. Then after five minutes they were usually winning 10–9.

He was that good. Lethal. He'd been capped

twice for the area schools' side, and was nearly certain to be playing in a month's time against Manchester boys.

Trouble was, he was lethal in other ways, as well.

Ever since Billy could remember Howells had been terrorising some poor mutt. If he wasn't swaggering and showing off his football medals, he was putting the fear of God into some poor soul. Next to giving people his autograph – a big flashy scrawl – it was the thing he liked most in the world. He'd been at it even when Billy was in the Infants'.

At one time you never saw him without this pin sticking in the top edge of his blazer lapel. It was easy to see if you knew where to look. Trouble was, teachers never did. Teachers never do. He used to call it his Pig-sticker. Nowadays though, Billy had heard he was more into elastic bands.

Lately he'd taken to using the outside bogs for his operations – hobby – call it what you like. It was an ideal place because of the Heap Big Stink that permanently lurked in there. All the teachers steered well clear of the place, especially Mrs Drury, who was always stuffing her ideas about Clean Air Policies either directly into your head or through your letter-box on scrappy bits of paper she duplicated on the school photocopier free of charge.

'Somebody's talkin' to you, Pea-brain!'

That was Barber, Howells' sidekick, who everybody called Sweeney Todd.

He'd just come out of the bogs with a titchy kid called Myers. Barber said something to Howells that made him laugh. He had lovely white teeth, Howells, just like an advert. His mam probably cleaned them every night for him as well.

Poor Myers looked so chewed up Miss Benfold's gerbil might have been at him for a fortnight (everybody called it Waste Disposal because it reduced Cornflake packets to scraps of confetti in two minutes flat).

'Come and see what I've got for you, weed!' shouted Howells. 'Got summat really nice!'

'Take no notice of him, Chuffy,' said Emma. She gave him one of her special smiles.

But it was doubtful if Little Chuff noticed her. He was looking across at Elvis instead.

Which wasn't surprising. Elvis usually stuck up for Chuffy. Only a week ago he'd put himself between Chuffy and Sid Butcher. And you didn't do that unless you'd grown tired of life all of a sudden.

Now, though, Elvis didn't seem to want to know about Chuffy. His head was down, he seemed to be concentrating on the ball, but then he mis-kicked – which wasn't usual – and the ball spun to Ossie Turnbull, who also mis-kicked – which was very usual – but who scored all the same, because Joey the Magic Goalie dived left instead of right.

Billy could only put Elvis playing this badly down to the fact that Mr Starr was never off his back nowadays. Plus a few of them – Daz and

25

Watty, particularly – were beginning to think it was him doing the nicking from the porches. Which was nuts and bananas.

'I'm counting to three, Lame-brain!' Howells shouted.

'Didn't know you could!' Emma shouted back at him. Emma was scared of nobody. 'Brain of Belton!' Then she turned to Chuffy, and said in a voice loud enough for Howells to hear, 'Tell him to get stuffed, Chuffy.'

'I berra go,' said Chuffy.

His face was whiter than whiter than white now, and his voice sounded almost as steady as a one-legged giraffe on stilts. He looked across at Elvis, who was still ignoring him and still mis-kicking like an England striker. Then Chuffy tipped his head back and sucked in a deep breath, and sort of shivered all the way through his body.

Although he was in Miss Benfold's now, Little Chuff was still inclined to wee his pants now and then, when things got a little bit too tough for him. Even his big sister still did. The Chuffs never got told off for it, though, because nearly all the teachers knew about it.

Mr Starr kept spare pairs of pants and that in his office for them, in case of accidents. Which was why Little Chuff and his sister were allowed to leave the room without putting their hands up. They could go out of assembly if they wanted to, even right in the middle of the Lord's Prayer.

'ONE!'

'Ignore him, Chuffy,' said Emma. 'He'll never

26

get to three, anyhow. He'll blow a fuse first.' She turned to look at Billy. 'We'll stick up for him, won't we, Billy?'

Billy wished she wouldn't say things like that. He pretended he hadn't heard her. But he felt his face going red.

'TWO!'

Chuffy was already on his way, clutching his battered old Amazing Spiderman bag. The way he held it tight reminded Billy of how Little Julie, his niece, clutched on to her favourite dolly when she came up to see them.

Billy could feel Emma still looking at him.

Eh, Billy? she seemed to be saying.

What did she expect him to do? Tie Howells in a reef knot and throw him over the school wall? He was only about a foot bigger, that was all. Only about two stones heavier. That was peanuts, of course!

'Billy?' she asked aloud.

Billy looked across at Elvis.

'What do you think? Should we do summat?'

'Aye,' said Elvis, 'fetch Owly Howells over here, an' I'll black his ankles for him!' He took a shot at goal — a hopeless shot — but it went in all the same, because Wonder Goalie Joe dived up instead of down. 'Or fetch us a ladder an' I'll black his eyes instead!'

The ball bounced off the wall and trickled to Emma, but she wasn't interested in the ball any more. Her mouth had gone as tight shut as a fridge door.

Billy had seen her like that before. She could be as awkward as a cuddy when she wanted to. When she got that feeling in her, she wouldn't let anybody stand in her way. Not Butch. Not even Howells. It was the same with her mam who was head of the dinner ladies. She was a right old bossy-boots. She even once told Mr

28

Fixby off for having too many second helpings of her roly-poly pudding.

That was how Emma was gradually edging her way into the school football team, because she wouldn't let anybody stand in her way. Because it wasn't any good just being a brilliant footballer, not if you were a girl. You had to have something else as well. You had to have a lot of neck.

'You want to cool it, Wardy,' said Elvis. 'You want to keep your hair on.'

Emma just glared at him. If looks could've killed, Elvis would have died on the spot at that moment.

'I think you're all soft, the whole lot of you!' she said. 'Soft as muck!'

'What can we do, man, Emma?' Billy said.

'Nowt,' said Elvis. 'Best to do nowt.'

He was right. It was a pity, but life didn't always turn out the way you wanted it to. And as Steven had said when they shut down Belton pit: *It's not a bit of good spitting into the wind.* That was why he and Sandra had upped their roots and taken Little Julie with them down to Barnsley, where there were some pits still open. *Might as well move wi' the tide*, he'd said to Billy's dad. Now, of course, there was talk of shutting the pit down there. So all the fuss and bother had been for nowt. Or as Steven had put it: *Out of the frying pan into the lavatory pan.*

Which was near enough where Chuffy was at the moment, because he'd just vanished into the bogs, closely followed by Owly and Sweeney Todd.

Emma had gone the colour of a turkey cock. She fired one last black missile of a look in Billy's direction, then swung away from them and went round the corner of Miss Benfold's.

'Where's she off?' Elvis asked.

Nobody answered. They all knew she'd gone for the duty teacher.

'Tapped,' said Elvis. 'She wants to mind her own business!'

'What for?' asked Billy. It seemed a good idea to him.

Elvis didn't answer. His face had gone as pale and mean as one of his ferrets.

Ossie Turnbull scored about nine goals in the next minute. He didn't seem to notice that everyone else had lost interest in playing.

As soon as Emma reappeared, dragging Miss Lipton behind her, everybody sauntered over towards the bogs, leaving Ossie to score goal after goal against himself in what was probably the most successful episode of his footballing career.

Miss Lipton was fresh out of college and taught computers. According to Mr Starr, when he introduced her to the school, she had more degrees than a ship's compass; but the funny thing was, whenever you passed her room the class was always flicking pellets about and generally running up the wall.

As soon as he saw her coming, Titchy Myers shot into the bogs to warn the others.

'Howells? Are you there?' Miss Lipton shouted over the lavvy wall.

30

'It's where he belongs, miss,' somebody in the crowd said.

'SILENCE!' shouted Miss Lipton, swinging round. She was one of those teachers who were always shouting 'Silence' at the top of their voices. Then she turned back to the bogs again. 'Howells! I want you out of there at once!'

Billy wondered if lady teachers weren't allowed in the boys' bogs. Or was it just the pong that was keeping her out?

Howells was still zipping up when he emerged.

'You've been a long time, Howells. What have you been doing till now?'

'Pardon, miss? Oh – number one, miss.'

He grinned round, displaying his perfect gnashers. A few of his cronies giggled.

'SILENCE!' shouted Miss Lipton. 'Are you trying to be clever with me?'

'No, miss. Honest, miss.'

'You'd better not be! Not with me! Now where is this boy Shufflebotham?'

'Shuffle what, miss?'

'You heard me! Shuffle –. This girl here says you ordered him to come to you a minute ago. Is that right?'

'Oh, you mean Chuffy, miss. I never knew what his proper name was. Everybody just calls him Chuffy, or Little Chuff—' another tooth-paste advert '—because that's what he is, miss.'

Another round of applause.

'Don't you prevaricate with me, young man! I wasn't born yesterday, you know!'

31

'Day before!' said somebody in the crowd.

'SILENCE, WHOEVER SAID THAT!' shouted Miss Lipton.

The whole crowd swung round to look. The only person behind them was Ossie Turnbull, still scoring goals against himself.

Miss Lipton turned back to Howells.

'Did you or did you not call this boy over to you?'

'Yes, miss. I wanted to give him some bubble gum.'

'He's lying, miss,' said Emma.

'SILENCE! I have listened to your version of the story already, have I not?'

'Yes, miss, but—'

'Don't you but me, madam! I am trying to get to the bottom of this matter and I simply cannot talk to two people at the same time! Do you understand?'

'Yes, miss.'

'Very good.' She turned back to Howells. 'You say you gave this person some bubble gum?'

'Yes, miss.'

'I heard him say he was going to give Chuffy summat, miss,' somebody shouted.

There was one born every minute.

'And where exactly is this person now?'

'No idea, miss. Soon as I gave him the bubbly he went on the bog!'

Further commercial, followed by further crony-crawling.

'Do not use that kind of foul language with me, young man! You hear me? And tell this

32

person – whoever it is – to come out at once!'

Chuffy came out at once. He came out so fast, it was almost as if somebody – Barber? – had given him a shove from behind. Naturally, he was chewing bubble gum.

'Are you this boy Shufflebotham?'

Chuffy didn't look totally sure.

When you first went into the Infants', Mrs Wendover always made you paint a picture of your grandad. She'd been doing it since the year dot. Chuffy gave his grandad ginger eyes and stuck them in his chin, and when Old Ma Wendover said, 'That's very nice, Ernest, but where are you going to put Grandad's mouth?' Chuffy stuck it on top of his napper.

Now Chuffy, dribbling pink bubble-goo, was looking up at Howells through his sticky-taped specs, waiting for a sign.

'Don't you know your own name!' sneered Miss Lipton.

The crawler brigade began to giggle.

Billy felt really sorry for poor Chuff. He was obviously totally flummoxed and scared. He was pink all over now, not just round his mouth. What they really needed was somebody like Butch to get Chuffy out of Howells' clutches. Butch would stand up to Howells. Trouble was, all Butch could think of at the moment was riding the new bike Daz had just got for Christmas.

'Haven't you got a tongue in your head – whatever-your-name-is!'

More crawler response.

'Say summat, Chuffy,' said Howells.

'Me bes' friend,' Chuffy muttered, looking straight at Miss Lipton.

'Pardon? Can you speak clearly? I can't hear you.'

'Me bes' friend,' said Chuffy, louder.

'Who? this boy here?'

'Me bes' friend.'

'You stupid child! Can't you say anything else? You sound like a needle on a record that's got stuck! Has this boy been sticking pins in you?'

'Me bes' friend,' said Chuffy.

'YOU IDIOT!' shouted Miss Lipton. 'YOU STUPID IDIOT!'

Chuffy suddenly went very pale. Most of them knew what that meant.

'Best not to shout at him, miss,' said Emma.

'SILENCE! You cheeky little child!'

'Look at his trousers, miss!' somebody shouted. 'He's peeing his pants.'

A lot of them laughed then.

Emma Ward darted forward and grabbed Chuffy's hand. 'I'll take him to Mr Starr, miss, to get cleaned up!'

And she'd dragged Chuffy across the yard and into the main building before anybody could interrupt or call her back.

Chapter 3

The idea of being a millionaire had never occurred to Billy until last night, when his mam had asked him what he was going to be when he grew up. But the more he thought about it, the more it seemed a reasonably good idea. He quite fancied having pots of money and driving around in a Rolls Royce, smoking a cigar that would last a fortnight.

Certainly Billy didn't want to end up like the tramp his dad let sleep the night in the greenhouse every winter on his way South.

Billy had only once caught a glimpse of him. He was a burly sort of chap in an old army great-coat, big red beard, probably couldn't even afford a razor. To Billy, he looked the sort of feller who wouldn't think twice about wringing a chicken's neck or helping himself to a dozen eggs. Billy reckoned his dad was daft to trust a chap like that.

As for being the leader of a crime-busting gang — Billy couldn't think why, but for some reason or other that idea seemed just a shade unrealistic to him all of a sudden.

It was five minutes since Mrs Drury had marked her register and taken in the Blind Dogs Appeal money (Soskiss was still in the lead by two and a half light-years). Now Mrs Drury was going round the class asking them

what they'd like to be when they grew up. It would take ages before she got to Billy and Elvis, because she always did the girls first.

'Because it's only polite,' she was always saying, 'and we do like politeness in 3D, don't we?' and the Swots Chorus would chant, 'Yes-Miss-ess-Dru-ry' in their sing-song voices, and Elvis would mutter 'No-Miss-ess-Drea-ry' under his breath and make everybody on their table laugh.

Another of Mrs Drury's sayings was 'Manners maketh man.' Elvis had once asked her if they didn't make women as well. He got a clout over the ear for that. He was always getting clouts over the ear from Mrs Drury. In theory Mrs Drury was all against wars, battery hens, electric chairs, white bread, hanging, atom bombs, and violence in general; but in actual practice she was never above giving Elvis clouts over the ear.

'Amelia, dear, what did you decide to be?'

'Please, miss, Miss World, miss.'

'More likely Miss Lavvy-brush!' muttered Elvis.

Amelia Petch was a long skinny lass with sticky-out ginger hair.

'Well, I think you stand a very good chance, dear,' said Mrs Drury. Billy sometimes thought she was a bigger liar than his grandma. 'And have you started preparing yourself?'

'Miss, Ah walk around every night wi' me eyes shut an' a book on me head in me bedroom.'

'Should try it on their roof!' Elvis muttered again.

37

'Is that to help your deportment, dear?'

'No, miss. Me mam sez it'll help us to walk proper.'

'I see,' said Mrs Drury.

Meanwhile Billy was gradually warming to the idea of being a millionaire and jotting down incredible ideas as his brain thought them out, taking care to lay down his pencil every time Mrs Drury swept her glance in his direction – just like these British prisoners had lain down every time the German guards swept their searchlight round in a war film he'd seen last week.

For a start, he'd have colour tellys in every room. Maybe one on the landing as well, just in case he missed a vital bit going from one room to another.

And he'd have to ban his dad from ever coming into a room when he was watching telly. His dad was a real menace when you were watching a really interesting picture, because he kept saying something like, 'Whatever are you watching this tosh for, Our Billy? I've seen it nineteen times already, and it's not worth watching.'

Or, worse still, just when you were wondering what happened in the end, he'd say, 'Want to know what happens in the end, Billy?' and when you said 'No' he'd say, 'In the end that nun is really a CIA agent and that Thermos flask she has in her hand now is really a laser gun, and the baddy falls out of the bomb-bay after a really long fight, and the pilot turns out to be

that other feller's girlfriend with a wig on.'

He was a genuine pain. Billy might even ban him from coming in the house altogether.

'Janine, dear? And what is it your ambition to be?'

'Nartist, miss.'

'Can hardlys draw her breath!'

'How very, very interesting, dear.'

He might even have a telly just for Dot. Nobody else in their house took much notice of her. She was particularly fond of nature films. When ducks skidded down on to ponds she tried to munch them off the screen. And when Wimbledon was on she was always trying to pinch the ball. Steven called her a canine delinquent.

Which somehow reminded Billy of Elvis.

Some kids called him Potty, and a lot of the time he was. First day in Mrs Drury's he put this Whoopee cushion on her chair and she didn't seem to get the joke at all. He was a right scruff to look at, always had about a ton of sleepy-dust in the corner of his eyes, and was always getting into trouble. Nowadays even Mr Starr was getting on at him, and he usually had a soft spot for Elvis because he was ace at football. Some people didn't want to knock about with him any more, because of this nicking from the porch business. Even Emma Ward was going off him. Billy just knew he was totally innocent.

Mind you, Billy wasn't too keen on Elvis at the moment, because last night Elvis had

crawled through this sort of sewer that went under the Great North Road, and the pong of the sort of sewer was still sort of clinging to him.

It was just as well they were sitting at the back, well away from Mrs Drury, who never budged out of her chair except in dire emergency (like when she sat on the Whoopee cushion), because Mrs Drury was sensitive all over, particularly in her nasal regions. It was likely that if she'd caught the faintest whiff of this particular pong she'd have passed out dead on the spot.

It was because of her sensitive nose that Mrs Drury couldn't eat school dinners or do canteen duty. She would have liked to, she kept telling them. Trouble was, she only had to catch the faintest hint of a suggestion of school sludge and she came over all funny. And it brought on her migraine. Mrs Drury had been attacked more times by migraine than Rome had been sacked by the Vandals.

Elvis didn't like school dinners either. His name for them was 'grotty mush'. Mrs Potter usually gave him a bag of crisps and a bar of choc for his dinner, he was dead lucky that way. And when the teachers were on strike and the kids had to get off the premises, she had let him go to the chippy.

One reason why Billy liked Elvis was because of football. Like Billy and Emma, Elvis had already played once for the school team, although they were still only in Mrs Drury's.

40

To look at him you'd never think Elvis could even lace up his boots, let alone play football. He was skinny as a runt, undersized, and always looked fit to drop. But he could go down the wing like a bomb, and he wasn't scared of anybody.

That was what was so amazing about this Howells business. Why hadn't he stood up for Chuffy?

Last year, for instance, when they'd played in this friendly match with St Oswald's, this big full-back (size of an elephant, feet to match) kept hacking Elvis down every time the referee wasn't watching. After a bit Elvis got tired of this; he turned round, gave the elephant a right welter on the shins and made the poor baby cry. The elephant kept hopping around on one leg and shouting 'Oooomelegooo!' (it was the first time Billy had seen an elephant do this), and after about five minutes they had to carry him off. They would have brought a stretcher for him, but they probably didn't have a stretcher big enough for an elephant. Elvis got a right telling off for it, and nearly got sent off as well. But Billy noticed that, when he came back on, the heffalump didn't come within five miles of Elvis.

Another thing about Elvis, he'd do anything for a laugh. He was brill at pulling ugly faces, for instance, which wasn't surprising really, because his normal one gave him a two-mile start over anybody else.

And last year when Miss Benfold took them

to the baths Elvis had dived off the top board, backwards, for two Smarties, and was eager to do it again. But Miss Benfold stopped him, because she said he'd only just missed the side with his head and if he'd hit it he might easily have damaged the tiles permanently.

'And now I think it's Alison's turn,' Mrs Drury was saying. 'And what would Alison like to be?'

'Please, miss, a ballet dancer,' said Alison Petworth.

'More like a clog dancer!' Elvis whispered,

while pretending to pick his nose. 'She teks size ten an' a halfs!'

'Now I think that's a lovely idea! Don't you think that's a lovely idea, 3D?'

'Yes-Miss-ess-Dru-ry!'

'No-Miss-ess-Drea-ry!'

Elvis was now drawing pin-men on what Mrs Drury called an Ideas Sheet – which was in fact an ordinary bit of paper.

He was always drawing pin-men. This time he had drawn a giant pin-man with umpteen pin-man arms stretching out all over the place, and stuck on the end of each pin-man arm there was a pin-man stone or circle – or was it a coin? All round Giant Pin-man, standing back in a big ring, there were titchy-witchy pin-men, all reaching up with their pin-men arms to worship him – or were they shaking their pin-men fists? Elvis wasn't exactly a brilliant artist, not like Joey.

'Please, miss, I'm doing tap at Mrs Porter's Academy of Dance,' said Alison Petworth. 'I've got me sustificates!'

'Well, that's marvellous.'

'And, please miss, Mrs Porter sez I can be in the pantomime this year, miss. Miss, it's *Babes in the Wood*, miss, and Mrs Porter sez I can be one of the dwarves, miss.'

'She *is* a dwarf, miss!' shouted Sid Butcher.

He grinned round and nearly all the lads laughed. Butch didn't exactly force you to laugh at his jokes, it was just that if you didn't you were liable to die at playtime.

'That will do, Butcher!'

Elvis was now drawing something cutting a circle round Giant Pin-man's feet. Was it a swordfish?

'And what would you like to be, dear?' Mrs Drury asked Emma.

'Astronaut, miss.'

'Good heavens! That's not a very lady-like choice, Emma dear!'

'Don't want to be a lady, miss.'

'Don't you really? You are a funny child! And what made you choose to be an astronaut?'

'I like getting scared, miss.'

'How very, very interesting,' said Mrs Drury, turning away. 'And now I think it's Samantha's turn. What would Samantha like to be?'

'Please, miss, when I grow up I'd like to be the sort of person who helps people in the un-developing countries, miss, working for some international organization like UNICEF or OXFAM, miss.'

Blinking heck! thought Billy. Soskiss had only said that because Mrs Drury was mad keen for them to win the Blind Dogs competition.

'Now I think that's a lovely idea, don't you, 3D?'

'I think it's a terrible idea,' muttered Elvis under his breath. Unfortunately, not far enough under.

'Did I hear you speak, Potter? Are we to understand that for once you have something valuable to add to the conversation?'

'Just clearing me throat, miss.'

44

'I've told you before, Potter, about a hundred times if I remember rightly, I do not like little boys who lie!'

She rose from her seat and began stalking down the aisle like the main part in the Midnight Horror Movie. Mrs Drury was one of the leading lights in the St Luke's Church Amateur Dramatic Society. She nearly always got the main parts because her husband played the church organ.

Billy glanced down at the piece of paper that Elvis was trying to cover with his hands.

He could see now it wasn't a swordfish. It was a saw. Somebody was sawing the ground from under Giant Pin-man's feet.

Mrs Drury had reached them now. She could make her eyes go worse than the Bride of Dracula's when she wanted to, and she obviously wanted to now.

'Take your grubby paws away,' she said. 'What have you been drawing?' And when the work of art was fully disclosed: 'What on earth is this, Potter?'

'Pin-men, miss.'

'I can see they're pin-men, you insolent child! What I want to know is, what are they doing on my paper?'

'These little 'uns are gettin' robbed, miss, and this big—'

'Be quiet, Potter! You know very well what I mean! Where are your notes? Turn over your paper. Let me see your work – you have done some work, have you?'

'Yes, miss.'

Billy's grandma was always saying that God worked in a mysterious way, and, looking at what he had written on the other side of his Ideas Sheet, it was easy to see that Elvis did and all.

There was one word scrawled on the page.

GINERSTESTER.

'What's this? What on earth is this supposed to mean?'

'It's what I want to be when I grow up, miss,' Elvis explained. 'Guinness tester.'

'I've never heard such stupidity in all my life!'

'It's not, miss,' said Elvis, 'me dad used to be one once.'

'Probably the only job he ever had, miss,' said Butch, and all those who wanted to go on living laughed again.

'SILENCE!' roared Mrs Drury, and Billy wondered if she'd been learning from Miss Lipton. 'I WILL HAVE SILENCE!' Then all of a sudden she seemed to notice Elvis's pong for the first time. She sniffed once, twice, then stepped back quickly, as if from danger. 'Good heavens, Potter, you smell exactly as if you've just crawled out of a sewer!'

'I have, miss.'

'What? WHAT?'

'I have just crawled out of a sewer, miss. Last night—'

'Away! Away! I have stood enough of your insolence for one morning! Off you go! You know very well where to go! Tell Mr Starr exactly

46

what you've just told me! AWAY! AWAY! AWAY!'
She waved her hand as if she was in one of the
church plays, and shouted 'AWAY!' again.

'Please, miss,' said Billy, 'it's the truth he's
telling you.'

'SILENCE!'

She definitely had been learning from Miss
Lipton.

'It is, miss!' Joe tried to say.

'SILENCE, WHITE!'

'Do you want us to go or not?' asked Elvis,
who was now standing up.

'AWAY! AWAY! AWAY!'

Elvis went.

There was quite a cuffuffle when he'd gone:
all the girls blew their noses and shoved their
hankies up their cardigan sleeves, and all the
boys made jokes about Tickler – Mr Starr's
bamboo stick. He wasn't allowed to use Tickler
nowadays, but he kept threatening to.

'And now, if we're all quite ready, 3D?'

Mrs Drury was more or less composed now,
though Billy could see that her fingers were still
trembling. She was always getting herself in a
stew over Elvis, just like his mam was over
Sandra and Steven and Little Julie, especially
now that Steven was talking of coming out of
the pits altogether.

'We may as well carry on from where we left
off,' said Mrs Drury, 'if that's possible, if that's
all right with everyone? Good. Let me see your
preparation, Billy Robinson. Hmmm. Not a
great deal, I see. Have you just written this?'

'No, miss.'

'I see. Perhaps you'd like to stand up and tell the rest of the class what you'd like to be.'

'Please, miss, a millionaire.'

Nobody seemed to think it was funny at first.

'Is that all? Just a millionaire? That's all Billy Robinson wants to be, 3D, just a millionaire!' One or two of them laughed then. 'You're sure that's all, Billy Robinson? You're sure you wouldn't rather be two millionaires – or three?'

They all thought it was funny then. They all laughed. Soskiss made another good effort at fetching up her tonsils.

Billy felt a right twit standing there, his face as red as a beetroot.

Chapter 4

Billy's grandma didn't think it was at all funny
that he should want to be a millionaire.

'Aim for the sky, pet,' she said. 'You never get
what you don't aim for, not in this world.'

She was sitting in her rocking-chair, smoking
the pipe that had been Grandad's before he died.
Billy had come up to visit her after seeing to the
hens and pigeons. His dad had sent some chrysanths up for her, and Billy had brought his
raffle tickets for the Blind Dogs Appeal. The
good news was that Grandma had bought
twenty from him. The bad news was that Soskiss had already been up and sold her five!

'Samantha Soskiss was one of them that
laughed at me, Grandma,' said Billy. 'They all
laughed at me.'

If I'd known that, I'd have told her me purse
was empty, pet. Mind, they might all soon be
laughing on the other side of their faces!'

'Howd'you mean, Grandma?'

'They don't know yet what I fetched you back
from the Darby and Joan Jumble Sale!'

'What is it, Grandma?'

'Wait and see, Our Billy. Everything comes to
them that wait!' She levered herself out of her
rocking-chair, grabbed her walking-stick, then
zoomed off in the direction of the kitchen 'First
we'll have a bite to eat. You mend that fire,

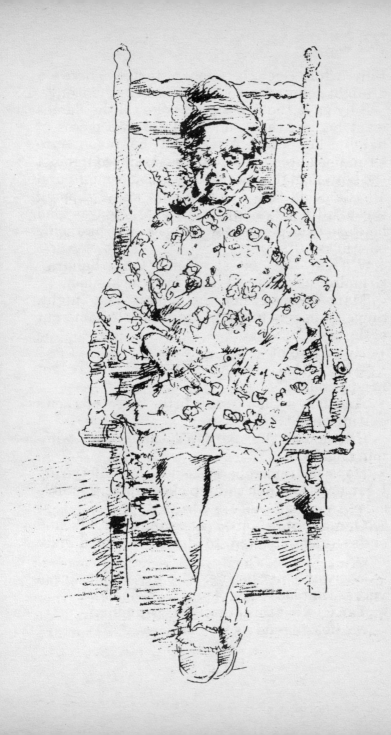

Billy, while I get the supper started. There's a draught going up my legs fit to freeze them off!'

Billy gave the fire a good poke till the flames leapt higher, then added one or two pieces of hand-picked coal. After that he made sure Grandma's woolly crocodile was shoved against the bottom of the door. There *was* a draught and all. He could feel it, like a cold knife, slipping through the crack under the door. He was glad he wasn't sleeping rough tonight – not like some poor folks.

'What's the latest from Our Sandra?' Grandma asked, as he came into the kitchen.

'Mam phoned her up again last night. Steven's nearly made his mind up to come out of the pits.'

'He does right.'

'What's this mysterious present you've got me, Grandma?'

'And how's that canny little bairn of theirs getting on?'

'Champion. Our Sandra's taken her swimming again.'

'Hope she remembered to use that safety-ring I got her. Another thing picked up at a jumble sale. And what else?'

'Our Sandra's joined a slimnastics club and she's forcing Steven to drink skimmed milk now.'

'She wants her head examining, that sister of yours. That lad needs plenty of beef in him!'

'Tell us what this present is, Grandma!'

'Me hearing-aid's gone deaf, pet.'

It was funny how her hearing-aid always went deaf at convenient moments. If you said 'Can you lend us twenty pence?' she never heard, but if they said on the telly her favourite programme was just about to start on the other channel, she twigged on every time.

She turned over the fish fingers and gave the instant potato a stir. She was a good cook, Grandma, not like Billy's mam who was always giving you what she reckoned was good for you, especially since she'd come under the Evil Influence of Sandra, who nowadays ate more nuts than a cartload of monkeys.

'Eh, Grandma?'

'Put them chrysanths in water, will you, Billy? Strip the bottom leaves off first, then they won't smell. That jug on the shelf'll do.'

'Tell us what it is, Grandma!' said Billy, as he filled the jug.

'Everything tastes better when you wait for it.'

'Just give us a clue.'

He knew that would get her.

'It's shaped this way on.'

She made a squarey shape with her hands.

'Is it a book?'

'Nothing like,' she said. But she hesitated slightly before she spoke, so Billy knew he wasn't far off the mark. 'It might look like a book but it isn't, if you see what I mean?' Billy didn't. 'Put them flowers out in the passage, will you, pet, it's over-hot for them in here.' When he came back into the kitchen she added, 'Mind,

53

I will admit this: there are words written down
the back – just like a book.'

'What do they say, Grandma?'

'Get the sauce out of the cupboard, pet. First
word starts with a haitch, second with a bee.'

'How many letters?'

'Get some bread out if you want some. Salt
and pepper. Four and five. Knives and forks.'

Billy tried to puzzle it out as he set out the
trays, but eventually she had to give him
another clue.

'I'm only glad the Vicar didn't see us picking
it up,' she said.

'What for?'

'He might've easy have been narked.'

Then Billy got it.

'Holy Bible!'

'That's what it says on the front. But in many
ways it's the very opposite.'

Did that mean it was a Yloh Elbib? Billy
hadn't seen a lot of them about, not recently.

'Want another clue, pet? It has a lot of numbers on it.'

'Pack of cards!'

'Warmer. In my day we used to call a pack of
cards The Devil's Book. And you're not far off at
that. It is something to gamble with, though.
You could make a lot of money with it. Not that
money is everything – look what happened to
Ada Troupe. Want another clue? There's something in it that spins.'

'Who's Ada Troupe, Grandma?' asked Billy,
because he was nine-tenths sure now he knew

what the surprise present was. He wasn't going to let on to Grandma, though. In many ways she was a bit like a kid – she liked to win now and then.

'Ada Troupe? I could easy have been one of the Bluebell Girls, if it wasn't for Ada Troupe.'

'What did she do?'

'Worked in Bishop Auckland pop factory. Put them two plates under the grill, pet, to warm up. It's a long story, Billy. Everybody knew I was the best high-kicker in Little Emmy's Dancing Girls. Ask anybody in Belton Buildings – they'll all tell you the same story.'

She flicked her left foot about six inches off the kitchen floor to prove her point.

'What happened?'

'She did the dirty on us, pet. That's what happened. That's what for I keep telling you never to trust a Potter.'

'I thought you said her name was Troupe?'

'The Troupes and the Potters are all the same stock, Billy. They share the same blood.' That sounded to Billy as if they swapped it round. *Here you are, Our Elvis, your turn for the blood tonight. I'll have it tomorrow night. Don't mek a noise, though, cos your dad's still asleep in his coffin.* 'Thick as thieves, the whole lot of them,' Grandma continued. 'Buy you at one end of the street and sell you at the other.'

'What did she do, though?'

'Kicked her clogs off.'

'But what were you wearing clogs for?'

'Because it was a clog dance. Are you listening

55

to what I'm telling you, or not, Billy? Get them plates down, and mind your fingers – they're hot. It was the high spot of the evening – me and Ada were the stars – and just when we got to the final chorus – five fish fingers, or six?'

'Six, please, Grandma.'

'She ups and deliberately kicks her clogs off, both of them. Deliberately on purpose, she did it – that was just like Ada. Fetch your tray in the other room, we might as well eat in comfort.'

'What happened after that?' asked Billy, when they were settled by the fire.

'Why, naturally, she made this big impression on this feller who had come up from London specially to see us.'

'You mean she hit him with her clog?'

'Not Ada. She was over-cute for that! She hit the fellers sitting either side of him. She was always a good shot. All the Troupes were. One of her brothers was a champion darts player, and the other got a medal for shooting a lot of Germans in the war.'

'Then what happened?'

'Why, this feller signed her up. There and then. What else do you expect to happen? Do you fancy the sauce? Don't drop bits on Grandma's best carpet, pet. So off she went to Paris, to join the Bluebell Girls, whereas all the time everyone knew it should've been me. She changed her name from Ada Troupe to Stella Knight and ended up top of the bill, whereas I ended up married to your grandad – a pitman –

so that was the end of the story.'

'And were you sorry, Grandma?'

'Not me, pet. I never wanted fame and fortune. Not me.'

Then she stabbed a fish finger and shoved it in her mouth, presumably to stop any more big fibs coming out.

'No,' Grandma was saying, 'me and your grandad never had a wrong word all the time we were married.' She was always telling that fib. They'd sided the supper things away and were sitting once more by the fire, Grandma puffing smoke from Grandad's pipe. She'd only taken up the habit when Grandad had died (because she didn't like to see a good thing go to waste), but she was already quite expert. 'I was always a proper Dainty Dinah as far as he was concerned. Wouldn't let me lift a hand's stir when he was in the house.'

But Billy wasn't really listening.

He was too interested in the present she'd given him.

This time she hadn't cheated, not a lot. It did look like a book. And the words *Holy Bible* were written down the spine.

But inside – as Billy had suspected before supper – there was a wheel that spun round and round, a wheel with numbers all round the rim.

And that wasn't all. There was a green baize cloth that unfolded to show red and black areas and a grid of squares, one for each number on the wheel, and one for the 0 as well.

There were bright-coloured plastic tokens

with £1, £5, £10, £20 written on them – all the way up to £100. There was a silver ball that bounced and whirred when you dropped it on to the spinning wheel, a well-thumbed *Book of Rules for the International Game of Roulette*, and even a plastic rake to gather in the loot.

It all reminded Billy of a film he'd seen about a place called Las Vegas. He couldn't remember the title, but it was about this chap who went to Las Vegas with only five dollars in his pocket and ended up raking in millions – simply because he knew how to beat the system. Billy remembered the scene where everybody was crowding round him, watching him win, and the heroine fell in love with him at first sight.

She'd been a dancing girl – perhaps like Ada Troupe? – but she'd lost her job, because she refused to kiss this fat ugly gangster who owned the casino where she worked. He even offered her a string of pearls, but she just couldn't have cared less.

The best bit was when the casino people had to send out for more money. It kept arriving in security vans, one after another, with escorts of police on motorbikes to protect them, lights flashing and sirens going.

Billy started to study the rules.

'He even gave me a fur coat once,' Grandma said.

'Did he, Grandma?'

That sounded like another fib. Grandma was always going on about how they all had to live on dripping-bread and fizzy pop (if they were

lucky!) in the Good Old Days of Yesteryear. She'd once told him that Grandad used to repair their shoes with bits of old car tyres. The old cobbler's last he'd used was still in her coal-shed. She didn't like to chuck it out, just in case it was ever needed again.

'A chinchilla one, pet. A chinchilla fur coat.'

'How could he afford that, though?'

Billy was still grappling with the rules. He imagined being able to beat the system, like the man in the Las Vegas picture. He imagined having X-ray eyes.

'He kept them, Billy. Hundreds and hundreds of chinchilla rabbits. He kept them for many a year. Until he had plenty of pelts to send off to make a coat for me – they had to match, you see. Of course, he never told me about it. Kept them up in his allotment and never said a word about it, till he walked in one day and handed it over complete.'

'And were you pleased?'

'Pleased? I felt a real swank! I paraded all over the village in it. I was the first one in Belton with a fur coat – even before the Co-op manager's wife, and she *was* a snob!'

There were a lot of funny words in the rules: *impair, passe, noir, rouge* and *manque*. Billy had a bit of idea what the last word meant, because a lot of people called Elvis that, so it probably meant grotty, as if you'd just come through a hedge backwards (or a sewer).

'Have you still got it, Grandma?'

'I haven't, pet. A tragedy happened. I went to

59

the pictures one night – it was to The Gaiety to see *Gone With the Wind* – I loved that picture, I saw it nine times altogether and never stopped crying – and when I came back the fur coat was gone with the wind and all.'

'Howd'you mean, Grandma?'

'Your Grandad's dogs had chewed it to bits, pet. You couldn't blame them, they were all Jack Russells. He was very partial to them at the time. Hunting was in their blood, see? They were all good working dogs. All that was left was little bits of fluff and half the belt-buckle. It was my fault for leaving the wardrobe door open. The smell must've excited them. They were only doing their duty, I never blamed them for it. But I never forgave myself for a long time after, and somehow I never felt the same about Jack Russells after that.'

'And did you never get another one, Grandma?'

'We never had the money, pet. We were poor, but content.'

'Did Grandad not want a lot of money, then, Grandma?'

'I can't say he did, pet. As long as he had his pint of beer and his dogs – and his pipe – he never grumbled.' Here she puffed smoke, which hovered for a second or so in front of the fire before it was suddenly whooshed up the chimney, almost as if Grandad was up there having twos-up. 'To my recollection there was only one thing he wanted in life, and that was a little Galloway – a pit-pony. And he never did get one

of those.'

'But he's got one now?'

It was what Grandma had told him before.
Grandad lived in Heaven now, with all the dogs
he'd ever had in life (1,275,951 at the last
count), and the little pit-pony he'd always
wanted. That had been a late arrival. Maybe
there'd been a change of government up there.
Grandma knew all this because he popped down
to give her a cuddle in bed every night and tell
her all the latest crack.

'Up in Heaven, I mean,' said Billy.

'Oh, yes. Certainly he has. No doubt.'

It was funny looking at her, all innocent in her flowery housecoat and funny woolly hat, and knowing all the time she was a bigger liar than Tommy Pepper.

'Want a game now, Grandma?'

'I don't mind if I do, pet.'

Billy was surprised to find she knew the rules already. She told him she had learnt them on a church outing to Blackpool. 'I only went into this gambling place because it was teeming down with rain,' she said. 'Only you needn't mention it to the Vicar if you see him.' Billy was going to ask her if she wouldn't mind being Banker – he fancied winning the money – but he didn't have to because she said, 'Shall I spin the wheel, pet?'

It was great getting all those tokens dished out to you. Billy had never had £1,500 in front of him before. It was a bit more than he got for his pocket money.

Grandma gave the wheel a spin and said, 'Fet vose chewers.'

'Beg your puddin?'

'It's what the French say. It means place your bets.'

Billy bet a hundred pounds on the red numbers winning, and scattered another sixty or seventy on some individual black numbers. It was a great feeling, not having to be mingy with your money. If he ever did get to be a millionaire, he would scatter hundreds – maybe even thousands – of pounds about wherever he went.

'Lay chewers son fet!'

'Come again?'

It sounded to Billy like something to do with teeth.

'The bets are placed,' explained Grandma. 'Ryan ne vat ploo.'

'Who's he when he's all there?'

'It means the betting is closed this round, pet. You can't add more money till the next go.'

Grandma dropped the silver ball on to the spinning wheel, and they watched it bouncing and whirling.

'Numero sixteen black est the winner!' said Grandma.

Billy had lost his hundred pound token – but he'd won on black sixteen, and when he worked it out he was fifty quid into pocket! Fifty quid! That was better than working for a living! It was nearly what he got in a year's pocket-money.

Billy liked this game.

They played for an hour, an hour that slipped away like a few swift seconds. Up and down went Billy's fortunes, round and round went the wheel. 'Fet vose chewers!' shouted Grandma. 'Ryan ne vat ploo!'

Suddenly Billy hit a winning streak. A strange feeling of excitement came over him, a feeling – a conviction – that he just couldn't lose. And he didn't lose. He knew then what Elvis's dad must feel like sometimes when he went to the races (he sometimes lost the rent money that Mrs Potter kept in a tin on the

mantelshelf). At one time Billy had over £6,000 amassed in front of him – that was even more than his dad had paid for their house when the colliery closed.

But then he did start to lose. Bit by bit and little by little. First he found he had no £1,000 tokens left. Then no £100 ones. Eventually he had only £55 left altogether.

'Fet vose chewers!' said Grandma.

Billy suddenly had a hunch. He just knew – deep inside him – that the black numbers were going to win again, just like the first time. It was as if someone – Grandad? – had whispered in his ear. Trouble was, should he play safe and bet on all the black numbers? Or should he risk everything on just one number? He had an idea that seventeen was going to win.

He decided to risk everything on the one square.

'Lay chewers son fet!'

She dropped in the silver ball. They watched it spin and bounce.

And land on a red number.

'What a shame, pet,' said Grandma, as she raked in his last few tokens. 'Never mind, it's time for *Sing Along With Stu*, and I couldn't miss him for worlds. Switch him on, will you, pet? He's moved over to the other channel now.'

Billy might have lost his money. But he had gained something: an idea. It began to dawn on him as he adjusted Grandma's patent coat-hanger aerial.

At first he had thought Grandma was win-

ning because she was cheating. She was a cheat. She was always hiding aces up her sleeve when they played whist for pennies down at their house, and pretending to be amazed when somebody spotted her.

Grandma's favourite singer, Stu MacPherson, swam into view, wobbled a bit, then settled himself down, as Billy did the fine tuning on the coathanger. He was singing a soppy song and had eyes like Samantha Soskiss's dog.

She probably had been cheating. But that wasn't the reason why she'd won, not this time. This time there was another reason, a pretty obvious one when he thought about it. It was just a pity that he hadn't thought of it before!

He smiled to himself as he rolled the discovery round in his head. It was a great discovery. An amazing discovery. One that could possibly open an awful lot of doors.

Just what on earth could he do with it, though?

Chapter 5

Billy was dying to try out his roulette game on Elvis, but he didn't risk taking it to school, because it was the sort of thing Mrs Drury would confiscate for nine hundred and ninety-nine years if she found it. He didn't even mention it to Elvis because he wanted to keep it a surprise.

He intended taking it round as soon as he got home, but his mam made him do his homework first, even before he'd had his tea. She was all of a fidget because of the letter they'd had from Sandra that morning.

Then, after tea, when he went up the allotment to see to the hens and pigeons, he had to cut some chrysanths because his dad was late back from the factory again.

When he got back home he twiddled the knobs on the telly, just to make sure he wasn't missing anything brilliant. There was a Tarzan picture on, so he watched that to the end.

It was great watching Tarzan throttling tiger-skins to death and swinging through trees in Technicolor. He particularly liked the bit where Boy ordered the elephants to rescue this lady who'd been captured by cannibals; he wouldn't have minded himself running about in a loin-cloth all day ordering elephants about and holding intelligent conversations with chimpanzees.

It would make a sight more sense than talking to a lot of people he knew at school.

Trouble was, as soon as his dad came in, he said, 'When's this tosh going off?' and every time his mam went through the room, she muttered 'Rhubarb!' not so much under her breath as well over the top of it.

It hadn't occurred to them, of course, that for the last ten minutes he'd been toying with the idea of being an actor when he grew up. They didn't realise that all the time he was watching Tarzan he was studying for his future career!

Grandma reckoned some of these actors earned a thousand pounds just for advertising dog meat and fitted kitchens. And Billy wouldn't have minded that – swearing blind he preferred Slurp dog food to any other, and then picking up the cheque.

But then, just when Tarzan was throttling a crocodile, he remembered there were snags to this acting business.

Like what had happened in the Nativity play last Christmas. Their class had done it and Miss Benfold had written a part for every single person. Pat Shufflebotham was an angel with only one word to say. She was supposed to lift up her hand and say 'Hail!' Everybody thought she'd end up saying 'Snow!' instead, but she didn't. On the night, she raised up her hand and said, 'Please, miss, I've forgot me lines,' but it made no odds anyhow, because all the audience knew the play off by heart to start with.

Elvis had been a cow. He had only two lines:

he had to say 'Moo' twice. In the rehearsals he kept making a muck of it and saying 'Baa' instead, or else grunting like one of Tommy Morgan's pigs.

Billy had been the Second Camel Driver (there were eight camel drivers altogether, it was a big class). He had only three words to say, but on the night he was so nervous he could only eat half his tea and kept burping and nearly being sick all over the table. His mother got real mad at him; she thought he was just acting about.

Then, just before he went on stage, he started going hot and cold all up and down his spine, and his legs started trembling and wobbling about all over the place, as if they had a life of their own.

The cause of all this was that he felt he'd get his words the wrong way round. He was supposed to say 'Look up yonder!' at the very moment Miss Benfold hoisted up this Star of Bethlehem they'd all slaved weeks over to make from silver bottle-tops, but Billy was totally convinced he'd end up saying 'Yuk up londer!' instead. It was an easy thing to do.

Another thing was he had to wear this short skirt-thing made from one of Sandra's old dresses, and it reached that high up his legs Sandra said she could see his knees knocking from the back row of the hall. Steven said he couldn't only see them knocking – he could *hear* them knocking as well. At first, he said, he thought somebody had started playing the xylophone.

When the Tarzan film ended Billy went upstairs, slipped the roulette game inside his bomber jacket and zipped it up. He checked in his wardrobe mirror to make sure nobody could see anything. His mam didn't notice it when he went into the kitchen, but, naturally, she didn't want him to go round the Potters' anyhow.

'What you want to go round there again for, Billy?'

'He's my best pal, Mam.'

'You must be hard up for friends, then,' she said. 'What's the matter? Isn't your own house good enough for you?'

'It isn't that, Mam.'

'What do you think, Dick?'

'There's nowt good round at the Potters',' his dad said.

'That's what I think. Should we let him go?'

'Let him suit himself, Alice.'

That was a change for him. He usually went on for a fortnight about the evils of the Potters' house.

'Well, if your father says you can go, you can go. Get yourself off. And get some of them Blind Dog raffle tickets sold on your way round there. You've hardly done a thing for that charity yet, Our Billy.' It was Sandra's letter that was making her this ratty. 'And don't fetch any fleas back, when you come!'

She was only saying that because the Potters kept their hens penned in under their kitchen table, and fed them with scraps down a hole cut in the middle.

70

And Mr Potter was looking after a greyhound that belonged to a friend of his over in Easington. Elvis said it was a famous racing dog, and they were giving it special training, but Billy had his doubts about this because all it seemed to do was eat. They weren't allowed to tell Billy its proper name, but they nicknamed it Hungry Horace.

On the way up Gordon Street he tried to sell some raffle tickets, but what was the use? Soskiss had been there before him. She'd sold seven books now. She was like the Evil Thing from Planet X.

At the top of Gordon there was this clarty black path that separated the colliery terraces from the allotments. This time of year there were always loads of kids up there under the street lamps, all playing marbles. One or two of them shouted to him, wanting him to join in, but Billy just shook his head.

Every year this obsession descended on just about everybody in their school. It was like a plague sent from outer space (was Soskiss responsible?). Kids played marbles at school, in the gutters on their way to school and back, and then at night up at the street tops till their mams shouted them in. They ate, slept and drank marbles. They even dreamed them. They couldn't think of anything else.

Billy couldn't see what the fuss was all about. What was the point of marbles? What difference would it make if you won ten thousand? None. If you walked into the Cheep-Cheep Store in

Bishop Auckland with ten million marbles in your pockets, they still wouldn't buy you a single dented tin of Wuff-Wuff.

He was just turning down Victoria backs when he heard somebody shout behind him.

'Hey! Uglymug!'

It was Butch riding Daz's new bike at ninety miles an hour over all the humps and hollows. Or, rather, what had been Daz's new bike. The wing-mirror had already been snapped off.

'Thought you knew your name!' shouted Butch, as he whizzed past under the street lamp doing a wheely.

Billy tried to smile back. He particularly wanted to keep on Butch's good side at the moment.

Then, just before Billy reached the Potters' backyard gate, he heard this terrific crash-bang-wallop, and guessed Butch had just had a slight disagreement with a lamp post. This time he smiled more easily. It wouldn't affect Butch much. The street lamp might be mortally wounded, Daz's bike might be demolished, but Butch would be okay. Butch was like that. Slightly indestructible. Billy had once punched Butch hard in the chest and he nearly had to send off for a new set of knuckles.

He had a job getting into the Potters' back-yard. The door dragged on the floor because one of its hinges had come off, and Mr Potter still hadn't had time to mend it – it had only fallen off about three years ago. Something – he couldn't think what – grated under his feet as

he crossed the yard.

Light was spilling out of the Potters' kitchen window, but he couldn't make them hear when he banged on the door. He went to the window and looked in. The Potters had no lace curtains, naturally. The Potters never bothered with fal-de-rals like lace curtains. They had no curtains up in their bathroom either, and the feller opposite had laid a complaint to the council about that, which Billy could sympathise with, because when all was said and done he *had* seen Mrs Potter emerging from her bath, which can't have been a pretty sight.

The light was on and the fire was burning. Billy could see Elvis's two ferrets, Pinky and Perky, nosing about in their cage on the sideboard, and the hens shuffling about under the table.

He knew they were in, though. There was this terrific racket coming from their front room. Billy recognised the music. It was from this film called *Fins*, and Mr Potter had made umpteen recordings of it to sell in Bishop Auckland market.

It was all about this perfectly innocent young shark that finds some nuclear waste dumped in the sea and decides to have a nibble. This results in the shark getting bigger and bigger until it ends up an absolute whopper.

At the same time it goes sort of funny in the head. It starts off eating titchy paddle boats — the sort little kids use at the seaside — and works its way up from there.

Billy went back to the door and knocked again.

It was just after that when he glanced to his left and saw something in a dark corner of the yard, beyond the window. It was just a quick glance, there and away. But it was sufficient.

There was something there. Or, rather, some *things*.

There seemed to be six or seven of them. They were about two feet high and had hooky chins and noses. They seemed to be vaguely familiar, but Billy couldn't remember where he'd last set eyes on them. They seemed to be lined up along the backyard wall. They seemed to be looking at him.

Billy knocked again. Harder.

Mrs Drury was always burbling on about the 'wonderful gift of imagination', but Mrs Drury hadn't a clue what she was talking about.

Billy knew he had to keep his particular 'wonderful gift' firmly bottled up. There were times when he let it out for a five-minute gallop round the room and it nigh-on frightened him to death.

The other night, for example, he'd distinctly heard a grizzly bear clumping up the stairs towards his bedroom. He even heard it sharpening its claws on the skirting-board, as it prepared to do him in. His mam and dad were just downstairs but Billy didn't fancy screaming for help, because his dad was watching the North East Regional Finals of the Egg Marketing Board World Tiddlywink Championships and,

quite naturally, wouldn't want disturbing.

So Billy got the Indian club (that he kept permanently under his bed to deal with burglars), and with remarkable coolness and courage advanced to the landing, determined to defend himself to the last drop of English blood.

That time it was only next door's kitten.

And one foggy night up the allotment last November, he had distinctly seen his dad's Brussels sprouts change into ten-headed invaders from outer space and start advancing through the mists towards him.

So he kept his eyes firmly on the Potters' back door and knocked again.

Chapter 6

This time he managed to set the greyhound off barking, and a minute later Elvis came to the door, with what looked like a nest of dead maggots clustered round his mouth.

'Having a chinky?' asked Billy, as he stepped into their kitchen.

Elvis nodded and scattered half a dozen bean sprouts on their clippy-mat. 'How you gless?' he asked, speaking from behind a mouthful of food, 'an' watchlin' *Flins* again – it's glate, man. What's tharrinya jthacket?'

Trust him to notice!

'Nowt,' said Billy, 'Just a game. Have we to watch the video first?'

'If you like. It's just clummin' to that good blit where the shark gets that feller wi' a wooden leg.'

Just then, from the front room, there came this scream followed by the sound of splintering wood, followed by another scream, followed by the kind of burble-wurble noise you can make by blowing out underwater in the bath.

'I think we just missed it,' said Billy.

Which was a pity because Elvis always laughed like a drain when the shark swallowed the feller and then spewed back his wooden leg, as if it was all of a sudden getting choosy (when only a minute ago it had swallowed a barge-load

of garbage without a moment's hesitation).

'We gorra lorra new furniture,' said Elvis, who had been working at creating more room in his mouth for words and was now able to speak more clearly. 'We gorra new carpet anna lorra pictures anna new settee an' all.'

Billy wasn't surprised. The Potters were always getting new things. They were always losing them as well. Cocktail cabinets, cuckoo clocks, bamboo plant-stands, three-piece suites, bits of fur to cover up their lavvy lid, even complete fitted kitchens, were continually whistling in and out of the Potters' with something approaching the speed of light.

'Me ma's gettin' hersel a new fur coat an' all – a nimitation one, anna new 'at.'

'Where'd you get all the money?'

'Me da won it on a hoss called Kuwait Sands.'

'Where's that?' asked Billy. It sounded like a seaside place to him.

'Kempton Park, two o'clock, sixteen to one,' explained Elvis.

Billy sometimes wished his own dad would have a flutter on the horses now and then. It might make life a bit more exciting. He'd just like to see him coming back honking of posh cigars and scattering ten pound notes round the house like confetti.

The shark in the video was just eating its first fishing boat as they went in the front-room. It was a good bit, this, brainy, because just as the skipper was eating this sausage-roll his wife had packed specially for him, the shark was

77

eating the skipper (and his boat, which, unfortunately, the skipper hadn't paid for), only he didn't know it till it was too late.

Mrs Potter was spread over most of the new settee, showing most of her flabby legs and occupying slightly more territory than the USSR.

The so-called Famous Racing Dog, now looking decidedly porky after its week of special training, waddled up to Billy and shoved its nose into his hand straight away. It had taken a fancy to Billy from the start.

'What you think to me new outfit, Billy?' Mrs Potter asked.

She stood up and spun round, nearly reducing the Wonder Racing Dog to bonemeal in the process. The fur coat looked to be made of nimitation rhino to Billy (though why anyone should wish to nimitate a rhino Billy couldn't nimagine), and the new hat was the sort Princess Di had a pash on six months ago. They were now selling them off cheap in the mid-mid-season sale at Bishop Co-op. To complete her ensemble Mrs Potter was wearing her pinny under her rhino-skin and her old carpet slippers, through which her bunions sprouted like bank robbers with nylons stretched over their fizzogs.

'Very nice,' said Billy.

She smiled and plonked herself back on the new sofa, making the same *whurrumph* noise the Whoopee had made when Mrs Drury sat on it that first day of term.

'And what do you think to our new house,

Billy?' she asked, waving her hand and disturbing assorted Chinese food freely all over the new carpet – a gesture Hungry Horace hurriedly showed his appreciation of.

Billy swept his eyes quickly round the room, not allowing them to linger too long in any one spot, for nothing he saw there was exactly a pretty sight.

The sofa was a yucky yellow and had tassels on it, one or two of which the dog had already chewed off as part of its special training.

'Like the colour?' Mrs Potter asked. 'It's called *Sahara Song.*'

Billy thought that *Droppings of Camel* might have been more appropriate, but he didn't say that. Instead he said: 'Subtle, Mrs Potter.'

'Mind, that's a clever word!' she said, glancing across at Elvis. 'What for can't you say clever words like that, Our Elvis? All you seem to know is mucky 'uns!'

But Elvis wasn't in a fit state to deal in words at the moment. He looked to have two tennis balls in his mouth.

Billy continued looking around. The first picture his eyes alighted on (momentarily) was of a lass with a green face and red eyes which glowed like coals, who – if Billy's eyes could be relied on – was apparently chewing on a rose and enjoying every minute of it.

The second picture showed two blue horses with green legs ending in spikes. The pair of them snorted fireworks down their nostrils as they stamped like billy-o on a purply rock.

79

'I do like a nanimal picture, don't you, Billy?'

Billy nodded his agreement. He was, in fact, very fond of nanimals.

The next thing Billy saw was even more shocking.

It was Elvis's sister.

Her real name was Marilyn, but everybody just called her Soss, which Billy always imagined was short for Sausage, probably because she looked like one! She was standing in front of the mirror over the fireplace, trying to do something about her face, and when she caught Billy's eye she waggled her finger at him.

'Like me new nails, Billy?' she asked.

They were about six inches long, curved like talons, pointed at the end, and covered in green gunge.

'Nice.'

'Blide of Dlacula!' was Elvis's comment.

'Give the feller some credit!' said Mr Potter, almost raising his head from his *Racing Times*. 'Even he's got more sense than that!'

Mr Potter and Soss were always having arguments. Sometimes Mr Potter even threw his *Racing Times* at Soss, and that just showed the depths of his exasperation, because Mr Potter wouldn't have damaged his *Racing Times* for anything.

'Why don't you just drop dead, Dad?' Soss inquired. 'Now would be as good a time as any.'

'Fancy a bite to eat, Billy?' asked Mrs Potter. 'Gerrim a plate, Elvis, and we'll all give him a dollop of ours. There's a clean one on the side in

the kitchen.'

If this was true, it was good news. People said the Potters never bothered with washing-up, they just licked their own plates clean. To be honest, Billy had never seen any sign of washing-up liquid in their house. And the only time he'd seen a drying-cloth Mrs Potter was wiping her nose on it. Come to that, he'd never even seen a tap running in the Potters'. But, then, he'd never seen the sun rise over Africa either. And you had to look on the bright side – hadn't you?

'What you mek of that one?' Mrs Potter asked, indicating a picture on the wall behind him which, perhaps mercifully, he hadn't spotted till then.

The moment he saw it his eyes skittered away from it. If his mam had seen it, she would have phoned for Scotland Yard and sent Billy upstairs to bed for a fortnight without any supper.

'What you think of that one, Billy? That's Mr Potter's favourite.'

'Got class has that picture,' said Mr Potter.

Billy looked at the picture, searching hard for class, but without success.

What he could see – what he could hardly avoid seeing – was a very large lady with no clothes on, lying on a beach where all the shells appeared to have grown ears and a lot of the fish were flying ones. The lady either resembled, or was turning into, one of those big fiddle things that jazz bands use to make the pom-pom noise

in the background, and a big clock just behind her left ear was melting in the heat of the sun (even though there didn't seem to be one).

Billy didn't know what to say.

'It's called *Spring Arising*,' Mrs Potter told him.

Billy wondered if the 'spring' bit had something to do with the clock; had it lost one, for instance? It seemed at least possible, because now that he looked carefully he saw that the clock had lost both hands as well. As for the 'arising' bit, maybe that had something to do with the fact all the flying fish were a-rising (as opposed to a-falling) through the air. But the more Billy thought about these things, the more he suspected they weren't the complete answer.

'I do like a picture with a story in it, don't you, Billy?' Mrs Potter said.

'Yes, Mrs Potter.'

Elvis came back in then with a plate and fork, both of which he appeared to be wiping clean on his backside, and all the Potters generously shovelled bits of food on the plate for Billy.

'I think it's dead mucky, me,' said Elvis, as he handed Billy the plate, and for a moment Billy panicked because he thought Elvis meant the plate – but a moment later he felt relieved when Mr Potter said:

'There's nothing mucky about that picture. It's your mind that's mucky!'

'Male chauvinist pig!' was Soss's response to her father.

'You wouldn't know a pig from a bull's foot!'

said Mr Potter.

'Wouldn't I?' asked Soss, turning from the mirror to look at him. 'Well, I'm looking at a pig now!'

'Eat up, Billy,' said Mrs Potter, 'always keep you belly full, that's what I say. Come and sit by me.' She patted the small area of settee beside her that was still unoccupied territory. 'That's better. Come closer! I'm not going to eat you yet – I've just had me supper!' She shrieked with laughter, and the famous racing dog almost leapt out of its already over-stretched skin.

Soss's make-up was going well by this time. Her cheeks were dead white and she'd put two black blotches round her eyes, so she looked like she'd been starved for a fortnight and then gone two hard rounds in the ring.

Meanwhile, on the video, the shark was eyeing up this ocean liner. The heroine, a girl with long legs and eyelashes, was in the bar drinking a cocktail. She was madly in love with this young officer, but one of the stewards was after her. He was a real nasty bloke. Billy had seen him in another picture where he was a sort of jailer, and he kept offering this girl (one with slightly shorter legs and eyelashes who was locked in a dungeon) bits of cheese on a plate and making what Billy's mam called 'suggestive' eyes at her.

'How's your mam and dad keeping, Billy?'

'Chumblebum,' said Billy. He had started on his food by now.

'Good. And how's your grandma?'

'She's chumblebum an' all.'

'What's her ears like nowadays?'

Big and blue, Billy felt like saying, red whiskers sprouting out of them.

'A lot better,' said Billy. 'She says she used to know a relation of yours, Mrs Potter. A dancer. She says she ended up on the stage.'

'She must mean Ada Troupe,' said Mrs Potter to her husband.

'Aye.'

'But that isn't how she ended up, Billy.' Mrs Potter pulled her nimitation rhinoceros-skin closer round her shoulders. 'She ended up with more money than she could count in her pocket, Ada Troupe. She ended up a lady, didn't she?'

'Aye.'

'Married to a Canadian lord or something of that sort. They were next door to getting invited to tea by the Queen when they come over here.'

'I thought you told me he was a lumberjack, Mam?' said Soss, who was putting on fluorescent-purple lipstick.

'He was a lumberjack,' said Mrs Potter, 'in a manner of speaking. He owned half of Canada.'

'An' a bit more,' said Mr Potter.

At that moment the shark bit off the end of the liner's propeller-shaft. Upstairs in his cabin the captain was writing a letter home to his wife. Her picture was on the table in front of him. He was very unhappy because she kept playing tennis with a younger man with hairy legs called Bruce. When the ship lurched he

84

looked thoughtful for a moment, perhaps thinking of Bruce, but then went back to his letter.

Downstairs in the bar the heroine was starting on her third cocktail; she also was very unhappy, because the young ship's officer didn't seem to fancy her. It was always the way in pictures. In actual fact, though, he fancied her a lot, but didn't think he was good enough for her because she had pots of money.

'And did your grandma get hersel' off them black-and-green pills like I told her to?' asked Mrs Potter.

'Yes,' said Billy.

A bit back his grandma had been plagued by earache. First Dr Samanti had tried pink pills on her, then little yellow ones, and finally, in desperation, he'd dosed her on these big black-and-green efforts that Billy's dad had said looked more suitable for shire-horses.

'And had that cured her?' asked Mrs Potter.

'Balaclava helmet cured her,' said Billy.

'Yer Grandma's surely to goodness not eating Balaclava helmets?' said Mr Potter, looking up from his *Racing Times*.

'Wearing one,' explained Billy.

'Ah!' said Mr Potter, grasping the point straight away. 'I was going to say, like.'

'Only I told her to watch out for them black-and-greenies, didn't I, Clarry?'

'Chap down Bertha reckons they made his eyes go round,' said Mr Potter.

'What shape were they before, Dad?' asked Elvis.

'Shut your cake-hole, you, clever-dick!'

'And how's your sister and that canny little bairn of hers down in Barnsley?'

'Champion,' said Billy.

'Finished, pet? Put your plate on the floor then, Billy,' Mrs Potter said, 'the dog'll lick it clean,' and at the same time she put her own down, which proved pretty conclusively that people were wrong when they said the Potters licked clean their own plates.

'They tell me that husband of hers is thinking of coming out of the pits,' said Mr Potter.

It was amazing how the Potters always seemed to know what was going on. It was only that morning they'd got to know themselves from Sandra's letter that Steven had definitely decided to take redundancy. That had put the wind up Billy's mother.

'He might be.'

'But they have offered him transfer to another pit down there?'

(It was no wonder the Potters never bothered to watch the news: they probably knew what had happened before it happened.)

'I think so.'

'He wants his head examining if he doesn't shift to another pit,' said Mr Potter. 'He wants to stick at a good job while he has chance, especially under this climate of opinion we're in at the minute.'

'Hark at the workaholic!' jeered Soss, sticking a curtain ring through her nose. 'Shove a shovel in front of him, an' he'd die of fright!'

'More likely to die of fright catching sight of your face!' said Mr Potter, chortling with mirth at his own sharp wittiness. When he'd recovered, he said to Billy, 'What shift's your dad on Friday?'

'Afters.'

'Is he?' Mr Potter seemed genuinely interested. He wasn't putting it on. And it wasn't like Mr Potter to be interested in work. Work was a four-letter word in the Potters' house. 'Champion.'

'Mr Potter's just gone into antiques, see, Billy,' said Mrs Potter, speaking as if she was explaining something. She was about to add something else, but Mr Potter caught her eye and she stopped.

'I see,' said Billy.

He was baffled.

As far as Billy knew, antiques were junky old bits of rubbish that nobody had any use for any more. Steven was always calling Grandma an antique. Though, when he thought about it, sometimes they could be worth a bit of money. His mam had seen a dressing-table set in the Trash 'n' Treasure shop at Bishop Auckland last month and told his dad about it. 'Made of silver and all, funny enough,' she'd said, though what was funny about that Billy hadn't a clue. 'How much?' his dad had asked her. 'Forty-eight pounds,' she told him. That made him nearly swallow his pipe.

'What sort of antiques?' Billy asked now.

'Mainly doorstops,' said Mrs Potter.

Billy was baffled some more by now.

On the video the shark had bitten a sizeable chunk out of the ship's hull. It was just digesting that when the first lifeboat crashed into the water beside it, so it swallowed the lifeboat (and its contents) as well.

'What's a doorstop for, Mrs Potter?' he asked.

'To stop a door with, dope,' said Elvis.

'Stop it what, though?'

'Falling off!' laughed Elvis, his eyes glued to the box.

General pandemonium now reigned on the liner. The decks were awash with people and men were diving overboard in their best suits. Hooters were hooting and lifeboats were being launched under the supervision of the young ship's officer. 'Women and children first!' he shouted at the top of his megaphone – surely an unfortunate oversight on his part, considering what had so recently befallen the occupants of the first lifeboat?

'If doorstops stopped doors falling off, we should've had one on our backyard door donkeys' years ago,' said Soss. 'That door's been falling off since before the Ark was thought of! What's me face like, Mam?'

'Lovely, Our Soss.'

'Undertaker's delight!' said Mr Potter.

'They're to prop doors open with, Billy,' Mrs Potter explained. 'Mr Potter's doing them like Punch and Judy. He's made six this afternoon. They're proper antiques, though – you wouldn't make fakes, pet, would you?'

'No way.'

Billy smiled. So *that* was what had nearly attacked him in the yard!

'They're all cast from the original mould,' said Mrs Potter. 'Mr Potter's supplying all the London shops wi' them. They can't get enough of them down there. Mr Potter's brother teks them down for him.'

Mr Potter's brother, Dasher, drove a lorry, off the back of which things were continually falling.

Just then Soss's boyfriend came roaring up the backs on his motorbike; they knew it wasn't anybody else because they heard him knock over half a dozen dustbins on the way up.

'Ta-ra, everybody!' shouted Soss, blowing a kiss from her fluorescent-purple lips to her mother.

'Good riddance to bad rubbish!' said Mr Potter.

As Soss went past Elvis, she fetched him a right welter round the neck and he punched her back on the thigh. They'd always got on well together.

A second later, as the motorbike took off down the backs, they heard another two dustbins go over; they must have been the only two left standing after the journey up.

'Ought to be locked up,' said Mr Potter.

'They're only young once,' said Mrs Potter.

The whuuuumph-whuuuumph noise on the telly had got really loud by now, and it was just coming up to the climax. The shark had just

eaten the engine room, including the chief engineer – a nice Scots bloke whose nice Scots wife didn't carry on with tennis players with hairy legs, but concentrated on more down-to-earth things like knitting the porridge and cooking roll-necked sweaters (she was slightly absent-minded) – and the funnel had just collapsed and crushed to death a nice old feller, who everybody was fond of because he continually looked on the bright side of life (in fact he was just saying what a lovely day it was when the funnel fell on his head).

'I hate this fillum, I really do,' said Mrs Potter, as she turned up the volume and opened a packet of biscuits, which till then she'd been sitting on. She handed them round and dropped two on the floor for the Famous Racing Greyhound. The biscuits were in as bad shape as the racing greyhound was, and, besides, the chocolate was melting, but Billy felt obliged to accept one.

The sea was all frothy and red now, looking like an advert for a new kind of deadly foam bath, and when the shark tore the rest of the bottom off the boat it made a sound just like the Potters' yard gate gronking on the floor. A girl, with only fairly long legs and eyelashes, looked down the shark's throat and was so shocked she dropped her handbag. A second later she and the handbag had vanished into its ever-open maw. At the same time an arm and a leg belonging to some unidentified person flew past the camera, and the steward with the sugges-

tive eyes and titbits of cheese was just hauling himself onto a liferaft when the shark suddenly snipped off his better half and he breathed his last.

'Anybody fancy another biscuit?' asked Mrs Potter.

People, dining-tables, steel filing-cabinets, Pekinese dogs (no expense was spared on this picture), were all sliding irretrievably by the dozen down the shark's throat now. At the same time Mrs Potter was demolishing one biscuit after another, all the time saying, 'I hate this fillum, I really do!' What did biscuits feel as they disappeared down into the gaping cavern of Mrs Potter's throat, Billy wondered; did they, too, have feelings? Would they want to cling onto the last shreds of life, just as this feller was clinging hard to the flappy bits of plastic filament at the entrance to the shark's throat?

'I'll have a nart attack, I really will!' said Mrs Potter, cold-bloodedly dispatching a ninth biscuit to its cruel fate among her gastric juices.

But it was nearly over now, apart from a little shot of the last hundred or so people — none of them really important — being sucked down screaming into the whirlpool made by the diving shark.

After that, all that happened was the girl with the long legs and eyelashes was rescued in the nick of time by the young ship's officer, and then they — and all the other important actors — were in turn rescued by the United States Air Force Strategic Bomber Command

(Laser Section) who lasered the shark to death, after which the President of the United States of America made a terribly moving speech about how necessary it was to rid the earth finally, totally and once and for all of violence of all kinds.

In the end you didn't feel too bad about it, because the only people who'd really died were those with walk-on parts.

The captain went down with his ship still wearing his cap, which had more gold braid on it than there were noodles round Elvis's mouth when Billy first came in. But when you remembered the way the Captain's wife was still clarting about with the tennis player with hairy legs called Bruce, even that was probably all for the best.

'Thank God that's over,' said Mrs Potter. 'What's on the telly?'

'The news,' said Mr Potter.

'We don't want that!' said Mrs Potter. 'Life's depressing enough!' She switched on to *Intimate Lives*, a quiz programme where people told about the naughty things they'd done. There were some really good prizes like food processors and microwave ovens. 'This is more like!' said Mrs Potter.

Billy picked up his own plate and Mrs Potter's, and took them through to the kitchen. He always made himself handy in other people's houses.

'What a canny lad!' said Mrs Potter.

Billy put the plates on the draining-board,

and placed the roulette game on the table as he passed it. Elvis had followed him in and started looking at the game straight away.

Billy went back in the other room to collect up the rest of the things. There was a cup behind the telly that didn't seem to want to leave the carpet and Billy wondered if it had been there that long it was starting to put down roots. A woman on the telly was admitting how she told a whole load of lies to her mother when she was a little girl.

'And you've never told anybody about this till now, Irene?' said Andy Divine, the compère. He had the sort of eyes that slid round corners and a smile that came and went.

'Not a soul.'

'Well, I think that's worth an electric bread-knife, don't you, folks?' Everybody clapped. 'Anything else, Irene? There must be something else deep down in there, just dying to get out. Would you like to go on for a microwave?'

'Yes, please!'

When Billy went back into the kitchen Elvis was reading the rule book. 'I like it! I like it!' he said, as Billy passed.

'Want a game?'

'Mucho grasso!' said Elvis.

Billy sat at the table. He couldn't wait to win all the money off Elvis. He couldn't wait to see his face in about half an hour. He started to count out the plastic tokens for him, first the £100 ones, then the £50s. When it was all ready — he'd been even more generous than his

Grandma had been with him – he pushed the £2000 towards Elvis, and said, 'That enough for you?'

But Elvis didn't touch the money. He just looked at Billy and said, 'You have the money, Billy. Tek as much as you like, I'd rather be the Banker.'

Most of the teachers at school rated Elvis as Extra Thick Plus Incorporated. And in a way that was understandable.

It was true, for instance, that when Elvis first heard about the Blind Dogs Appeal he thought it was the dogs that were blind.

Also, in answer to one of Mrs Drury's Royal Family quiz questions – nearly all Mrs Drury's quiz questions were about the Royal Family – Elvis had written the word Chukuvednbra.

Last year Miss Benfold had given him a gold star for not coming bottom of the class in a spelling test, and Mr Fixby always called him 'the Missing Link'.

But there were times, just now and then, when Billy suspected that most teachers were as wrong about Elvis as they were about most other things in life.

Chapter 7

The next morning Elvis told Billy that he'd been up half the night thinking about the roulette game. It didn't seem to have affected him much, though. He still looked half-alive, washed-out and mucky.

'I like it! I really like it, man!' he kept saying, as they walked to school, stepping over or round the army of marble-nuts who littered the pavements and gutters all along Station Road.

There was a strange, mad, faraway look in his eyes, the sort loony professors got in horror pictures when they first thought of the idea that would solve all the world's problems (and blow it up in the process).

Billy knew this could mean only one thing: Elvis had a brainwave coming on.

Elvis didn't have too many brainwaves, but when they *did* arrive on the scene they tended to be pretty earth-shattering occasions – like the time Sandra had blown off the top of the pressure cooker and redecorated the kitchen ceiling with boiled rice.

'I like it! I like it!' he kept repeating all the time the rest of them were having a kick-about just before going in (he was so obsessed with the roulette game he didn't even play, but just stood not watching on the sidelines).

When Emma did a flying header to knock in

one of Billy's crosses Elvis didn't even notice.

He didn't even notice when Chuffy came out of the bogs after another session with Howells, his ears blazing red, and not with embarrassment either.

All this concentration was another sign that a Potter Brainwave was imminent. Elvis always got in-turned, almost unaware that the rest of the world was going on, just like Billy's dad had got when the colliery had shut down and he'd lost his job.

Something was cooking in there all right. Or festering. And Billy had a feeling that it wouldn't be long before Elvis's lid blew off. He could just imagine Elvis's brains being plastered on the ceiling of Mrs Drury's classroom. He could just imagine her looking up and saying 'What a mess, Potter! What a typical mess!'

Just after Mrs Drury had taken in the Blind Dogs money (Soskiss was three and a half light-years ahead by now), a monitor came in to say Elvis had to report again to Mr Starr.

But Elvis was back after only five minutes, grinning as he swaggered down the aisle all bouncy. When Billy asked him what had been going on, he said he had to stand outside Mr Starr's office again at break-time, because somebody had put a plastic doggy's doo-doo in Mr Fixby's desk and the headmaster suspected him.

'What did you say?' asked Billy.

'Told him I would've put it there, only the dogs round our way don't do plastic ones.'

You couldn't always believe these stories of Elvis's.

'Quiet, you two!'

Mrs Drury was even more snap-crackle-and-poppish than usual this morning. She was having another of her migraine attacks. Billy's Grandma said what caused them was that her husband, who played the organ at church, was making eyes at another woman who went to church in bit hats, but this was probably a lie. Billy's grandma was always telling lies, especially about the Drurys. She hated them like rat poison.

Anyroad, Mrs Drury made them play Three of a Kind again that morning, which she always did when she was feeling off-colour or had to do yard duty.

She wrote a list of subjects on the board – houses, ships, nuts, games, and so on – and the class had to write down three of a kind in absolute silence, because her head would split right open if they didn't. Ten minutes before the end of the lesson they usually swapped papers and marked them themselves; that was to save time.

When Billy reached the third subject he wrote:

> NUTS
> cocoa-nuts
> peanuts
> Elvis Potter

Billy wasn't bad at spelling (though you will

probably have noticed he wasn't quite as brilliant as he thought!).

He dug his elbow into Elvis's ribs and pointed out what he'd written. Elvis responded by screwing up his face, crossing his eyes and poking out his tongue. Billy admitted this was a definite improvement but said it still didn't make him look human, not fully.

So far Elvis had managed to squeeze this out of his pencil:

> HOUSES
> bog
> cole
> publik

Since then he'd concentrated on drawing pinmen, another sign that momentous thoughts were being cooked up deep in the Potter brain. Billy knew just what a dangerous and delicate operation this must be, so he didn't disturb him after that.

It was nearly ten o'clock when Elvis started acting about. First he started trembling all over, as if he was being convulsed by electric shocks by the Evil Alien From Outer Space. He always did that when he was in grip of an Extra-special Brainwave.

Then he dropped his head on the desk and forced spit to drool out of the side of his mouth.

Then his hands started scrabbling over the table like blind grey crabs, that wouldn't have looked out of place in Mr Potter's favourite

picture among the shells with ears and the
vertical take-off fish.

'Elvis Potter! I sometimes wonder if you're
right in the head! *Non compos mentis!'*

'No need to call us a bag of compost, miss!'

'You know very well I said no such thing, boy.
I simply meant you aren't right in the head.'

'Oh, that's all right then.'

'What in Heaven's name is the matter with
you now, child?'

'Miss, I haven't had no breakfast this mornin',
miss.'

'What on earth has that to do with it?' she
asked, raking in her handbag for her pills.

Mrs Drury was always rattling on about the
importance of coming to school on an egg (especially a free-range one). The first time she told

them she always came to school on a free-range egg, Elvis said he thought she always came on a Volvo 245 instead and got a clout over the lughole.

'Please, miss, I think I'm that hungry I can't think.'

'You never could think, Potter. I doubt you ever will! Get up! Go and stand by the radiator, that's it. Now, put your hands behind your back, where I can see them, and face the wall! Maybe that will help you to think!'

Billy knew Elvis wouldn't mind that much. There was nothing he liked better than looking at walls, especially if it meant he didn't have to work.

But it meant that Billy had to wait till play-time to hear what the brainwave was. Elvis told him as they were scuttling along the corridor towards the indoor bogs. They were allowed to use them for the first five minutes of break. Mr Fixby was already on duty there, watching them like a Martian Overlord while they peed in the urinal (it was from this cloakroom where most of the nicking had taken place).

And when Billy heard the brainwave he didn't say a word.

He couldn't. He was absolutely flabbergustipilated.

'Good, eh not?' said Elvis, just before he parted from Billy to go and stand outside Mr Starr's office, which was just along the corridor from the bogs.

Billy still didn't reply.

101

But the same loony professor look was in his eyes.

Billy didn't speak for a long time after that.

But he knew at once he was going to make a fortune. Or, rather, *they* were. Because he was going to work with Elvis. They would work together, as a team. *Billy's Boys.* They would go shigs-together all the way. Halfy-halfies. Right to the end.

When he went out into the yard, he scarcely noticed the sunshine or heard Emma shouting for him to come and play football with them.

Because sunshine and football were things of the past now.

He'd show blinking Drury and the rest of them! He'd soon make them laugh on the other side of their faces, just like Grandma had said.

He didn't like Phase One of Elvis's plan. Phase One would be boring. Phase Two was a titchy bit more interesting. Phase Three would be really great.

When Emma called him again he didn't hear her at all. Nor did he notice Chuffy trail past him on the way to the bogs, his face all white and tense. Billy walked among the screaming maelstrom of kids that constituted a normal morning break and didn't notice a single thing.

How could he? In a sense, he wasn't there at all.

He was somewhere else.

He was walking along a beach, alone, barefoot.

Well, not quite alone. Elvis had come for a fortnight's holiday. He was up with the monkeys who lived on the rock. He wanted to join in their tribe, but they wouldn't have him because he didn't groom regularly enough.

To Billy's left there was the steady murmur of breakers rolling shoreward. To his right there were palm trees waving, and coconuts plopping on to sand.

He was on his very own island. It was somewhere in the middle of the Pacific. He'd just flown there himself, in his private jet. It was so secret nobody else in the world could find it, not even the Americans. The President of America had just had to resign because even his spies couldn't find it. The reason was Billy has just installed a hundred billion pounds-worth of radar jamming devices.

That was what money could buy for you. Peace. Contentment. Happiness.

And, boy, did he have plenty of money now, thanks to the roulette game!

He had money in the bank. His business enterprises and investments were thriving. And, as luck would have it, he'd just discovered a hoard of treasure left on his island donkeys' years back by pirates: gold doubloons, amethysts, emeralds, gold chains – the usual sort of stuff. Christie's of London were begging him to let them come out and hold an auction (they'd already agreed to be blindfolded on the way out), but he wasn't sure he wanted his peace disturbed.

And as if that wasn't enough, he was making a tidy bit on the side by selling coconuts (his mam had been wrong about money not growing on trees).

His mam was here now. Billy had invited her and dad out for a holiday, a *short* holiday. She was keeping a low profile in the distance as she swept the beach, trying to keep the sand tidy. She would never change now, she was too old. After she'd finished tidying the sand she was going to give the jungle a bit of a dust. It was sad, but that was life.

He had just presented his dad with a cheque for £100,000, just so he and mam would be all right for bits and bobs when they got home (his dad was always going on about the price of things in the shops – especially sports shops; the last time Billy got a new pair of footer boots his dad went on for half an hour about how when he was a lad you could buy ten pairs of football boots, six footballs, a pump, and still have some change left over from twopence halfpenny).

For a moment his dad had been speechless. He looked so funny: white and pathetic, his trousers rolled up to display his disgustingly knobbly knees. In contrast Billy was clad only in a loincloth (like Tarzan's), and his body had gone all muscular and brown (also like Tarzan's) with his new life – windsurfing, signing cheques, playing golf and the Stock Exchange.

'It's over-much, son,' his dad had finally said. 'How ever can me and your mam ever pay you back?'

There were tears in the old man's eyes.

'It doesn't matter, Dad,' said Billy. 'Money doesn't matter at all.'

And he was right, of course. Money didn't matter at all. Money didn't matter a tittle, when you had millions of pounds.

Chapter 8

By the time Billy and Elvis got to the top of Gordon all the best pitches under the streetlamps had been grabbed by the marble brigade, so they spread out the green baize cloth on a flattish bit close to the main path up through the allotments.

Elvis put the tokens in piles and made sure the wheel was spinning free, while Billy arranged their marbles in a tidy heap. They'd just been down to Nobby Bolton's and bought two quids' worth. That was their investment. Even in the weak light that reached them the marbles seemed to glitter with promise.

All the same, the going was slow at first.

Dead slow.

In fact, slower than that.

Non-existent.

After a bit Elvis started shouting out, 'ROLL UP! ROLL UP! ALL THE FUN OF LAS VEGAS!' but nobody took a bat of notice, except a big kid from Spenny Comprehensive who told him to shut his trap or he'd re-arrange his face. So Elvis desisted after that.

There was a nip in the air that night, a cold that seemed to reach everywhere. Billy zipped up his jacket and wriggled his toes in his trainers.

Under the streetlamps the cobbles down Gor-

don fronts glinted like hard knuckles, and the
windscreen of Mr Harle's old Cortina was so
frosted over you couldn't see through it. He had
bought it three years ago and had never
actually got it started. The Harles were not
what you'd call dead lucky. When Mr Harle's
brother got his redundancy from the pit he went
skiing for a fortnight in Austria and ended up
on the first day with a cast on his leg.

Five minutes passed. Or perhaps it was an
hour?

Emma Ward came up Gordon fronts in her
new tracksuit and trainers. She nodded and
smiled at Billy but didn't come over to them.

She wasn't too keen on Elvis at the moment.
She hadn't said anything, but Billy suspected
that by now she was pretty convinced it was
Elvis nicking the money from the porch.

She leaned against the wall and pretended to
watch a game of marbles. But Billy knew she
was keeping her eye on them.

Elvis called out again. This time the big
comprehensive school kid took a much more
reasonable line and only displayed his fist.

Billy's dad and Dot passed them shortly after
that. Billy's dad usually took Dot for a walk
about this time. He was carrying a can of
paraffin. This meant he was going up the allotment to light the lamp in the greenhouse. If the
frost got to the chrysanths it killed them off.

'Whatever are you doing, Our Billy?' his dad
asked, glancing down at the roulette game.

'Playing marbles, Dad.'

107

'Funny sort of marbles!'

He shook his head. Then he swung open the gate to the allotments, and soon he and Dot vanished into the dark.

Billy wondered if the tramp was up there already. It wouldn't be long now before he did turn up.

Elvis was blowing bubbles with his gum. He was ace at things like that. He could even pull his lower lip right over his nose, if he wanted to. It was a pity he didn't do it more often because it really improved his appearance.

A titchy kid, a kid they didn't know, had wandered over to them. The lenses of his specs were cracked.

'What's this game, mister?'

Elvis had never been called that before.

'Just a way of winnin' a lot of marbles, kiddar,' he said.

'Where you from?' asked Billy.

'Up the village.'

'What you doing down here, then?'

'Come down wi' me mam to see me grandma. She give us these.' He opened his hand to show them three marbles. 'Can I play wi' these?'

'Certainly you can, kiddar,' Elvis said. 'They're just the sort we're lookin' for.' He winked at Billy. 'Give us your marbles an' I'll give you three tokens. That's it. Now put the tokens wherever you like. Put them on any number you fancy. You can put all three on one number, if you like. You win more that way.'

The kid did that.

And lost.

'Hard Cheddar,' said Elvis, raking in the tokens.

'I thought you said it was a way of winnin' marbles,' said the Cracked-specs kid.

'So it is,' said Elvis. 'For us! Go and ask your grandma if she has any more marbles she wants to chuck away, will you?'

The kid looked at him for a moment. He obviously wasn't used to that kind of joke. Then he wandered off down Kitchener backs.

'Like tekkin' milk from a bairn!' said Elvis to Billy.

Emma must have heard him. She'd come over without either of them noticing.

'That wasn't very fair,' she said.

'How'd you mean?' asked Elvis.

'Tekkin' them marbles off that little kid. You should've let him win.'

'It was his choice. It's a free country.'

Steven was always saying that. That it was a free country – as long as you had the money.

'Is it?' She looked at Billy. 'What do *you* think, Billy?'

Billy wasn't sure. He enjoyed winning the three marbles. On the other hand—

But by that time Emma had turned away from him and marched off.

'Temper, temper!' Elvis called out after her. He jiggled the three marbles up and down in his hand. 'I like it! I like it!' he said. Billy still wasn't so sure. 'Mind you, Wardy's right,' Elvis said.

'How'd you mean?'

'We should've lerrim win. If we had of done, that might've brought other suckers running!' There was something about his grin that reminded Billy of the one the shark in the video was wearing, just before it swallowed its first kids' paddleboat when it got in the boating lake.

'Anyroad, we couldn't've let him win even if we'd wanted to,' said Billy. 'It's impossible.'

'It's impossible, impossible!' Elvis started singing. He bent down, picked up the wheel, and stuck a spot of bubble gum on the bottom of it. Then he put it back where it belonged and spun it three times. Each time the wheel stopped with the ball on number sixteen.

'Looks like number sixteen just got lucky all of a sudden,' he said to Billy, winking and looking all sly.

It was a minute after that when a kid called Barraclough came over to try his luck. Elvis advised him to bet on number sixteen, but he didn't trust Elvis at first. The second time he did, though.

'YIIIIIIIIPPPPPPPPPEEEEEEEEEEEEE!'

That meant Barraclough had won.

'Pay him out, Billy,' said Elvis. 'That's THIRTY-FIVE marbles.' He spoke the words loud so everybody would hear.

While Billy counted them out, he noticed Elvis stoop and remove the blob of bubble gum from the wheel. Barraclough wasn't in a fit state to notice anything. His eyeballs were nearly popping out as Billy counted out his winnings.

And after that the rush started.

Hands reaching out to offer them marbles, hands grabbing tokens, hands hovering over the green baize wondering where to place their bets; nervous hands, wandering hands, wondering hands, hands begging you to take their marbles first and nobody else's, hands clenched with disappointment, hands greedy with their winnings.

Kids poured in from all over the place: from Kitchener, Gordon, Haigh, Clive, Victoria, Wolsey, Nelson – from all the streets. By seven o'clock they were queuing up for a turn, jostling and fighting, the big kid from Spenny Comp keeping them in order (Elvis and Billy were paying him with marbles). And all the time the pile of marbles at Billy's feet was growing larger.

By half-past seven there were even kids from Chapel Row and Station Road playing. They must have heard it on the grapevine. And not long after them came kids from the council estate, from as far away as Coniston Road and Thirlmere Avenue and Windermere View.

Hands, marbles, tokens, hands; grab, rake, hands, push, shout, win, lose, hands . . .

Billy didn't even notice his dad and Dot come back down the allotment path and walk past them.

By eight o'clock Phase Two had started; they were selling marbles back to kids now. That meant the mountain of marbles began to dwindle slightly. But that didn't bother Billy. There

were pennies in Billy's pocket now. A real weight of them. A real solid weight of money. And that was a feeling Billy liked.

And he liked it even better when Phase Three started, and they stopped playing with silly marbles and started playing with pure money instead.

At nine o'clock, when the supply of money and marbles had dried up, they went back to Elvis's to divide and count up their loot.

They each had £1.95, together with a joint stockpile of a hundred and seventeen marbles. Not bad for a night's takings!

Billy made out two identical accounts, one for him and one for Elvis. He wrote at the top of each ROULETTE EARNINGS, and put the date against the sum. That was Elvis's idea. He insisted on it.

Billy didn't dare take his money home. He could just imagine what his mam would say if she found out. And she *would* find out. She had a nose like an anteater at times.

So Elvis put Billy's money in an old baccy-tin and hid it in the ferret cage. He said it would be safe there; his dad had a habit of grabbing any money that was left lying around, especially when he felt he was on to a Sure-Fire Certain Definite Winner (which he always was).

Elvis said he was going to keep his own money and account slip somewhere else, somewhere nobody would ever find them, somewhere nobody would ever suspect. He wouldn't even tell Billy.

When Elvis's sister came in with six chop-suey rolls and chips for their supper, she had a red-white-and-blue Mohican and she'd painted white triangles under her eyes.

Elvis fell off the chair and pretended to faint.

'What's up wi' you, Our Elvis?' said Soss.

'Just seen your haircut!' Elvis said.

She waited till he got back on his chair, then knocked him off it on to the floor again.

It was at a time like this that Billy really envied Elvis.

Chapter 9

It was the following day that Elvis had his second brainwave, the really important one.

It was also the day when Elvis was on the receiving end of a not-so-loving whop from Mrs Drury for making a disgusting sign behind her back as she was stalking away from him down the aisle.

It had been a particularly hard day for Mrs Drury. First she caught Elvis singing *Climb Every Butter Mountain* in assembly. Then second period in the afternoon she caught him picking his nose for the second time that day (not the second time he'd picked it, the second time she'd caught him picking it). And just before the end of school there was the Disgusting Sign Incident.

When he started answering her back again – Elvis had a bigger mouth than Tynemouth – nobody was surprised when she sent him to Mr Starr for about the umpteenth time that week.

'I just cannot imagine why somebody like you should associate with people like that!' she said to Billy. She looked all hot and flustered, her hands were still shaking long after Elvis had swaggered out of the classroom. There were times when even Billy thought Elvis went slightly over the top. 'And you are not to wait for him after school – you hear me, Robinson?'

'Yes, miss.'

'Is that clear now?'

'Yes, miss.'

Of course Billy did wait for Elvis. He always did when he was kept behind after school. When nobody was watching he tucked himself behind the rhododendron bushes which, despite all the odds, still managed to flourish alongside the outside bogs.

Mrs Drury would never find him there. For a start, she'd never come within a five hundred-mile range of anything so smelly, not with her sensitive nose.

The only one who regularly invaded the Danger Zone of the Bog Block was Mr Fixby, and he probably couldn't smell anything because he was so smelly himself to start with. He always had this dead lethal pong on his breath. You had only to catch a whiff of it and you felt like retiring from life. Some people said it was because he was a dedicated fagger and puffed his way through forty a day. Other people said he ate garlic sandwiches – Storm Pickersgill reckoned she'd actually *seen* him with her own eyes eating a garlic sandwich when she was coffee monitor one week. Other people said he never cleaned his teeth because he was too mingy to buy a toothbrush. In Billy's opinion it was probably a combination of all three.

All the same, somebody did come into the bogs just after Billy had tucked himself into hiding. It made Billy jump when he heard him – or them? – make a clattering noise in one of

the stalls, just the other side of the wall where he was leaning.

It surprised him because he'd seen nobody cross the yard and he could see right down it, right to the gate where the two duty teachers were frisking people as they went through, trying to find some of the money that had been nicked that day. He'd seen Miss Lipton search Howells only a minute or two ago. He'd hoped she would find something on him and order him back, but of course she didn't.

Anyhow, whoever it was in the bog didn't stay long, hardly long enough for a Jimmy Riddle.

When he was quite sure they'd done a bunk, Billy poked his nose out to have a gander at who it was. And that was another funny thing: there was neither sight nor sound of anybody in the yard. So they'd either hugged the wall right opposite Mr Starr's office, where he could have easily seen them through his windows, which was daft. Or it was the Invisible Man who'd just called in for An Extremely Short Swift One.

The teachers weren't allowed out of school till four o'clock (Emma Ward's mam had told her that), and about two milliseconds after that Mrs Drury burst out of the staff entrance like the so-called Famous Racing Dog was supposed to erupt from its starting trap – if Elvis was to be believed (which he wasn't).

Not that Mrs Drury looked much like a racing greyhound. She was wearing her heavy gear in order to combat the January cold; as well as her quilted coat (which could have taken on Siberia

and won 3–0), she was wearing her leather boots that stopped short just south of her navel and a fur hat that, at first glance, Billy took to be a fat black cat curled up asleep on her head. Apart from the two best weeks in July she always did dress as if the Third Ice Age was just round the corner of the school gates.

However, despite this weight-penalty, she still crossed the yard in record time and was into the staff car park in two seconds flat. She did rather like to be reasonably quick off the mark. In no time at all she'd clunk-clicked and, after giving Mr Fixby's cronky Ford a close shave, she zoomed out of the yard in her brand new Volvo.

Billy caught a glimpse of her face as she went. She looked none too happy. Maybe it was right what his grandma said. Maybe her husband really was having a carry-on with a woman who wore big flashy hats. Or maybe it was Elvis that was getting her down.

Billy could never quite sort out his feelings about Mrs Drury. She was ace at reading stories – even better than Miss Benfold had been. And he agreed with her about battery hens, Saving the Whale and that sort of thing. He didn't want to see any animal vanish for ever. Like Mrs Potter, Billy had a soft spot in his heart for nanimals – most naminals. (Killer sharks were a different matter altogether, weren't they? Or were they?)

Trouble was, Mrs Drury kept getting all high and mighty with everybody. A lot of teachers

were like that. Maybe they were trained for it in college? She especially had it in for Elvis.

And – a thing that really stuck up Billy's crop – when he was in Miss Benfold's he was always getting top marks for his stories, even beating Soskiss. For the first week or two in Mrs Drury's he'd been top as well, but since then she'd seemed to go off him (probably because of Elvis), and nowadays he sometimes came as low down as fifth or sixth, even behind bird-brains like Julia Batty, who always wrote the same blinking words – about her blinking pony, Dinky – in increasingly neater blinking handwriting.

It just wasn't fair. Miss Benfold always used to write BRILLIANT IDEAS! *Spelling a bit wonky!* To begin with, Mrs Drury used to write more or less the same. But then after the first three or four stories she started writing ATROCIOUS SPELLING! *Some very good ideas* instead. There was a world of difference between these two.

Elvis emerged soon after Mrs Drury had gone. By now all the kids had been cleared off the premises and the duty teachers had gone inside. Elvis stood at the bottom of the yard, making-on he was trying to guess where Billy was. He was always pretending he was dafter than he was, and that can't have been easy.

Billy wondered if he should come out of hiding. If the school caretaker spotted Elvis he'd get into trouble. His real name was Mr Lafferty, but everybody called him either Laffy or Mona Lott because he went round with a face longer than a Durham dole queue.

Mr Lafferty wasn't terribly keen on kids hanging about after four o'clock. Come to that, he wasn't keen on kids hanging about before four o'clock either. In fact, Mr Lafferty wasn't keen on kids, full stop. In his opinion they only made his school look untidy.

He went particularly bazonkers if you played football round his dustbin area. He sometimes went for you with his yard brush when you did that. Elvis said he was probably a member of the RSPDB (Royal Society for the Protection of Dust Bins).

Elvis was halfway up the yard, when the front door of Mr Lafferty's bungalow burst open and he shouted out, 'Hoy! What the devil are you doing here at this time of night? Get yersel' off home!'

Mona's guard-dog — a sabre-toothed Yorkshire Terrier everybody called Fang because it only had one tooth (it was permanently on display) — rolled threateningly down the path of the titchy front-garden like a small clump of annoyed fuzzy-felt, and stood or lay (it was hard to tell which, its legs were that short) yapping at the stockade fence itching to get its sabre tooth into Elvis. If anybody came within ten yards of that fence, Mona used to open his gate and set Fang on you, and if that failed he reached for his ultimate weapon — the yard broom.

'Mr Starr kept us in,' Elvis said.

'And now Ah'm chuckin' you out!' said Mona, almost breaking into a smile of genuine amusement.

'I can't wait,' said Elvis.

'Can't wait for what?'

'Can't wait for you-know-what,' said Elvis, pushing his hands between his thighs, crossing his legs, and nodding towards the bogs. 'If I don't go quick I'll have to go in Station Road.'

'Cheeky young *$£%!*!' said Mona. He was always swearing, especially if he caught you using the handbasins just after he'd given them their annual wipe-over. 'See you're off these premises in two minutes, or I'll give you you-know-what – and no mistake!'

He called Fang, and when he-she-or-it was safely corralled again, banged the door shut behind him.

Elvis carried on up the yard till he nearly reached the bogs, then called out:

'I spy with my little eye, something beginning with S.'

Billy came out from behind the rhododendron bush.

'What's S stand for?'

Elvis said a rude word.

'How'd you know I was there, though?'

'Could smell you a mile off!'

They started walking down towards the gate.

'How did you know I was there, though?'

'Saw you through the window, man.'

At first Billy didn't catch on. Elvis couldn't have seen him if he'd been standing in the corridor outside Mr Starr's office. There wasn't a window there. Then he realised Elvis must have got bored of standing, and nipped along

121

the corridor to look out of one of the windows further along. Or else he'd been looking out of Mr Starr's office window.

'Who was it went in the bog?' Billy asked.

'When?'

'Just after I got hid.'

'Nobody did.'

'They did, man. I heard them.'

Elvis stopped talking. And walking. He looked at Billy.

'Are you sure somebody was in there?'

'Positive, man. I heard all this clatter. They were only in a tick.'

'Blinkin' heck!'

Elvis had turned round and was heading for the bogs.

'What's up?' Billy called after him. For a sec he thought Elvis had been telling the truth to Mona. But that was highly unlikely.

Meantime Elvis had dived straight into the bogs. He came out after a tick. He had a funny glazed look in his eyes. At first Billy thought it might be the stink, but then he realised it was something more important than that. He'd seen that look in the eyes of a feller in a film, who got accidentally frozen to death for five hundred years, then came alive again and started chasing people with an axe because his heart had got frozen in the process.

'What is it, Elvis?'

But he didn't really have to ask.

'Just had a brainwave.' His eyes were still glazed over. 'A really brilliant one.'

'What about? About the game?'

'Na. More important than that.'

'What do you mean?'

Elvis never answered that question, either then or later.

But eventually Billy had an idea what the answer should have been.

Chapter 10

That night, and all day Saturday and Sunday, and Monday night as well, Billy and Elvis took out the roulette game and continued to rake in the loot.

By Monday night each of their account sheets read like this:

PROFITS

Thursday	25th January	. . .£1.95
Friday	26th January	. . .£2.45
Saturday	27th January	. . .£0.71
Sunday	28th January	. . .£0.47
Monday	29th January	. . .£0.24

Things looked good. At least at first glance. They'd each made a profit of £4.82 on their original investment of £1.00. And they had a stockpile of marbles. Not bad!

But, as Elvis pointed out after they'd counted their profits and were playing with the ferrets on Monday night, the bottom had dropped out of the market.

They'd taken their last marble on Saturday morning, and if you looked carefully at the figures you could see the money was fast running out as well. As a matter of fact, on Monday night only three punters had turned up, and all three of them were skint after half an hour.

'We'll just have to think of summat else,' said

Elvis, as he spun the wheel and watched the silver ball bounce up and down before coming to rest. 'This racket's finished. Lay chewers son fet, as they say.'

But his mind didn't seem to be really on the job. It hadn't been all night for some reason. The whole time he'd seemed to be thinking of something else.

Come to think of it, he hadn't been himself all day. Mrs Drury hadn't had to send him once to Mr Starr, and most of the time he'd acted (almost) like a perfectly normal human being.

The funny thing was, despite what he'd just said, he was still smiling like a cat that just had the canary.

In any case, Billy was feeling only half-hearted himself about the whole roulette business.

Of course, it was nice to have a hoard of marbles hidden under your bed and in the bottom of your wardrobe (like buried treasure). And it was nicer still having nearly six quid of dosh tucked away in the ferret cage.

But there was another side to Getting-Rich-Quick, a side of drawbacks. Heap Big Drawbacks and Heap Plenty Troubles.

In fact, you could draw up another kind of account sheet about the roulette game, a balancing side of losses that had nothing to do with money and more to do with a bonny lot of other things in life. Things which as each day passed seemed to loom larger and larger in Billy's mind.

Firstly, for example, there was the problem of MATES.

Billy hadn't really noticed how important mates were before. They'd just been there; like air, or water, or another slice of jam and bread for tea.

But suddenly they all seemed to be moving further and further away from Billy and Elvis: Daz, Mitch, Ibbi, Totter, Fletch – even Joe and Emma – they were all moving away.

When they'd first come into Mrs Drury's she'd once mentioned, just in passing, that the universe they lived in was constantly expanding and that the stars in it were all the time drifting further and further apart.

It hadn't meant much to Billy at the time. It had hardly registered on his mind. But it did now.

He knew just how those stars felt as they watched their best mates drifting even further and further away from them; they felt colder, lonelier, more isolated with every second that passed.

Of course, none of them had actually said anything – except Emma, who'd dropped a pretty hefty-sized hint that first night when they'd taken the marbles off the kid with cracked lenses in his specs.

Apart from that, none of them had actually said anything. None of them had actually come straight out with it and said, 'Don't want to play with you any more, Robbo.'

They might as well have done, though.

Billy could understand Ossie Turnbull stopping them playing with his ball at school. That was the sort of thing you expected from Ossie Turnbull. He'd lost all his marbles and twenty pence that first night anyhow, which probably left him scarred for life. And Ossie Turnbull was always the sort of kid who'd take First Prize in a Moaning Competition any day.

It was the rest of them that bothered Billy. None of them had said a dicky-bird when Ossie picked his ball up and said Elvis and Billy couldn't play any more. Not even Emma Ward chirped up.

And it wasn't just that they didn't really want to play football with you any more. They didn't want to swap comics with you. They didn't tell you any jokes. When you told them jokes they didn't listen properly. All the time you were with them you felt they had somewhere else more important to go. Nobody punched you in fun, or kicked you up the backside.

And that was an awful feeling. The feeling that you could bend over to tie your shoelace in the playground and nobody – nobody – would boot you up the backside and shout, 'Caught you bending!'

It was a feeling that Billy liked less and less as time went by.

Secondly, there was HOWELLS.

It really narked Billy that Howells was benefiting from the game. It had narked him from the start. He hadn't liked it that first night when Howells had followed them down the

backs. He ought to have spoken out then, but he hadn't.

'What you after, Owly?' Elvis had asked, turning round.

'Me cut of the lolly, Pottyman, that's all.' He held out the palm of his left hand and stroked it with the fingers of his right. 'Spondoolicks. Dosh. Dough. Ackers. Gelt.'

It was the first indication Billy ever had that somebody could be as daft as a backward budgie and still know an awful lot of words that stood for money.

'I don't get it,' said Elvis. 'What you on about?' He was always pretending he hadn't a clue, when in fact he had everything worked out from start to finish.

Certainly Billy knew what it was about. He'd seen all this happen in the film about Las Vegas. It was what was called a protection racket.

As soon as the hero of this film had got rich and started investing in nightclubs and casinos, these gangsters from Chicago had muscled in – big gorillas with brains like a well-sucked wine gum – and they had explained that he needed protection.

Protection! Big joke! What they meant was, if he didn't shig-out to them fast he'd end up in the harbour wearing concrete wellies. Outsize concrete wellies.

'Gimme-gimme-gimme,' said Howells, still stroking his big daft hand.

'What for should I pay you money, though, Owly?'

128

'Yer what?'

'I mean, who do I need protectin' against?'

Even in this dim light you could see Howells' brain trying its best to work. You could practically hear the cogs creaking. It seemed to be quite an ordeal, but after about three weeks Howells came up with an answer.

'Somebody might offer you a bit of this,' said Howells, holding up his fist.

'Oh yeah,' said Elvis, 'never thought of that, Owly. OK. How much d'you want?'

At the time Billy thought Elvis was going soft in the head. He was wrong of course. But that's what he thought at the time.

He watched them settle for fifty pence a night. Fifty pence for a – for a you-know-what like Howells. Billy would sooner have chucked the money away in the sea.

He was about to shove his sort of oar in but, before he could actually get his tongue round the words, Elvis had pulled this bit of paper from his jacket (he seemed to have it prepared) and shoved it under Howells' nose. It was appropriately entitled OFFISHAL RECEEPS.

'What's this?'

'Just sign yer moniker.' Elvis had a pencil in his hand now (naturally, it was a school one). 'Just so we're all square. I've always wanted yer autograph, anyhow, Owly.'

Howells grinned. That was something he could understand: somebody wanting his autograph.

He signed his name with a flourish. He had a

right flashy signature that everybody could recognize and nobody could read – like a doctor's in a panic.

'Thanks a lot, Owly,' said Elvis, ogling up at him.

Billy nearly yucked up.

So that was it. Every night they handed over their fifty pence protection money, and Howells signed with his well-known flashy flourish and grinned a ghoulish grin.

And every night Billy got more and more sick of the whole rotten business.

But the MARBLES situation was even worse . . .

The marbles, which had started as a minor irritation, had blossomed into a major catastrophe, and were now fast developing into a non-stop nightmare.

It wasn't only that they seemed to have syphoned off every marble for miles around (which was one reason why a lot of mates weren't mates any more). Billy's dad had practically called him a miser when he'd seen all the marbles. And now his mother was starting to complain. And that could be serious.

Billy could see now he'd gone wrong on that first night, when Elvis had said if he was looking after all the money it was only fair if Billy looked after all the marbles.

It had seemed a reasonable idea at the time. Trouble was, by Friday night they had about a zillion marbles.

Even then they would have been all right if it hadn't been for Billy's mother. On Saturday

morning, when she was out of the way, Billy got some sweet boxes from Nobby Bolton, packed them all in there and shoved them under his bed and in the bottom of his wardrobe, all neat and tidy. Well, sort of.

How was he to know she would start spring cleaning when she got back from Bishop Auckland?

That was the trouble with Billy's mother. In many ways she was entirely unpredictable. And she didn't just spring clean in spring. She spring cleaned in autumn, summer and winter as well. Plus the bits in between.

Why couldn't she be more like Mrs Potter? Mrs Potter didn't altogether hold with spring cleaning (or any other cleaning for that matter). She said that if you went about housework with a whole load of 'flap and doodle', all you did was force muck and dust to shift from one end of a room to another. And she couldn't see any sense in that. In her opinion, moving dust about wasn't the reason why God had put us on earth.

And on the rare occasions when she did clean she had a rule never to shift things if it could be at all avoided. So that, apart from those objects in the Potter household that were in a continual flux of coming and going (due to the ups and downs of Mr Potter's speculations on the gee-gees and wuff-wuffs), it was reasonably true to say that Mrs Potter never shifted anything at all.

'If it hasn't moved, Billy, I fail for the life to me to see how there can by any muck under it,'

she was always telling him, 'and if it hasn't any muck under it, why bother to move it in the first place?'

And Billy was inclined to agree with her.

Billy's mother, however, was made of different stuff.

When *she* was cleaning a room her motto seemed to be: if you can see an object, move it! She moved beds, wardrobes, and dressers that weighed three tons. If by chance a mountain had strayed into the room she was currently cleaning she'd have moved that as well. She'd have lifted the floorboards if they hadn't been firmly nailed to the joists with six inch nails.

The result was that when she shifted Billy's cardboard boxes they started to show their frailty. First little cracks and openings appeared, and soon these developed into what job adverts called 'Promising openings for young marbles with initiative, courage, and two GCSEs', and before she knew what was what, the more adventurous of the marbles had started emigrating to the four corners of the room, and one had shown enough enterprise to reach as far afield as the landing at the top of the stairs.

You can imagine what a carry-on this caused!

When he came in for his tea on Saturday afternoon, she held up the poor marble between finger and thumb, and said, 'I could've easy slipped on this little devil, Our Billy, *and* broke me neck coming down them stairs!'

Billy didn't say anything.

133

'Load of daftness!' said his dad.

'Why should I have to get down on my hands and knees to shift things like that about, Billy? Do you think I've got nothing better to do?'

'Sorry,' said Billy.

He was always saying 'Sorry' nowadays. And he was getting blinking sick of it.

But things actually got worse after that.

First Dot did her Famous Marble Swallowing Act. Or *might* have done. They were never quite sure about that. It was one of Life's Great Unsolved Mysteries.

Billy's mam definitely saw her pick up a marble in her teeth. Then she threw back her head (Dot, not Billy's mother) and there was a clicky sound which might – or might not – have been the marble hitting her teeth (Dot's, not his mother's) and bouncing out; but after that all she (Billy's mother) could be certain of was that she'd searched high and low without finding sight or sound of a marble.

What sort of a sound does a marble make, anyhow, Billy had found himself wondering.

Chuffy would probably know. On Friday Miss Benfold had been showing her class how to play What Am I? and, to make it easy, the first one she wrote on the board was:

1. I have a smooth skin.
2. I have two legs.
3. I can talk . . . What am I?

And when everybody had flung their hands

up she'd asked Chuffy for the answer (because Chuffy didn't often put his hand up – well, not to answer), and Chuffy's answer had been: 'A carrot.'

'It might easy have caused a stoppage of the insides, mightn't it, Dick?'

Billy's mam had a tendency to look on the bright side of things.

'Easy.'

And Billy's dad had a tendency to support her.

But when Billy told Mrs Potter about it on Sunday morning she thought it was highly unlikely. She was reading a book called *Wild and Reckless Lover* and eating chocolates at the same time as she was watching the bit in *Fins*, where hairy-legged Bruce was teaching the captain's wife the correct grip for the first time (of her racket).

'What goes in must come out, Billy,' she said, as she swallowed a Caramel Nougat, 'that's what folks say.'

'What goes up must come down,' corrected Mr Potter.

'Eh?'

'Never mind.'

'The answer to that's a numbrella, isn't it?' said Soss, who was putting on her anti-nuclear earrings (which made a nice change from her safety pins).

'Up a spout up,' said Elvis, trying to help, 'or down. Or summat.'

So that altogether Billy wasn't terribly reassured.

And in any case things were to get much
worse.

In fact on Sunday night the Worst thing in
the World happened. The Thing Billy's Mam
Dreaded Even More Than The Atom Bomb
Falling On Belton Buildings While They Were
Using Their Best Tea Set In Their Front Room.

Yes – you've guessed it – the vacuum cleaner
stopped working. The Holy Machine gave up the
ghost.

What had happened was half a dozen marbles
seemed to have wedged themselves in its throat,
probably deliberately.

When Billy's mam referred to them as 'little
devils', it reminded him of a war film he'd seen
about Japanese kamikaze pilots hurling themselves to death on the decks of American aircraft carriers, and his estimation of marbles
went up immediately.

'Whatever shall we do, Dick?' asked Billy's
mam.

It sounded like the End of the World Was
Nigh. Maybe it really was, in a way, as far as
Billy's mam was concerned. And what about the
Jehovah's Witness feller who was forever
knocking on their front door in a tidy suit and
a spotless shirt, telling them the world was
going to come to a full-stop next week if everybody didn't pull their socks up sharp and do
something about it quick? Maybe he was right.

Was there, in fact, life after the vacuum
cleaner?

'Keep calm lass, I'll see what I can do,' said

Billy's brave dad, and he soon came galloping back to the rescue with his tool box to carry out an emergency tonsillectomy there and then on the carpet of Billy's bedroom.

Billy held the patient on its back, trying to calm its nerves, while his mam put it to sleep (by yanking out its plug), and his dad fished expertly about in its throat with a pair of screwdrivers and a giant medieval tin-opener Grandma had bequeathed to them yonks back, which looked like a weapon for finishing off

knights in armour. Eventually he struck gold, or, rather, marbles, and they all breathed a sigh of relief (not the marbles, the humans), except Billy's mother, who breathed three.

Four of the suicide-divers had got stuck in the suction pipe, and they found another three, crouching like undercover agents, in the dust-bag.

'Mind, this carry-on'll have to stop, Our Billy,' said his dad. 'Just look at all these marbles!' Not many of them had rolled into view, actually; only about a million. 'It's more like a miser's hoard than owt else. You ought to be ashamed of yourself, son. However did you come by all this many?'

He knew very well how Billy had got them, of course.

'Just playing, Dad.'

'Just playing me foot!'

'All I know is they'll kill somebody before long,' said Billy's mam.

Billy could just see it in the newspaper: *Ten million marbles launched a mass-attack on cheerful Northern housewife Alice Robinson yesterday as she was preparing to Spring Clean her son, William's, bedroom for the fourth time since Christmas.*

'You hear what your mother says? We'll all end up wi' broken legs.'

'Yes, Dad.'

'I want them out of this house by Wednesday night,' said his mam. 'And I don't want them taking up your grandma's. I don't want them

killing her instead, not just yet.'

How on earth could anybody get rid of a zillion marbles by Wednesday night? It was Mission Impossible.

And, anyhow, who'd ever heard of a homicidal marble?

That night Billy dreamed that a race of alien marbles had invaded planet Earth. They came in spaceships disguised as toffee boxes from Nobby Bolton's, and got under people's feet and made them fall down. Everybody had crutches and broken legs. Even the dogs had broken legs. Billy was talking to a farmer and there was a solid wooden object leaned against a wall. When Billy asked him what it was he said it was a wooden leg for his bull. His mother was down the street carrying on a lone fight against the alien invaders. She kept saying, 'It's all Our Billy's fault!'

So that on Tuesday morning Billy woke up feeling full of worries.

But he had a lot more to worry about by Tuesday afternoon.

Chapter 11

Mind you, Tuesday started off normally enough:
Mr Starr sent for Elvis during registration.

But this time he was back after five minutes.

And he came in looking all pink round the
gills. He might even have been blushing. Billy
fancied he was even trying to cover up a smile
as he swaggered down the aisle to their table.

'What did Mr Starr say?' Billy asked him.

'Nowt.'

Five minutes later, just when Mrs Drury was
going to scramble all their brains with another
general knowledge quiz about the Royal Family
and battery hens, a prefect from the top class
came in and said they all had to go to the hall
at once.

Mr Starr came into the hall, just as Mrs
Wendover was shepherding her Infants down to
the front and trying to get them to behave like
normal human beings.

They were always last to arrive because they
had to cross the road, and then what Mrs Wendover (who everybody called Tank-top because
she looked like one, especially at the top) called
'the Big Yard', and they kept wandering off and
getting lost, despite the fact that Mrs Wendover
was always fussing over them like a mother hen
disguised in tweeds, woollies, and big wooden
beads the size of pigeons' eggs.

141

'Now then,' said Mr Starr, when something like sanity was threatening to creep in. 'I have something very important to tell you this morning. Something very important, indeed. Something you'll all be glad to hear.'

'Please, sir,' said one of Mrs Wendover's kids, 'our dog 'ad pups last night.'

'Shush!' said Mrs Wendover, leaning forward and rattling her beads.

'How very interesting,' said Mr Starr. His specs flashed under the lights and everybody heard him click his false teeth. He always did that when he was getting his paddy up.

'Ten o' them, sir,' added this gobby Infant. 'It 'ad ten last year an' all, sir. Please, sir, me mam sez it 'as ten every year.'

'Shush-shush!' said Mrs Wendover, shaking her beads like a rattlesnake. 'Shush!'

'Lately,' said Mr Starr, 'we've had a spate of thieving in our school, something we don't often get. In fact, all the time I've been at Belton Buildings school I cannot recall a time when so much money has been stolen.'

'Please, sir, I 'ad twenty pence nicked outa me pocket in the porch last week,' said a little kid down the front.

'So have I, sir!' said this midget from Miss Benfold's. Everybody called him the So-Have-I kid because no matter what you said – it could be *Please, sir, I've been to Spain last week and our plane nearly didn't take off,* or *Every night I go to bed, sir, I have this nightmare about black puddings wi' arms* or *Please, sir, we went to*

142

Spend 'n' Save, and we gorra blue balloon, and
when we got home it blew over our backyard wall
– this kid was bound to say, 'So have I, sir.'

Mr Starr slowly angled his head round till he
was staring straight down at the So-Have-I kid.
He had a way of looking like the Zombie From
Twenty Thousand Fathoms when he wanted to.

'I've just about had enough of these interruptions,' he said.

For a minute, when Billy saw the So-have-I
kid's head bob and wiggle, he thought he was
going to stand up and say, 'So have I, sir,' but
he didn't, which was just as well for all of them
(and especially for the So-Have-I kid).

'I really don't know what the world's coming
to nowadays,' said Mr Starr, 'what with bomb
outrages, kidnappings – and, now, people inter-
rupting teachers. I don't know where it's all
going to stop. In my day it was an unheard of
thing for a child to interrupt a teacher when he
was speaking – or she. Unheard of. Nowadays
there's half of you people up all hours of the
night watching horror movies on the television.
In my day children were in bed by half-past
seven – best place for them at that time of night.
And anybody that did interrupt a teacher would
have been hung, drawn and quartered on the
spot.' His eyes swept round the room. He may
have winked. 'Probably the best thing for it as
well. Still . . .'

He gazed out at them like an annoyed lighthouse. There were no interruptions this time.
Even Elvis didn't say anything under his breath

143

– and that *was* unusual.

'I don't suppose many of you remember Adolf Hitler?' asked Mr Starr.

Pat Shufflebotham put her hand up.

'Yes, thank you, Patricia, you can put your hand down now.'

Pat Shufflebotham would have put her hand up if Mr Starr had asked whether anybody remembered Julius Caesar or even Moses in the Bulrushes. She was always eager to please.

'Well, I do remember Hitler,' said Mr Starr.

He was probably speaking the truth. Mr Starr had been born such a long time ago that he had even fought in the war against the Germans. Some people said he had flown a Spitfire, other people said he had been in tanks (not flying them, though).

But these questions were so far back in the remote past that nobody would ever know the answer for sure, just like nobody – according to Mrs Drury – would ever know for certain why the dinosaurs had finally kicked the bucket (though in her opinion it was probably all due to pollution, which is one reason why she kept on doing her nut about chip papers scattered along Station Road).

'And I remember invading Germany in 1945 and freeing Berlin – me and a few others, of course.'

Here he flashed his glasses to signal to the teachers that he'd just cracked one of his corny jokes, and a few of them giggled. Mrs Drury didn't even pause in her knitting.

144

'I don't suppose any of you have the faintest idea what impressed the German people about Adolf Hitler, have you?'

'I have, sir,' said the same barmy infant who'd told Mr Starr about his pups.

'So have I, sir,' said the So-Have-I kid.

'I shall do something naughty in a minute, Mrs Wendover,' said Mr Starr. 'Something very naughty and illegal, I shall probably be arrested shortly afterwards and sent to jail, but all things considered it will probably be worth it!'

Mr Starr's false gnashers were going like agitated castanets by now – a really bad sign.

'As I was saying before I was so rudely interrupted, what impressed the German people most about Adolf Hitler was the fact that they could leave their purse on the side in the kitchen and nobody would touch it. Can you imagine that? The mother of one of our children was telling me only the other day that she hung her husband's long underpants on the washing line for five minutes last week and when she went back to get them, somebody had actually stolen them. And I want no laughter! This is not a laughing matter.'

Mr Starr waited until the sniggering had stopped.

'Now,' he said, 'can anybody tell me why you could leave your purse on the dresser top and nobody would pinch it when Adolf Hitler was around? Hands up if you know the answer.'

'Please, sir, were they all dead?'

'Not quite. Good try, though. No, something a

little less drastic than that. Anybody guess? Nobody? Well, I'll have to tell you, then. It was because Hitler passed a law to say that anybody caught thieving had to have his hand chopped off. And, from what the German people told me, that apparently stopped thieving overnight.'

Billy could just imagine it would.

It was the sort of law Mona Lott would be in favour of. Billy could just imagine him borrowing Tommy Morgan's scythe and going around cutting people's legs off. That would stop them playing football round his bins.

He turned to look at Elvis, to see what he thought – it was a wonder he hadn't made a crack already – and was surprised to see how white Elvis's face had gone. Whatever for, he wondered.

'Anyhow, I'm glad to say we won't have to go quite that far to stop thieving in our school – though I'm sure one or two of my staff would probably think it a good idea.'

Again he gave a I-Have-Just-Cracked-A-Joke twinkle of his glasses. He was probably thinking of Mr Fixby, whose favourite hobby was twisting your lugs off or keeping you in all playtime on sunny days. Certainly he was all in favour of bringing back hanging because he'd told them so once in a Scripture lesson. And he personally thought football hooligans should be flogged to death with a cat o' nine tails before the next game started. He reckoned it was the only way to stamp out violence once and for all in society.

147

'It won't be necessary, because we've found the culprit.'

Mr Starr's head moved slowly to take in the whole school. For one moment Billy was uncomfortably certain that Mr Starr was looking directly at him and he found himself wondering if *he* was the culprit after all.

Had he, in fact, been nicking the Blind Dog money all along, without knowing it? Like a feller he'd seen in a film, a mad pianist who was given a murderer's hands (by accident) in an operation, and kept throttling people all over the shop, without knowing it was him.

In any case, he *had* been robbing people – with the roulette game. Elvis and Billy were just as much to blame as the person who'd been nicking from the porch – weren't they?

'A lot of you will get a great surprise when you hear who the thief is, because he's a bit of a blue-eyed boy.'

Billy felt a surge of relief when he heard this, and not only for himself. Elvis didn't have blue eyes, either. Elvis's eyes were a sort of frogspawn-grey.

'A boy who has won many accolades,' said Mr Starr.

'Please, sir, what's a naccolade?' asked the Ten-Pups-A-Year kid.

'Furthermore, a boy who is an outstanding sportsman. You don't expect a sportsman to be a thief.'

Mr Starr was saying that because back in the Dark Ages he'd played football himself. He'd

played football for the Athletic when they'd won the cup (that was two seasons before Noah built his ark), and although he was so ancient he could still kick a ball when he wanted to.

'However,' said Mr Starr, 'I don't want to keep you here all morning. I can see some boys at the back itching to get on with their maths and spelling tests. So, without further ado, I'll come straight to the point.'

Here he paused, so that everybody could laugh at the Extremely Boring Joke (No. 3), which he'd just cracked.

'But perhaps I might first mention another boy, one who doesn't want his name mentioning at all – and that is another surprise, because I wouldn't have thought this particular specimen was modest at all. My goodness, we do seem to be having a lot of surprises this morning, don't we?'

'Yes, sir,' said Pat Shufflebotham.

'Thank you, Patricia,' said Mr Starr. 'By coincidence this boy is also a good – but perhaps I'd better not say too much, otherwise I might give the game away! All I'd better say is this: the boy has almost single-handedly brought the culprit to justice after nearly a fortnight of clever initiative on his part, a fortnight in which he has selflessly given up many of his play-times in order to keep watch – and one in which some misguided people have given him an even blacker reputation that he enjoys already.'

Here Mrs Drury stopped her knitting; in fact she almost dropped it.

'So, without disclosing his name, I want to say a big thank you to this boy on behalf of all of you. Thank you, Sherlock Holmes!'

Mr Starr smiled and began to clap. The whole school joined in, squiggling round to try and find out who it was.

Mr Starr seemed to be looking at Billy again. Had he, in fact, solved the crime without really knowing what he did? Was that it? He tried to think back to what he'd done in the last week or so.

Then he realised who the Sherlock Holmes really was. He turned to look at Elvis. He was screwing his neck round to look at the back, just like all the rest. His face and neck were scarlet. That could be the strain of turning round, of course.

Or was it something else?

'And now we have another matter, a less pleasant one to deal with. The boy who was the mastermind behind all this thieving did not even commit the crimes himself. He was too cowardly for that. He used two younger boys to steal the money from other people's pockets, just like some modern-day Fagin. We knew it was going on, of course. We knew for a long time. It was pinning the crime on the real perpetrator that was difficult, catching the villain red-handed. But we did that last night, thanks to a tip-off from our young Sherlock Holmes.'

'Please, sir, I've seen Sherlock Holmes on telly.'

'So have I, sir,' said the So-Have-I kid.

'What our thief was doing was gathering up the money in the outside boy's toilet and hiding it there. That was why our spot-checks at the gate failed. Then after school he was going into the farmer's field and climbing back over the wall into the outside toilets. That's how he was collecting his ill-gotten gains. Clever, eh? Until Monday night, when he was caught with the money in his hand!'

'Who was it, sir?'

'I was just coming to that. Would the thief please stand up!'

Billy turned round and was just in time to see Howells, powerful, heavy, and white-faced with anger rising to his feet.

Chapter 12

It was just before afternoon break when the thunderbolt came.

'Robinson, Potter, the headmaster wants to see you at once.'

Billy had known the piece of paper had his name written on it the moment the monitor had brought it into the classroom.

All day, ever since that first little jab of conscience in assembly, he'd felt uneasy, as if something not very nice was about to descend on him from an extremely great height.

And he'd felt sure of it twenty minutes before when he'd seen Mrs Soskiss stalking across the yard. She always leaned forward when she walked, as if she was heading determinedly into a gale-forced wind, but this afternoon she looked particularly leany and determined.

And Billy could guess why.

As soon as Mrs Drury spoke, everybody swivelled round to look at him and Elvis including Samantha Soskiss, who had been swivelling round that much since her mam had first set foot in the yard it wouldn't have surprised Billy (or disappointed him, overmuch, either) if her head had swivelled off in the process.

Billy felt his face go red. At the same time he felt something cold and clammy take possession of his belly (which reminded him of a film he'd

seen at Elvis's about an alien from outer space that had dived head-first down some poor fella's throat, and taken up residence in his stomach till it felt it was ready to burst out on to the world).

Elvis was already out of his seat and swaggering up the aisle. He didn't look too worried. It was all right for him. He was used to it.

Billy had only once before been in Mr Starr's office, and that was to get a lollipop prize when he was in Mrs Wendover's for learning to tell the time properly on her cardboard clock.

'I think you should use a comb before you go into Mr Starr's office,' said Mrs Drury. 'Don't you, Elvis?'

She'd been a lot nicer to Elvis since assembly, treating him almost like a humanoid. She'd even told him his writing had improved, which was true; you could more or less read it today, sort of.

Billy suspected that (like him) she thought Elvis was the mystery Sherlock Holmes that everybody had been yacketty-yacking about at play-time. Naturally, Elvis denied it. But Elvis always denied everything anyway (and especially if he'd done it) – so what was the truth?

'Haven't got one, miss.'

'Oh, dear, what a pity.'

She made a pretence of rummaging in her handbag for one. 'I seem to have forgotten mine as well. Has anybody in the class got a comb Elvis can borrow?'

Nobody had.

You couldn't blame them, really. They probably didn't want to mix the breeds.

'Well, you'll just have to go in to see him like that. Heaven only knows what he'll think.' She glanced at Billy. 'You're passable,' she said.

She was full of compliments today.

Mr Starr was sitting behind his desk when they went in. He wasn't smoking now, but you could still smell the smoke.

'Come in, boys. I've just had a parent in to see me and I'd just like a little chat with you both.'

That sounded friendly enough.

'Now, for a start, have either of you two lads got anything you'd like to get off your chests before we begin? Anything bothering your minds at all?' He paused for a long time. Billy felt his face going redder all the time. 'No? Are you quite sure? I mean, the last thing I want to do this afternoon is punish somebody, Elvis. You do appreciate that, son?'

'Yes, sir.'

Mr Starr glanced quickly at Billy.

'But I do have to get to the bottom of this business, even if there has to be some unpleasantness. You do understand that, Billy?'

'Yes, sir.'

'And you've nothing to tell me?'

'No, sir,' Billy croaked.

'Elvis?'

'No, sir,' said Elvis.

'Well, that's a pity,' said Mr Starr. 'A great pity. I'm sorry to hear it, for your sakes. And for mine.'

He stood up and pushed his chair back, making a horrible screechy sound.

'There's one thing I like in this world, boys. Do you know what that is? It's the truth.'

Billy had thought he was going to say it was football. Because Mr Starr was nuts and bananas about football. That was the only thing that stood them in good stead at the moment, because both Elvis and Billy were knocking on the door of the school team. Not that it had helped Howells much. Mr Starr had told him that if he got into any more trouble that term he wouldn't be playing for the area team.

Mr Starr was standing by the window now, the light behind him.

'Let me put it this way, boys. Have the pair of you been up to anything devious in the last week or so?'

'What's "devious" mean, sir?'

'Dodgy, Elvis. Not quite above board. Shady. I feel sure you must know what that means.'

'Yes, sir.'

'Thought you might. Well? Have you?'

'No, sir.'

'You disappoint me.'

'Don't know what you're on about, sir.'

'I think you do, Elvis,' said Mr Starr. A sharp edge had come into his voice now. 'I think you know very well what I'm on about – as you put it. Think hard.'

Elvis thought hard. You could tell he was thinking hard because he put his I-Am-Thinking-Hard face on. It was easy to recognise

156

because he didn't often use it.

Light seemed suddenly to dawn in his eyes. 'Do you mean all the collectin' for charity that—'

'I do not, Elvis! You know very well that is not what I mean!'

'But we 'ave been collectin' for the Blind Dogs Appeal, sir,' said Elvis. He had his Totally Innocent Angel face on now. Billy knew why he'd said that. To soften the blow, when it came. 'It's the God's truth I'm telling you, sir!'

Blinking heck! thought Billy.

'I see,' said Mr Starr. 'You're placing me in a very difficult situation – you see that, don't you, Elvis? But if that's the way you want it, that's the way you shall have it!'

He went to his cupboard and took Tickler down from the top shelf. He placed the stick on his desk, where they had a perfect view. It was a thin bamboo stick, a bit frayed at the end.

Then Mr Starr came in front of his desk and sat on it, just to the side of Tickler.

He was so close to them that Billy could see the craters in his face, especially the big ones clustered round the end of his nose. It was like looking at a bumpy part of the moon after a pretty bad shower of meteorites.

'I'm sorry it's come to this, boys, and as I say, especially for you, Elvis.'

He looked at Billy. His eyes were sparkly and bright for an old feller's. It was no wonder he still balanced the books at the Club where Billy's dad was also on the committee. There

was a wart on the lid of his right eye that Billy had never noticed before.

'I'm sorry for you as well, Billy Robinson, because this is the first time you've ever been in trouble of this kind, and I know how disappointed your father will be when I see him at the committee meeting tonight. You realise I've no option but to tell him?'

Billy nodded.

'But especially for you, Elvis, in view of what's happened—' (he nearly said today) '— recently.' He looked at Elvis for a moment and shook his head. 'A lot of my staff don't agree with me, but I've never thought you were a bad boy at heart.'

He was only saying that because Elvis was ace at football. If he hadn't been, Mr Starr would cheerfully have crucified him years back with the full blessing of half the staff.

'And we all know you don't get as much help as you might from other sources.' He was probably referring to Mr Potter, who once tried to claim compensation for a strain in the leg he got standing in a queue in the dole office. 'And to cap it all you're a first-rate footballer. I hate to see a first-rate footballer go to waste.' He shook his head again. 'You're both good footballers, that's what's so sad about it. And I've punished enough good footballers already for one day!' He drew in breath so sharply that Billy saw all the hairs in his nose bend violently in the updraught. 'But I can't beat about the bush mincing words all day. I've got Mrs Quincy, the

159

English Adviser, coming to see me in ten minutes, so I'll have to be brief and come to the point. A parent has just been in to see me – can you guess who?'

Both boys shook their heads.

'Mrs Soskiss. You know her, of course?'

Both boys nodded.

How could anybody not know Mrs Soskiss? The Soskisses lived in Lindisfarne View where all the houses had front gardens. If a dying man sat on her front-garden wall for one second, Mrs Soskiss would come out and ask him to move on because it was private property. She was always timing how long the dustbin men had for their tea-break, and then writing a letter a yard long to the papers about it.

'Mrs Soskiss told me a rather distressing tale. Matthew Soskiss, her son, also a member of this school community, the same one that you belong to, has happened to lose the grand total of sixty-six marbles and all his pocket-money in one night!'

All his pocket-money? All they'd taken from the Soskiss kid was fifteen pence. Was that all they gave the poor kid for his pocket money? It was possible. Anything was possible with the Soskisses. They had a notice on their front garden gate that said BEWARE OF THE DOG, and all they had was a King Charles spaniel.

'Now I call that a pretty remarkable achievement, don't you? To lose all your pocket-money and sixty-six marbles in one night. And what I'd like to ask you boys is this: do either of you

know anything about it? A simple, straightforward yes or no will suffice.'

'Yes, sir,' said Elvis, his voice remarkably
firm and clear.

'Yes, sir,' said Billy, more shakily.

'Excellent! I do believe we're beginning to get
somewhere! The truth is beginning to leak out
at last! Good heavens, boys, it's like trying to
squeeze toothpaste out of last year's tube.'

'But, sir—' started Elvis.

For some reason he was beginning to hop on
one foot.

'But me no buts, Elvis – and for Heaven's sake
stand still, lad! You're making my eyes go all
joggly! Time is ticking away and I haven't all
day. I now come to my second point. It isn't just
that one lad has lost all his marbles – and you
can wipe that smile off your face, Elvis – that
was not meant to be funny! Other boys are
concerned, or so I am given to understand. Not
two, not ten. Not twenty. Perhaps the number
is much vaster than that. The fact is – if my
information is correct – there is not a single lad
left in this village with a marble to call his own!
Not a single solitary soul! What do you think of
that, eh? Do you think it is possible?'

'Yes, sir,' they both answered.

'And do you think this lamentable fact can in
any way be connected to your own recent mach-
inations?'

'Yes, sir,' Elvis answered straight off.

Billy was a millisecond behind him.

'Excellent again!'

161

'But, sir—' started Elvis, hopping again.

'Elvis! I have warned you once! I shall not do so again! I now come to my third point. And this is by far the most serious one as far as I am concerned; almost a criminal matter, a matter for the police, you understand me?'

'Sir.'

'Sir.'

'It appears that not only have you been systematically robbing these boys of their marbles, hundreds – perhaps thousands – of them. But you have been carrying on an illicit trade in selling them back to the same boys – the very same boys you robbed them of in the first place.'

'But, sir—' said Elvis, starting to hop again.

'SILENCE! And for heaven's sake stop hopping up and down, lad! You're beginning to resemble a frog! STAND STILL! That's better. Now what it comes down to is this. If I'm not mistaken you two boys are in possession of a large sum of money, together with a substantial quantity of marbles, which ought, by rights, to be residing in the pockets of a large number of boys in this school. Am I right, or am I wrong?'

'Sir,' said Elvis, 'that's what we've been trying to tell you all along. We've been collecting it for the Blind Dogs, sir. It's all for the charity.'

'What?' A blank look had begun to cloud over the sparkle in Mr Starr's eyes. 'What exactly are you trying to tell me, lad?' he asked in a stony voice.

'We did it all for the charity, sir. We knew we couldn't sell many raffle tickets because

Horsekiss – I mean Soskiss, sir – was sellin' them to everybody.' Mr Starr was staring at Elvis like a wall. But Elvis was used to being stared at by walls. 'So we thought up this idea, sir, me and Billy, to use the roulette game instead.'

Mr Starr continued to stare at Elvis for a moment or two, then – probably seeing it was useless – suddenly switched his gaze to Billy.

'Billy? Is what Elvis has just said correct?'

'Not exactly, sir.'

'I see! What exactly do you mean by "not exactly", lad?'

'It wasn't exactly *our* idea, sir. It was more my grandma's.'

'You're surely to goodness not implicating your poor old grandma in this highway robbery the pair of you've been up to!'

'She gave us the roulette game, sir. It was the night I went up to sell her some raffle tickets. Samantha Soskiss had just been up. She thought it would be a good way to get me own back.'

Mr Starr looked from one to the other. Under normal circumstances Billy might have flinched. But it was the truth he was speaking, in a sense. Well, close enough to the truth to pass for it.

And there was another thing that made him put a brave face on it. He felt he was part of a team. It was him and Elvis – *Billy's Boys* – versus the rest of the world.

'I don't know what to believe,' said Mr Starr.

163

'It's the God's only truth we're tellin' you, sir,' said Elvis. 'Cross me heart and hope to die.' For some reason he didn't. 'I've brought the money to school today, sir. We were going to hand it in tomorrow when the competition closes. We were going to surprise everybody.'

He started hopping again, and for a moment Billy thought he was going into his frog routine again, but this time he managed to snatch off his right trainer. From inside it he took out some coins and handed them to Mr Starr.

'It's all there, sir,' he said. 'Five pounds.' He dug his hand into his jacket pocket. 'And here's the other eighty-two pence.'

Mr Starr looked down at the money in his hand. He checked it.

'But how do I know—'

Elvis was already holding out his account sheet.

'You'll see it tallies exactly, sir. Billy wrote it out every night because he's a better reckoner-up than me.'

'Well . . .' said Mr Starr, after a long pause. 'I don't know what to think.' He moved his hand and accidentally knocked Tickler to the floor. Billy picked it up and replaced it alongside Mr Starr. 'I really don't.'

'Sir?' said Elvis.

'Yes?'

'That Mrs Quinky's here.'

The English Adviser was crossing the yard from the staff car park. Mrs Quincy had once taken a lesson when they were in Miss Ben-

fold's, but nobody had understood a word of it. And Pat Shufflebotham had peed her pants when Mrs Quincy, purely in an effort to help them all write creatively, had flapped her arms and run down the aisle in a convincingly good imitation of a pterodactyl on the rampage.

'Oh, Mrs Quincy. Well . . . Perhaps you boys had better go. It does seem on the face of things that I've misjudged you, possibly. I do hope so. Perhaps I'd better see you again later on. I may even owe you something of an apology.'

'It's all right, sir,' said Elvis, smiling generously back, and opening the door just in time for Mrs Quincy, like a polite little angel.

Chapter 13

Billy and Elvis felt chuffed as they walked home together that night.

Even after splitting Billy's share of the roulette money, they still had nearly three pounds each! A tidy bit of money!

And that wasn't all.

At tomorrow's assembly, when Samantha Soskiss was presented with her winning book token, Billy and Elvis were going to get a consolation prize. Mr Starr had hinted at a football.

And even this wasn't all they had to smile about.

That afternoon break something great happened. Something terrific.

It was Emma who drew their attention to the fact that Howells was up to his old tricks with Little Chuff again. As soon as they heard her yelling, Elvis stopped playing football and stomped straight towards the outside bogs, with Billy following.

'You can stop out, Wardy!' they'd heard Howells shout from inside when they got near. 'You're not a boy yet – not quite!'

'What's up, Emma?' Elvis asked.

'Howells is doing Chuffy over in there.'

Elvis bounced straight in this time. No messing. Billy followed him. Though, mind you,

what they were going to do about it Billy hadn't
a clue.

Poor Chuffy was in one of the cubicles, shaking like a leaf. His hair was plastered onto his
napper. He'd obviously been shoved head-first
down the bog.

'It wasn't me, Owly, honest,' he was saying,
though you could hardly make out the words he
was shuddering and shaking that much.

'What's going on in here?' Elvis asked.

'This is private business, Pottyman. Shove
yer big nose out, unless you want your face
altering.'

'It *is* my business,' said Elvis. 'Chuffy's a mate
of mine.'

Billy thought Elvis had gone out of his tiny
mind at that moment.

Howells obviously did as well. His eyes nearly
popped out of their sockets as he looked down at
Elvis.

'I'll shove *you* down the bog in a minute,' he
said.

'You won't,' said Elvis.

'Yer what?' said Howells. He just couldn't
believe his own lugholes now (despite their
size). 'You seem to have forgotten who I am,
Pottyman.'

'It's you that's forgotten something,' said
Elvis.

'What?'

'These.'

Elvis took out some papers from his pocket
and held them out to Howells.

'What are these supposed to be?'

'Just your signatures for all the money you've been doing us out of.'

'Let's have a look at them.' He took them from Elvis. 'I'll show you what I'll do wi' them!' He pushed Chuffy out of the way and went to the bog. He tore up the slips of paper, dropped them in the bog, then pulled the chain. 'Thanks very much, Pottyman.'

'Won't do you any good. They were only photocopies. I ran them off in the library. I've still got the originals.'

'What about it, anyhow? What you going to do with them?'

'Show them to Mr Starr. Then you'll never get in the area team.'

Howell's face had gone suddenly white.

'You wouldn't do that, man.'

'I would, you just watch me!'

'Well, you *!$?*!'

Howells called Elvis a very rude word.

'I don't like being called that!'

'What are you going to do about it?'

'Show Starr your signatures. Unless you say you're sorry.'

It took Howells a long time to say he was sorry. But he managed it in the end.

Then Elvis made him swear he wouldn't touch Chuffy again. After that he said he didn't like being called Pottyman.

'So I don't want it any more – OK, Owlyman?'

'Sure, Elvis.'

'Just don't forget. And I want all our fifty

pences back. All right?'

'Anything you say, Elvis.'

A big crowd had gathered in the bog by now. Howells was looking as sick as a dog.

A minute later when they came out into the yard with Chuffy, Billy asked Elvis what he was going to do when Howells had paid back all his money.

'Then I'll show Starr all the receeps,' said Elvis, grinning like a shark. 'That'll really drop him in it!'

Billy knew something was wrong the moment he stepped over the threshold into the back kitchen. He knew at once something was wrong, because Dot didn't leap up and try to knock him over with her usual love and adoration as he came through the door.

'Where's Dot, Mam?'

His mam was rolling out pastry to make an apple pie.

'You might well ask, Our Billy!' she said, shaking her head.

'Where is she?'

'Look under the table.'

Dot was lying under there by the wall on her old blanket. She had her favourite toy with her, an old golliwog she'd taken an instant liking to. It had lost both its legs weeks back and now one of its ears was fast becoming extinct.

She wagged her tail at Billy, but only in a feeble sort of way. Usually when she wagged her tail it was enough to break a table-leg.

'How do, Dot, what's up wi' you, old lass?'

'Leave her be, Billy. She's best not disturbed. Unless I'm very much mistaken she's broken a leg.'

'Broken a leg?'

He jerked upright as he spoke, almost banging his head on the underside of the table.

'That's what I said.'

'How'd she do that, Mam?'

'How'd you think? Them blinking marbles of yours.'

'How'd' you mean?'

'All them bags and boxes of them up in your room. They must've broken out again. I'm sick to the eye-teeth with them. It's like a tip up in that room.'

'But what did she do wi' them?'

'She must've been playing with them, Billy, She's got them all over the landing and stairs. I daren't go up there. It's more like a minefield than anything else. You'd better get them tidied before your dad gets in from work.'

'But what did she do?'

'Skidded on them, as far as I can make out. She came down them stairs like a ton of bricks. I've never heard such a commotion in all my born days.'

'Blinking heck!'

'I've told you before not to swear in this house, Billy. Do what you like in the Potters' house, but not in here.'

'And is she in agony?'

'She isn't pleased about it, if that's what you

mean.'

'And what'll happen now?'

'Well, she'll likely have to go to the vet's. We'll just have to wait until your dad comes in.'

Billy had an anxious half-hour after that. He rounded up the escaped marbles, but all the time was thinking of a film he'd seen where they had to shoot a racehorse because its leg was broken.

But his dad reassured him on that point as soon as he got home.

'Shoot her, Billy? She's not a blinking race-horse. She might look like one. She might eat like one. But she's not one, not yet at any rate. Anyroad, if I'm not mistaken, it's not her leg that's gone at all. It's her kneecap. She'll likely need a pin through it.'

He stood up from examining her. Billy's dad knew all about these things because he was in the St John Ambulance.

'What we going to do, then, Dad?'

'Best get her up to the vet's as fast as we can. They shut at half-past five. I'll just sup this tea, and then we'll be off.'

They didn't speak a word as they drove to the vet's in the factory van. Billy sat in the back with Dot to give her a bit of comfort. She did feel sorry for herself. She kept whingeing and show-ing the whites of her eyes as they steamed up the hill.

Billy noticed some grains of sand on the floor of the van, and that reminded him of another place where he'd come across sand recently, and

171

that put an idea in his head; but he considered
it wiser not to speak his thoughts aloud.

Luckily, they didn't have to wait long at the
vet's. When they went into his cubicle, he ran
his hands over Dot's legs and body. Billy's dad
held her head, because she kept gurning her lip
up and showing her teeth every time the vet
touched a sore spot.

'What do you reckon?' asked Billy's dad.

'I think you're right, Mr Robinson. Her leg
seems all right. Fell down the stairs, you say?
A normal dog could have easily broken a leg
like that.'

'She's never been exactly normal.'

'I suspect it's her kneecap that's slipped. A dog's kneecap isn't exactly like ours.'

'I'd heard as much.'

'Two sheaths run down the side of the joint, here.' The vet touched Dot's knee and she curled her lip again. 'I'm pretty sure the sheath on this side has slipped out of place a little. I'll have to pin it. Tell you what: leave her here for the night and I'll tranquillize her. Then tomorrow morning I'll have another look; if necessary I'll operate on her then, and you can pick her up in the evening. Fair enough?'

'Champion. And what'll be the damage?'

'The bill, you mean? Not more than twenty-five pounds, I shouldn't think. That's including VAT.'

Twenty-five pounds seemed an awful lot to Billy. He wondered, for a moment, if he should become a vet. But then he remembered seeing a film about a vet. There were some good bits in it; but then he didn't fancy having to deal with an uppity bull or put a whole flock of sheep to sleep because they'd caught something.

'Got off lightly there,' said Billy's dad, as they clambered back into the van. 'Might easy have cost a bonny lot more than that.'

'I can give you summat towards it, if you like, Dad.'

Billy spoke without really thinking; but once the words were out he wasn't sorry he'd said them.

'Can you, son? That's mighty generous of you.'

He put the van into gear and pulled away smoothly. Billy had noticed he was getting better all the time. 'No, you keep your hard-earned money, Billy.' They overtook a bus and went past The Black Bull. 'As it happens, I came into a bit last night.'

'Did you, Dad?'

'I've been doing a few odd jobs for a feller I know, like — largely to get that dressing-table set your mam fancied — and he give us a hot tip on a dog race.'

'And did you win, Dad?'

'I certainly did! The favourite came in last by a long chalk, and the dog I bet on had odds of thirty-three to one.'

'Did you win a lot?'

'Enough to get your mam's silver wedding present, pay for the vet — and five quid left over. That's the way money is, son. Roundabouts and swings. Comes and goes. Talking of which, you'll have to get shot of them marbles.'

'I'm going to dish them out tonight, Dad. Give them away.'

'That's the way, son. Let them circulate.' They'd turned the corner at Manor Farm now and were heading downhill. 'Marbles's like ten pound notes. You can have too many of them for your own good. Look what happened to Ada Troupe.'

'I thought she finished off living like a lady?'

'Is that what Elvis's mam told you? She had pots of money, all right. But she ended up with a bottle of gin in every room so she wouldn't

have far to go for a drink. Killed herself with booze in the end, that's how happy she was.'

It reminded Billy of the film about Las Vegas. In the end the gambler had started bumping people off left, right and centre, just to protect his money, and the dancing girl had got really tight and had driven into a truck.

'To be honest,' said his dad, 'I was never too happy about the way you came by all those marbles, Billy.'

'It was all in a good cause, Dad.'

'I'm not over-sure of that, Billy.'

'It was, Dad. We raised over five pounds for the Blind Dogs, me and Elvis.'

'Oh, aye?'

Billy's dad didn't sound too convinced.

'Mr Starr's going to give us a special prize. You can ask him at the committee meeting tonight, if you like.'

'Oh, aye?' He still looked suspicious.

When they'd stopped outside their house and before they got out, Billy's dad said:

'By the way, Billy, not a word to your mam about her present – or about that bet of mine. Your mam's not over-keen on gambling.'

It was just as well he said that.

When they went in, there was a report on the local television news about a dog race at Spennythorpe. The stewards were holding some sort of enquiry. The red-hot favourite had come on the track looking like Two-Ton Tessie, and had scarcely moved out of its trap. As soon as Billy saw a photo of the favourite he recognised

it as Hungry Horace, though it wasn't the name they gave it on the telly.

It was Billy's turn to look suspicious now.

But his dad was all smiles and the picture of innocence.

Chapter 14

Normally Billy didn't mind seeing to the hens and pigeons every morning. He quite liked climbing up through the allotments when the sun was just getting out of bed, and giving the pigeons their first wing-stretch of the day and the hens their first poddle about in their run.

But this morning was different.

For a start, he missed Dot. He missed her poking her nose through other folks' railings and leaving what Grandma called her 'trade-mark' at every twist and turn of the allotment path.

And there was a special reason why he would have been glad of her company this morning.

Last night the tramp had called at their house and asked if he could sleep the night in their greenhouse. Billy hadn't seen him. He'd been round at Elvis's at the time. But he'd heard about it when he got back.

It wasn't that Billy was scared of the tramp. There was probably no harm in the feller. But Billy particularly didn't want to get done in this morning, not when he and Elvis were going to get their presentation at assembly.

But in any case the tramp seemed to have gone now. When Billy got to the allotment gate there was no sign of him. And when he peered

in the greenhouse, all he could see were some bits of newspaper spread on the floor where the tramp had been sleeping.

Billy started whistling. He let the pigeons out first. They waddled out on to their ledge and ruffled their feathers against the cold, then after a bit of argy-bargy they whooshed off suddenly, all together, for a look round at the morning.

The sudden flurry of them, the way they'd all rushed off together, reminded him of how people had crowded round him and Elvis last night when they'd doled out all the marbles. They'd nearly got killed in the rush. Of course, they'd made sure little Chuff had got more than anybody else. About two hundred more, to be precise. And, of course, he'd lost them all by the end of the evening. But at least he'd been king of the midden for an hour or so.

Billy went to the hen-run. He lifted the pophole and the hens came stalking out. They were all there. He counted them, just to make sure. He fed them, then lifted the top of the coop. Seven eggs. The tramp didn't seem to have pinched any of them either.

In a way, eggs were like money. He'd often thought of making a fortune out of hens. Trouble was, to make a fortune out of hens you'd probably have to keep them in battery cages. And Billy was in total agreement with Mrs Drury as far as battery hens were concerned. Maybe that was the trouble with money. Maybe in order to make a real heap of it you had to—

It was then that he heard the noise behind him.

He swung round, just in time to see the tramp squeezing his way through the hawthorn hedge that bounded the top edge of the allotments. He must have been out on the Edge, a narrow strip of grass and gorse that eventually dropped sharply down to the Old Line far below.

For a moment they looked at one another without speaking. Billy hoped he didn't look too scared. The tramp had one hand behind his back, as if hiding something.

He hadn't changed a lot since Billy had last caught a glimpse of him through their back door. Old army great-coat fastened with baling string. A big red beard. A greasy black beret with the remains of a pom-pom on top.

'You'll be Billy?'

Billy nodded.

'Your dad's told us all about you. What's he up to this morning?'

'He's on early shift.'

'Serve him right. Keep him out of mischief.' He smiled. He brought his hand from behind his back. 'Thought one of these might come in handy.' He was holding two rabbits. He walked over to the hen-run and dropped one down on the ground. The other he stowed away in a gigantic pocket inside his greatcoat. 'Nowt like a bit of rabbit pie,' he said.

He winked and plonked his backside on the top of the hen-coop. He started rolling a cigarette with his fingers, using a strip of blank

newspaper and a tiny wisp of baccy from a small pouch hung round his neck.

'Where you off to this morning?' Billy asked, trying to keep his voice steady.

'South, Billy.' He licked the strip of paper, then rolled it expertly between the fingers and thumb of one hand. 'Just been up north to see me mother. Generally call in this time of year, like, just to mek sure she's behavin' herself.'

'Where's she live?'

'Jarrow. She still lives in the house where I was born.'

'What for did you leave her?'

'In the first place I left to get a job, Billy. That was the original intention, like. Shipyard closed where I worked, and somehow I didn't fancy passing me life away in a dole queue, so I went looking. I had no option.'

'And couldn't you find anything?'

'I did, like. Here and there. Now and then. Nowt that really took me fancy, though.' He lit his home-made cigarette with a single match he took from his pocket and struck against his thumb nail. He squinted, smiling up at Billy. 'You might say I never looked hard enough, Billy. You could put it like that.'

'How d'you mean?'

'Point is, son, once I got on the road, legging it, like, I more or less took a fancy to the life. It sort of suited us.'

'What's good about it, though?'

'Freedom, Billy. Ever heard of that word?

Nobody barking down your neck all day, telling you what to do. Do what you like, when you like.'

'Bet it's cold, though, sometimes.'

'Cold? Fit to freeze your particles off some nights. But you have to tek the rough with the smooth in this life. I never knew a job yet without drawbacks. Do you, Billy? Thought not. Choose what shift you like, there's always snags to it.'

He paused to inhale. The edges of his cigarette were ragged and black.

'Then there's travel, Billy. I've seen a canny bit of England in the last year or so. Length and breadth of it. I wouldn't have done that if I'd stopped in the shipyards, would I?'

'Suppose not.'

'No suppose about it, Billy. Like Tintagel for instance. That's where I'm headin' for now. Ever heard of that? Pity. It shows a deficiency in your education, son. Tintagel's a smashing place. You ought to go there, Billy. It's where King Arthur used to live, him and his Queen Gwinny-whateveryercaller.'

'Is it?'

'Certainly is. Get yer dad to tek you there one day. Champion atmosphere. Battlements, seagulls galore. You can stand on them ramparts lookin' down and near enough see them old knights knocking hell outa one another. You can practically hear them – clattering and that.'

'Sounds all right.'

'It's what I term the Living Past meself, like. That's just my name for it. I generally lie up in an old tin-mine down there. That's a place full of ghosts an' all.'

'Is it?'

'Chock-a-block. Many a score of them. Most of them bit bairns – from the good old days, like.'

'And what do they do?'

'Just have a bit crack with us, man. That's all they want, just a bit of jaw. Took them a bit o' time to learn me lingo, but they're all right now.'

Billy smiled at him. He was the sort of feller whom his dad called 'dry'. That meant you never quite knew when he was kidding or not. But like Billy's grandma as well. Never quite sure when he stepped over the thin line between fibs and facts.

'And is that all you do?' Billy asked him. 'Talk to ghosts and tramp around?'

'Certainly not. I'm not altogether idle, you know! Sometimes I tek a job. When I'm absolutely forced into it, when I'm running short of the old spondoolicks. Bit of hop-picking, bit of road-mending, a bit of fruit-picking – I generally come through the Vale of Evesham on me way back up north again. But never over-much, Billy. That's the secret with work – never let it become your master. Enough is sufficiency's always been my motto.'

His cigarette was almost finished now. He rubbed what was left between his fingers and

carefully put the remains back into his little pouch.

'Ah well, I'd better be off,' he said, rising to his feet.

'How far will you get today?' asked Billy.

'As far as I get, Billy – and that'll be far enough!' He winked and smiled. 'Ta-ra then, bonny lad. I'll mebbies see you again, next year about this time. Hope yer mam likes the rabbit, and say thanks to yer dad from me. Ta-ra.'

'Ta-ra. And thanks a lot for the rabbit.' It was then, as the tramp was moving towards the hedge, that Billy remembered he had the £2.91 in his pocket. He had wrapped it up in his hanky at Elvis's, so his mam wouldn't hear it chink. A great idea came into his napper. 'Mister?' he called.

'What?'

'Can I offer you some money? Just to help you on your way, like?'

The tramp took only a second to decide.

He smiled. 'That's very canny of you, son, but just for the noo I'll say no.' He smiled again. 'I haven't a lot of use for money nowadays, Billy. I find the stuff just weighs us down!' He waved his hand; a second later he'd squeezed through the hedge and was gone.

Billy put the rabbit into the corn pail, then put the eggs in beside it. He shut the gate of the hen-run behind him, then scattered some corn to fetch the pigeons back down.

He wondered how far the tramp had got by

now. Probably halfway along the Old Line. Just fancy him refusing money!

When all the pigeons were back down, Billy squeezed through the hawthorns and out on to the Edge. The tramp was almost to the Great North Road. In a minute he'd scramble up the bankside right beside the sewer-pipe Elvis had crawled through last week.

If he was lucky, a lorry driver might pick him up in no time. It would be snug in the cab, the heat from the engine would warm his feet. Then maybe he'd get dropped off in a place he'd never seen before. But he wouldn't mind. He'd just sniff the new air as if he enjoyed it, and he wouldn't get lost because he knew how to find his way by the stars. That night he'd sleep in a barn full of hay, and the next morning he'd set off in the direction of Tintagel and King Arthur's castle, his pockets empty and his face full of smiles.

Billy wouldn't have minded seeing Tintagel. He shut the allotment gate behind him. He wouldn't mind going to London as well. Or Honolulu. The African Jungle. The Sahara Desert. Kuwait Sands. There were a bonny lot of places to see. A *bonny* lot.

Because you didn't have to stop in England – once you gave up this silly idea of making lots of money. You could go anywhere. There was a whole world – India, tropical islands . . .

Billy could see himself walking along a beach. To his left there was the steady murmur of ˙˙˙ves breaking on the sand, to his right the

sighing of a gentle wind through the palm trees. He was alone, barefoot, clad only in a loincloth, all sunburnt, living only on seaweed and coconuts, not a penny to his name, and as happy as Larry . . .

He wondered . . . Was *that* what he ought to be?

GHOST DOG

by Dick Cate

'If you do just happen to see an enormous dog – grey, with luminous eyes – coming towards you out of the mist . . .'

Billy Robinson just can't stop thinking about the ghostly wild dog spotted at the local colliery. The whole community is warned and the creature is soon the talk of the town. Though Billy's parents seem more interested in his sister's problems, Billy fears that the beast is out there, waiting just for him . . .

A fast-moving, action-packed adventure not to be missed.

SBN 0 440 862116

YEARLING BOOKS

CHARLIE COPPINS

by Neville Crine

'So I don't know much about being a cat, but I can find out, can't I? You just watch. I'm going to get to know so much about cats, you'll think I'm a real one.'

Ever since getting the part of a cat in the school pantomime, Charlie Coppins has been behaving oddly. Determined to get his cat-walk right, he's been up on the kitchen wall watching Mr Flint's cat Barney – staring at it as though he wanted to eat it. Charlie's best mates, Colin and Wayne, think he's gone potty.

But then Barney disappears! And his mates remember how fascinated Charlie was by that science lesson on worms, which learned by eating chopped-up bits of other worms. When Charlie's hair starts turning ginger, and the vicar's cat attacks him on sight, Colin and Wayne reckon they know what Charlie's up to. . . .

A hilarious story from an exciting new author.

SBN 0 440 862043

YEARLING BOOKS

If you would like to receive a Newsle[tter about our new]
Children's books, just fill in the c[oupon below with]
your name and address (or copy it on[to a separate piece]
of paper if you don't want to spoil yo[ur book] and send
it to:

The Children's Books Editor
Transworld Publishers Ltd.
61-63 Uxbridge Road,
Ealing
London W5 5SA

Please send me a Children's Newsletter:

Name..

Address..

....

....

All Children's Books are available at your bookshop or newsagent,
or can be ordered from the following address:
Corgi/Bantam Books,
Cash Sales Department,
P.O. Box 11, Falmouth, Cornwall TR10 9 EN

Please send a cheque or postal order (no currency) and allow 60p
for postage and packing for the first book plus 25p for the second
book and 15p for each additional book ordered up to a maximum
charge of £1.90 in UK.

B.F.P.O. customers please allow 60p for the first book, 25p for the
second book plus 15p per copy for the next 7 books, thereafter 9p
per book.

Overseas customers, including Eire, please allow £1.25 for postage
and packing for the first book, 75p for the second book, and 28p
for each subsequent title ordered.

Also available by Dick Cate
and published by Yearling Books:

GHOST DOG

Available shortly:

FOXCOVER

'Grandma dropped the silver ball on to the spinning wheel, and they watched it bouncing and whirling.

"Numero sixteen black est the winner!" said Grandma.

Billy had lost his hundred pound token – but he'd won on black sixteen, and when he worked it out he was fifty quid into pocket! Fifty quid! That was better than working for a living! It was nearly what he got in a year's pocket-money.

Billy liked this game.

They played for an hour, an hour that slipped away like a swift few seconds. Up and down went Billy's fortunes, round and round went the wheel. "Fet vose chewers!" shouted Grandma. "Ryan ne vat ploo!"

Suddenly Billy hit a real winning streak. A strange feeling of excitement came over him, a feeling – a conviction – that he just couldn't lose.'

Billy has finally decided what he wants to be when he grows up. A millionaire! His only problem is how to get started. Then his grandma gives him the perfect present, and Billy and his friend Elvis begin to rake in the loot. But Billy soon discovers that wealth has its drawbacks . . .

Dick Cate is an award-winning author who has written many books for children. TWISTERS is the second book in his well-observed and entertaining trilogy about Billy Robinson, his family and friends.

Zanzibar

THE BRADT TRAVEL GUIDE

THE BRADT STORY

The first Bradt travel guide was written by Hilary and George Bradt in 1974 on a river barge floating down a tributary of the Amazon in Bolivia. From their base in Boston, Massachusetts, they went on to write and publish four other backpacking guides to the Americas and one to Africa.

In the 1980s Hilary continued to develop the Bradt list in England, and also established herself as a travel writer and tour leader. The company's publishing emphasis evolved towards broader-based guides to new destinations – usually the first to be published on those countries – complemented by hiking, rail and wildlife guides.

Since winning *The Sunday Times* Small Publisher of the Year Award in 1997, we have continued to fill the demand for detailed, well-written guides to unusual destinations, while maintaining the company's original ethos of low-impact travel.

Travel guides are by their nature continuously evolving. If you experience anything which you would like to share with us, or if you have any amendments to make to this guide, please write; all your letters are read and passed on to the author. Most importantly, do remember to travel with an open mind and to respect the customs of your hosts – it will add immeasurably to your enjoyment.

Happy travelling!

Hilary Bradt

Hilary Bradt

19 High Street, Chalfont St Peter, Bucks SL9 9QE, England
Tel: 01753 893444 Fax: 01753 892333
Email: info@bradt-travelguides.com
Web: www.bradt-travelguides.com

Zanzibar

THE BRADT TRAVEL GUIDE
Fifth Edition

David Else
Heather Tyrrell

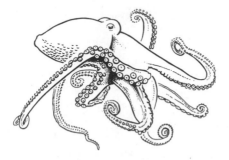

Bradt Travel Guides, UK
The Globe Pequot Press Inc, USA

This fifth edition published in 2003 by Bradt Travel Guides Ltd,
19 High Street, Chalfont St Peter, Bucks SL9 9QE, England
web: www.bradt-travelguides.com
Published in the USA by The Globe Pequot Press Inc, 246 Goose Lane,
PO Box 480, Guilford, Connecticut 06475-0480

First published in 1993 by Bradt Publications

British Library Cataloguing in Publication Data
A catalogue record for this book is available from the British Library

ISBN 1 84162 063 7

Photographs
Front cover Ariadne Van Zandbergen
Text David Else (DE), Matt Richmond (MR), Heather Tyrrell (HT),
Ariadne Van Zandbergen (AZ)

Illustrations Annabel Milne, Carole Vincer
Maps Steve Munns

Typeset from the author's disc by Wakewing
Printed and bound in Italy by Legoprint SpA, Trento

Authors and Contributors

AUTHORS

David Else is a professional travel writer, specialising in Africa. Since 1983 he has worked and travelled all over Africa, on all sorts of transport, from train, plane and car, to camel, bike and dug-out canoe, and crossed the continent several times, from Alexandria to Cape Town, and from the Atlantic coast in Senegal to the Indian Ocean shorelines of Kenya and Tanzania – via most of the bits in between.

David first reached Zanzibar in 1985, sailing by dhow from Dar es Salaam. Since 1992 he has visited Zanzibar regularly (using more comfortable modes of transport) to collect information for the various editions of this guidebook. As well as this guide to Zanzibar, David has written and co-written around 20 other guidebooks for independent travellers in Africa, and also contributes to magazines and other publications. His areas of particular interest are the mountains of East Africa, including Kilimanjaro and Mount Kenya, where he occasionally leads groups of trekkers for specialist tour companies.

When not in Africa, David lives in the north of England, which is still within reach of some impressive mountains, but a long way indeed from a tropical coastline.

Heather Tyrrell studied languages and anthropology at the University of Durham, specialising in primate behaviour. She first travelled to Africa with the British Schools Exploring Society, on an expedition to the Kalahari in 1989. Later she returned as a BSES leader to Namibia where she scaled the Klein Spitzkoppe and Brandberg mountains to map rock art, and collect insects for Namibian researchers. Since then she has researched and travelled extensively in Namibia, Zimbabwe, Botswana, Zambia, South Africa and Mozambique. She now runs the East African programme for Sunvil Africa – one of the UK's leading specialist tour operators to Africa.

Heather spent much of 2001 and 2002 researching in southern Tanzania, and the Zanzibar and Mafia archipelagos. In 2003 Heather is mounting a small expedition around the remoter parts of western Tanzania, where she plans to see chimpanzees for the first time.

When not in Africa, or the Sunvil Africa office, you'll find her rowing on the Thames or doing dubious bits of DIY on her flat.

MAJOR CONTRIBUTORS

The following people made major, and greatly appreciated, contributions to this guidebook:

Philip Briggs provided information for the *Southern Tanzania Safaris* chapter. He is the author of the Bradt Travel Guides to Tanzania, Uganda, Ethiopia, Malawi, Mozambique, Ghana, and East and Southern Africa, and co-author of their guide to Rwanda. He also contributes regular travel and wildlife features to *Travel Africa*, *Africa Geographic* and *Africa Birds & Birding* magazines.

Sarah Chanter wrote the original *History* chapter and many of the historical items throughout this book. She has a keen interest in the history and culture of Zanzibar, has worked as a teacher in Kenya, and has travelled extensively throughout East and southern Africa. Sarah's first visit to Zanzibar was in 1984. Now based in Britain, she has returned to Zanzibar on many occasions.

Said el-Gheithy is a medical anthropologist who has undertaken research on general practice in rural Wales and inner-city London. He is the director of the Centre for African Language Learning (London) and the Princess Salme Institute (Zanzibar/London). He lives and works in both Zanzibar and London, and kindly provided information for the *Language* and *History* sections.

Dudley Iles is a keen ornithologist and conservationist, and provided information on the wildlife of Zanzibar. From 1993 to 1995 he worked for the Commission for Lands and Environment in Zanzibar, helping to set up environmental clubs and train conservation officers. He has since returned to Zanzibar each year to study natural history and design nature trails, particularly on Pemba, Chumbe Island and Mafia Island, and in Jozani Forest.

Gemma Pitcher is a travel writer who has lived and worked in Zanzibar for the past three years, as well as travelling widely throughout eastern and southern Africa. Gemma has published articles in magazines and newspapers worldwide, and provided sections on various aspects of the people and culture of Zanzibar for this book. Some of the text used in this book originally appeared in *Zanzibar Style*, written by Gemma Pitcher, with photographs by Javed Jafferji, published by Gallery Publications, and is reproduced with permission.

Dr Matthew Richmond is a marine science and fisheries expert who has lived and worked on Zanzibar and around the western Indian Ocean since 1989. He spent six years at the Institute of Marine Sciences, based on Zanzibar, preparing *A Guide to the Seashores of Eastern Africa and the Western Indian Ocean Islands*. Matt is involved in marine education and biodiversity projects in the region, and provided the *Marine Wildlife* section of this book.

KEY TO STANDARD SYMBOLS

—·—·	International boundary	🏛	Historic building
······	District boundary	✝	Church or cathedral
------	National park boundary	♨	Buddhist temple
✈	Airport (international)	🏠	Buddhist monastery
✈	Airport (other)	♨	Hindu temple
✛	Airstrip	ç	Mosque
🚁	Helicopter service	▶	Golf course
▬	Railway	🏃	Stadium
········	Footpath	▲	Summit
--🚢--	Car ferry	△	Boundary beacon
--🚢--	Passenger ferry	◉	Outpost
⛽	Petrol station or garage	✕—✕	Border post
🅿	Car park	◖	Rock shelter
🚌	Bus station etc	▫—◉—▫	Cable car, funicular
🚲	Cycle hire	═	Mountain pass
M	Underground station	○	Waterhole
⌂	Hotel, inn etc	✳	Scenic viewpoint
Ⓐ	Campsite	❀	Botanical site
♠	Hut	♧	Specific woodland feature
♉	Wine bar	🌴	Lighthouse
✗	Restaurant, café etc	≖	Marsh
✉	Post office	🌴	Mangrove
(	Telephone	🦅	Bird nesting site
e	Internet café	🐢	Turtle nesting site
✚	Hospital, clinic etc	∽∽	Coral reef
🏺	Museum	➤	Beach
🐘	Zoo	🐟	Scuba diving
i	Tourist information	🐋	Fishing sites
$	Bank		
♣	Statue or monument		
∴	Archaeological or historic site		

Other map symbols are sometimes shown in separate key boxes with individual explanations for their meanings.

Contents

Acknowledgements

David Else wrote the first four editions of the Bradt *Guide to Zanzibar*. This fifth edition was jointly researched and written by David Else and Heather Tyrrell. Thanks are due to the many people who have helped us with advice, information and contributions throughout the book's long and interesting history.

Firstly, many thanks to Sarah Chanter, who provided the original *History of Zanzibar* chapter and many of the historical 'boxes' scattered throughout the book; her endless enthusiasm was contagious and invaluable. Special thanks also to Peter Bennett, another Zanzibar aficionado, who helped research and gather information for four editions of this book, and to Patrick and Gilly Dudgeon, and Sylvie Mbugua.

Over the years, and over all the past editions, further help has come from the following people (in Zanzibar, Britain and elsewhere around the world): Abdel Wahid Hassan, Salim Abdullah, Msanif Msanif, Suleiman Hassan, Naila Majid Jiddawe, Abdi Salim Abdi, Allis Montensson, Derek Chartres, Paddy Hogan, John Baile, David Gray, Fatma Rashid, Emerson Skeens, Tom Green, Tahir Ishaq, Helen Paul, Mahboub Machano, Paul Lie, Sybylle Riedmuller, Eleanor Carter, Rodney Lebow, Tim Hendriks, Mubeen Jamal, Farhat 'Raf' Jah, Paul Stockley, Fabian Fernandes, Javed Jafferji, Amit Gondalia, James Hutchins, Greg Welby, Antje Forsle and Rainer Yusuf Vierbotter (Green Ocean), Mary Silver (Professor of Ocean Science, University of California), Andrew Cooke (Zanzibar Protected Areas Project), Ramadan Mwinyi (Ministry of Information, Culture, Tourism and Youth, Zanzibar), Mohamed Feruzi (Zanzibar Tourist Corporation, Pemba), Pippa Heylings (Commission for Lands and Environment, Zanzibar), Abdul Sharif (University of Dar es Salaam), Flo Liebst, John da Silva and Balkishna Gorolay (historians, whose deep insights helped us enlarge and further improve our *History* section), Fiona Clark and Jim Boggs (for input on wildlife and culture), Osmo Seppala (Zanzibar Urban Water Supply Project), Timo Vihola (Zanzibar Forestry Development Project), and Celia Kisson (Tanzania Desk, Department of Trade and Industry). For wildlife contributions, thanks to Rob Wild (Conservation and Development Coordinator, CARE-International, Tanzania), Dr Nadia Corp, zoologist (School of Psychology, University of St Andrew's, Scotland), Lorna Slade, ecologist (Zanzibar Sea Turtle Survival Project), Dudley Iles, ornithologist, Dr Per Berggren (Department of Zoology, Stockholm University, Sweden) and to Hildegard Kiel and Yusuf Mahmoud (Dhow Countries Music Academy, Zanzibar) for much-appreciated help updating the music and dance section. Particular thanks to Matt Richmond PhD, marine biologist (Marine Education, Awareness & Biodiversity Programme, Zanzibar) who provided a great deal of information on Zanzibar's marine wildlife, plus ideas, inspiration and good company, and also rounded up several other natural history experts to help provide further details. Thanks also to: Toufiq Juma Toufiq, senior ranger Ngezi Forest, Pemba; Ali Addurahim, ecologist and chief bird guide; and Ali Khamis

Mohammed, bird guide, Jozani Forest, for local insights; to Jeff Fleisher (Department of Anthropology, University of Virginia) and Adria LaViolette (Asst Professor, Dept of Anthropology, University of Virginia), for help on historical, archaeological and anthropological matters. For travel information, many thanks to Michael Sweeney (Zanzibar Travel) and Roger Gook (Footloose Travel) for constant updates from the front line. Thanks also to Ariadne Van Zandbergen for the photographic information; to Philip Briggs, author of Bradt's *Tanzania* (and other fine works too numerous to list!), for additional facts and figures, and to Dr Jane Wilson-Howarth and Dr Felicity Nicholson for the health section.

Finally (almost), thanks must also go to our official book testers, and all the readers of previous editions who wrote in with news and ideas to help us keep this edition up to date. These include: Adam Sachs, A Cotcher, Klaus Richter, Susan Robinson, Jacky Sutton, Anna Asheshov, Sandy Orton, Maggie Mattock, Tamsin Pearce & Edward Scarr, N F Green, Christian Steer, William Ackroyd, Therese Allan, Nicola Moody, Laura Wade and Samantha Witman (Friends World Program, Long Island University, USA), Peter and Amy Lumley-Wood, Janet Carroll, Christian Steer, Sue Pryde, Marilyn Reynolds, James Gillies, J P Krejci, Janet Carroll, Alex Liambey, Jason Dalrymple, Anne Rutter, Amanda Botha, Rochelle le Roux, Chris & Robin Watson, Raihana Ehsanullah, Andrea Funkhouser, Gwen Griffiths, Andy Hamilton and Vivien Hicks.

Your letters were all very useful, and I hope readers of this edition will continue to send me corrections and suggestions. Finally (really), thanks also to the many Zanzibaris, and to the travellers from around the world, who willingly – or unknowingly – supplied their comments and impressions.

THE NEXT EDITION

Our readers play a vital role in updating books for the next edition. If you have found changes, or new and exciting places, or have a story to share, do write. The most helpful contributions will receive a free book. Email or write to: Bradt Travel Guides, 19 High Street, Chalfont St Peter, Bucks SL9 9QE, UK; tel: 01753 893444; fax: 01753 892333; email: info@bradt-travelguides.com

Perspectives on Zanzibar

Zanzibar is one of those magical African names, like Timbuktu, Casablanca and Kilimanjaro. For many travellers, the name itself is often reason enough to come. And when you arrive, you'll discover for yourself many other reasons and the many different faces of Zanzibar.

Some of Zanzibar's early visitors seem to have been favourably impressed:

> This place, for the goodness of the harbour and watering and plentiful refreshing with fish, and for sending sorts of fruits of the country, as cows...and oxen and hens, is carefully to be sought for by such of all ships as shall hereafter pass that way.

James Lancaster, captain of the *Edward Bonaventure*, first English ship to visit Zanzibar (1592)

> Truly prepossessing was our first view...of Zanzibar. Earth, sea and sky all seemed wrapped in a soft and sensuous repose...The sea of purest sapphire...lay basking...under a blaze of sunshine.

Richard Burton, British explorer (1856)

> An artist could find genial occupation for years; but your matter-of-fact...tourist would vote the place slow, of course, see nothing in it, and sigh for a future of broad streets and civilisation, broad-cloth, bottled beer and blacking; and from such revilers of the picturesque I trust a kindly Providence may long deliver the quaint, queer, rambling old Arab town of Zanzibar.

J F Elton, *Travels and Researches among the Lakes and Mountains of Eastern and Central Africa* (1879)

Not all travellers were so impressed, however:

> The stench from the...exposed sea-beach, which is the general depository of the filth of the town, is quite horrible. At night, it is so gross and crass, one might cut a slice and manure the garden with it. It might be called 'Stinkibar' rather than Zanzibar.

David Livingstone, British explorer (1866)

> February 19th. We anchored off Zanzibar at dawn. A day of fierce heat. The island is said to enjoy a cool season. I have never struck it. An hour's stroll ashore sufficed to revive old memories, then I retired to the ship for a cold bath and an afternoon under the electric fans.

Evelyn Waugh, *Tourist in Africa* (1959)

The name of Zanzibar crops up in all sorts of places, such as popular fiction, magazines, and newspaper travel sections:

> And then they had reached the town and were threading their way...through streets so narrow that neighbours living on opposite sides...could surely shake hands with each other from their upper windows. Tall whitewashed houses, so high that the streets were deep canyons and crevasses. Hot white walls, hot black shadows...The smell of strange eastern spices and hot dust; the scent of sandalwood...and cloves. A sound of laughter and music and drums...
>
> M M Kaye, *Death in Zanzibar*

> Zanzibar engulfs you. Arabic dhows wait in the harbour. The old Stone Town is heavy with the scent of spice, heat and decay... Muezzins call the faithful to prayer and behind intricately carved doors there is a vacuum of silence, of families and half-empty offices guarding secrets.
>
> Richard Lutz, *The Independent* (1989)

> Gradually, through the mist, I saw Zanzibar Island, newly-born in the early dawn...glistening in the distance...These are not the crisp whitewashed buildings one sees on travel posters of the Greek islands...The buildings exude an atmosphere of palpable decay; of a still-inhabited, picturesque ruin. If buildings could speak, these would be crying out for restoration.
>
> Dana Seidenburg, *Signature Magazine* (1990)

> Zanzibar gleamed in the late afternoon sun like a fairytale set in a harbour of aquamarine. Zanzibar – even more exotic than its name. It really is a fairytale place. You know you've seen it before, imagined it as a child, when you step from the wharf and find yourself right in the heart of the old Stone Town. Palm trees lean beside Arabic whitewashed houses and against a bright blue sky; men walk by wearing long white robes; women wrap the black *bui-bui* around bright dresses; and on the harbour Arabic sailing boats – dhows – glide by. Any minute you expect to spot Ali Baba or maybe the odd genie.
>
> Leanne Logan, *TNT Magazine* (1990)

> Zanzibar is full of ghosts, a time capsule heavily laden with the past.
>
> Mark Ottaway, *The Sunday Times* (1994)

> In most parts of the world today, the traveler tends to get a sneaking feeling that he has arrived too late; in Zanzibar the traveler is rewarded with that rare feeling that for once he got there in time. The island has been sensitively cleaned up since the Marxist excesses of the seventies, but has not yet been wrecked by Western development.
>
> William Dalrymple, *Condé Nast Traveler* (1995)

ZANZIBAR IN SONG

Why do the wrong people travel, travel, travel,
When the right people stay back home?
What compulsion compels them
And who the hell tells them
To drag their cans to Zanzibar
Instead of staying quietly in Omaha?

Noel Coward, *Sail Away*

I've got the old man's car,
I've got a jazz guitar
I've got a tab at Zanzibar
Tonight that's where I'll be.

Billy Joel, *Zanzibar*

Pemba is like the straight man in a successful double act, the one nobody can remember. It is part of Zanzibar, an entity that consists of two islands. The main island has taken the name, the adulation, the money and all the best architecture, leaving Pemba as its forgotten partner. Most of the tourists who are now busy rearranging Zanzibar's economy have never heard of Pemba. To me, this seemed a pretty good recommendation...

Stanley Stewart, *The Sunday Times* (1995)

All your desert island fantasies come true as you approach Zanzibar. Indeed, all the fantasies you ever had about travel suddenly crowd around. The sea is preposterously aquamarine, the sand implausibly golden and the airport impossibly empty. Check the map in the in-flight magazine to make sure you are not dreaming...

Simon Calder, *The Independent* (1996)

Each morning the call of the muezzin breathes life into centuries-old Stone Town and daylight reveals a haphazard agglomeration of coral-rag buildings, corrugated iron roofs and hanging balconies separated by an arms length over a maze of busy narrow alleys.

Meals were very much an order-early-and-we'll-see-what-we-can-get-affair [on the coast], but the crystal clear water here provided an interesting variety of sea delicacies. Consequently snorkelling was good, although many of the larger fish had already been grilled and served with pilau rice.

Cathy Lanz, *Getaway Magazine* (1996)

The insanitary old Stone Town that Burton and others first clapped eyes on was left to crumble...and it might well have done so entirely had not the Aga Khan given a "something must be done" speech...then primed the pump for the restoration process with funds from his Foundation. His involvement has not been without controversy, but anyone who starts such a project not with something flash and showy, but by fixing the drains, gets my vote.

Mark Ottaway, *The Sunday Times* (1997)

It is one of the many beauties of Zanzibar that the needs for both the indigent and the industrious are catered for. There's plenty to do, but the temptation to relax on a palm-fringed beach is always there. The trick is to make sure you spend enough time on Zanzibar to do both.

Richard Hopwood, *Yorkshire Post* (1998)

What is it about Zanzibar? What makes it seem so exotic to people who haven't been there, and hardly know where it is?...Well, it could be the name: all those sensual zzzzs, the fact that it used to be the centre for the spice trade...redolent of merchant adventurers, swaggering traders, Omani pirates. The reality is more mundane but every bit as enticing. The heart of the capital is Stone Town...a warren of scruffy streets and tall buildings with massive ornate doors and plaster falling off the walls...There is a constant clatter of furniture being made, and genuine African artefacts being conjured up. There is a fish market and spectacular smells.

Richard Holledge, *The Independent* (1998)

Some places whisper, some shout, and some prattle...like small talk. Zanzibar sings. Zanzibar is the stuff of grand opera; it's a score from the wildest imagination, composed from a rich melody of aromatic spices...But the tale of Zanzibar is also written in blood and rooted in historical reality.

Getaway Magazine (1999)

Stone Town exuded an atmosphere of palpable decay. In many ways it was the ancient crumbling time capsule I had always imagined. But the years have not passed it by completely. The occasional Coca-Cola sign is perhaps inevitable, and here and there, a satellite dish has taken root. From some of the intricately carved wooden doorways emanated the timeless and pungent aroma of cloves, but others advertised email services.

William Gray, *Wanderlust* (2000)

Over the various editions of this book, we have received many letters from readers who have travelled to Zanzibar, and their impressions and opinions also make interesting reading:

Sailing into the port was like entering a giant Christmas Cake. The smell of cloves and spices is amazing.

The history of Zanzibar fascinates me. Sultans, princesses, palaces, explorers, pirates, ivory traders...Wow!

Zanzibar Town must rate as the Venice of Africa. Narrow streets of beautiful buildings, all in danger of crumbling away. And after rain these streets turn into canals!

I didn't enjoy Zanzibar Town. The decrepit buildings, the dirt and the filth all depressed me. But the beaches. Man! What a great place to hang out.

Compared to other African cities and towns, Zanzibar was so clean and airy. I loved it. I could have stayed for weeks.

I enjoyed the atmosphere of the town. The history and the romance of the place. I've never been anywhere else like it. And the 'lost palaces' around the island – it was like walking through the pages of Arabian Nights. The beaches on the east coast were great too, but I don't need to go halfway round the world for a good beach!

I was completely lost for words when I first saw the beaches on the East Coast. They are beautiful and as yet unspoilt, although there was building galore.

Zanzibar has left a great impression on me, mostly favourable, although it did take me a day or so to become accustomed to the squalor, dirt and smells of the Stone Town.

Many travellers rave about the beaches on Zanzibar, and they are in fact idyllic: clean white sand, palm trees, not many tourists, and photogenic fishing boats. But it seems very narrow-minded to come here just for the beach. There's much more to it than that. If Zanzibar becomes just another beach resort it will certainly cheapen the experience. I hope Zanzibar doesn't go the way of Kenya's Lamu and Malindi.

I enjoyed walking around the Stone Town, always getting lost, and taking a different way home every night. I'll always remember the amazing colour of the sea and the beautiful, beautiful sunsets. And no tourists! But it won't stay like this for long. I'm glad I went when I did.

For most visitors to Zanzibar, the greatest impression the islands make is the 'un-spoiltness' of it all. Although more visitors come to the islands now than ever before, it's still only a trickle compared to some other tourist destinations in Africa. Zanzibar may have lost some of its isolation, but many parts of the islands still retain their unique atmosphere of peace, charm and remoteness.

The Zanzibar government departments with special responsibility for tourism officially aim to exercise strict control over the development of hotels and other facilities. Promises have also been made about keeping the development relatively low-key, and the hotels not too obtrusive, and providing some benefits for the local people without destroying their culture or environment. These laudable aims are not always much in evidence on the ground, but to keep Zanzibar 'un-spoilt' much of the responsibility also lies with us, the visitors – tourists and travellers all.

If we behave in a sensible and appropriate manner, treat the local people with consideration and respect, support local businesses and conservation schemes, travel with an open mind and see the islands of Zanzibar as a community, not just a theme-park in the sun, our experiences here will be so much the richer for it.

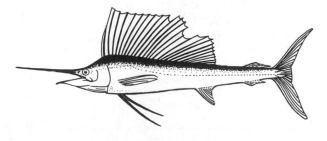

Part One

General Information

Zanzibar – A Profile

This is an introductory chapter describing in brief many different aspects of Zanzibar. More detailed information on subjects such as history, population, culture, wildlife and vegetation are given elsewhere in later chapters of this book.

Location
Zanzibar consists of two large islands, plus several smaller ones, about 40km (25 miles) off the coast of East Africa, in the Indian Ocean, about 6° south of the Equator. The two large islands are Unguja (usually called Zanzibar Island) and Pemba.

Size
Zanzibar Island is about 85km long and between 20km and 30km wide, with an area of just under 1,500km² (about 640 square miles). Pemba Island is about 75km long and between 15km and 20km wide, with an area around 850km² (about 380 square miles).

Topography
The islands of Zanzibar are generally flat and low lying. The western and central parts of Zanzibar Island have some low hills, where the highest point is about 120m (390ft) above sea-level. Pemba Island has a central ridge, cut by several small valleys, and appears more hilly than Zanzibar Island, although the highest point on Pemba is only 95m (310ft) above sea level.

The islands of Zanzibar are surrounded by coasts of rocky inlets or sandy beaches, with lagoons and mangrove swamps, and coral reefs beyond the shoreline.

Climate
The climate of Zanzibar is characterised by wet and dry seasons. The main rains fall from mid-March to the end of May, and there is a short rainy season in November. The dry seasons are from December to February and June to October. Humidity is generally quite high, although this can be relieved by winds and sea breezes. Average daytime temperatures on Zanzibar Island are around 26°C (80°F) from June to October, and around 28°C (83°F) from December to February. Pemba tends to be cooler and gets slightly more rain than Zanzibar Island.

Vegetation and agriculture
The islands were originally forested, but human habitation has resulted in widespread clearing, although a few isolated pockets of indigenous forest remain. The main crops grown in Zanzibar are coconuts and cloves. Bananas, citrus fruits and other spices are also grown commercially. Maize, cassava and other vegetables and cereals are grown for local consumption.

Wildlife

There are no large wild animals on Zanzibar, as found on the African mainland. Forest areas are inhabited by monkeys and small antelopes. Civets and various species of mongoose are found all over the islands. Birdlife is varied and interesting, with over 100 species being recorded, although bird populations are not as high as in other parts of the East African region. The marine wildlife, in the coral reefs that surround the islands, is particularly rich.

History

The monsoons that blow across the Indian Ocean have allowed contact between Persia, Arabia, India and the coast of East Africa (including the islands of Zanzibar) for over 2,000 years. The first European arrivals were Portuguese 'navigators' looking for a trade route to India. They reached Zanzibar at the end of the 15th century and established a trading station here and at other points on the East African coast.

At the end of the 17th century the Portuguese were ousted by the Omani Arabs. During this period, Zanzibar became a major slaving centre. In 1840, the Omani Sultan Said moved his court from Muscat to Zanzibar, and the island became an Arab state and an important centre of trade and politics in the region. Many European explorers, including Livingstone and Stanley, began their expeditions into the interior of Africa from Zanzibar during the second half of the 19th century.

Zanzibar was a British protectorate from 1890 until 1963, when the state gained independence. In 1964, the sultan and the government were overthrown in a revolution. In the same year, Zanzibar and the newly independent country of Tanganyika combined to form the United Republic of Tanzania.

Population and settlement

The population of Zanzibar was around 600,000 in 1988, the last date at which reliable figures were available. In 1992, the population was estimated at around 700,000 with a 3–4% annual growth rate. Based on these figures, the population is estimated at around 900,000.

Zanzibar's largest settlement is Zanzibar Town (sometimes called Zanzibar City), on Zanzibar Island (Unguja), with about 100,000 to 150,000 inhabitants. Other towns on Zanzibar Island include Chaani, Bambi, Mahonda and Makunduchi, but these are small. Outside these towns, most people live in small villages and are engaged in farming or fishing.

On Pemba the overall settlement pattern is similar. The largest town is Chake Chake, with a population of about 10,000 to 15,000; other smaller towns are Wete and Mkoani.

Language

The language of Zanzibar is Swahili (called *Kiswahili* locally). Visitors with a basic grasp of this language will be understood anywhere, although there are many forms and dialects found in different areas. Arabic is also spoken. English is widely used in the towns and tourist areas. More details on Swahili are given in *Appendix 1* at the end of this book.

Religion

Islam is the dominant religion, and practised by most Zanzibaris. All towns and villages have mosques. In Zanzibar Town there are also churches and temples for the small populations of Christians and Hindus.

Government

Zanzibar is a separate state within the United Republic of Tanzania, governed by a Revolutionary Council and House of Representatives, whose members are elected or appointed. The president of Zanzibar is also the vice-president of Tanzania.

Economy

For the people of Zanzibar, fishing and farming are the main economic activities. From the beginning of the 19th century to the mid-1970s Zanzibar exported a large proportion of the world's supply of cloves, and the islands' economy was based largely on this commodity. Some diversification has occurred since then, but cloves are still a major export, along with coconut products and other spices. In recent years, seaweed has also become an important export commodity. The potential for tourism to be a major earner of foreign currency has been recognised and this is being developed. The number of tourists visiting Zanzibar is still relatively small, but increasing every year.

Currency and exchange rates

As part of Tanzania, Zanzibar's unit of currency is the Tanzanian Shilling (TSh). Visitors (non-Tanzanians) to Zanzibar must pay for some items, such as air flights, ship tickets and hotels, in foreign ('hard') currency, usually US dollars (US$). The prices for many other items, such as tours or rental cars, are quoted in US dollars, although these are payable in hard currency or in TSh at the current exchange rate. This situation means the US dollar is an unofficial second currency in Zanzibar.

Prices in TSh, and exchange rates against hard currencies, are likely to vary considerably in the future, but prices in US dollars will remain more constant. Both currencies are used in this book. In November 2002, when this book was going to press, the exchange rates were:

1 US dollar = 1,016 TSh
1 UK pound = 1,606 TSh
1 euro = 1,026 TSh

A History of Zanzibar

Sarah Chanter
with additional contributions by Jeff Fleisher, archaeological researcher,
Department of Anthropology, University of Virginia

First inhabitants and early visitors

The first human beings (*Homo erectus*) evolved in the East African Rift Valley, within a thousand miles of Zanzibar, about 1.5 million years ago. They migrated throughout Africa and later Asia and beyond, becoming hunter-gatherers. Near rivers and coasts these people developed fishing techniques, and it is possible that Zanzibar's first human inhabitants were fishermen who crossed from the African mainland in dug-out canoes sometime during the first millennium BC.

At around the same time, or even earlier, the East African coast (including the islands of Zanzibar) may have received visitors from many parts of the ancient world, such as Mesopotamia (present-day Iraq) and Egypt. The Egyptian pharaohs sent expeditions to the land they called Punt (present-day Somalia) in around 3000BC and again in 1492BC, which possibly continued southwards down the East African coast. This theory is supported by carvings on temple walls at Luxor showing sailing boats with slaves unloading gold, ivory tusks, leopard skins and trees of frankincense.

Other visitors may have included Phoenicians, a seafaring people from the eastern shores of the Mediterranean. Around 600BC, a Phoenician fleet sailed south along the coast, past Zanzibar, and is believed to have circumnavigated Africa before returning to the Mediterranean three years later.

By the 1st century AD Greek and Roman ships were sailing from the Red Sea down the East African coast, searching for valuable trade goods such as tortoiseshell, ebony and ivory. Around AD60, a Greek merchant from Alexandria wrote a guide for ships in the Indian Ocean called *The Periplus of the Erythaean Sea*. This is the first recorded eyewitness account of the East African coast, and describes 'the Island of Menouthesias' (most likely the present-day island of Unguja, also called Zanzibar Island) as 'flat and wooded' with 'many rivers' and 'small sewn boats used for fishing'. Another Alexandrine Greek, Claudius Ptolemaeus (usually called Ptolemy), also mentioned Menouthesias in his book *Geographike*, written about AD150.

At about the same time, it is thought that Arab and Persian trading ships from the Persian Gulf were also sailing down the coast of East Africa. Using the seasonal monsoons, they sailed south on the northeast monsoon between November and February, carrying beads and cloth, and even Chinese porcelain that had come via India. Then, between March and September, after the winds changed direction, they returned north on the southwest monsoon, carrying the same tortoiseshell, ebony and ivory that had attracted the Greeks and Romans, plus mangrove poles for timber and other goods. The Arabs and Persians traded with the local inhabitants but they remained visitors and, at this stage, they did not settle.

During the 3rd and 4th centuries AD, other groups of migrating peoples started to arrive on the east coast of Africa. These people were Bantu (the name comes from the term used to define their group of languages), and they

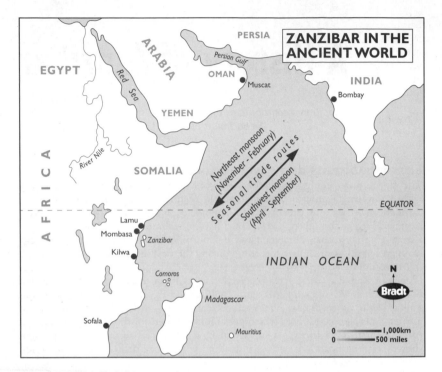

originated from the area around present-day Cameroon in the centre of the continent, then spread throughout eastern and southern Africa over the following centuries. On the East African coast, these people established settlements, which slowly grew into towns, and were eventually to become the major trading cities such as Kilwa, Lamu and Mombasa on the mainland, and Unguja Ukuu on the island of Unguja (Zanzibar Island). These coastal settlers traded with the Arabs, exporting ivory, rhino-horn, tortoiseshell and palm oil, and importing metal tools and weapons, wine and wheat.

The Arab traders called the East African coast 'Zinj el Barr', meaning land of the black people, from where the modern name Zanzibar is derived. 'Zinj' comes from *zang*, the Persian word for 'black', and *barr* is the Arabic word for 'land'. The Arabs may also have derived the word from *Zayn za'l barr*, meaning 'Fair is this land'. Zanzibar remained the name of the whole coast, including the islands of Unguja and Pemba (which together make up the present-day state of Zanzibar), until the late 15th century.

Early Arab settlers

The 7th century AD saw the rise of Islam in Arabia. At the same time wars in this area, and subsequent unrest in Persia, caused a small number of people from these regions to escape to the East African coast, where they settled permanently, bringing the new Islamic religion with them.

There are several accounts of emigrations from Arabia to East Africa. (The history of this period is largely based on stories handed down by word of mouth through generations, which are difficult to separate from myth and legend.) One story tells of two Arab chiefs from Oman who arrived in East Africa with their families around the end of the 7th century, and settled on the island of Pate, near

Lamu. Another story tells of an emigration from Shiraz, in Persia, some time between the 8th and 10th centuries. The Sultan of Shiraz and his six sons migrated with their followers in seven boats. One of the sons stopped at Pemba, while others settled in Mombasa and Kilwa. The 9th-century Arab tale of *Sinbad the Sailor*, one of the stories in *The Arabian Nights*, was most probably inspired by accounts of journeys by Arab sailors to East Africa and Southeast Asia.

The rise of the Swahili

During the second half of the first millennium, the coastal Bantu people developed a language and culture (in fact, a whole civilisation) which became known as Swahili. This name came from the Arabic word *sahil* meaning 'coast'. Their language, Kiswahili, although Bantu in origin, contained many Arabic words. It also included some Persian words, mainly nautical terms. The Swahili people seem to have accepted the small numbers of early Arab and Persian settlers. There was some intermarriage, and the Swahili adopted many Arab customs and traditions, including the Islamic religion. On Unguja (Zanzibar Island), Shirazi settlers are believed to have married into the family of the island's Swahili king. Several centuries later, the *Mwinyi Mkuu* ('The Great Lord'), the traditional ruler of Unguja, continued to claim descent from a Shirazi prince.

By the 7th century, the Swahili people were trading regularly with Arab and Persian merchants, who continued using the vital monsoons to sail between Africa, Arabia and Persia. In the same way, Swahili dhows (traditional ships based on an Arab design) also became involved in the trade and sailed regularly to and from the Persian Gulf, carrying gold, ivory, rhino-horn, leopard skins, tortoiseshell, and ambergris from whales. African slaves were also carried to the Persian Gulf, probably to work in the marshlands of Mesopotamia.

Over the following centuries the trade between Africa and Arabia increased, and trading links between East Africa and Asia also continued to grow. Ivory was exported to India, and later China, while Indian cloth and Chinese porcelain and silk were imported to Arabia and Zanzibar. At around this time, Indonesian sailors from Java and Sumatra are thought to have reached East Africa and Madagascar, possibly introducing coconuts and bananas.

From this period (7th to 10th centuries) archaeologists have discovered a very distinctive kind of local pottery, known as Tana Tradition, which looks the same at sites along the whole East African coast, from northern Kenya to southern Tanzania, and out to the Comoros Islands. The similarity of this pottery over such a large area shows how closely linked the people of the coast were, and also shows – for the first time – a sense of commonality and shared experience. Imported ceramics, called Sassian Islamic, from the Persian Gulf have also been discovered.

Archaeological, linguistic and historical research conducted since the early 1980s has also led to a shift in the way that the early history of the coast is interpreted, rejecting some of the ideas put forward by scholars working during the 1950s, 1960s and 1970s. In essence, this research suggests that at its core – its foundation – Swahili culture and history is an African phenomenon. Until recently, archaeologists had proposed that the large towns of the East African coast (such as Kilwa, Lamu, Mombasa and Unguja Ukuu) had been built by Persian or Arab settlers, and the local Bantu people had then intermarried and 'Africanised' the Arabs, thus resulting in the Swahili people. But, through extensive excavations at many of these towns, it is now known that they were founded by people from the interior of Africa and instead of simply starting as grand towns, were actually built up slowly over time by these same people.

Unquestionably, the links to the Indian Ocean trade were some of the most important for these towns, and it is through these links that they became successful. Islam and prestigious goods from Arabia, Persia and China were also symbols of power and authority. But there is little evidence that there were *large scale* migrations from Arabia or Persia to the coast of East Africa until the middle of the second millennium.

Zanzibar enters the second millennium

On Unguja (Zanzibar Island), one of the earliest remaining examples of permanent settlement from Persia is a mosque (which can still be seen today) at Kizimkazi, on the southern part of the island. It contains an inscription dated 500AH (*Anno Hegirae*), which corresponds to the Christian year AD1107, making this the oldest known Islamic building on the East African coast. From the end of the 12th century, Omani immigrants also settled in Pemba. At around the same time the settlement that was to become Zanzibar Town also began to grow.

As the trade between Africa, Arabia and the rest of the Indian Ocean continued to expand, Zanzibar became an increasingly powerful and important commercial centre. Major imports included cotton cloth, porcelain and copper from Dabhol, a port on the west coast of India, and exports included iron from Sofala (in present-day Mozambique). By the 13th century, Zanzibar was minting its own coins, and stone buildings were starting to replace more basic mud dwellings. In 1295, the Venetian traveller Marco Polo wrote of Zanzibar: 'The people have a king...elephants in plenty...and whales in large numbers', although he never visited the island. Other writers of the time noted that the kings and queens of Zanzibar and Pemba dressed in fine silks and cottons, wore gold jewellery, and lived in stone houses decorated with Persian carpets and Chinese porcelain.

Many Chinese imports had come to Zanzibar via India, but in the early 15th century the ports on the coast of East Africa were trading directly with China. Gold, ivory and rhino-horn were transported to the East, as well as a small number of slaves, mainly for domestic labour and military service. In 1414, a dhow from the city of Malindi (in present-day Kenya) carried a giraffe to China, as a present for the emperor. A few years later, the Chinese admiral, Cheng Ho, visited Mogadishu, Malindi and possibly Zanzibar. The trade came to an abrupt end in 1443 when the new Ming Emperor banned Chinese merchants from going abroad. However, the demand for ivory remained, which the Arab dhows supplied via markets in India.

By the mid-15th century the islands of Zanzibar, along with Mombasa, Malindi, Lamu and Kilwa, formed a chain of thriving Swahili Islamic city states, each with its own sultan, spread along the East African coast. Positioned on the edge of the Indian Ocean, these cities had close trading links with Arabia, Persia, India and Southeast Asia, and although many of the trade items came from the African interior no significant attempts were ever made to penetrate or colonise this vast region. As it was, commerce had become very profitable, and it seems that the Sultans of Zanzibar and the other city states were more than happy for their territories to remain as gateways or conduits for the trade between Africa and the Indian Ocean.

This flourishing Indian Ocean trade might have continued successfully for many more years but it was severely disrupted at the end of the 15th century by the arrival of the Portuguese on the coast of East Africa.

Portuguese rule

By the mid-15th century, Prince Henry 'the Navigator' of Portugal was encouraging voyages of exploration around the African coast. He hoped to find a sea route to the East, as well as the Christian kingdom of the legendary Prester John (or 'Priest-king') of Abyssinia. With the rise of the Ottoman Empire in 1453, all goods from the East, including the increasingly valuable spices, now reached Portugal through potentially hostile Muslim countries. Prices were high as the sultans of Egypt and the Ottoman Empire charged considerable levies for the passage of goods across their lands.

In 1487, Prince Henry's successor, King John II, dispatched two expeditions to the East: one by sea around the southern tip of Africa, the other overland through Egypt. By 1488, Bartholomew Dias had rounded the Cape of Good Hope (so called because of the hope that it led to a sea route to India) before turning back. Meanwhile, Pedro da Covilhan had sailed across the Mediterranean to Alexandria, crossed Egypt in disguise as a Muslim honey merchant and then sailed from the Red Sea to India. On his way back (around 1489) he made a diversion along the coast of East Africa, sailing past Zanzibar to Sofala (in present-day Mozambique) before returning to the Red Sea.

In 1497, another Portuguese navigator, Vasco da Gama, encouraged by the reports of Dias and da Covilhan, rounded the Cape of Good Hope and sailed northwards up the coast of East Africa, on the way to India. He passed Zanzibar and landed at Mombasa, where he received a hostile reception from the sultan. But he got a warm welcome in Malindi, an old enemy of Mombasa. Da Gama built a pillar of friendship on the shore at Malindi and employed an Omani navigator called Ahmed bin Majid to guide him across the Indian Ocean. On his return from India in 1499 he moored for a day off the island of Unguja (Zanzibar Island).

More Portuguese ships followed in the wake of da Covilhan and da Gama. They needed safe provisioning and repair bases for their voyages to and from the Far East, and so garrisons were established in the harbours of Unguja (Zanzibar Island), Pemba and Mombasa.

Any early friendship that may have existed was soon forgotten when the Portuguese took control of Unguja in 1503. A ship commanded by Rui Lorenco Ravasco moored off the southern end of the island while Portuguese sailors captured over 20 Swahili dhows and shot about 35 islanders. The Mwinyi Mkuu (king of Zanzibar) was forced to become a subject of Portugal, and agreed to allow Portuguese ships free access to Zanzibar to be supplied with fresh food and water. Additionally, the Mwinyi Mkuu was required to pay an annual tribute to the Portuguese crown.

Portuguese domination of the region continued. In 1505 they took control of Mombasa, and in 1506 Pemba came under Portuguese control. Between 1507 and

THE PORTUGUESE LEGACY

Zanzibar was occupied by the Portuguese in the 16th and 17th centuries. They introduced many new foods, brought from their colonies in other parts of the world, and the Swahili words used for these today are borrowed directly from the Portuguese language: cassava or manioc is *muhogo* in Swahili (from the Portuguese *mandioca*) and the cashew nut is *mbibo*, from *bibo*, both plants originally grown in Brazil. Avocado is *mpea* and guava is *mpera*, both from the Portuguese word *pera*. The Portuguese also introduced the use of dung (Swahili: *mboleo*, Portuguese: *boleo*) for cultivation, and the iron nail (Swahili: *parafujo*, Portuguese: *parafuso*) for boat-building.

Source: Oliver Roland and Matthew Gervase,
A History of East Africa (Oxford University Press, London, 1963)

1511 the Portuguese also occupied territories in the Arabian Gulf, including Muscat and the island of Hormuz.

By 1510 Unguja's tribute had fallen short and the people of Pemba had also become hostile to the Portuguese. Under Duarte de Lemos, the Portuguese looted and set fire to settlements on Unguja, then plundered the town of Pujini in Pemba. They soon regained both islands and by 1525 the whole East African coast, from Lamu to Sofala, was also under Portuguese control and a vital part of their trading empire. Gold, ivory, ebony and slaves from the interior were carried to Portuguese colonies in India or back to Portugal. Iron ore and garnets from Sofala, and coconut fibre and gum-copal (a tree resin) from the islands were also exported. Cloth, beads, porcelain and metal tools were imported to the East African coast from Oman and Portugal.

Around 1560 the Portuguese built a church and small trading settlement on a western peninsula of Unguja. This was to become Zanzibar Town. But although the Portuguese occupied Unguja, and forced the local people to trade under their supervision, the islanders continued to pay allegiance to the Mwinyi Mkuu, their own king.

Portugal was not the only European power with interests in the Indian Ocean. In November 1591 the *Edward Bonaventura*, captained by Sir James Lancaster, became the first English ship to call at Zanzibar. It was supplied with fresh food and water by the Mwinyi Mkuu. Soon, more European ships were calling at Zanzibar on their way to and from the Indian subcontinent and islands of the East Indies.

John Henderson, a Scottish sailor from one English ship, was reportedly held captive on Zanzibar in 1625. He later escaped, but not until he had fallen in love with a Zanzibari princess who escaped with him back to Scotland. Today, their portraits are in the collection of the Scottish National Portrait Gallery in Edinburgh.

With the advent of English ships in the Indian Ocean, the Portuguese needed to strengthen their position on the coast. In 1594 they built a fort at Chake Chake in Pemba, and from 1593 to 1595 Fort Jesus in Mombasa was constructed. Settlers arrived from Portugal, and a Portuguese garrison was established in Fort Jesus, brutally suppressing the local population. Mombasa became known as *Mvita*, 'the place of war', and the Portuguese governor, *Afriti*, 'the devil'.

Despite these fortifications, however, the Portuguese position in East Africa began to weaken. In Arabia, Hormuz was regained by the Persians in 1622, and in January 1650 Muscat was regained by the Omani Arabs. Following this victory, the Sultan of Oman's navy sailed to Zanzibar to help the Mwinyi Mkuu, Queen Mwana Mwema. The Omanis raided the Portuguese settlement on Unguja, killing many people and imprisoning about 400 in the church. They also attacked and burnt the Portuguese settlement on Pemba. By 1668, virtually the entire coastal area was in Omani hands. The only garrisons still held by the Portuguese were at Fort Jesus in Mombasa, and on the western peninsula of Unguja.

In 1679 the queen of Pemba, who had given her island to the Portuguese, had become a Christian and was living in Goa. In 1682 the Portuguese persuaded her to return, but this attempt to install a friendly ruler in Pemba was frustrated when her own subjects drove her out. The last Portuguese inhabitants were expelled in 1695.

By this time, Queen Mwana Mwema of Zanzibar Island had been succeeded by her son, Yusuf. After he died, towards the end of the 17th century, the island was divided between his two children, Bakari and Fatuma. King Bakari ruled the southern part of the island, with Kizimkazi as his capital, while his sister, Queen Fatuma, ruled the northern part. Fatuma supported the Portuguese, so her capital was built near the garrison on the western peninsula which later became the site of Zanzibar Town

When the Omani fleet arrived at Mombasa and laid siege to Fort Jesus in March 1696, Queen Fatuma sent three dhows full of food to help the Portuguese defenders. The dhows were captured and burnt by the Omanis, who then attacked Zanzibar itself, forcing Queen Fatuma and her followers to flee into the interior of the island.

The siege of Mombasa lasted until December 1698, when the Omani forces took Fort Jesus and installed an Omani governor. Once again, the Omanis attacked Zanzibar. They drove out the last of the Portuguese settlers, captured Queen Fatuma and took her to Oman, where she spent the next 12 years in exile before returning to resume her rule. While she was away, her son Hassan took the title Mwinyi Mkuu, but paid allegiance to Oman.

Thus the Portuguese were finally ousted from the whole East African coast, and the Omanis were firmly in control of the entire region as far south as present-day Mozambique (which remained in Portuguese hands until 1972).

Omani rule and the rise of the slave trade

From 1698 the Sultan of Oman ruled the islands of Zanzibar from Muscat, his capital, through appointed governors and occasional armed raids to put down minor rebellions. To consolidate his grip on the islands, a fort was built in Zanzibar Town, on the site of the Portuguese church, and by 1710 about 50 Omani soldiers were garrisoned there.

By this time, Oman had become a major trading nation. One of its major exports was dates, and the expansion of date plantations created a demand for cheap slave labour. The rules of Islam forbade the enslavement of Muslims, so Africans were imported in large numbers, many of them transported through Zanzibar. It is estimated that there were about 5,000 African slaves in Oman at the beginning of the 18th century, with about 500 new slaves arriving each year. Although most slaves were used on the plantations, others were employed as domestic workers or concubines, and some were re-exported to Persia or India.

In 1744, in Oman, the ruling Yaa'rubi dynasty (which had been in power since 1624) came to an end after a long civil war. It was succeeded by the new Busaidi dynasty led by Ahmed bin Said al Busaidi, an Omani merchant and ship-owner. Ahmed was made Sultan of Oman and the East African coast; one of his first moves was to install a new governor in Zanzibar.

At this time, the governors of the East African city states paid allegiance to Oman, but in practice they enjoyed a great deal of autonomy. Zanzibar, Pemba, Lamu and Kilwa were all ruled by members of the Busaidi family, but Mombasa was controlled by a rival Omani family, the Mazrui. In 1746 the Mazruis declared Mombasa independent of Oman, and overthrew the Busaidi force on Pemba. In 1753 they tried to capture Zanzibar, but the governor here remained loyal to Oman and repelled the attack.

During this period, the Mwinyi Mkuu, King Hassan, had died and been succeeded by his son, named Sultan, who in turn was succeeded by his son Ahmed, and then by his grandson Hassan II.

Zanzibar was now a major commercial centre and had also become very important strategically. From the middle of the 18th century there was a flourishing trade in slaves from Zanzibar and Kilwa to the Mascarenes (present-day Mauritius and Réunion) where slaves were used on sugar and clove plantations. By the 1770s these numbered about 3,000 slaves a year. In the same period Dutch ships came to Zanzibar in search of slaves to work on plantations in the East Indies.

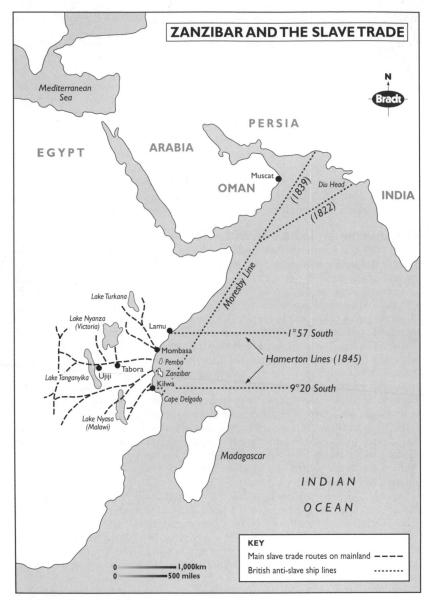

ZANZIBAR AND THE SLAVE TRADE

N

Bradt

Mediterranean
Sea

PERSIA

EGYPT

ARABIA

OMAN

Muscat

(1839)

Diu Head

INDIA

(1822)

Moresby Line

Lake Turkana

Lake Nyanza
(Victoria)

Lamu

1°57 South

Mombasa

Hamerton Lines (1845)

Pemba

Lake Tanganyika Ujiji Tabora Zanzibar

Kilwa

9°20 South

Cape Delgado

Lake Nyasa
(Malawi)

Madagascar

INDIAN

OCEAN

KEY

Main slave trade routes on mainland – – – –

British anti-slave ship lines ·········

0 ——— 1,000km
0 ——— 500 miles

Until this time African slave traders had brought captured slaves to the coast, but by the end of the 18th century the demand for slaves had increased to such an extent that Arab and Swahili traders from the coast and islands were penetrating the African interior. By the 1770s caravan traders had already travelled inland as far as Lake Nyasa (present-day Lake Malawi). (For more details, see the *East African Slave Trade* box, on page 172.)

In Oman a new sultan, whose name was Sultan bin Ahmed, came to power in 1792. He needed a strong ally to help him combat the Mazrui of Mombasa and also to keep the Persians out of Oman. He found this ally in Britain, by this time a powerful maritime nation with an empire expanding all over the world. In the late 18th century, Britain was at war with France and knew that the French emperor, Napoleon Bonaparte, was planning to march through Persia and capture Muscat, on his way to invade India. So Britain also needed an ally, and in 1798 Britain and Oman agreed a Treaty of Commerce and Navigation. Sultan bin Ahmed pledged himself to British interests in India, and his territories became out of bounds to the French. He allowed the British East India Company to establish a trading station in the Persian Gulf, and a British consul was posted to Muscat.

As well as defeating Bonaparte, the British had another motive for the treaty with Oman: they wanted to put pressure on the sultan to end slavery, which had been declared illegal in England in 1772. At this time, the trade from Africa to Oman was still buoyant with about 3,000 African slaves passing through Zanzibar every year.

At the same time, Zanzibar's position as an important trade centre was bolstered further when the supply of ivory from Mozambique to India collapsed due to excessive Portuguese export duties. The traders simply shipped their ivory through Zanzibar instead.

Sultan Said and the birth of the spice trade

In 1804 Sultan bin Ahmed of Oman was killed in battle, and his sons Salim and Said (aged 15 and 13) jointly inherited his kingdom with their cousin Bedr acting as regent. Two years later the young Said killed Bedr, who he believed was plotting to kill him; in 1806 he was proclaimed Sultan of Oman and the East African coast.

Said ruled his kingdom from Muscat and did not visit his African territories for several years. He maintained good relations with Britain because, like his father, he hoped for British help against the Persians and the Mazruis. During this period, wars and drought had drained Oman's economy, and many Omani merchants migrated to Zanzibar to participate in coastal trading and the caravans to the interior.

Meanwhile, in Europe, a campaign led by William Wilberforce resulted in the abolition of the slave trade within the British Empire in 1807. The USA passed a law against slave trading in 1808; the French and Germans did the same a few years later.

In East Africa, however, about 8,000 slaves were brought from the mainland to Zanzibar every year, many of them carrying ivory. This led to a surplus of slaves – a serious problem for the traders and for the Sultan of Oman. The answer to this problem came in 1812, when a Muscat-born Arab called Saleh bin Haramil al Abray introduced clove trees into Zanzibar from the island of Bourbon (now Réunion). Zanzibar's surplus of slaves was diverted to work on clove plantations and demand increased once again.

As the demand for slaves and ivory continued to expand, Arab traders from the coast pushed further inland. In 1820, they established a trading centre at Kazeh (near present-day Tabora, in Tanzania), over 800km (500 miles) from the coast. From Kazeh, trade routes branched north to the shores of present-day Lake Victoria, northwest to Buganda (now Uganda), and southwest to the southern end of Lake Tanganyika. (See *Zanzibar and the Slave Trade* map, opposite.)

Early British anti-slaving attempts

To combat this expansion in slavery the British consul in Muscat continued to put pressure on Sultan Said to end the slave trade. In September 1822 Said signed an anti-slavery treaty with the British Captain Fairfax Morseby which prohibited slave transport south and east of the 'Moresby Line' drawn from Cape Delgado, the

AL BUSAIDI FAMILY TREE

Ahmed bin Said SOZ 1744–83

Hilal (blind)

Said SOZ 1783–89
Hamad SOZ 1789–92

Qais
Azzan
Qais
Azzan (SO 1868–71)

Thuwaini SO 1856–66
Muhammed
Turki SO 1871–88

Hamad (1853–96) SZ (6) 1893–96
Haroub
Salim SO 1866–68
Hamoud (1847–1902) SZ 1896–1902(7)
Faisal SO 1888–1913

Khalifa (1879–1960) SZ 1911–60(9)
Ali(8) (1884–1911) SZ 1902–11
Taimur SO 1913–32

Abdulla(10) SZ 1960–63
Said SO 1932–70

Jamshid(11) SZ 1963–64
Qaboos SO 1970–

Seif

Bedr SOZ 1804–06 (regent)

Azze (Said's first wife)

Khaled (1815–54)
Shembua
Farashuu

Sultan SOZ 1792–1804

Salim (1789–1821)
Hamad
Moza (Barghash's first and only wife)

Said (1791–1856) SOZ 1804–56 (1)

Majid(2) (1834–70) SZ 1856–70
Barghash(3) (1837–88) SZ 1870–88
Khaled
Khole
Salme (1844–1924)
Rudolph
Khalifa(4) 1854–90 SZ 1888–90
Ali(5) 1852–91 SZ 1890–93
Abdid
Aziz

SOZ Sultan of Oman and Zanzibar
SO   Sultan of Oman
SZ   Sultan of Zanzibar

Note: Only names of the most prominent family members are given

southern limit of the sultan's domain in Africa, to Diu Head on the coast of India. (See *Zanzibar and the Slave Trade* map, page 14.)

This treaty meant that the transport of slaves from Zanzibar to the Mascarenes and to India was banned, but still permitted between Zanzibar and Oman. The sultan was also banned from selling slaves to Christians, which included the French for their Indian Ocean islands. British warships gained the right to confiscate any dhows found carrying slaves in forbidden waters.

Ironically, British prohibition of the slave trade to the Mascarenes only led to an increased development of the slave trade in Zanzibar itself. Sultan Said lost the revenue he would have received as duty on all slaves sold, so to make up the shortfall he encouraged the development of more clove plantations.

Meanwhile, Sultan Said continued to attempt to oust the Mazrui Sultan of Mombasa. In 1823 a British ship HMS *Barracouta* docked at Mombasa and the sultan asked for British protection against Oman. The ship's captain passed on the request to his senior officer, Captain William Owen of HMS *Leven*, who saw that he could use this local dispute to Britain's advantage: he sailed to Muscat and informed Sultan Said that he intended to grant the Mazrui request for British protection unless Said agreed to end the slave trade. Said refused to do this, so Owen declared Mombasa a British Protectorate, along with the coastline from Malindi to Pangani, on condition that the Mazrui sultan agreed to abolish the slave trade. The sultan agreed, but the agreement was short-lived. Within a few years, the Mazrui reverted to slave trading, and the British Protectorate was lifted in July 1826.

Sultan Said in Zanzibar

In 1827, Sultan Said sailed from Muscat to Zanzibar to inspect his far-flung territory. Here he met one Edmund Roberts, an American merchant from Portsmouth, New Hampshire, who suggested a commercial treaty between Said and America. Soon Zanzibar was supplying large amounts of ivory to America and Western Europe. African ivory was soft and easy to carve into combs, piano keys and billiard balls. Asian ivory, in contrast, was hard and brittle. The Americans also purchased animal hides and gum copal, a tree resin used in the manufacture of varnish. In return, cotton cloth (called 'Amerikani'), guns and gunpowder were imported into Zanzibar for distribution along the coast and to Arabia. (So great was the American demand for ivory in the 1830s that a town called Ivoryton was established in Connecticut, with a factory making piano keys and billiard balls out of ivory imported from Zanzibar.)

Sultan Said realised that trade with Europe and America would increase Zanzibar's wealth and strength, and thereby consolidate his own position, so at the end of the 1820s he decided to develop further Zanzibar's clove industry. His first move was to confiscate the plantations of Saleh bin Haramil al Abray, who had introduced cloves to the island in 1812. Said's reason for this was that Saleh was the leader of a political faction competing for power, and had also continued to send slaves to the Mascarenes after the Moresby treaty had made this illegal.

Vast plantations were established on Zanzibar and Pemba, and the islands' prosperity soon grew dramatically. Said decreed that three clove trees must be planted for every coconut palm, and that any landowner failing to do so would have his property confiscated. Said became the owner of 45 plantations scattered over the island, with about 50 slaves working as labourers on the smaller plots and up to 500 on the larger ones. Cloves fetched a high price abroad and by the end of Said's reign Zanzibar was one of the world's leading clove producers.

Said valued Zanzibar's large harbour, abundant freshwater supply and fertile

SULTANS

To help you place the sultans of Oman and Zanzibar in chronological order, the following lists will be helpful. The dates refer to their years as sultan. Note that *bin* means 'son of', and that some sultans were given the name Sultan. See also the family tree on page 16.

Sultans of Oman and Zanzibar

Ahmed bin Said	1744–83
Said bin Ahmed	1783–89
Hamad bin Said	1789–92
Sultan bin Ahmed	1792–1804
Bedr bin Seif	1804–06 (regent)
Said bin Sultan	1804–56

Sultans of Zanzibar

Said bin Sultan	Nov 20 1804 – Oct 19 1856
Majid bin Said	Oct 28 1856 – Oct 7 1870
Barghash bin Said	Oct 7 1870 – Mar 27 1888
Khalifa bin Said	Mar 29 1888 – Feb 13 1890
Ali bin Said	Feb 13 1890 – Mar 5 1893
Hamad bin Thuwaini bin Said	Mar 7 1893 – Aug 25 1896
Hamoud bin Muhammad bin Said	Aug 27 1896 – Jul 18 1902
Ali bin Hamoud	Jul 19 1902 – Dec 9 1911
Khalifa bin Harub bin Thuwaini	Dec 16 1911 – Oct 17 1960
Abdulla bin Khalifa	Oct 17 1960 – Jul 1963
Jamshid bin Abdulla	Jul 1963 – Jan 12 1964

Sultans of Oman

Thuwaini bin Said	1856–66
Salim bin Thuwaini	1866–68
Azzan bin Qais bin Ahmed	1868–71
Turki bin Said	1871–88
Faisal bin Turki	1888–1913
Taimur bin Faisal	1913–32
Said bin Taimur	1932–70
Qaboos bin Said	July 23 1970 – present day

soil. He also recognised the strategic importance of a Busaidi power base on the East African coast, and decided to spend several months on the island each year. A large house was built for him at Mtoni, on the west coast of the island about five kilometres north of Zanzibar Town.

Over the next few years, Said came under increased pressure from the British to abolish slavery. This call was strengthened in 1833, when the Emancipation Act abolished slavery throughout the British Empire and all slaves in British territories were freed. Recognising the need for strong allies, in the same year Said formalised the trade agreement suggested earlier by Edmund Roberts and signed a Treaty of Amity and Commerce with the United States of America. This gave the Americans freedom to set up trading posts at Zanzibar and on the mainland. In return, Said hoped for armed assistance against the Mazrui and for British anti-slavery pressure to ease.

To assist further in his attempts to take Mombasa, in December 1833 Said sent an envoy to Queen Ranavalona of Madagascar asking for her hand in marriage and for soldiers to help him fight the Mazrui. Queen Ranavalona declined his proposal of marriage, but offered him as many soldiers as he needed. She also asked Said to send her a coral necklace, which she would pay for but, disappointed by the queen's rejection, Said did not take up her offer of reinforcements.

Despite the lack of help from Madagascar, and the continued anti-slavery demands from Britain, in 1837 Said finally managed to oust the Mazrui from Mombasa and install his own garrison of soldiers in Fort Jesus. His presence along the coast of East Africa was finally complete.

Links between Zanzibar and America became increasingly cordial, and a consul, Richard Waters, was appointed in March 1837. Said presented him with a horse and a boat, and Waters was often the sultan's guest at Mtoni Palace. In November 1839 Said sent his trading ship *El-Sultani* to America. The ship arrived in New York in May 1840, the first Arab boat ever to visit an American port, and returned to Zanzibar with a cargo of arms and ammunition, china, beads and 'Amerikani' cloth.

Zanzibar becomes the capital of Oman

In December 1840 Sultan Said established his capital in Zanzibar, transferring it 3,000 miles from Muscat. He made this move at a time when Zanzibar's prosperity was increasing rapidly, and Oman's was in decline. Said also believed that the dual powerbase of Zanzibar and Oman would help safeguard his territories on the African mainland and maintain his dominance over Indian Ocean trade. Many of Oman's most influential merchants were already based in Zanzibar, and more followed him in the move from Muscat.

Said's title was now Sultan of Zanzibar and Oman. He ruled Zanzibar directly while his eldest surviving son, Thuwaini, remained in Muscat as governor of Oman. Zanzibar's own king, the Mwinyi Mkuu, presided over local matters but Said's government took control of trade and international affairs. Zanzibar Town began to expand: when Said had first arrived in the 1820s the buildings were mostly huts of mud thatched with coconut fronds, but by the 1850s many impressive stone buildings had been constructed by the new immigrants from Oman.

Said was also followed to Zanzibar by Captain Atkins Hamerton, who had originally been installed in Muscat to act as British Consul. In December 1841 he became the first British consul in Zanzibar. France also established diplomatic relations with Zanzibar: a French consulate was opened in 1844.

Meanwhile, despite the restrictions imposed by the Moresby Treaty, the slave trade continued to expand. In 1841 Arab traders had established a trading colony at Ujiji on Lake Tanganyika, almost 1,600km (1,000 miles) from the coast, and in 1843 the first Arab caravans had reached Buganda (now Uganda) on the shores of present-day Lake Victoria. By the end of the 1840s, Arab traders had gone even further, reaching the Upper Congo (now Eastern Zaire), the Central Highland area around Mount Kenya, the Rift Valley lakes of Baringo and Turkana, and southern Ethiopia. About 13,000 slaves a year were arriving in Zanzibar from the mainland. (See *Zanzibar and the Slave Trade* map, page 14.)

Britain's opposition to the slave trade

Sultan Said became increasingly concerned that British attempts to abolish the slave trade would weaken his power in the region. In 1842 he sent his envoy Ali bin Nasur to London on the ship *El-Sultani* to plead his case. Said's gifts for Queen Victoria included emeralds, cashmere shawls, pearl necklaces and ten Arab horses.

In reply, the British government told the Zanzibari ruler that it wished to abolish the slave trade to Arabia, Oman, Persia and the Red Sea. To soften the blow Queen Victoria gave Said a state coach and a silver-gilt tea service. (The state coach arrived in pieces and had to be assembled. It was still unused a year later, as Zanzibar had no roads. The tea service was considered too ornate to use and was taken to the British consulate for safe keeping.)

Britain continued putting restrictions on the slave trade. In October 1845 Said was virtually forced by Captain Hamerton to sign another anti-slavery treaty, which allowed slave transport only between lines of latitude 1° 57" south and 9° 20" south (between Lamu and Kilwa, the northern and southern limits of Said's dominions on the coast). This meant slaves could still be imported into Zanzibar but could no longer be exported to Oman. (See *Zanzibar and the Slave Trade* map, page 14.)

Ships from the British navy were employed to help enforce the treaty by capturing any dhows carrying slaves. When a dhow was captured, it was set on fire and the slaves were taken to Aden, India, or a free-slave community on the mainland coast, such as English Point in Mombasa. However, with only four ships to patrol a huge area of sea, the British navy found it hard to enforce the treaty, so the slave dhows continued to sail. Ships from France, Germany, Spain, Portugal and America also continued to carry slaves, as there were still huge profits to be made. And on the mainland slave traders continued to push further into the interior. The job of the British navy captains was made even harder following a decree that no dhow could be destroyed until the ship's papers had been removed. But very few dhows' captains carried any documents and on the rare occasions when papers were produced, they were usually in Arabic or Swahili which few British could read anyway.

Early European explorers

In the 1840s, European missionaries and explorers began to venture into the East African interior. In Britain, an Association for Promoting the Discovery of the Interior Parts of Africa had been formed as early as 1788, and had since merged with the Royal Geographical Society (RGS). In the following years it would play a leading role in the search for the source of the River Nile.

Zanzibar became the usual starting point for journeys into the interior. Here, the European missionaries and explorers paid their respects to Sultan Said, who 'owned' most of the land they would pass through. They equipped their expeditions with supplies and porters, before sailing to Bagamoyo on the mainland. Many explorers followed the established slaving routes into the interior, often employing slave traders to act as guides.

In 1844, the English Church Missionary Society, unable to find any British recruits, sent the German Johann Krapf to East Africa in an early attempt to convert the local people to Christianity. He was followed by his missionary colleague, Johann Rebmann, who arrived in Zanzibar two years later. Rebmann was introduced to Sultan Said by the British consul, Hamerton, before joining Krapf in Mombasa. They travelled widely across the areas now known as southern Kenya and northern Tanzania. In May 1848 Rebmann became the first European to see Kilimanjaro and in December 1849 Krapf was the first European to see Mount Kenya. (See *Exploration in East Africa* map on page 22.)

Meanwhile on Zanzibar the slave trade continued. By the 1850s about 14,000 to 15,000 slaves a year were being imported into Zanzibar from the mainland, providing Sultan Said with a large income from duties. Zanzibar traders pushed even deeper into the interior, reaching what is now northern Zambia. In 1852 a caravan reached Benguela (in present day Angola) having completely traversed the continent from east to west, while the following year another group reached Linyanti, in the present-day Caprivi Strip of Namibia.

Through the slave caravans Said had become the nominal ruler of a vast commercial empire stretching along the coast from Mozambique to the Somali ports, and inland to the Great Lakes of Nyasa (Malawi), Tanganyika, Nyanza (Victoria) and Turkana. By the end of his reign Zanzibar's empire covered about 2.5 million km² (1 million square miles), or 10% of the African continent, including the whole of present-day Tanzania, plus sizeable parts of Malawi, Zambia, Zaire, Uganda and Kenya. The Arabs had a saying: 'When the flute plays in Zanzibar, they dance on the lakes.' But it was an empire in name only and Said never attempted to conquer or develop the area.

The end of Said's reign

Sultan Said made periodic visits to Muscat, leaving his son Khaled as governor of Zanzibar in his absence. Khaled had a predilection for French goods and called his principal country estate Marseilles, after the French Mediterranean port. The house had floors inlaid with black and white marble and the inside walls were covered with large mirrors. When Khaled died of tuberculosis in November 1854, an order came from Said in Muscat appointing another son, the 20-year-old Majid, as governor.

In September 1856 Said sailed for Zanzibar again in his boat *Kitorie*. He travelled with his family, including his son Barghash, now 19 years old. Said ordered some loose planks of wood to be loaded on to the ship, saying that if anyone should die on board, the body must not be buried at sea according to Muslim custom, but embalmed and taken to Zanzibar in a coffin. Said seemed to know it was he who was about to die: he began to suffer severe pains from an old wound in his thigh followed by an attack of dysentery. On October 19 1856 he died on board the ship. He was 65 years old.

Barghash put his father's body in the coffin and took command of the fleet. He knew his elder brother Majid would succeed his father as the new Sultan of Zanzibar, but Barghash also realised that Majid would be unaware of their father's death. On arrival at Zanzibar, Barghash did not anchor in Zanzibar harbour, but went instead to Chumbe Island, about 10km to the south. That night, Barghash came ashore secretly and tried to take control of the palace at Mtoni and the Fort in Zanzibar Town, but he was unable to muster enough supporters and his attempt to seize control was thwarted.

On October 28 1856 Majid bin Said was proclaimed Sultan of Zanzibar. A ship was sent to Oman with the news, but Said's eldest son Thuwaini refused to acknowledge Majid as sultan, believing that he was the legitimate successor. Majid agreed to pay Thuwaini 40,000 Maria Theresa dollars (the trade currency of the time) annually as compensation, but after a year the payment ceased.

Later European explorers

By this time, the reports of early explorers like Rebmann and Krapf encouraged the British Royal Geographical Society to send an expedition to East Africa to search for the source of the White Nile. The leaders were Lieutenant (later Sir) Richard Francis Burton and Lieutenant John Hanning Speke.

In December 1856, on the last day of mourning for Sultan Said, Burton and Speke arrived in Zanzibar. After preparing for the expedition, they sailed for Bagamoyo and followed the slave route towards Lake Tanganyika, which they hoped was the source of the Nile. When they arrived, in January 1858, local Arab traders told them that a river at the northern end of the lake flowed into the lake

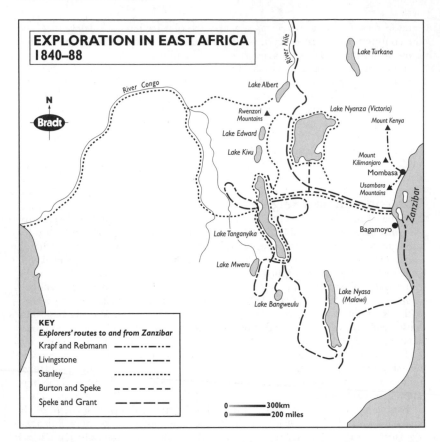

EXPLORATION IN EAST AFRICA 1840–88

N

Bradt

River Congo

River Nile

Lake Turkana

Lake Albert

Rwenzori Mountains

Lake Nyanza (Victoria)

Mount Kenya

Lake Edward

Lake Kivu

Mount Kilimanjaro

Mombasa

Usambara Mountains

Zanzibar

Lake Tanganyika

Bagamoyo

Lake Mweru

Lake Nyasa (Malawi)

Lake Bangweulu

KEY
Explorers' routes to and from Zanzibar
Krapf and Rebmann — · · — · · — · · —
Livingstone — — — — — —
Stanley · · · · · · · · · · · · · ·
Burton and Speke — — — — —
Speke and Grant — — — — —

0 ══════ 300km
0 ══════ 200 miles

(not out of it). Burton and Speke wanted to check for themselves, but were unable to reach the point where the river met the lake.

Bitterly disappointed, they began to return eastwards to Zanzibar. Burton became ill, and was forced to stop, so Speke struck out northwards on his own, and became the first European to see the great *Nyanza* (meaning 'lake') which he named Lake Victoria, certain it was the source of the White Nile – although he was unable to prove it at the time. Speke and Burton returned to Zanzibar in March 1859, and then separately to London.

To verify his theory, Speke returned to Zanzibar in 1860 with the Scottish explorer James Grant. Together they travelled inland to Lake Victoria, and this time found a great river emptying Lake Victoria at a waterfall, which they named the Ripon Falls after the president of the Royal Geographical Society. Although they were still unable to prove without doubt that this river was the Nile, it was the closest any explorer had got to settling the great geographical question of the age.

The division of Oman and Zanzibar

Meanwhile, back on Zanzibar, a power struggle was developing between the Omani rulers. Sultan Thuwaini of Oman planned to overthrow Sultan Majid of Zanzibar, as his promised tribute had not been paid. In February 1859 Thuwaini sailed southwards but was intercepted by a British cruiser at the eastern tip of Arabia. The British government wanted to keep control of the sea route to India, and did not want a civil war to develop in this area. Captain Hamerton, the British consul, had died, but Thuwaini was persuaded to submit his claims to the arbitration of Lord Canning, the Governor-General of India. Thuwaini agreed and returned to Muscat.

But Majid was in danger from another member of the family. His brother Barghash was still plotting to overthrow him and proclaim himself Sultan of Zanzibar. Majid learnt of the plot but Barghash escaped to the Marseilles plantation. He was finally captured and exiled to India for two years. (For more details see *The Escape to Marseilles* box on pages 24–5.)

In April 1861 Lord Canning declared that Oman and Zanzibar should be completely separate states. The annual tribute from Zanzibar to Oman was reinstated and in March 1862 Britain and France signed an Anglo-French declaration which recognised Majid as Sultan of Zanzibar and his territories as an independent sovereignty.

Although the Mwinyi Mkuu still lived in the palace at Dunga, his power was now negligible. Hassan II was succeeded by Mohammed, who died in 1865, aged 80. He was succeeded by his son, Ahmed, who died of smallpox in March 1873, leaving no male heir. The line of the Mwinyi Mkuu of Zanzibar had come to an end, and its passing was hardly noticed.

In 1866, in Oman, Thuwaini was murdered in his sleep by his son, Salim, who succeeded him. Majid discontinued the payment of the tribute on the grounds that Salim was a usurper, and Oman withdrew into isolation. (This isolation lasted for over a hundred years, until the accession of Sultan Qaboos bin Said in 1970.)

David Livingstone and 'Stinkibar'

In 1866 the Scottish missionary and explorer David Livingstone arrived in Zanzibar. He had already travelled across much of central and southern Africa, and written at great length about the horrors of the slave trade. He wanted to introduce what he regarded as essential elements of civilisation – commerce and Christianity – to Africa as a way of defeating the slave trade. He had also been asked by the Royal Geographical Society to clarify the pattern of the watersheds in the area of Lake Nyasa and Lake Tanganyika and their relation to the source of the White Nile – still an unsolved problem for the geographers of the day.

By this period, Zanzibar's increasing trade and growing population had created its own problems and Livingstone did not enjoy his stay: 'No-one can truly enjoy good health here,' he wrote, later adding: 'the stench from...two square miles of exposed sea-beach, which is the general depository of the filth of the town, is quite horrible. At night, it is so gross and crass, one might cut a slice and manure the garden with it. It might be called "Stinkibar" rather than Zanzibar.'

During the same period, other European visitors arriving by ship claimed they could smell Zanzibar before they could see it. In the town itself, the freshwater springs were not particularly fresh. Dr James Christie, an English physician who arrived in Zanzibar in 1869, reported that the springs consisted of the 'diluted drainage of dunghills and graveyards'. Not surprisingly, this led to frequent bouts of dysentery and epidemics of smallpox and cholera. Malaria and bilharzia were also problems. Cholera epidemics had occurred in 1821 and 1836, and smallpox in 1858. Later cholera epidemics in 1858 and 1869–70 killed one-sixth of the population of Zanzibar Town, and 35,000 people throughout the island.

At this time, slavery had still not been abolished on Zanzibar. In the early 1860s an average 15,000 slaves a year were being imported into Zanzibar from mainland Africa, and by 1866 this had grown to 20,000 a year. The slave population had reached its peak and clove production entered a phase of overproduction and stagnation, so prices dropped.

THE ESCAPE TO MARSEILLES

In October 1859 Barghash was plotting to overthrow his brother, Majid, who was Sultan of Zanzibar. Barghash was living in a house in Zanzibar Town, close to the palace of Beit el Sahel, with his sister Meyye and 11-year-old brother Abdil Aziz. Two more sisters, Salme and Khole, were living in a house immediately behind his, separated by a narrow street. Two of his nieces, the princesses Shembua and Farashuu, also lived nearby. All these siblings supported Barghash and wanted Majid overthrown, and their three houses formed a centre for the conspiracy.

Majid, aware that his brother was plotting against him, arranged to have the three houses watched and ordered Barghash's house to be blockaded. Several hundred soldiers were posted outside the front of the house with strict orders to shoot any suspicious person and cut off all communications. But Barghash had plenty of provisions, and his fellow conspirators smuggled water to him through the back of the house.

Meanwhile, at the fortified plantation of Marseilles, in the centre of the island, the conspirators stored arms, ammunition and food supplies in preparation for a siege. (The plantation had been named Marseilles by another brother, Khalid, who had a predilection for all things French.) Princess Salme played an important part in the preparations because she could write, and prepared secret messages to be carried between the other conspirators. She later referred to herself as 'secretary to the alliance of rebels'.

At midnight on October 8 1859 Salme and Khole went to Barghash's house with a large escort including Shembua and Farashuu. Bluffing their way past the soldiers on duty (Arab women did not normally speak to strange men), they were allowed to pay the prisoner a short visit. They brought women's robes and veils and Barghash wrapped himself in a voluminous black robe, which left only his eyes free. The tallest women walked alongside him to make his height less conspicuous, and the guards on the door made way respectfully for the royal party when they left the building.

Salme and Khole had arranged a rendezvous with some of Barghash's other

As a result of the declining profitability of clove production, there was a greater interest in the production of coconut and sesame seed oils, mainly for export to France. There was also a revival of sugar production, and rubber plantations were established along the coast.

Livingstone, Stanley and the relief expeditions

David Livingstone had left Zanzibar in March 1866. Lack of news in the outside world led to speculation on his whereabouts, and in January 1871 the American journalist Henry Morton Stanley arrived in Zanzibar, having been commissioned by the *New York Herald* to search for the 'lost explorer'. In November the same year Stanley arrived at Ujiji, where he found Livingstone and greeted him with the now immortal phrase, 'Doctor Livingstone, I presume?' (For more details on the explorations of Livingstone see the *David Livingstone* box, under *Places to Visit near Zanzibar Town* in *Chapter 5 – Zanzibar Town*. See also the *Henry Morton Stanley* box on page 26.)

After Stanley had found Livingstone, and returned alone to Zanzibar, Livingstone stayed at Kazeh until August 1872, then set off southwards on another expedition to find the source of the Nile, which he thought would take no more

supporters outside the town. Here Barghash threw off his disguise, while his sisters returned to Zanzibar Town. Majid soon heard news of Barghash's escape, and knew that he had reached Marseilles with many followers. Majid mustered 5,000 soldiers and appealed to the British consul, Sir Chistopher Rigby, for help in quelling the revolt. Rigby provided Majid with nine soldiers and a gun from the British warship HMS *Assaye*.

Majid marched to Marseilles and started to bombard the house, but Barghash's supporters emerged from their fortifications, and fought off Majid's troops until sunset. Several hundred lives were lost. Majid retreated for the night but, as he and his army slept, Barghash and his supporters slipped back into town. On the morning of October 16, Majid re-advanced on Marseilles and smashed open the gates, only to find it abandoned.

By this time, Barghash had returned to his house. Realising that his plans were thwarted, he remained concealed, refusing even to go to the window. Rigby arranged for HMS *Assaye* to be anchored just offshore, and a detachment of marines landed and marched to the front of Barghash's house.

On October 17 Rigby called on Barghash to surrender. When there was no answer, the marines started to fire their guns at the front of the house. Khole, calling from her house across the street, persuaded her brother to surrender. Contemporary reports describe how cries of '*Aman!*' ('Peace!') were heard from inside the house and how, after the firing had stopped, Rigby rapped on the door with his walking stick and demanded immediate surrender. When Barghash emerged, Rigby arrested him and put him on board the *Assaye*. He was taken to India, where he lived in exile for two years. Abdil Aziz insisted on accompanying his elder brother and stayed in India after Barghash's return in 1861.

Princess Salme was rejected by her family, and in 1866 met a German trader called Heinrich Ruete. They became lovers and moved to Germany, where Salme changed her name to Emily and later wrote a book about her life at the court of Zanzibar. (For more details see the *Princess Salme* boxes, pages 180–1.)

than a few months. (He had already been in the interior for six years at this stage.)

Meanwhile the RGS in London was unaware of Stanley's 'find' so in February 1872 the Livingstone Search and Relief Expedition, led by Lieutenant Llewellyn Dawson, was dispatched to Zanzibar in the steamship *Abydos*. Two months later, the expedition arrived in Zanzibar, where their ship was caught in the freak hurricane of April 14. Contemporary accounts record that it began to blow at 23.00 and continued until 13.30 the next day, when it abated for about half an hour. The storm then suddenly burst upon the island in greater fury, and raged for another three hours. Every ship and dhow in the harbour was driven ashore except the *Abydos*, although the expedition's accounts were blown away. The town was wrecked, many people were killed, and over two-thirds of the coconut and clove trees on the island were uprooted.

A few weeks after the hurricane, in May 1872, Stanley arrived at Bagamoyo, where he met Dawson and told him that Livingstone was safe and would be arriving after a few more months. Dawson cancelled the Search and Relief Expedition and returned to London. But by the end of 1872 Livingstone had still not arrived back at Zanzibar as expected, so in February 1873 a second Relief Expedition, led by Lieutenant Verney Lovett Cameron, set out from Zanzibar to find him.

Unknown to Cameron, and the rest of the world, Livingstone's short expedition had become much longer than he had intended. He had grown ill again, and the attacks of dysentery had returned. On May 2 1873 he died in the village of Chitambo, near Lake Bangweulu (in present-day Zambia), 800km (500 miles) south of Ujiji, and even further from the actual source of the Nile. Two of his companions carried his body back towards Zanzibar. In August 1873 they reached Kazeh, where they met Cameron and told him of Livingstone's death.

Cameron decided to march on to Ujiji which he reached in February 1874 and where he found Livingstone's papers. From Ujiji, Cameron continued westwards, eventually reaching the Atlantic coast in November 1875, thereby becoming the first European to travel across this part of Africa from east to west.

Sultan Barghash and John Kirk

By this time, on Zanzibar, Sultan Majid had died, aged 36. His only child was a daughter so his brother Barghash (who had twice already tried to seize the throne and had returned to Zanzibar from exile in India in 1861) finally succeeded to the throne, and was proclaimed sultan on October 7 1870. In the same year, Dr John Kirk (who had originally come to Zanzibar as a medical officer on Livingstone's expedition) was made acting British consul.

After the hurricane of April 1872, Sultan Barghash had announced plans to grow new plantations, and the slave trade picked up once again. By late 1872 around 16,000 slaves had been imported into Zanzibar. (The hurricane only hit the southern tip of Pemba, leaving most of the clove trees on that island untouched. By the 1880s Pemba was producing about 80% of the total clove harvest from Zanzibar and Pemba.)

At the same time, the anti-slavery movement continued to grow, fuelled in America by the publication of *Uncle Tom's Cabin*. In January 1873 Sir Bartle Frere,

HENRY MORTON STANLEY

The man known to the world as Henry Morton Stanley was born John Rowland on January 29 1841 at Denbigh in Wales. He spent nine years in a workhouse and two years as a farmhand, before joining a ship from Liverpool to New Orleans, which he reached in 1858. In New Orleans he was adopted by his employer, a cotton merchant, from whom he took his new name, Henry Stanley. 'Morton' was added later.

By 1869 Stanley was a correspondent for the *New York Herald*. The manager of the newspaper, James Gordon Bennett, despatched him to Africa with orders to cover the inauguration of the Suez Canal, and then find Livingstone if he were alive, or bring back his bones if he were dead.

Stanley arrived in Zanzibar on January 6 1871. He borrowed a top hat from the American consul, John Francis Webb, and went to visit Sultan Barghash who gave him letters of recommendation to show his agents in the interior. Stanley set off from Zanzibar in March that year, just two days before the start of the rainy season. His provisions included American cloth, beads of glass, coral and china for trading, plus two silver goblets and a bottle of champagne for the day he met Livingstone.

Stanley finally met Livingstone at Ujiji, on the eastern shore of Lake Tanganyika, on November 10 1871. According to Stanley's own description of the meeting, Stanley took off his hat, held out his hand, and said, 'Doctor Livingstone, I presume?' When Livingstone answered, 'Yes,' Stanley continued with, 'I thank

a special envoy from Queen Victoria, arrived in Zanzibar to negotiate a treaty which he hoped would finally put an end to the Arab slave trade. Sultan Barghash was naturally reluctant to end slavery as he was still earning a great deal of revenue from import duties, and needed the slaves to work in the clove plantations. Frere sailed for England at the beginning of March 1873 without a treaty and almost immediately the British navy began a blockade of every slave port on the mainland. The number of slaves passing through the Customs House in Zanzibar Town between January and March dropped to 21, compared to 4,000 in the same period the previous year.

In June 1873 Sir John Kirk, the British consul, informed Sultan Barghash that a total blockade of Zanzibar Island was imminent. Reluctantly Barghash signed the Anglo-Zanzibari Treaty which provided for the complete abolition of the slave trade in Barghash's territories, the closing of all slave markets and the protection of all liberated slaves. Transport of slaves was forbidden, and slaves could no longer be exported from mainland Africa to Zanzibar and Pemba, except for domestic purposes.

The large slave market in Zanzibar Town was closed immediately. The site was bought by missionaries of the Universities Mission in Central Africa (UMCA), and work started on the cathedral which can still be seen in Zanzibar Town today. (See *Chapter 5 – Zanzibar Town*.)

One of the main effects of the treaty, now that slavery was illegal, was to push up the price of slaves and the trade continued in a clandestine manner. Through the 1870s smugglers were estimated to be exporting between 10,000 and 12,000 slaves a year.

In 1875 John Kirk brought Sultan Barghash an official invitation to visit Britain to ratify the Anglo-Zanzibari Treaty. In June the same year Barghash and Kirk arrived in London where Barghash received the Freedom of the City at the

God that I have been permitted to see you,' to which Livingstone gravely replied, 'I feel thankful that I am here to welcome you.'

After these traditional English niceties, and the seemingly mundane phrase that was to dog Stanley for the rest of his life, Stanley and Livingstone travelled in the area together for some time, but Livingstone was still determined to discover the source of the Nile and pressed on southwards alone. Stanley returned to Zanzibar on May 7 1872, before travelling to London.

Two years later, Stanley gave up journalism to return to Africa as an explorer. He reached Zanzibar again in September 1874, and left for the mainland in November the same year. On this expedition he rounded the southern shore of Lake Victoria, went through Buganda (now Uganda), and followed the Congo River (through present-day Zaire) to the Atlantic Ocean, which he reached on August 12 1877, thus crossing Africa in 999 days.

From 1879 to 1884, Stanley returned to the Congo for King Leopold II of Belgium. He established and governed the Congo Free State (which was to become Zaire, now renamed the Democratic Republic of the Congo), and the town of Stanleyville (now Kisangani) was named after him.

After another expedition from 1887 to 1889, Stanley returned to Britain a celebrity. He was married in Westminster Abbey in 1890, elected to parliament as a Liberal Unionist for North Lambeth in 1895, and knighted in 1899. He died in London on May 10 1904.

Guildhall and attended a state banquet at Mansion House. During his visit Barghash went to the Ascot and Doncaster races, Hyde Park and the British Museum. He had guided tours of the General Post Office, Woolwich Arsenal, Aldershot Camp and Brighton. He also went to the manufacturing towns of Birmingham, Liverpool and Manchester, where he witnessed the might of the Industrial Revolution. A firework display was given for him at Crystal Palace.

Barghash also visited Queen Victoria at Windsor, and the Prince and Princess of Wales at Marlborough House. He was surprised to see the young princes Albert and George wearing sailor suits, which he regarded as the uniform of working men.

While Barghash was in London, his sister Salme had come from Germany (where she had gone in 1866 with Heinrich Ruete – see the *Princess Salme* boxes, pages 180–1) hoping to be reconciled with her brother. But Barghash refused to meet Salme. The British government supported this action as they thought Salme might persuade her brother to reject the treaty.

On July 15 1875, after four weeks of intensive sightseeing and entertainment, Barghash and his party went from Folkestone to Calais and thence to Paris. A few days later, they travelled by train to Marseilles and sailed for Zanzibar, arriving home in September.

For the British, Zanzibar was no longer a distant, obscure island, and links between the two countries became even more firmly established. In 1869 the Suez Canal had opened, making the sea voyage between Britain and the coast of East Africa much shorter and simpler. In 1872 the British India Steamship Navigation Company started a monthly mail service between Zanzibar and Aden. It brought the first scheduled passenger and cargo service to Zanzibar, which allowed merchandise to be exported quickly. Communication was again improved in 1879, when the Eastern Telegraph Company completed their cable from Zanzibar to Europe via Aden, and a telegraphic link with Europe was established.

Inspired by his visit to Europe, Barghash decided to make many changes on Zanzibar. Advised by John Kirk (now firmly installed as the power behind the throne), he appointed Lieutenant William Lloyd Mathews to reorganise his army and enforce his sovereignty over the interior. (For more details see the *William Lloyd Mathews* box, page 186.)

During his exile in India, Barghash had seen the opulent wealth of the Indian palaces and he tried to emulate them on Zanzibar. Many luxurious palaces were built, including Chukwani, to the south of Zanzibar Town, and Maruhubi Palace, to the north, for his harem. Another palace, in the town, became known as the *Beit el Ajaib*, or House of Wonders, as it was the first building on Zanzibar to have electric lighting. In all his palaces, Barghash upgraded the dinner services from silver to gold. Divan coverings of goat and camel hair were replaced by silks and taffetas, and French carpets covered the floors.

Barghash introduced Zanzibar's first clean water system to replace supplies from local wells and rainwater: aqueducts and conduits brought pure water from a spring at Bububu into Zanzibar Town, a distance of some six kilometres. Other developments introduced by Barghash included a police force, an ice-making factory, electric street lighting, and telephones to connect his city and country palaces. Barghash also built and improved the roads on the island, and every year he provided one of his private steamships for Muslims wishing to make the pilgrimage to Mecca.

The scramble for Africa

In 1884 Dr Karl Peters, founder of the Society for German Colonisation, arrived in Zanzibar, then sailed for the mainland where he made 'treaties of eternal friendship' with the local African chiefs in return for large areas of land. By the time he reached Kilimanjaro he had annexed more than 6,000km² (2,500 square miles) of land, which were still nominally under the control of Sultan Barghash.

Britain was concerned at the presence of a rival European power on its patch, but was distracted by events elsewhere. In January 1885 Khartoum, the capital of Anglo-Egyptian Sudan, fell to the forces of the Mahdi. The British General Gordon was killed and the British governor of Equatoria Province, south of Khartoum, was cut off. (Ironically, the governor was actually a German called Eduard Schnitzer, although he had adopted the name Emin Pasha and was working for the British.)

Otto von Bismark, the German chancellor, saw the Mahdi's victory as a sign of Britain's weakness and believed that Germany could consolidate its claims in East Africa without British opposition. In February the same year the General Act of Berlin, signed by Kaiser Wilhelm of Germany, officially proclaimed a German protectorate over the territories annexed by Karl Peters. Sultan Barghash was only formally told about his loss of land in April of the same year. He hoped for support

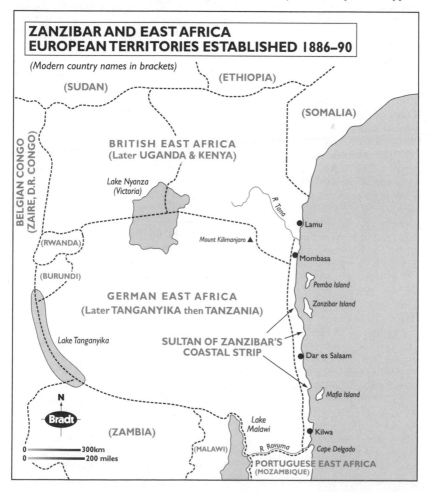

**ZANZIBAR AND EAST AFRICA
EUROPEAN TERRITORIES ESTABLISHED 1886–90**

(Modern country names in brackets)

(SUDAN)   (ETHIOPIA)

(SOMALIA)

BELGIAN CONGO
(ZAIRE, D.R. CONGO)

BRITISH EAST AFRICA
(Later UGANDA & KENYA)

Lake Nyanza
(Victoria)

R Tana

Lamu

(RWANDA)

Mount Kilimanjaro ▲

Mombasa

(BURUNDI)

Pemba Island

GERMAN EAST AFRICA
(Later TANGANYIKA then TANZANIA)

Zanzibar Island

Lake Tanganyika

SULTAN OF ZANZIBAR'S
COASTAL STRIP

Dar es Salaam

Mafia Island

N

Bradt

(ZAMBIA)

Lake
Malawi

Kilwa

0 ──── 300km
0 ──── 200 miles

(MALAWI)   R Rovuma   Cape Delgado

PORTUGUESE EAST AFRICA
(MOZAMBIQUE)

from the British, but Britain did not want to make an enemy of Germany, and so declined.

In June 1885 the Germans claimed another protectorate over Witu and the mouth of the Tana River, near Lamu, and in August the same year five ships of the German navy, commanded by Carl Paschen, arrived in Zanzibar harbour. Paschen demanded that Sultan Barghash recognise the German protectorates. Kirk had to obey the recommendations of the British government, which was to persuade Barghash to submit.

A few days after the arrival of the German fleet, another German ship entered the harbour, carrying Barghash's sister Salme (who had eloped to Germany in 1866). She was with her son Said-Rudolph, now 16 years old, and two other children. Kirk believed that the Germans would propose Said-Rudolph as sultan. Then, if Barghash arrested him or Salme, now German citizens, this would justify the Germans in declaring war on Zanzibar. So, advised by Kirk, Barghash tolerated Salme's presence. He did not arrest her, but offered no hospitality, nor did he meet her.

Barghash sent his formal recognition of the German protectorate to Carl Paschen and two months later, in response to the German action, the British government arranged for a joint commission between Britain, Germany and France to establish their own boundaries in the mainland territories that were still officially under the control of the Sultan of Zanzibar.

After lengthy discussions the first Anglo-German agreement was signed by Germany and Britain in late 1886. Barghash's lands were reduced to Zanzibar, Pemba, Mafia, Lamu and a ten-mile (16km) wide coastal strip stretching around 1,200km (about 750 miles) from the Tana River, near Lamu, to the Rovuma River, near Cape Delgado. The rest of the mainland, east of Lake Victoria and Lake Tanganyika, was divided between Britain and Germany. Britain took the northern portion, between the Tana and Umba rivers, which became British East Africa, later Kenya. Germany took the southern portion, between the Umba and Rovuma rivers. This became German East Africa, later Tanganyika. (See *Zanzibar and East Africa* map, page 29.)

Given no option, Barghash agreed to this treaty in December 1886 and the French government signed it a few days later. In June 1887 Barghash leased the northern section of his coastal strip (between the Tana and Umba rivers) to the British East African Association (BEAA), which had been formed by William Mackinnon in May the same year. Meanwhile the Germans and Portuguese met in Barghash's absence to discuss their own border, and Portugal gained more of Barghash's land in the south.

In February 1888 Barghash sailed to Muscat, to visit the healing Bushire Springs on the Persian coast, to recuperate from tuberculosis and elephantiasis. He returned to Zanzibar on March 26, arriving at 20.00. He died five hours later, on March 27, at the age of 51.

On March 29 1888 Barghash's brother Khalifa bin Said was proclaimed sultan. In April the same year, the British East African Association became the Imperial British East Africa Company (IBEA), with its capital at Mombasa, which was beginning to take Zanzibar's place as the commercial centre for Africa. Without the income from the slave trade, Zanzibar's prosperity was in decline.

In March 1889 Karl Peters arrived back in Zanzibar as head of the German Emin Pasha Relief Expedition, to rescue his countrymen who had been cut off by the Mahdi in Equatoria in 1885. Under the guise of this expedition Karl Peters planned to travel inwards from the German-held enclave of Witu (near Lamu), north of the British territory, to seize Uganda for Germany. In August the same year the IBEA sent a British expedition into the interior, led by Sir Frederick Jackson, also to make contact with Emin Pasha.

Meanwhile, unbeknown to both the German and British expeditions, Henry Stanley (who had left Zanzibar on his own relief expedition in 1887) had already found Emin Pasha on the western shore of Lake Albert in April 1888.

A British protectorate

On September 13 1889 Khalifa signed an agreement with the British government agreeing to abolish slavery in his territories. Anybody who entered the sultan's realms, and any children born, would be free. Britain and Germany were awarded a permanent right to search for slaves in Zanzibar's waters. As a sign of Britain's appreciation, Khalifa was knighted, but less than a month later he died, aged 36.

Khalifa's brother, Ali bin Said, was proclaimed sultan. Ali was the fourth and last of Said's sons to become Sultan of Zanzibar. On August 1 1890 Ali signed an anti-slavery treaty forbidding the purchase and sale of slaves. With the end of the slave trade, the only viable export from the interior was ivory, by now a rapidly waning asset.

Meanwhile in the interior Karl Peters entered Uganda in February 1890 and claimed the territory for Germany, just ahead of Sir Frederick Jackson from England. But Britain was unhappy about Germany's claims; the British politician Lord Robert Salisbury realised that control of the Upper Nile could lead indirectly to the control of the Suez Canal and thus the trade route to India. So Germany was persuaded to renounce any claims over Uganda in return for British support of the Kaiser against the major European powers of the day, France and Russia.

By the second Anglo-German agreement (the Treaty of Zanzibar) of July 1 1890, Germany agreed to recognise a British protectorate over the Sultanate of Zanzibar, and to abandon any claim to Witu and the country inland as far as the Upper Nile. Germany also abandoned any claim to the west of Lake Nyasa but, in return, gained sovereignty over the coast of German East Africa, later to become Tanganyika. The British–German border was continued westwards across Lake Victoria to the boundary of the Belgian territory of Congo, thus securing Uganda for Britain. The British coastal strip (which still belonged to the Sultan of Zanzibar) was removed from the control of the British East Africa Company and administered by the British East Africa Protectorate, later to become Kenya and Uganda.

In exchange for the thousands of square miles of East African territory, including the islands of Zanzibar (Unguja and Pemba) which it gave up to British control, Germany gained Heligoland, a small island off the German coast which lay near the mouth of the Kiel Canal. This was of strategic importance to Germany, but Karl Peters was disgusted and wrote that 'two kingdoms had been bartered for a bath-tub in the North Sea'.

In 1891 a constitutional government was established in Zanzibar, with General Sir Lloyd Mathews as first minister. But although Zanzibar enjoyed the status of a British protectorate, the island's importance as a commercial centre was declining further in favour of Mombasa.

The British now controlled Zanzibar, so when Sultan Ali died in March 1893, without making a will, they proclaimed Hamad, son of Thuwaini (the former sultan of Oman), as sultan even though there were two other claimants: Khaled bin Barghash and Hamoud bin Mahomed bin Said, a nephew of Thuwaini.

During Hamad's reign, in November 1895, Zanzibar issued its first stamps (from about 1875 the island had been using Indian stamps with 'Zanzibar' overprinted). Then a newspaper, *The Gazette for Zanzibar and East Africa,* was produced. It was followed by others in English, Arabic, Swahili and Urdu.

Also in 1895, the Mazrui family leaders made a final attempt to break away from Zanzibar and rule Mombasa themselves once again. A year later, defeated, their leaders fled from British-held Mombasa into German territory where they were taken to Dar es Salaam and imprisoned.

The last years of the 19th century

Sultan Hamad became ill in 1896, and died in August that year. The British recommended Hamoud, a cousin of Hamad, as sultan. But Barghash's son, Khaled, who had already tried to seize power from Hamad, made a second attempt at snatching the throne. He was briefly successful this time but was ousted by the British, after 'the shortest war in history' (see *The Shortest War in History* box, opposite). Khaled escaped to Dar es Salaam, in German territory.

On August 27 1896 Hamoud was conducted into the Customs House and proclaimed Sultan of Zanzibar, amidst the salute of the ships. The new sultan supported the British government and on April 5 1897 he signed a treaty to abolish the legal status of slavery in Zanzibar and Pemba. Shortly after this Queen Victoria awarded him the Grand Cross of the Most Distinguished Order of St Michael and St George. Hamoud sent his son Ali to school at Harrow in England where he represented his father at the coronation of King Edward VII.

Sultan Hamoud died on July 18 1902 and the British proclaimed the 18-year-old Ali as the new sultan. From his school days he spoke English fluently, and continued to travel in Europe during his reign. He often received medical treatment in Switzerland and Germany and also visited Paris and Constantinople. In May 1911 Ali attended the coronation of King George V in England. While in Europe his health deteriorated and he abdicated in December 1911. He spent the last seven years of his life in Europe, and died in Paris in December 1918. Khalifa bin Harub, a cousin of Ali, became Sultan Khalifa II on December 16 1911.

Zanzibar enters the 20th century

Sultan Khalifa bin Harub proved to be a moderate but influential ruler, and proceeded to guide Zanzibar through the first half of the turbulent 20th century with skill and diplomacy.

Soon after Khalifa gained power, changes were made to the British way of overseeing their interests in Zanzibar. In July 1913 responsibility for Zanzibar was transferred from the Foreign Office to the Colonial Office. The post of British Consul became British Resident, subject to the control of the governor of the British East Africa Protectorate. At the same time a Protectorate Council was established. This was an advisory body with the sultan as president and the British Resident as vice-president.

During World War I the German and British armies, with conscripted African soldiers, were involved in several campaigns on the mainland. The war did not affect Zanzibar directly except for one incident when the British ship *Pegasus* was bombarded and sunk by the German ship *Königsberg* in Zanzibar Town harbour. (Graves marking the bodies of sailors killed in this incident can still be seen on Grave Island.)

Towards the end of the war, in 1917, the British army drove the Germans out of their territory and marched into Dar es Salaam. Khaled, who had tried to seize the throne of Zanzibar during 'the shortest war' in 1896, was still there and was captured. He was exiled to the Seychelles, then allowed to return to Mombasa in 1925 where he lived quietly until 1927.

After the war, the German East African territory was administered by Britain under a League of Nations mandate and called Tanganyika. Later, in 1920, the British East Africa Protectorate became known as the Kenya Colony.

In 1925 the British Resident on Zanzibar was made directly responsible to the

THE SHORTEST WAR IN HISTORY

Sultan Hamad died on August 25 1896 while the British consul, Arthur Hardinge, was on leave in England. The acting British consul, Basil Cave, recommended that Hamoud (Hamad's cousin) be appointed sultan, but when Cave and Sir Lloyd Mathews reached the palace of Beit el Sahel in Zanzibar Town they found the doors barred. Khaled, the son of Barghash (and another cousin of Hamoud), had arrived before them with about 60 armed men, entered the palace by climbing through a broken window, and had been quickly joined by more than 2,000 supporters.

Khaled proclaimed himself sultan, and raised the red flag of Zanzibar on the palace roof. But Basil Cave refused to recognise his claim: British ships in the harbour landed guards of marines, which were posted at the British consulate (where the British women sought refuge), the Customs House, and elsewhere around the town. Many foreigners gathered on the roof of the English Club, where they had a clear view of the harbour and the palace.

On the morning of August 26 the three British ships were reinforced by the timely arrival of two others, and the following day, at dawn, the British fleet under Rear-Admiral Harry Holdsworth Rawson delivered an ultimatum: Khaled was to surrender, disarm, evacuate the palace and be at the Customs House by 09.00, or the British ships would open fire. At 08.00 Khaled sent an envoy to Cave, asking for a chance to discuss peace, but his request was refused.

The palace clock struck three (09.00 British time) and at 09.02 the bombardment started. In half an hour Beit el Sahel and the adjoining palace of Beit el Hukm were badly damaged. The lighthouse outside the palace was in flames and the nearby House of Wonders was also hit a few times. Many of Khaled's supporters had fled, leaving 500 dead and wounded lying about the palace grounds.

At 09.40 Khaled surrendered. He lowered the flag, the firing ceased and the war was over. This dispute over the succession is listed in the *Guinness Book of Records* as the shortest war in history.

Khaled escaped through the narrow streets and fled to the German consulate, where he was given asylum. As the steps of the consulate led on to the beach, Khaled was able to board the German warship *Seeadler* without risking arrest. Khaled was taken to Dar es Salaam where he lived in exile. He died in Mombasa in 1927, aged 53.

Colonial Office in London, and a new Legislative Council was established. The ten-mile (16km) wide strip of land along the coast of Kenya, including Mombasa, which had been leased to Kenya in 1895 was still technically 'owned' by the sultan of Zanzibar and the new Kenya government continued to pay the lease of £11,000 per year.

During World War II, Zanzibar was not involved in any military action. The war's main effect was to interrupt the supply of rice, a staple food for the Asian and African people, that had until then been imported from Burma.

The road to independence

After World War II Britain gradually allowed the local people of Zanzibar to become involved in the island's government. Several local political parties were formed and Zanzibar's first elections were held in July 1957. The Afro-Shirazi Union (which later became the Afro-Shirazi Party – ASP) defeated the Zanzibar Nationalist Party (ZNP). Broadly speaking, the ASP was dominated by Africans, the ZNP by Arabs.

In October 1960 Sultan Khalifa died, after ruling for 49 years, and was succeeded by his only son, Abdullah. In November the same year Zanzibar was granted a new constitution which allowed for the elections of the members of the Legislative Council. Elections took place in January 1961, producing no clear result, and again in June 1961, but these were marked by serious inter-racial rioting. Nevertheless the ZNP, along with the aligned Zanzibar and Pemba People's Party, won 13 of the seats on the council, while the ASP won ten.

Britain realised that internal self-government for Zanzibar was inevitable, and this was finally granted in June 1963. In July that year Sultan Abdullah died. Throughout his short reign he had suffered from severe pains in his legs, which had eventually been amputated. Abdullah was succeeded by his eldest son Jamshid.

On December 10 1963 Zanzibar became an independent sultanate, and the coastal strip was finally ceded to Kenya, which became independent two days later. Zanzibar was made a full member of the British Commonwealth and on December 16 became a member of the United Nations. But the new sultanate was short-lived: on January 12 1964 the Zanzibari government was overthrown in a violent revolution.

Revolutionary Zanzibar

The leader of Zanzibar's Revolution was a Ugandan called John Okello who had been living in Pemba. The local African population supported Okello with great enthusiasm, and went on a rampage through the islands, in which more than 17,000 Arabs and Indians were killed in one night. The leader of the Afro-Shirazi Party, Sheik Abied Amani Karume, was installed as president of the newly proclaimed People's Republic of Zanzibar, which included the islands of Unguja and Pemba.

Karume and other prominent ASP members formed the Revolutionary Government of Zanzibar (*Serikali ya Mapinduzi ya Zanzibar*, or SMZ). Most of Zanzibar's Asian and Indian people left the islands; their property was confiscated and their land nationalised. (On the mainland Sultan Jamshid was given temporary asylum in Dar es Salaam, then went to Britain where he lived in exile in a town on the south coast.)

Meanwhile, Tanganyika had also become independent in December 1961, with Julius Nyerere elected as president the following year. Nyerere had known and supported Karume since the mid-1950s but the Zanzibar Revolution created problems in Tanganyika, inspiring an attempted coup in Dar es Salaam only a few days later. (To suppress this coup Nyerere received help from Britain in the form of a battalion of commandos.)

Once Nyerere had regained control he approached Karume to discuss a political union. Karume agreed, and on April 24 1964 the two countries joined to form the United Republic of Tanganyika and Zanzibar. In October the same year the country was renamed Tanzania (from 'Tan' in Tanganyika and 'Zan' in Zanzibar). Nyerere became the president of the new state while Karume became vice-president. The SMZ was to control all local affairs on the islands of Unguja and Pemba, while foreign affairs would be handled by the Tanzanian government.

(During the negotiations John Okello had gone to the mainland to meet Nyerere. On his return to Zanzibar in March 1964 security forces immediately sent him back to Dar es Salaam. He made no further public appearances.)

Despite the so-called union Karume kept Zanzibar separate from the rest of Tanzania in many respects. The clove plantations on Unguja and Pemba were developed and the earnings from exports continued to increase, but this revenue was not shared with mainland Tanzania.

After the Revolution almost all the European and Asian residents had left Zanzibar. To fill the vacuum caused by the departure of these skilled people Karume attracted technical and military assistance from Cuba, China and the then Eastern bloc countries of East Germany, Bulgaria and the Soviet Union. Engineers from East Germany designed and built new blocks of flats in Zanzibar Town, and in 'new towns' elsewhere on the islands of Unguja and Pemba. In 1970 Karume's government was accused of human rights violations against political opponents. Nyerere spoke out strongly against this, but it seemed to have little effect.

On April 7 1972 Karume was assassinated whilst playing cards in the ASP headquarters in Zanzibar Town. Aboud Jumbe Mwinyi, who had been a member of the ASP since before independence, became the new leader of the Revolutionary Government. Mwinyi was less hard-line than Karume and introduced several reforms. He was also more sympathetic towards Nyerere and mainland Tanzania. On February 5 1977 the ASP united with Nyerere's party, the Tanzania African National Union (TANU), to form the Chama Cha Mapinduzi (Party of the Revolution).

After this unification, both leaders began to relax some of their policies on nationalised industries and state financial control. Relations with some Western nations, including Britain, slowly improved. In July 1979, as a sign that Tanzania was regaining some international respect, Queen Elizabeth II of the UK visited Zanzibar. During her tour, she was shown a tree that had been planted by her sister, Princess Margaret, in 1956.

The 1980s and economic changes

In 1980 the first presidential elections took place, and Aboud Jumbe Mwinyi was officially elected as president of Zanzibar. In 1984 Ali Hassan Mwinyi was elected president. A year later he became president of Tanzania, following Julius Nyerere's resignation. Idris Abdul Wakil was then elected president of Zanzibar.

On the economic front, Zanzibar was in trouble. During the 1980s there was a drastic decline in the world market price for cloves, dropping to US$1,000 per ton from almost ten times that amount in the 1960s. Zanzibar was unable to pay its full annual contribution to the government of Tanzania and had to look for alternative ways of generating income. Gradually, the government of Zanzibar started to encourage private-sector (rather than state-controlled) operation of the economy.

In 1989, seaweed farming was introduced on the east coast of Unguja (Zanzibar Island) and has since become a vital source of income for coastal villagers. The seaweed is planted and tended on beach areas between the high and low water marks (see *Seaweed farming* box, page 71). It is harvested and dried, collected in Zanzibar Town, and then exported to several countries in Europe and Asia for use as a food thickener or stabiliser. Seaweed is now a valuable addition to Zanzibar's traditional exports of coconuts, cloves and other spices. (For details on cloves and coconuts see boxes, pages 52 and 55.)

Despite the success with seaweed, exports are limited, and Zanzibar imports many basic foodstuffs, including rice (from Pakistan, Thailand, Vietnam, Indonesia, India, China and the USA), maize (from mainland Tanzania), cooking oil (from Kenya, Tanzania, Singapore and Dubai), sugar (from Brazil), plus wheat and flour (from France, Germany and the USA). Other imports include mineral water (from the Gulf states) and beer (from Denmark).

The 1990s and the growth of tourism

In the elections of 1990, Dr Salmin Amour was elected president with an overwhelming majority, and his government continued actively to encourage private-sector economic investment. As part of this strategy, in 1992 the government announced a major project to make Fumba, about 20km south of Zanzibar Town, into an Economic Free Zone (EFZ) with factories, warehouses and a jetty to bring in raw materials easily. Potential investors were offered a range of incentives including exemption from import and export duties, and it was envisaged that Fumba would become a manufacturing centre for a wide range of products which could then be exported to Africa, the Gulf and elsewhere in the region. A similar EFZ was also planned for Micheweni on Pemba. By 2001, although the plans had not officially been shelved, there was no sign of development at either Fumba or Micheweni. However, if all goes to plan, history will have turned full circle, and Zanzibar will once again be a major player in the Indian Ocean trade block.

The first half of the 1990s also saw a dramatic increase in the development of another Zanzibar industry – tourism. The Zanzibar Commission for Tourism was founded in 1987 to promote Zanzibar as a tourist destination. The drive was further strengthened in 1992 with the creation of the Zanzibar Investment Promotion Agency to encourage overseas investment, particularly in tourism projects.

By 1995, over 50,000 visitors were arriving in Zanzibar each year. This grew rapidly and by the end of the 1990s this figure had risen to around 100,000. While still way below the figures recorded by many other popular East African tourist destinations, it marked a significant annual growth since the lows of the early 1980s. There was a corresponding growth in hotel construction, and by 1994 most of the best coastal sites had been allocated for hotels and related schemes, mainly to European developers. By 2000, at least 30 new hotels of different sizes had been built along the coast of Zanzibar Island, and construction was in progress or near completion on several other sites. The latest statistics indicate that tourism represents about 15% of Zanzibar's gross domestic product (GDP). This contrasts with clove production and export, which accounts for around 45% of GDP and 85% of foreign exchange earnings, but as export earnings from this traditional commodity continue to fall (for more details see the *Cloves* box in the *Flora* section on page 52), the income from tourism continues to expand. Although tourism makes up a relatively small proportion of the overall figures, some observers say that within ten years it could be Zanzibar's major foreign exchange earner, and is definitely plugging the gap left by the drop in demand for cloves.

It's not all good news though. Although the growth in tourism may benefit Zanzibar financially, the island may suffer in other ways. For example, the frequent use of saline beach sand and coral blocks for building hotels and bungalows may lead to structural weaknesses in the not too distant future. Of more cause for concern are the reports about huge amounts of sand for construction being taken from beaches, meaning sea-erosion in some areas is now a major problem. This is exacerbated by the unsustainable growth in the use of poles cut from mangroves (which naturally protect coasts from wave actions) for use in new buildings. In some areas the coast is believed to be receding at a rate of one metre per year.

Even more worrying is the increase in water consumption that comes with tourism. As a low-lying island, Zanzibar's supplies are precarious at the best of times, and as the number of hotels continues to increase, so supplies of fresh ground water are being depleted. One recent survey concluded that tourists on average consume 180 litres of water per day (this of course includes all use – washing, laundry, hotel cleaning, etc) compared to the average local Zanzibari's daily consumption of less than 40 litres. In recent years several wells, often caves in the coralline rock used for generations by villagers, have seen drops in water levels, become saline or even gone dry.

And it's not only water which is being used up faster than it can be replaced. All around Zanzibar, sea creatures such as crab, lobster, squid and octopus are being caught at an unsustainable rate to provide for the growing number of restaurants catering for tourists. As these animals get harder to find, the prices the restaurants pay get higher, and this gives further incentive to the fishermen. Although catching and eating sea creatures are not necessarily problematic, if the supplies run out, locals will be deprived of a vital source of income.

Despite these potential problems, as we enter the 21st century, hotel-building continues rapidly on Zanzibar Island, and is now beginning to take hold on Pemba. In the face of such development, although tourism undoubtedly creates local jobs and is a healthy opportunity for overseas investors, some observers point out that Zanzibaris could suffer as their culture, land, traditional livelihoods and even their water supplies are destroyed. Additionally, rapid development could spoil the natural beauty of the islands and thereby stem the flow of vital tourist dollars. Officially, the government recognises this problem, and back in 1992 introduced a National Environmental Policy for Zanzibar, stressing that the quality of life of the Zanzibaris should not be harmed by the destruction of their environment, and that cultural and biological diversity should be preserved. In the words of President Salmin Amour, 'unchecked development could soon become unsustainable for our people and our small islands'. Fine words, but building and development were already rampant on many parts of Zanzibar's coast by the time the policy was introduced, and almost ten years later still appear to be growing.

Alongside the growth in hotels, from the late 1990s, another worry for local tour companies has been the influx of major operators from the Tanzanian mainland and further afield, who set up offices in Zanzibar. Some of these operators bring in their own employees, and offer complete packages to tourists from overseas, thus edging out the local tour companies and forcing them to lay off staff. On a smaller scale, many of the beach-boys and hustlers that earn money from Zanzibar's tourist industry are also outsiders – mostly from places like Dar, Mombasa and Arusha. The new arrivals naturally annoy the locals who see themselves as unable to benefit from the visitors on their own patch. Some observers claim that this resentment, unemployment and overall disempowerment is partly to blame for the rising crime levels.

Political developments

While Zanzibar has seen many changes in tourism in the decade or so since the early 1990s, there have also been major developments on the political front. Zanzibar, along with the rest of Tanzania, ceased to be a one-party state in 1992. For the first time in almost twenty years Chama Cha Mapinduzi (CCM) was faced with several new opposition groups, which quickly coalesced into parties. The Civic United Front (CUF), led by Seif Sherif Hamad from Pemba, became the major opposition party for Zanzibar. Elections were not held immediately, but planned for October 1995, as all parties agreed that a gradual transition to a multi-party political system would be beneficial. Salmin Amour remained Zanzibar's president and CCM leader, while on the mainland the CCM chose a new president, Benjamin Mkapa, in July 1995. This followed the resignation of Julius Nyerere, the 'father of the nation' who had ruled since independence, although he remained an important figure behind the scenes.

Elections were duly held in Zanzibar on October 22 1995, a week before the mainland vote. It was a simple two-horse race between Salmin Amour and Seif Sherif Hamad for President of Zanzibar, and between CCM and CUF candidates in the islands' parliament. There was a very high turnout (over 95% of registered voters) and voting itself passed peacefully, but the counting took much longer than expected (three days for just over 300,000 votes).

As is common in politics, particularly in many parts of Africa, the ruling party's control of the government structure gave it an in-built advantage, but despite this head start it soon transpired that the CUF was polling strongly. After two days, when reports surfaced that the candidates were running neck and neck, the CCM protested that the election process was flawed. Later they withdrew these comments when it transpired that Amour had won with 50.2% of the vote. Then the CUF picked up the claim of unfair procedures. International observers from the United Nations agreed that there was evidence of serious irregularities, but the nominally independent Zanzibar Electoral Commission refused to hold a recount or to compare their figures with some of those recorded by the UN. On the mainland, a divided opposition and an even more shambolic election, not to mention the possibility of vote-rigging (the count took almost a month), meant that CCM and President Mkapa stayed in power.

Some donor nations protested about the irregularities, but after a while the dust settled, and although some aid funds were frozen, little effective action was taken. Former president Julius Nyerere called for a government of national unity, to reflect the equal support enjoyed by both parties, but this was ignored. Amour's two-seat majority in the Zanzibar parliament was boosted by an additional nine CCM MPs, appointments he was allowed to make according to rules in the national constitution. The CUF brought a high-profile legal case against the CCM on the grounds that the results and the whole election process were not representative of the wishes of the people, but this was bogged down in the courts and finally dismissed in 1998.

There were more legal shenanigans that same year, as several leading members of the CUF were arrested, then held in prison for 18 months before being tried on charges of treason. CUF supporters claimed that the arrests and charges were politically motivated, and in January 2000 there were riots outside the High Court in Zanzibar Town when the accused CUF leaders were brought to trial.

Despite these distractions (or maybe because of them), President Amour and the CCM remained firmly in power through 1999 and early 2000. In the lead-up to elections due in late 2000, Amour rocked the boat a little by announcing he would stand for a third (and unconstitutional) term as president. The instant response among the people of Zanzibar was a sharp swing in support for the CUF. An equally quick response from CCM high command meant Amour was relieved of his post, and Amani Karume, son of the president Karume who had been assassinated in the 1960s, was ushered in as Zanzibar's new CCM leader and presidential candidate.

At a grassroots level, there was still considerable support for the CUF, and its leader Seif Sharif Hamad, but the strong Pemba following this party enjoyed meant that ostensibly political differences stood a danger of degenerating into inter-island (or 'tribal') conflicts. This sense of grievance also translated into separatist aspirations; since the end of the 1990s, the desire of many Zanzibaris to be independent of mainland Tanzania has been stronger than it has been for many years. The urge for separation is also partly due to the death in October 1999 of former president Julius Nyerere, who conceived the Union of Tanganyika and Zanzibar, and held it together throughout his 30-year rule.

Elections were held on October 29, 2000, and thanks to a divided opposition on the mainland, President Mpika and the CCM romped home with huge and increased majorities. The people of mainland Tanzania seemed happy (in fact, many seemed indifferent) about the result, and international observers agreed that voting had been free and fair.

On Zanzibar, however, it was a different story. In the period leading up to the election, fist-fights erupted on several occasions between CUF and CCM supporters, local party offices were attacked or burned, and CUF demonstrations were broken up by the police and army. On the election day, several polling station opened late or remained closed all day, or simply had no ballot papers. In 16 constituencies, things were so bad that the whole process was cancelled, and a re-run vote arranged for November 5. In frustration, CUF demonstrations turned into violent protests, especially in Zanzibar Town, and these were met with police tear gas, rubber bullets and even live ammunition.

In disgust, the CUF pulled out of the election process, leaving the November 5 re-runs to be easily won by CCM candidates. In total, the CCM won 34 of the 50 seats in the Zanzibari House of Representatives, while Amani Karume won almost 70% of the vote for President. Commenting on the whole process, in sharp contrast to their report on voting on the mainland, the Commonwealth Observers Group called the Zanzibar election a 'shambles'. The CUF's response was to announce its continued boycott of procedures in the House of Representatives.

In one of his first moves as newly elected President of Zanzibar, Amani Karume called for peace and reconciliation between the two sides, which he backed up by releasing from prison the group of CUF leaders who'd been held on charges of treason since 1998. Hopes for peace were dashed shortly afterwards when a series of bombs exploded in Zanzibar. The police blamed the CUF, while the CUF said it was a government set-up – just another excuse to arrest CUF supporters again.

The trouble simmered on, with more CUF street protests in January 2001. This time the police used even stronger tactics to break up things up: in a single day, between 20 and 70 demonstrators were shot, one policeman was killed, and many more were injured. Other protesters were arrested, and claimed they were tortured at police stations. The events were reported in media around the world, the USA and the donor nations of Europe expressed concern, and aid money which had been frozen following the discrepancies of the *last* election (in 1995) remained firmly out of reach.

In March 2001, at the direct behest of President Mkapa, leaders from the CCM and the CUF tentatively started to discuss their differences, and in October that year, after a long series of negotiations, the two sides signed an accord to end their dispute over the election results. Although much of the politicking had little effect on tourists, the safety warnings for foreigners were lifted. Through 2002, things were on the up. The islands returned to their traditional calm and peaceful atmosphere, and Zanzibar was fully open for business once again.

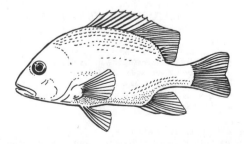

Background Information

PEOPLE AND CULTURE
People

It is thought that Zanzibar's original inhabitants came from the African mainland around 3,000 to 4,000 years ago, although this is not certain and no descendants of these early people remain, having been completely absorbed by later arrivals.

A few thousand years later, the records get a little clearer, and historians know that African peoples of Bantu origin migrated from central Africa and settled across East and southern Africa during the first millennium AD. (For more details see the *History* chapter.) Those who settled on the East African coast and offshore islands, including Zanzibar, came into contact with Arab traders who had sailed southwards from the Red Sea region. The Bantu adopted some customs of the Arabs and gradually established a language and culture which became known as Swahili.

From the 10th century, small groups of immigrants from Shiraz (Persia) also settled at various places along the East African coast, and especially in Zanzibar, and mingled with the local people. Over the following centuries, small groups of Arab and Persian peoples continued to settle here and intermarried with the Swahili and Shirazi. The largest influx occurred in the 18th and 19th centuries, when Omani Arabs settled on Zanzibar as rulers and landowners, forming an elite group. At about the same time, Indian settlers formed a merchant class.

Today, most of the people in Zanzibar are Shirazi or Swahili, although clear distinctions are not always possible. They fall into three groups, the Wahadimu (mainly in the southern and central parts of Zanzibar Island), the Watumbatu (on Tumbatu Island and in the northern part of Zanzibar Island), and the Wapemba (on Pemba Island), although again distinctions are hard to draw, and in fact, often not made by the people of Zanzibar themselves. The islands' long history of receiving (if not always welcoming) immigrants from Africa and Arabia has created a more relaxed attitude to matters of tribe or clan than is found in some parts of Africa.

Zanzibar is also home to groups of people of African origin who are descendants of freed slaves, dating from the 18th and 19th centuries. In more recent times, a large number of Africans have immigrated from mainland Tanzania. Additionally, some Arabs who were expelled after the 1964 Revolution have returned to Zanzibar.

Other people on Zanzibar include small populations from Goa, India and Pakistan, mainly involved in trade or tourism, and a growing number of European expatriates and volunteers, many working in the tour industry, with others employed as teachers, doctors and engineers.

Religion

Most of the people in Zanzibar are Muslims (followers of the Islamic faith) and all towns and villages on Zanzibar Island (Unguja) and Pemba have mosques. Visitors to Zanzibar Town cannot fail to hear the evocative sound of the muezzins calling people to payer from the minarets, especially for the evening session at sunset. And

THE SHETANI OF ZANZIBAR
Gemma Pitcher

Throughout the centuries Zanzibar Island (Unguja) and, to a greater extent, Pemba Island have been famous as centres of traditional religion and witchcraft, alongside their better-known role as centres of the spice and slave trades. Today the cult of the *shetani* (meaning a spirit or spirits, the word is singular or plural) is still going strong in Zanzibar and Pemba – a dark undercurrent unseen and unknown by the majority of visitors.

According to local traditional beliefs, *shetani* are creatures from another world, living on earth alongside animals and humans, but invisible most of the time and generally ill-intentioned. Many of the ebony carvings on sale in Zanzibar's curio shops depict the various forms a *shetani* can take – for example, a hunched and hideously twisted old woman, a man-dog hybrid, or a young girl with the legs of a donkey.

There is no real way, say the locals, of protecting yourself from the possibility of being haunted or attacked by a *shetani*. The best thing is simply to keep out of their way and try to make sure they keep out of yours – for example by hanging a piece of paper, inscribed with special Arabic verses, from the ceiling of the house. Almost every home or shop in Zanzibar has one of these brown, mottled scraps, attached to a roof beam by a piece of cotton.

Should the worst happen in spite of these precautions and a *shetani* decide to take up residence in your home – or even, in the worst case scenario, your body – the only thing to be done is to visit a *mganga* (sorcerer). To be a *mganga* is a trade that generally runs in families, with secrets and charms passed on from father to son or mother to daughter. *Waganga* (plural of *mganga*) meet periodically in large numbers to discuss their business (patients must pay handsomely for their services) and initiate new recruits. A committee of elderly, experienced practitioners will vet a younger, untested *mganga* before declaring him or her fit to practise.

Each *mganga* is in contact with ten or so *shetani*, who can be instructed to drive out other *shetani* from someone who is possessed, or to work their power in favour of the customer. The *waganga* are also herbalists, preparing healing medicines where spirit possession is not indicated, or combining both physical and occult treatment in severe cases.

But there are some *shetani*, goes the current thinking, which even a *mganga* cannot control. The latest and most famous of these was (or is) Popo Bawa – a phenomenon of far greater significance than just a run-of-the-mill *shetani*, which gripped Zanzibar's population in a wave of mass hysteria in 1995.

Popo Bawa (the name comes from the Swahili words for 'bat' and 'wing') began

---

visitors cannot fail to notice the effects of the holy month of Ramadan, when most people fast during the day, and the pace of life slows down considerably. (For details on dates see the *Public Holidays* section on page 105.)

Islam

Islam was founded by the Prophet Mohammed, who was born around AD570 in Arabia. He received messages from God during solitary vigils on Mount Hira, outside his home town of Mecca. When driven out of Mecca by his enemies, he migrated to Medina. Here, at the age of about 53, he started to convert the world to Islam, and his message spread rapidly through the Arab world and beyond.

Mohammed died in AD632, but fired by evangelist zeal Arab Muslims had

on the island of Pemba, where he terrorised the local population to such an extent that they called upon their most powerful sorcerers to drive him across the sea to Zanzibar. There the reign of terror of the 'shetani-above-all-shetani' continued.

The experiences of those who claimed to be visited by the demon were terrifying. They awoke in the middle of the night to find themselves paralysed and with the feeling of being suffocated. They then saw a squat, winged figure, around one metre, or slightly smaller, and with a single eye in the middle of its forehead, approaching the bed. Helpless, they were powerless to move or cry out as the demon raped them, men and women alike. Only when Popo Bawa had departed were they able to raise the alarm.

During the height of the Popo Bawa hysteria, people took to the rooftops and village squares, following a rumour that said safety could only be had by those who slept outside, in a group. Despite precautions like these, tales of the demon's progress around the island spread, until the government was forced to broadcast announcements on the radio pleading for calm. Despite this, a helpless, mentally handicapped young man was beaten to death by a mob that had become convinced he was the demon. This seemed to be the climax of the whole affair – after that, the hysteria abated somewhat and Popo Bawa retreated. He is widely expected to return, however, and when local people talk of him, it's with a nervous laugh.

American psychologists came to Zanzibar to study the events and write papers, and stated that the case of Popo Bawa is simply a Zanzibari version of a phenomenon known as a 'waking dream'. One of the characteristics of such a dream is a feeling of being weighted down or even paralysed. Other characteristics include extreme vividness of the dream and bizarre or terrifying content. It is this same phenomenon that is used by sceptics in the USA to explain the stories of those who claim to have been abducted by aliens.

Nevertheless, to the people of Zanzibar, Popo Bawa was very real and proof that shetani exist. Of course, they are not all as horrific as Popo Bawa; the lesser shetani come in all shapes, sizes and colours – beautiful Arabic women, hideous Ethiopian hags, or tall, handsome white men. Shetani can be forced to work for humans, but it's a risky business. Some successful businessmen are said to keep a whole room of shetani in their houses to promote material success and make mischief on their adversaries. But the price of such supernatural intervention is high – a goat, a chicken or a cow must be sacrificed regularly and its blood sprinkled in the four corners of the room. If this sacrifice is not faithfully and regularly made, the shetani will take a terrible substitute – it will demand instead one of its master's male children...

conquered all of northern Africa by the early 8th century, and introduced the new religion there. By AD1100 Islam had spread from Arabia and the Horn of Africa along the East African coast, through the current countries of Kenya and Tanzania, all the way down to Sofala (in present-day Mozambique). Today, Islam is the dominant religion of these coastal areas, which includes the islands of Zanzibar.

The five main tenets of Islam are prayer (five times a day), testimony of the faith, fasting (the period of Ramadan), almsgiving, and the pilgrimage to Mecca (the Haj). The Muslim calendar dates from the Hejera, the flight of Mohammed from Mecca to Medina, which corresponds to July 16 AD622 in the Christian calendar. The Muslim year consists of 12 lunar months of 29 or 30 days each, making 354 days. Eleven times in every cycle of 30 years a day is added to the year. This means Muslim festivals fall 11 or 12 days earlier every year, according to the Western calendar.

Other religions

In Zanzibar Town there are also churches and temples for the small populations of Christians and Hindus. The two most notable churches are the Anglican Cathedral Church of Christ and the Catholic Church of St Joseph. Both are described in detail in *Chapter 5*.

Alongside the established world faiths, traditional African beliefs are still held by most local people, and there Is often considerable cross-over between aspects of Islam and local customs. See the *Shatani* box for more details.

Music and dance

Hildegard Kiel, Yusuf Mahmoud

It is said that nothing tells you more about the soul of a nation and its people than its music. When you have the good fortune to visit Zanzibar you will find that the peoples' souls are very rich. As you wander around town, like in so many countries, you will hear calls to prayer from the many mosques but you will also hear the sounds of American rap music and Jamaican reggae. Around the next corner, however, you are also likely to hear film music from India or the latest chart-toppers from Egypt and the Gulf States. Thankfully the islands have not entirely lost their own cultural traditions, and equally popular in Zanzibar are local musical forms, in particular the style known as *taarab*.

Taarab

Zanzibar has been at the crossroads of trade routes for thousands of years as peoples of Africa, India, Iran, China and other parts of Asia and the Arab world have all played their parts in influencing the music, architecture, food and culture of the region. In its origins, *taarab* was court music, played in the palace of Sultan Barghash. The sounds of Arabic musical traditions, India, Indonesia and other countries of the 'Dhow region' (the Indian Ocean basin) are clearly distinguishable even today, mingling to form a unique flavour and providing the frame for the Swahili poetry which makes up the heart of *taarab* music.

Currently, two major *taarab* groups exist in Zanzibar: Nadi Ikhwan Safaa and

BI KIDUDE

A description of the music of Zanzibar would not be complete without mentioning Bi Kidude – now at the fine old age of about 90 years, and still one of the island's most famous singers. She used to perform with Siti bint Saad, has toured the world and sold thousands of cassettes. She herself claims to feel like a 14-year-old when she is performing, and seeing is believing in this case. Her voice is raw and unfiltered, and her singing and drumming with a large drum strapped to her hips is an experience of sheer energy. She has the agility of a teenager and the sly wisdom of a thoroughly experienced performer. Her stage presence is absolute and intense and she is most famous for her performance of *unyago ngoma*, which is played at all-female initiation rituals for brides to prepare them for their wedding night, featuring explicit lyrics as well as movements.

RECOMMENDED RECORDINGS OF ZANZIBAR MUSIC
The Music of Zanzibar, Vols. 1–4, (Globestyle Recordings, 1988)
Mila na Utamaduni – Spices of Zanzibar (Network Medien GmbH, 1996)
Kidumbak Kalcha: Ng'ambo – The other side of Zanzibar (Dizim, 1997)
Zanzibar: Music for Celebration (Topic Records, 2000)
Bashraf: Taarab Instrumentals from Zanzibar (Dizim, 2000)
Beni ya Kingi – Brass Band Music of Zanzibar (Dizim Records, 2003)

Mila na Utamaduni (also called Culture Musical Club, or just Culture). Of the two, Culture is the more professional and has become quite well known internationally, not only through CD releases such as 'Spices of Zanzibar' or the more recent 'Bashraf' albums, but also because they have successfully toured Belgium, France, Germany, Switzerland, the Arab Emirates, Réunion and many other countries. Nadi Ikhwaan Safaa, affectionately known by local people as Malindi Music Club, is Zanzibar's oldest group, who trace their roots back to 1905. The group plays a style of *taarab* in which the distant Middle Eastern origins are still very much to the fore.

Different theories abound about the real origins of taarab in Zanzibar. Legend has it that in the 1870s Sultan Bargash sent a Zanzibari to Cairo to learn to play the qanun, a kind of zither, common to the Arab-speaking world. Among the first singers to record taarab music in Swahili language was the legendary Siti binti Saad, who was taken to India by a film director. Siti stopped performing in the 1940s, but her records – solo and in duet with Sheikh Mbaruk – continued to be issued on 78rpm throughout the 1950s and are still much in demand. Besides the qanun, other instruments that came to feature in the taarab groups (or orchestras) include the oud, violins, ney, accordion, cello and a variety of percussion. Hence much of the traditional taarab music sounds like a more africanised version of some of the great Egyptian popular classical orchestras that played alongside singers like Oum Kulthoum, who is still played on Radio Zanzibar to this day.

The best way to experience taarab is at a local concert, but visitors to Zanzibar are also welcome at the orchestras' rehearsals in Malindi or at Vuga Clubhouse in the evening. What Andy Morgan (Roots magazine) says in an article on Zanzibari music definitely holds true: 'There's hardly anything in the whole of Africa as uplifting as the swelling sounds of a full taarab orchestra in full sail.'

Kidumbak

The suburb of Ng'ambo – the 'other side' of Zanzibar Town, where the lower-class living areas spread out and where poorer families and more recent arrivals to the city live – is the home of kidumbak. This music style, which is less refined and more upbeat than *taarab*, could be located musically somewhere between Stonetown big-orchestra *taarab* and the rural *ngoma* music. It is most often performed at weddings and other celebrations and is closely related to *taarab*. In fact, contemporary kidumbak often makes use of the latest *taarab* hit songs and is sometimes called *kitaarab*', which means 'a diminutive type of *taarab*' or 'derived from *taarab*'. Historical evidence suggests that Swahili *taarab* was originally performed in a very similar way to kidumbak and only later changed to resemble court orchestra music.

The kidumbak ensemble consists of a single melodic instrument, customarily a violin (played in frantic fiddle-style), a sanduku, or tea-chest-bass, two small clay drums (ki-dumbak), which form the rhythmic core of every such ensemble, and other rhythm instruments, such as cherewa, a kind of maracas manufactured from coconut shells filled with seeds, or mkwasa, short wooden sticks played like claves. In contrast to taarab, kidumbak is much more rhythmic and the lyrics more drastic than the poetic settings of the taarab songs, often criticising other people's social behaviour. At wedding performances, the singer has to be able to string together a well-timed medley of ngoma songs, and she or he must have the ability to compose lyrics on the spot. At a Zanzibar wedding, one kidumbak set usually lasts for an hour; as one song joins the next, the intensity heats up, with the main attraction being the interplay between the music and song of the players and the dancing and chorus response of the wedding guests.

Beni

This brass band music originated around the end the 19th century as a mockery of colonial style military bands. It was soon incorporated in the competitive song-and-dance exchanges so popular on the Swahili coast and spread from there all over East Africa. Beni (from English 'band') is a popular wedding entertainment with a strong focus on rhythm and dance, and audience participation.

Beni borrows choruses from the latest *taarab* hits and arranges them in extended medleys with the female wedding audience joining in for the chorus and as dancers. It is funny music, vivacious, raucous and lively. If you can imagine a deranged military marching band playing as loud as possible on half-broken trumpets, trombones, drums – only vaguely in tune with each other, but having a great time – then you will get the idea!

In Zanzibar, beni is performed both as a street parade and, stationary, for a wedding dance. The band Beni ya Kingi usually kicks off the opening parade for the Festival of the Dhow Countries (see Festivals below), which winds its way slowly through the narrow streets of Stone Town before reaching Forodhani Gardens at the waterfront with a great crowd which then turns into a wild and lively party.

Ngoma

Ngoma literally translated means 'drum' and is a term used to encompass all local African traditional forms of dancing, drumming and singing. There are literally hundreds of different *ngoma* styles throughout Tanzania, variations often being so slight that untrained eyes and ears can hardly notice the difference. A number of these originate from Zanzibar and Pemba and all are spectacular to watch. The often-elaborate native costumes emphasise the unity of the dancers' steps and the rhythm section which usually consists of several handmade drums and percussion instruments (such as oil tins beaten with a stick). *Ngoma ya kibati* from Pemba, for example, consists of a very rapid declamatory style of singing which is an improvised dialogue to drum accompaniment with singers/dancers coming in for a chorus every so often. Even if you can't follow a single word of the firework-like exchange between the two main singers, kibati is hilariously funny; if you understand all the references and hints implied, it is of course even more so. Another example is msewe, supporting the rhythm section, and named after the material which is strapped to the ankles of the male dancers.

Each *ngoma* style has its own special costume. In kyaso, men dance dressed in shirts and *kikois* (special woven cloth from the East African coast) with a long, narrow stick in their hand, all movements beautifully coordinated. In ndege women in colourful dresses all hold bright umbrellas, moving forwards with slightly rotating steps and movements of the hips. In bomu, the women dress up like men and in other funny costumes and dance around in a circle.

The variations are endless and performances are never dull. According to Abdalla R Mdoe, choreographer for Imani Ngoma Troupe, a privately initiated performance ensemble that specialises in all kinds of *ngoma*, three different types can be differentiated: ceremonial *ngomas*, which are performed at weddings, circumcision and other festivities; ritual *ngomas* (eg: *kisomali* to cure a sick person, or *pungwa* to avert evil); and religious *ngomas*, which in Zanzibar are closely related to the Muslim festivities of Zikri, Duffu, Maulidi and Hom.

Modern taarab
Undoubtedly a pop-phenomenon (and therefore time-limited) is a modern style of *taarab*, called rusha roho, which translates literally 'to make the spirit fly' and has some untranslatable meaning approximating to 'upsetting someone' or 'making the other one jealous'. Modern *taarab* is also the first style of *taarab* that's designed to be danced to, and features direct lyrics, bypassing the unwritten laws of lyrical subtlety of the older groups. Much of modern *taarab* music is composed and played on keyboards, increasing portability; hence the group is much smaller in number than 'real *taarab*' orchestras and therefore more readily available to tour and play shows throughout the region. This fact has led to enormous popularity in Zanzibar, boosted by the prolific output of cassette recordings, which, though not up to European studio quality standards, still outsell tapes by any other artist local or international.

Venues and recordings
To get a flavour of the unique experience of Zanzibar music, recommended recordings are listed below. For an unforgettable live experience, your best option is the Festival of the Dhow Countries around the beginning of July each year. (See the *Festivals* section, page 50, for more details.) You can also stop by Dhow Countries Music Academy, Zanzibar's first music school, which opened in the old Customs House on the waterfront of Stone Town in 2002. The school provides music lessons as well as instruments at minimal cost to anyone interested in studying music from the Dhow region or acquiring mastery of an instrument. Particular emphasis is on teaching traditional Zanzibar music styles, with most of the teachers coming from Zanzibar. It is a great place to meet local musicians and get further information on Zanzibar music and cultural events.

Tingatinga paintings
Among the visual arts, by far the best-known contemporary Zanzibari style is Tingatinga (or Tinga-Tinga). Paintings in this distinctive style can be found for sale at souvenir stalls and shops all over Zanzibar, as well as at tourist centres on the Tanzanian mainland, and in Kenya. The subjects of Tingatinga paintings are usually African animals, especially elephants, leopards, hippos, crocodiles and gazelles, as well as guineafowl, hornbills and other birds. The main characteristics of the style include images which are both simplified and fantastical, bold colours, solid outlines and the frequent use of dots and small circles in the design.

The style was founded by Edward Saidi Tingatinga, who was born in southern Tanzania in 1937 and came to Dar es Salaam looking for work in the 1950s. After doing various jobs, in the early 1960s Tingatinga became unemployed and looked around for a way to earn money. At that time, carvers and sculptors, notably Makonde people, were producing some indigenous work, but most local painters favoured pictures based on European representational styles or

ZANZIBAR DOORS

When a house was built in Zanzibar, the door was traditionally the first part to be erected. The greater the wealth and social position of the owner of the house, the larger and more elaborately carved his front door. The symbolic designs and quotations from the Koran were intended to exert a benign influence. Patterns include waves of the sea climbing up the doorpost, representing the livelihood of the Arab merchant to whom the house belonged, and frankincense and date-palms symbolising wealth and plenty. Some designs are thought to date from before the Koran: the stylised lotuses could be associated with Egyptian fertility symbols, and the fish could possibly represent the Syrian protecting goddess Atargatis, or the ancient fish-god of the Egyptians.

Many doors are studded with brass spikes and bosses. This may be a modification of the Indian practice of studding doors of medieval castles with sharp spikes of iron to prevent their being battered in by war elephants. In AD915, an Arab traveller recorded that Zanzibar Island abounded in elephants, and around 1295 Marco Polo wrote that Zanzibar had 'elephants in plenty'. But the elephants must have been extinct long before the Arabs built houses in Stone Town, and the studs and bosses seen today are purely for decoration.

The oldest carved door in Zanzibar, which dates from AD1694, is now the front door of the Peace Memorial Museum in Zanzibar Town.

Congolese styles from Central Africa. (In fact, in the 1950s and 1960s many painters from Congo and Zaire came to Kenya and Tanzania to sell their work to tourists and well-off residents.) Legend has it that Saidi Tingatinga decided he could do what the Congo artists did – paint pictures and sell them for money.

With no training, his own pictures were initially simple and straightforward. Subjects were the animals and people he remembered from his home in southern Tanzania. He used just four or five different colours (actually house paint – and the only colours available) and painted on wooden boards. But despite this humble beginning, Tingatinga quickly sold his early paintings, mainly to local European residents who admired the original, 'naïve' style.

Within a few months, Tingatinga's paintings were in high demand. He couldn't keep up with the orders which flooded in, so he employed several fellow painters to help him produce more. There was no concept of copyright, and Tingatinga encouraged his colleagues to base their works on his style. As their success grew, soon the artists were able to afford to use bright enamel paints (the type used for touching up paintwork on cars and bicycles) and painted on canvas so tourists could take home pictures more easily. By the end of the 1960s, Tingatinga painting had become recognised as truly original contemporary African art.

In 1972 Saidi Tingatinga died, but the artists he'd encouraged formed a group named in his honour, and continued to produce and sell works in his style. Today, demand from tourists is still high, and vast numbers of Tingatinga artists produce paintings on cloth, wooden boards and other objects such as trays, plates and model wooden cars. There's even an aeroplane at Zanzibar airport with its tail decorated in Tingatinga style.

With so many Tingatinga paintings available in Zanzibar and around East Africa, the quality of the work varies considerably; many pictures for sale in the streets have been bashed out quickly with little care or attention to detail. But if you

BARAZA BENCHES
Gemma Pitcher

Baraza benches, often simply called *barazas*, have been a focal point of community life in Zanzibar for centuries. These thick benches of solid stone are built into the walls around courtyards or flank the heavy doors of distinctive Arab-style townhouses. The houses which line the long, narrow streets of Stone Town often have *barazas* outside – and you will also see *barazas* on the verandas outside traditional Swahili homes, while in the villages a palm-leaf shelter, flanked by wooden seats, fulfils the same function.

Barazas evolved as a way for Islamic men to receive visitors in their homes without compromising the privacy of their womenfolk. Coffee and sweetmeats would be served on the *baraza* to anyone who arrived, with only the closest friends or family members being invited into the house. The Omani sultans held public meetings, also known as *baraza*, outside their palaces to receive petitioners or give visiting dignitaries a public audience.

Today, *barazas* are still a meeting point for all sections of Zanzibari society. Every urban *baraza* is lined with people lolling on the warm, smooth cement benches, gossiping, playing games of bao or cards, drinking sweet, thick Arabic coffee or simply idling away a long afternoon with a nap. Draughts boards are scratched in chalk on the stone surfaces, ladies sit comfortably to plait each others' hair, and for traders with no market stall of their own, a *baraza* provide a flat surface on which to pile their tiny pyramids of oranges, tomatoes and mangoes.

In the rainy season, when torrents of water, sometimes laced with rubbish, make walking down the streets of Stone Town uncomfortable and even hazardous, the *barazas* outside the houses provide a useful elevated pavement, and pedestrians jump from one to the next in an attempt to keep their feet dry.

The *baraza* as an architectural feature is an idea that seems to have caught on in a big way among the designers of Zanzibar's smarter hotels; almost every courtyard, nook and cranny – and even bathroom – now boasts its own *baraza* bench, often whitewashed to match the coral walls or inlaid with mosaic tiles.

search hard among the dross, or visit a shop where the trader has an interest in stocking better quality stuff, you can often find real works of art (and still at reasonable prices) which do justice to the memory of Saidi Tingatinga – the founder of a fascinating, entertaining and quintessentially African style.

Traditional games
Gemma Pitcher

Stroll casually around any village or town on the islands of Zanzibar, and eventually you'll be sure to come across two hunched, intent figures seated on a *baraza* bench – their grunts of satisfaction or derision accompanied by the click of counters on wood. Sometimes a crowd of spectators will have gathered, pointing and shouting garbled instructions. Look closer and you'll make out the object of all this excitement – a flat wooden board, 32 little round holes, and a lot of brown polished seeds. This is **bao** – Zanzibar's favourite pastime.

Games of *bao* – the name simply means 'wood' in Swahili – can go on for hours or even days at a time. Experienced players develop little flourishes, scattering the counters (known as *kete* – usually seeds, or pebbles, or shells) expertly into holes or slapping handfuls down triumphantly at the end of a turn. *Bao* is played, under various different names and with many rule variations, across Africa, western India and the Caribbean. Swahili people are proud of their version, known as 'king' *bao*, and claim it as the original and purest form of the game. Tournaments are held periodically in Zanzibar and on the coast of the mainland – as in chess, one grand master eventually emerges.

The object of the game is simple: to secure as many of your opponent's counters as possible. *Bao* masters (usually old men) are said to be able to think strategically five to seven moves ahead, a level comparable with professional chess players. Children learn *bao* as soon as they can count, scratching little holes in the ground in lieu of a board and using chips of wood or stones as counters.

The African love of carving has produced a proliferation of *bao* boards of many different sizes, shapes and forms – the board can be represented as resting on the back of a mythical beast, grows human heads from either end, or is smoothed into the shape of a fish. *Bao* boards make excellent souvenirs and are sold in almost every curio shop, often along with a badly photocopied set of printed instructions that are guaranteed to bamboozle even a maths professor. Far better to find a friendly local to teach you – the game is actually surprisingly simple to pick up.

Keram is the second most popular game in Zanzibar, and probably first arrived here from India. It's a fast-paced, raucous game played on a piece of wood carefully shaped into a small, square snooker table with cloth pockets at each corner. The game is similar to pool, with nine black disks, nine white disks, one red 'queen' disk and one larger white striker. Players flick the striker from their side of the board in an effort to get their own-colour disks into the pockets. Boards are kept smooth and speedy by liberal applications of talcum powder.

Bao and *keram*, like their Western equivalents chess and pool, have very different characters. While bao is traditionally a daytime game, played in shady village squares by elderly, dignified men, keram is popularly played at night in bars, often in the midst of a noisy and tipsy crowd of jack-the-lads.

Festivals

Without a doubt, the highlight of Zanzibar's artistic and cultural calendar is the **Festival of the Dhow Countries** – a 16-day event usually held in early July every year, and touted as East Africa's premier cultural event and among the most significant cultural events in all of Africa. The 'dhow countries' are those of Africa and the Indian Ocean basin, and so include East and southern Africa, northern East Africa, West and Central Africa, the Horn of Africa, Arabia, Iraq, Iran, the subcontinent of India, Madagascar and the Indian Ocean Islands, plus what the organisers call 'their global diaspora'.

The festival has grown from strength to strength since its humble beginnings at the Zanzibar International Film Festival (ZIFF) back in 1998, and now includes theatre, performances of traditional and contemporary music and dance, plus exhibitions of paintings, sculptures, craftwork and photography. However, a central part of this event is still the large, interesting and eclectic mix of films from all the dhow countries and places further afield. Several film-makers are also present, there are prestigious awards for new films (short and long features, and documentaries), and the festival also includes workshops, talks and discussions, as well as an energetic series of entertainments called the Children's Panorama.

In 2002, top of the bill was the powerful and moving film *Lumumba*, by Haitian director Raoul Peck, that year's Festival Guest of Honour; others include *100 Days* (directed by Nick Hughes, Rwanda/UK); *Under the Skin of the City* (Rakhshan Bai Etemed, Iran); *The Name of a River* (Anup Singh, India/UK); *Soviet Implosion* (Martin Cheketa, Zimbabwe); *Boubacar Traore: I Will Sing For You* (Jacques Sarasin, France); and *Rage* (Newton Achuaka, UK).

Music fans enjoyed an equally intriguing mix in 2002, and the line-up included U-Cef and Momo (both Morocco/UK), Avijit Ghosh (India), Apache Indian & The Soldiers (India/UK), Al Urmawi Group (Palestine), Traditional Bushehrei Music Ensemble (Iran), Abdul Halim Nwira Orchestra and Al Quithara Group (Egypt) and Asia el Kindy (Oman/Zanzibar). From the Tanzania mainland came African Revolution Band (Wana Tam Tam), The Kilimanjaro Band (Wana Njenje), Parapanda Arts, Amani Ensemble and Mionzi Dance Theatre, plus some intruing Swahili 'bongo flava' rappers, while Zanzibar was represented by the legendary Bi Kidude, Nadi Ikhwaan Safaa (Malindi *Taarab*), Culture Music Club and the Zanzibar Stars Modern *Taarab*. Festivals in future years will undoubtedly offer a similarly tempting choice.

On the more serious side, film and media-related workshops included Women Film-makers, Making Current Affairs Programmes for African Audiences, Constructing African History in the Cinema, and Creative Journalism.

The main venue for the festival is the open-air theatre at the Arab Fort, with films and performances on the main stage of the amphitheatre and live music in the adjoining Mambo Club, while other events are held at the Palace Museum, the House of Wonders, and the Old Dispensary (Stone Town Cultural Centre). The Old Customs House, which became the home of the Dhow Countries Music Academy in 2002, is the venue for musical Master Classes. There's also a series of free shows in Forodhani Gardens, just outside the Fort.

Many events are free and admission charges are kept to a minimum (around US$0.50 for Tanzanian residents, US$5 for non-residents) to encourage local participation. There's also an ambitious (but highly successful) programme of 'Village Events', which transports a selection of everything the festival offers in Zanzibar Town (film, music, theatre, women's workshops, children's shows, etc) out to the rural areas of Unguja and Pemba islands. The Festival of the Dhow Countries' organisers are keen to promote July as 'culture month' on Zanzibar, and this is undoubtedly an excellent time to visit the islands, although of course it's likely to be busy at this time. You can get more information from ZIFF, the festival organisers – postal address: PO Box 3032, Zanzibar; physical address: The Old Fort, Stone Town, Zanzibar; tel: 00 255 (4) 747 411499; fax: 00 255 (4) 747 419955; email: ziff@ziff.or.tz; web: www.ziff.or.tz.

In a very different vein, the festival of **Mwaka Kogwa** is held every year in several villages around Zanzibar, but most famously and most flamboyantly at the village of Makunduchi, in the south of Zanzibar Island. The traditional festival originated in Persia and celebrates the arrival of the New Year according to the Shirazi calendar. This one-day festival normally occurs during July, but it would be better to check this locally as changes are possible. For more details on the festival itself see the *Mwaka Kogwa* box on page 219.

ZANZIBAR FLORA

The vegetation of Zanzibar, as anywhere else, is largely determined by the quality of the soil, which in turn is determined by the underlying geology, although the indigenous vegetation of Zanzibar has been altered greatly by clearance and cultivation.

The islands of Pemba and Unguja (usually called Zanzibar Island) were formed about 27 million years ago and seven million years ago respectively. Both islands were originally coral reefs which became exposed as sea levels dropped, so the main rock type is a coralline limestone, known locally as 'coral rag'.

On the eastern side of Zanzibar Island, and in parts of the northern and southern areas, the landscape is very flat where coralline rock is exposed or covered by a thin layer of a calcareous sandstone soil, which supports low scrubby bush, known as coral rag thicket, quite dense in some areas. The western and central parts of the island are slightly more undulating, with a deeper soil cover: red, iron-rich and more fertile. Additionally, the western sides receive more rain than the eastern sides of the islands. Thus the western parts of Zanzibar Island were once covered in forest, similar in most respects to the low coastal forest which existed on the East African mainland, but today, very little of Zanzibar's indigenous natural forest remains, as it has mostly been cleared and used for agriculture. Local people grow crops on a subsistence basis, and this area is also where most of Zanzibar Island's commercial farms and spice and fruit plantations have been established.

The only significant areas of natural forest remaining in Zanzibar are at Jozani, a forest reserve on the south-central part of Zanzibar Island, and at Ngezi, a forest reserve in the north of Pemba Island, although smaller patches do exist elsewhere. The water table around Jozani is particularly high (during the rainy season the water can be over one metre above the ground) and the trees are mainly moisture-loving species.

CLOVES

Cloves are the buds of a tree which, when dried, produce a pleasant taste and smell. Their name comes from the French word 'clou' meaning nail, which the buds resemble. Clove oil was originally a highly prized ingredient used in cooking and preserving. Later it also became important in the food, cosmetic and pharmaceutical industries.

Cloves were introduced to Zanzibar from the end of the 18th century from the French colonies of Seychelles and Ile de France (now Mauritius) and Réunion, where they had earlier been introduced from the Moluccas in Indonesia by French sailors. Sultan Said (sultan from 1804 to 1856) recognised their value and encouraged the setting up of plantations on Zanzibar and Pemba.

At the height of the clove trade (the second half of the 19th century and the early 20th century) the islands of Zanzibar produced more than 90% of the world's supply of cloves, and the power and wealth of Zanzibar were based largely on this trade.

Clove trees (their scientific name is *Eugenia aromatica* or *Eugenia caryophyllata*) grow to a height of around 10–15m and can produce crops for over 50 years. In the first eight years of growth the buds are not picked, and turn into colourful pink flowers. When a tree reaches maturity the buds are picked by hand before they open (normally the harvest period is between July and January, with a break during the November rainy season), then separated from their stems. Buds and stems are dried in the sun on palm-leaf mats or on a special stone platform called a *sakufu*. Cloves are green when picked but turn brown during the drying process.

All cloves have to be sold to the government, who buy at fixed rates, then sell on at market rates to the users and producers. Sometimes the government

Despite the establishment of forest reserves such as Jozani and Ngezi, Zanzibar's forests continue to be cut down at an unsustainable rate. Timber is used for boat- and furniture-making, and as fuel, both for domestic purposes and to burn coral to produce lime for building construction. (This latter use has grown particularly quickly as the number of hotels in Zanzibar has increased.)

Mangrove wood from coastal areas is also being cut at an unsustainable rate. Forestry Department figures show that in 1992 about 10 million poles were cut in Chwaka Bay Forest, compared to 2.5 million in 1990. This wood is used for fuel and furniture, and in the construction and repair of buildings, but unfortunately the cutting of poles in the mangrove swamps leads to beach erosion and the destruction of habitats for fish and other marine life.

To replace some of the disappearing forest, through the 1990s, the Zanzibar Forestry Department planted acacia, casuarina and eucalyptus trees in Unguja and Pemba, as well as orange, coffee and cinnamon plants in Pemba. Another scheme, called the Zanzibar Cash Crop Farming System Project (ZCCFSP), discouraged farmers from cutting clove trees for firewood. All logging, and even the removal of dead wood, has officially been stopped in the Jozani and Ngezi reserves, although how carefully this new rule will be policed remains to be seen.

A new project outside Zanzibar Town is engaged in the use of timber from coconut palm trees, which are found all over Zanzibar and Pemba islands. Traditionally, palm has not been used as a timber because it is very hard to cut or plane. However, modern high-quality joinery tools mean coconut wood can now be

rates paid to the clove growers are so low that a harvest is not economically viable, and the cloves are left on the trees. In recent years some plantations have been completely abandoned.

Of the cloves that are harvested, most are sent to Zanzibar Town where they are processed into oil in the distillery near the port. This oil is used mainly as a flavouring device in foods such as cakes, pickles, cooked meats and ready-made mixes. It is also used in some antiseptic solutions, such as mouthwashes and in mild painkillers for toothache. Its other major use is in cosmetics, where it gives a sweet-spicy note to many different kinds of perfumes.

The best quality dried buds are kept separate and used whole in cooking, pickling or the making of spiced wines and liqueurs. These buds are also distilled into a high-grade oil for use in particularly fine perfumes. In the cosmetics industry the oil from good Zanzibar clove buds is reckoned to be the best in the world.

Today, Zanzibar is still a major exporter of cloves and clove products, representing about 45% of Zanzibar's gross domestic product (GDP) and 85% of foreign exchange earnings. However, export levels are falling every year as, due to an increase in the use of synthetic or alternative products in the food, cosmetics and pharmaceutical industries, the worldwide demand continues to drop. Consequently, agricultural diversification is encouraged.

When the plantations were established in the last century, it was found that growing conditions on Pemba Island were superior to those on Zanzibar, and the bulk of the produce actually came from there. Today, this is still the case, with about 75% of the islands' total produce coming from Pemba. During the harvest season, you can often see sacks of cloves being unloaded on Zanzibar Island at the port, or on the beach near the Tembo Hotel, and then carried by truck to the distillery.

COCONUTS

Coconuts are the second most important crop on Zanzibar after cloves. They grow on a certain species of palm tree which is generally planted where clove trees cannot survive, although as diversification is encouraged it is not uncommon today to see coconut palms and clove trees on the same plantation.

Coconuts are picked throughout the year, and large quantities are consumed locally as food. The pickers skilfully climb up the palm trunks using only a short loop of rope, then drop the nuts to the ground. The outer husks of the coconuts are removed by striking them onto a sharp stick or metal bar fixed in the ground. This is also a skilful process.

Coconut products – mainly the 'kernel' (the white edible parts) – are also exported. The process involves splitting the coconuts in two and leaving them to dry so that the white fleshy kernels can be easily removed from the shells. The kernels are then dried for a few more days in the sun or in a special kiln. Gangs of workers, separating the husks and kernels, and small coconut kilns, can be seen in the plantation areas outside Zanzibar Town.

When the kernels are properly dried, the substance is called 'copra'. It is widely used in the food industry as a flavouring, or for decoration. Copra is also processed into an oil, which is used in some foods and in the production of soap, candles and hair-oils. In the days before aerosol foam, copra was particularly good for making shaving soap as it helped produce a good lather.

The coconut husks are not wasted: they are buried under sand on the beach for several months, which helps to soften the fibres and make them separate from the rest of the husk. They are periodically dug up and beaten on rocks to help this process, and then buried again for another few months. The fibre is called 'coir', and is used for mats and rope-making. In the areas outside Zanzibar Town you will often see local women working with coir in this way.

turned into beautiful furniture and fittings such as doors and window frames. The aim of the project is to use the local palm trees after they have come to the end of their natural fruit-producing life. By using this local source of timber, it is hoped that other trees will not be cut down or imported to Zanzibar from the mainland. Several of the hotels and tour companies around Zanzibar are now using coconut wood items.

Other trees occurring on Zanzibar include mango, which is used for its fruit and as timber for boat-building, and kapok (capoc), which produces a substance similar to cotton, traditionally used to make stuffing for mattresses and pillows. Other fruit-producing trees, grown in plantations or singly around local villages, include guava, breadfruit, orange and pomegranate.

As well as the famous clove trees, other spice plants found on Zanzibar and Pemba include black pepper, cinnamon, cardamom, jasmin, chilli and henna. The main crops grown by local people for their own consumption include maize, cassava, bananas and pumpkins.

History of Zanzibari agriculture

The earliest peoples on Zanzibar are thought to have been hunter-gatherers who made little impact on the natural vegetation. However, the first Bantu settlers, who probably arrived some time in the 3rd or 4th centuries AD, started to clear patches of natural forest to plant crops such as millet and sorghum.

At some stage, plants such as bananas, coconut palms and yams were introduced, possibly by peoples from Madagascar who in turn had originally migrated from the islands of Indonesia. As these crops became more popular, more indigenous forest was cleared.

In the 16th century, Portuguese traders established bases along the East African coast, including those on Zanzibar and Pemba, and introduced plants, such as cassava and maize, from their colonies in South America. More forest was felled as the local people cleared the land required to grow these crops.

After the Omani Arabs gained control of the islands in the early 18th century, and the trade in ivory and slaves expanded, Zanzibar became an important import and export centre. Cassava was used for feeding the vast numbers of slaves who passed through the island's infamous market. Another major export at this time was copra (produced from coconuts) which meant more land was cleared for coconut palm plantations.

At the turn of the 19th century cloves were introduced from other islands in the Indian Ocean. They soon became a major export crop. Other spices, such as vanilla and cardamom, were also grown and yet more forest was cleared for plantations.

Throughout the 19th century, the powerful nations of Europe put pressure on the sultans of Zanzibar to restrict the trade in slaves. As this was reduced, the trade in cloves and other spices became even more important. During the colonial period, plantations continued to be developed and the natural forest continued to be reduced. A Department of Forestry was established to exploit the forests' timber supplies, but apparently, it was not until the 1950s that it came to the attention of the Forestry Department that there was very little indigenous forest left on the island of Zanzibar. The largest remaining area, Jozani Forest, to the southeast of Zanzibar Town, was purchased from an Arab landowner by the department and the felling of trees was restricted. In 1960, Jozani was declared a protected nature reserve.

ZANZIBAR WILDLIFE
The following sections provide a good overview of the wildlife of Zanzibar. For more detail, some field guides are listed in the *Further Information* appendix at the back of this book. For keen zoologists, the natural history section of the National Museum in Zanzibar Town has a good, but very tatty, collection of exhibits and more information about all the animals and birds found on the islands of Zanzibar.

Mammals
As described above, much of Zanzibar's indigenous forested area has been cleared, so natural habitats for all wild animals are severely restricted. Probably the best places to see indigenous mammals are the Jozani Forest Reserve on Zanzibar Island and the Ngezi Forest Reserve on Pemba Island.

In this section, scientific names of species are given according to information provided by Jozani Forest Reserve and Ngezi Forest Reserve. Other authorities disagree on some classifications and nomenclature, especially regarding subspecies, but this is unlikely to be important for most visitors.

Jozani Forest Reserve is well known for its population of **red colobus monkeys** (see colour section). This animal is found elsewhere in Africa, but those on Zanzibar form a distinct species, called Zanzibar red colobus or Kirk's red colobus (*Procolobus kirkii*), endemic to the island and one of the rarest primates in Africa. (This truly Zanzibari species is now becoming a symbol of national pride –

you can even find its picture on Air Tanzania sugar sachets!) Although rare, and hard to see in the forest canopy, one group of red colobus in Jozani is partly habituated to human presence, so you are quite likely to spot some if you visit. These monkeys are mainly reddish-brown in colour, with a darker back and 'cap', and a paler forehead patch. On closer inspection, particularly of facial areas, you will notice that each monkey has slightly different coat patterns and colourings.

In Jozani and some other patches of forest you are likely to see the **blue monkey**, also called Sykes' monkey, mitis monkey or the Zanzibar white-throated guenon (*Cercopithecus mitis albgularis*), which on Zanzibar is bluish-grey, or even a greenish-grey, with a distinct white throat-patch.

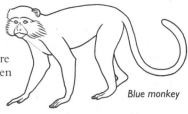
Blue monkey

Although the two types of monkey compete for some food items, they are often seen foraging peacefully in mixed groups. The Swahili word for monkey is *kima*. On Zanzibar, the blue monkey is more commonly given this name. When distinguishing between the two, the blue money is called *kima mweusi*, and the red colobus *kima punju* – 'poison monkey' (probably because the colobus has a stronger smell than other monkeys, and is reputed to have an evil influence on trees where it feeds).

A local species of **vervet monkey** (*Cercopithecus aethiops nesiotes*) occurs on Pemba, but it is thought not on Zanzibar Island. This monkey is smaller than the red colobus and the blue monkey, generally greyish with a dark, rusty brown back and black feet.

Other mammals found on Zanzibar, mainly in forested areas, include **bush pig** (*Potamochoerus porcus*), although its numbers are reported to be greatly reduced; **Zanzibar tree hyrax** (*Dendrohyrax arboreus neumanni*), a rodent-like animal the size of a rabbit (this subspecies is endemic), with hoofed feet and rounded ears, and a loud piercing scream when threatened; **Aders' duiker** (*Cephalophus adersi*), a species of small antelope found only on Zanzibar and, until recently, the Kenyan coast; and **Zanzibar suni** (*Nesotragus moschatu moschatus*), another endemic subspecies of antelope which is even smaller than the duiker. The endemic **Pemba blue duiker** (*Cephalophus monticola pembae*) occurs at Ngezi Forest. All these animals are nocturnal or extremely shy and are unlikely to be seen.

Aders' duiker

Leopard (*Panthera pardus adersi*, or *chui* in Swahili) have been recorded in Jozani, and elsewhere in Zanzibar. Again, this is an endemic subspecies, smaller than the mainland version and with finer markings, and also very unlikely to be sighted. Recent studies have concluded that this animal is now extinct on Zanzibar. For more details see the *Leopards in Zanzibar* box opposite.

The greater and lesser **galago** or **bushbaby** (*Otolemur garnetiti garnettii* and *Galago senegalensis zanzibaricus*) both occur in Zanzibar. The greater galago (*komba* in Swahili) is about the size of a rabbit, generally brown, with very distinctive large ears and eyes, and a large

Zanzibar leopard

LEOPARDS IN ZANZIBAR

The Zanzibar leopard (*Panthera pardus adersi*) is a local subspecies. Two different types have been recorded: the kisutu, which is similar to the mainland leopard, but with a more compact spot pattern and lighter background; and the konge, which is larger than the kisutu with dark fur and faint spot pattern.

Leopard tend to be shy, and mainly active at night. Perhaps because of their elusive, nocturnal habits, they have traditionally been considered unlucky by local people, and are often associated with witchcraft, so have been actively hunted. They are also hunted because they are seen as vermin by farmers, and for their skins which can be sold to dealers. The leopard has been further pushed to the edge of extinction by an ever-growing loss of suitable habitat, as forest areas are cleared, and by a loss of prey, as Zanzibar's small antelopes are also hunted unsustainably.

By the 1980s the leopard was believed to be extinct in Zanzibar, but in 1994 an American researcher called Scott Marshall found evidence of three leopards on Unguja (Zanzibar Island), including prints, droppings and a suspected den near Chwaka. In his report, Marshall suggested that these leopards were trapped and 'domesticated' at a young age, to be used in ceremonies by local witch-doctors or traditional healers. He also suggested that there may be several more leopards similarly kept in captivity at other villages in Zanzibar, although this assumption was based on local anecdotal evidence, rather than on positive sightings.

However, in 1998, the South African wildlife experts Chris and Tilde Stuart published a report in *Africa Environment and Wildlife* magazine, which described their exhaustive methods to locate any signs of leopard on Zanzibar Island, and concluded that none existed in a wild state. They also looked into the possibility of a few 'kept' leopards remaining in existence but found no hard evidence. They further concluded that even if a small number of 'kept' leopards were being held in secret, there was no hope at all for long-term survival of this species on Zanzibar.

bushy tail. The lesser galago (*komba ndogo*) also has large eyes and ears, but it is smaller (about half the size of the greater galago) and grey in colour. Both animals are nocturnal, especially active at dawn and dusk, and have distinctive cries – sometimes like a child crying (hence their name), other times loud and shrill, and positively spine-chilling. They are known to be inquisitive and will forage around huts and villages at night. They are attracted to bowls of locally brewed palm wine, and often get captured when intoxicated and incapable of escape. A local saying, '*mlevi kama komba*', means 'as drunk as a bushbaby'!

Also found in Zanzibar is the **African civet** (*Viverra civetta schwarzi, orngawa* in Swahili); it looks like a very large cat with a stocky body, thick tail, and black, white and grey markings which form rough stripes. The **Javan civet** (*Viverricula indica rasse*) occurs on Pemba and Unguja, probably introduced by Southeast Asian traders.

Smaller mammals include the **Zanzibar slender mongoose** (*Herpestes sanguineus rufescens*), most often seen running across roads with its tail vertical, and the **bushy-tailed mongoose** (*Bdeogale crassicauda tenuis*) – rarely seen anywhere. The **marsh mongoose** (*Atilax paludinosus rubescens*) occurs only on Pemba and may be seen at Ngezi Forest. The **banded mongoose** is a non-indigenous species, introduced to Zanzibar Island.

Populations of rats, mice and shrews (plus 14 species of bat) occur on both Zanzibar and Pemba islands. Those worthy of note include the **Zanzibar four-toed elephant shrew** (*Petrodromus tetradactylus zanzibaricus*) with distinctive long slender legs and a trunk-like snout for eating insects, and the **Pemba flying fox** (*Pteropus voeltzkowi*), a large fruit bat with distinctive rufous colouring and fox-like face, found only on Pemba Island.

Reptiles and amphibians

Of all the reptiles on Zanzibar, undoubtedly the easiest to spot are the **giant tortoise** (*Geochelone gigantea*) that inhabit Prison Island, a few kilometres offshore from Zanzibar Town, and also live in the garden of the Peace Memorial Museum. They were introduced here from the island of Aldabra, in the Seychelles archipelago, in the 18th century.

If you visit Jozani, you'll probably see some of the forest's population of tiny black and gold **frogs**. In the rainy season, when the ground floods, you'll see their tadpoles too. **Chameleons** can also be seen in Jozani and other parts of the island. Like the mongoose it is often seen crossing roads, but often very slowly, and *very* precariously. Other reptiles include snakes (rarely seen) and geckos (frequently seen on the inside walls of buildings – particularly the budget hotels in Zanzibar Town – although this is no cause for worry as they're small, timid and harmless).

Flap-necked chameleon

One of the best places to see some of Zanzibar's reptiles (among other animals) is at the Zanzibar Land Animals Park (ZALA) a few kilometres west of Jozani Forest on the road to Kizimkazi. For more details see *Chapter 6 – Zanzibar Island*, page 189.

Birds

Dudley Iles

Zanzibar is not noted as a major birdwatching area, but over 200 species of bird have been recorded on the islands of the archipelago (that is, Unguja – usually called Zanzibar Island – and Pemba, plus the numerous offshore islets). The avifauna of Zanzibar includes the resident birds, plus visitors – migrants and sea birds. For any keen birdwatcher travelling on the East African mainland, polishing off the holiday with at least a few days on Zanzibar can make the trip-list even more impressive – the islands boast several species and races which are unique. Even for the more casual birdwatcher, Zanzibar provides some fine opportunities. Knowing the name of the bird that flew over the beach, or sings from a bush in your hotel garden, will make your time in Zanzibar even more rewarding and enjoyable.

Overview

Like the majority of offshore islands, Unguja and Pemba have a smaller avifauna than the mainland of East Africa. Unguja can claim about 220 species, and Pemba slightly fewer. Of these, about 35 have been added since 1994, an indication of increasing tourist interest and observations. On Zanzibar, visitors are able to make a larger contribution to natural history records than on the mainland, since there have been fewer observers until recently.

Although Unguja and Pemba are similar in size, geography and position, they provide an interesting avifauna comparison. Unguja has woodpeckers, shrikes, cuckoo shrikes and bulbuls, while Pemba has none of these. But Pemba has its own species of green pigeon, scops owl, white-eye and sunbird found nowhere else in the world.

As well as the resident birds, migrants from Eurasia, the Middle East and southern Africa pass through or remain to winter on the islands. Those from the north arrive in September/October and leave again in February/March. For European visitors it is a delight to see a familiar spotted flycatcher in the hotel garden, or hear the sound of a curlew calling from the shore at low tide.

Habitats

The main bird habitats on Zanzibar, and some of the species found there, are described below. If the name of a bird is singular (eg: golden weaver), it refers to one species. If the name is plural (eg: bee-eaters, kingfishers), it refers to several species of the same or similar genus.

Parks and gardens

Perhaps surprisingly, some of the best places to see birds are the parks and public gardens of Zanzibar Town, or the gardens of the many hotels situated along the coasts of Unguja and Pemba. The seed- and fruit-bearing trees, and the insects they attract, in turn attract many **mannikins**, **warblers**, **coucals**, **sunbirds** and **swifts**.

A bird you cannot miss in towns and around the big hotels on the coast is the **Indian house crow** – see the box on page 62 for more information.

Farmland

The more fertile areas of Zanzibar, mostly the centre and west of Unguja and much of Pemba, are occupied by the majority of the rural population. Over the centuries natural coastal scrub and forest has been cleared and turned over to agriculture, either for small-scale subsistence farming, or for commercial plantations growing fruit and spices. The plentiful supplies of seeds, fruits and insects here attract many birds, including the beautiful long-tailed **paradise flycatcher** and parties of **golden weaver** (the only widespread weaver in Zanzibar). You may also see **green wood-hoopoe, crested guineafowl** (although these are now rare) and the diminutive **emerald-spotted wood dove**.

The telegraph wires along the roads provide vantage points for **lilac-breasted roller** and occasionally for the rufous-coloured **broad-billed roller**, and in winter for the **blue-cheeked bee-eater**.

Striped swallow hunt for flying insects over the countryside, and visit pools to collect mud for nest building. In areas where there are coconut palms you will see **palm swift**.

Freshwater ponds and grasslands

Some farming areas consist of grassland, grazed by cattle, and often flooded after rain. Some of these wet areas are used to grow rice. Here you will see **black-winged bishop**, a small bright red finch, plus **herons** and **egrets**, especially **cattle egret**, and maybe even a **goshawk** or **harrier**.

Where undisturbed, ponds and marshes support breeding **jacana** (or lilytrotter) and **black crake**, and possibly **Allen's gallinule**. You may also see small parties of **pygmy goose, white-faced whistling duck** and occasionally the rare **white-backed duck**. In winter months, **purple heron** and **yellow wagtails** (from Eurasia) feed in the rushes along pond edges.

Other birds seen in these areas include **little grebe, red-billed teal** and **moorhen**.

Bush

Many areas of Zanzibar, especially the north and east of Unguja (Zanzibar Island), are not fertile and have not been cleared. They are covered in low scrubby vegetation called coral rag bush. It grows on well-drained rock which was once a coral reef, but was exposed when sea levels dropped many millions of years ago. The poor vegetation here does not attract great numbers of birds, but a few exciting species can be seen, especially in the early morning or late evening, including the **pale-eyed sombre bulbul**, **eastern bearded scrub robin**, **crowned hornbill** and **collared sunbird**. You might also see birds of prey such as **African goshawk** or **black kite**, plus **rollers** and **shrikes**. With luck a **Gabon nightjar** may rise suddenly from near your feet.

Crowned hornbill

Forests and woodland

Only a small percentage of Zanzibar's indigenous forest remains, following centuries of clearing for farms and plantations. The main areas are Jozani Forest on Unguja and Ngezi Forest and Kiyuu Forest on Pemba, characterised by tall trees with buttressed roots and a convergent canopy, interspersed with ferns and smaller bushes. Masingini Forest near Bububu north of Zanzibar Town can also be rewarding. The forest birds of Zanzibar are shy and hard to spot, but your chances are better in the early morning, when you might see **Fischer's turaco**, **wood owl**, **crested guineafowl** or **tambourine dove**, plus **swifts**, **hornbills**, **woodpeckers** and **weavers**.

In patches of woodland, on the edge of areas which have been cleared for farming, you may see more weavers, plus coucals, sunbirds, flycatchers and bulbuls.

Mangroves

Mangroves occur on small offshore islands or around estuaries, in or near areas which are covered by water at high tide. Individual mangroves can grow to 5m in height, and close together, which creates a forest-like atmosphere. (The mangrove vegetation of Zanzibar is discussed in the *Seas and Shores* section that follows.) This habitat is rich in marine life, which is exploited by humans as well as resident and migrant shore birds including **herons** and **kingfishers**. Other species you are likely to see include **mouse-coloured sunbird** and **blue-cheeked bee-eater**.

Seashore and sandbars

Naturally, as a group of islands, Zanzibar is surrounded by seashores, made up of beaches, low cliffs, creeks and tidal coral-mud flats. On the beaches you will find various wading birds, including **plovers**, **whimbrels** and **sandpipers**; many of these will be familiar to European naturalists, as Zanzibar becomes an increasingly important wintering ground for these northern species.

Also look out for the **greater sand plover** (which comes from central Asia) and the striking **crab plover**, which breeds along the Somali coast. Another notable shore bird is the **dimorphic heron**, which feeds along the tide line: about 49% of these birds are mouse grey, and another 49% are pure white, while the rest show intermediate plumages. Perhaps the most striking seashore bird is the **African fish eagle**, which may be seen in some areas.

On the numerous sandbars off the west coast of Zanzibar you can see more waders, plus flocks of **terns**, **gulls** and **cormorants**. The **sooty gull** often seen here is a visitor from the Red Sea.

Open sea
Some birds spend most of their time at sea, in (or above) deeper water, and rarely come to the shore. You will only see these if you are out on a boat, possibly diving or fishing, or crossing to Zanzibar Town on a ship from Pemba or Dar es Salaam. Oceanic birds are rare, but you may occasionally see **frigatebirds** or a **roseate tern**, or a **masked booby** from the breeding colony on Latham Island, south of Zanzibar.

Birdwatching areas
There are many places where you can watch birds on Zanzibar, and we list just a few recommended areas here.

The People's Gardens
In Zanzibar Town, formerly known as Victoria Gardens (see the *Places to visit in Zanzibar Town* section in *Chapter 5*), this small park has flowers and flowering trees and attracts a good range of birds. Here you might see **scarlet-breasted sunbird**, the Indian race of **house sparrow**, **bronze mannikin**, **black and white mannikin**, and the neat but skulking **green-backed camaroptera**, a complex name for Zanzibar's only widespread resident warbler. Overhead, parties of **little swift** hawk for insects.

Mbweni Ruins Hotel garden
On the outskirts of Zanzibar Town (described under *Places to stay* in the *Zanzibar Town* chapter), this good hotel has a beautiful garden, and is an excellent birdwatching area. You don't have to be a guest to come here for lunch and a walk around their nature trail. At least 50 species have been recorded here by the hotel management who are very knowledgeable on local wildlife, and can advise on good birdwatching places on Zanzibar. The hotel's dining veranda overlooks a beach, where many shore birds, including **oystercatchers**, **whimbrels**, **sooty gull** and **lesser crested tern**, await the retreat of the tide. Nearby is an area of mangrove. In the hotel gardens you'll see **bronze mannikin**, **mangrove kingfisher**, **little swift** and **scarlet-chested sunbird**, plus **Eurasian golden oriole** and **blue-cheeked bee-eater** in winter. During the heat of the day, the hotel pond is beloved by **black-breasted glossy starling**, **dark-capped bulbul**, **golden weaver** and as many as 50 **Java sparrows** (introduced around 1857, but now resident).

Bwawani Marsh
Situated near the port, on the edge of Zanzibar Town, this is the largest reed swamp on Unguja, although it was formed by accident when the Bwawani Hotel was built. Some 20% of Unguja's birds have been recorded here including a few, like the **hottentot teal** and **purple gallinule**, which have not been recorded elsewhere on the island.

Other species to look out for are **lesser swamp warbler**, **Allen's gallinule**, **jacana**, **wood sandpiper**, **night heron**, **purple heron** and the African race of the **little bittern**. The best viewing spots are on the Bububu road and on the

THE INDIAN HOUSE CROW

from information provided by Dudley Iles, updated by Helen de Jode, Zanzibar Ecotourism Association

The Indian house crow (*Corvus splendens*) was introduced to Zanzibar in 1891. The bird is a scavenger and 50 crows were sent by the Indian Government to help clear domestic waste building up in Stone Town at the time. Although the Indian house crow did consume some of this rubbish, it is by nature an aggressive bird and it began to attack many of the island's small birds and their eggs. As early as 1917 it was realised that the crows had become a pest, and they were subject to various control efforts including trapping, shooting and poisoning, but to little effect. By the 1940s the Indian house crow had spread throughout Zanzibar Island, and by the 1970s their population had increased to such an extent in Zanzibar Town that many small bird species were rarely seen.

The crow population continued to grow and by 1990 their impact on the indigenous bird population had become considerable, with the town becoming virtually devoid of all other species. In addition the Indian house crow was affecting agricultural and livestock production: feeding on germinating maize, sorghum and soft fruits, eating young chicks and ducklings and attacking calves and sometimes even cattle.

Between 1990 and 1995 the Finnish International Development Agency funded a control programme organised by wildlife expert Tony Archer and a team from the Zanzibar Commission for Lands and Environment. They used firstly a Malaysian-designed crow trap, and later a poison which was developed in the USA to control starlings as agricultural pests. The trapping and poisoning

smaller road leading to the hotel. Unfortunately, the swamp has become a dumping ground for local rubbish. Beware!

Jozani Forest

A good area for keen birders, particularly if you visit early or late in the day, is Jozani Forest Reserve, although the birds here typically hide themselves in the undergrowth or high canopies. The area south of Jozani Forest itself, on the other side of the main road, where the semi-habituated monkeys are found, is also good for birding. (For more details see the *Jozani Forest* section in the *Zanzibar Island* chapter, page 227.) Birds occurring here include the **olive sunbird**, the **little greenbul** (a racial endemic), **dark-backed weaver**, **paradise flycatcher**, **east coast batis** (a neat black-and-white flycatcher), **crowned hornbill** and **cardinal woodpecker**. Local specials include the **east coast akalat** and **Fischer's turaco**. At dawn or dusk you may also see **African wood owl**.

In the nearby mangrove forest, where a walkway has been constructed, you can see **mangrove heron**, **mangrove kingfisher**, **mouse-coloured sunbird** and maybe **tropical bulbul**.

Chwaka Bay

This is the largest and most complex area of mud and sand on Zanzibar. It is an important area for local fishing, seaweed production, and for wintering shore birds, most notably the crab plover. Much of the east coast, from Chwaka to Nungwe, can offer good birdwatching along the shore – and even beyond the reef at low tide. Birds occurring here include **waders**, **terns** and **gulls**, plus **herons** such as the **green-backed heron** and **dimorphic heron**.

strategies were combined with a bounty on the collection of Indian house crow eggs and chicks during the breeding season. According to a report issued by Tony Archer, almost 45,000 crows were killed between 1993 and 1995. An estimated 95% of the crow population were killed in Stone Town and 75% across the island as a whole, allowing the small bird populations to return.

Unfortunately, since 1995, as funding dried up, there has been little continued effort to control the numbers of crows in Zanzibar. Increasing amounts of rubbish generated by a growing human population in Zanzibar Town, and a growth in tourism in coastal areas, are partly to blame for the rise in the number of crows. Current levels are having a serious impact on the indigenous bird population and are becoming an environmental health hazard.

In Dar es Salaam, where a similar crow problem exists, the Wildlife Conservation Society of Tanzania (WCST) has succeeded in killing over 43,000 crows using crow traps paid for by hotel owners and with some limited funding from the Canadian Fund for Local Initiatives.

In Zanzibar, since 1999 a small voluntary organisation, registered as the Zanzibar Ecotourism Association (ZEA), has been encouraging hotels to become part of a similar sustainable programme for Zanzibar, but lacks financial support. Under ZEA coordination several hotels and individuals around Unguja have now established their own crow traps, but many more are needed if the island is to be rid of the Indian house crow.

For more information, ZEA can be contacted by email: ecotourism-znz@twiga.com

Matemwe

This is a small village about halfway between Chwaka and Nungwe – with typical east coast conditions. There is a wide beach here, backed by palm groves and coral rag bush, and each habitat attracts typical species. The Matemwe Bungalows garden also attracts **sombre greenbuls**, **collared sunbirds** and **paradise flycatchers**, among others.

Chumbe Island

This small island lies off the west coast, within easy reach of Zanzibar Town. About 63 bird species have been recorded here since 1992, but these are mostly sea and shore birds. The resident land birds are limited to about six common species, including **African reed warbler**, and most notably the small colony of **mouse-coloured sunbird**. Perhaps Chumbe's main avian interest lies in the vagrants which occasionally appear, such as a **wood warbler** (only the third recorded sighting in all Tanzania) and in 1999 a **peregrine falcon**. In 1994 around 750 pairs of **roseate tern** bred on two islets off Chumbe but, although some 500 young were reared, the birds have not returned. House crows, fish eagles, rats (now eliminated) and bad weather were the probable reasons for their staying away.

Misali and Panza islands

Misali Island lies close to Pemba Island while Panza Island lies off Unguja. Each has coastal forest and typical shore habitats. Like all small islands they are limited in bird species but are attractive for migrants. Misali is noted for a small population of **Fischer's turaco**, while on Panza **brown-necked parrot** occurs. Panza also has large colonies of fruit bat and white-winged bat which attract **bat hawks**.

Ngezi Forest

On Pemba Island, Ngezi Forest is a good birding destination. Birds recorded here include **palm-nut vulture**, **African goshawk**, and four endemics: **Pemba scops owl**, **Pemba white-eye**, **Pemba green pigeon** and **Pemba violet-breasted sunbird**. Ngezi is also home to a good population of fruit bat, once again attracting **bat hawks**.

THE SEAS AND SHORES OF ZANZIBAR

Matt Richmond PhD

For anyone visiting the islands of Zanzibar, Mafia Island or the coast of mainland Tanzania, the diversity of marine life in the surrounding shallow waters may not be immediately obvious. However, the main marine habitats (mangroves, coral reefs and seagrass beds) are part of an extremely diverse, productive and vitally important marine ecosystem. Other marine habitats are the beaches and cliffs fringing the shore, and the vast areas of open water. The species of plants and animals which make up these habitats around Zanzibar and off mainland Tanzania are mostly the same as those found elsewhere in the western Indian Ocean (eg: Mozambique, Madagascar, Mauritius and Seychelles), though slightly different from those in similar habitats as far away as Southeast Asia, Australia and the South Pacific islands. Some species of fish and other creatures do, however, span this entire Indo-Pacific region.

Marine habitats

Beaches and cliffs

Around the main islands of Zanzibar (that is, Unguja and Pemba), many shores are fringed by either coconut-lined coral-sand beaches, where **ghost crabs** scamper, or rocky limestone cliffs – remains of ancient reefs once below the sea (over 100,000 million years ago), then exposed as sea levels dropped, now undercut and battered by high-tide waves. The cliffs provide a home to the brilliant red-yellow **grapsid rock crabs** and the bizarre eight-plated **chiton snail**, plus numerous other small snails, rock oysters and rock-skipper fish.

Mangroves

In sheltered bays and inlets, where wave action is reduced, mangrove stands and forests are commonplace. Mangrove trees are specially adapted to survive in the sea, and all ten species found in the western Indian Ocean occur in Zanzibar. At high tide mangroves attract numerous species of fish, crabs and shrimps which depend on the forests as nursery grounds for their young. At low tide, red-clawed **fiddler crabs** carry out their formal challenges when not sifting the mud for food, while **mud-skippers** flip from pool to pool, or from branch to branch when the tide is in. One of the best places to experience these fascinating marine forests is the mangrove boardwalk at Jozani Forest – especially when the tide is in. You can also snorkel around a mangrove forest on Misali Island, off Pemba, or in many other inlets around the main islands.

Seagrass beds and lagoons

The intertidal areas or zones lie between the high- and low-tide marks. Where beaches slope sharply, this is a narrow strip. Where old coral beds slope imperceptibly and are almost flat, this area may extend 2km or more. Intertidal zones provide a habitat for thousands of molluscs, crabs, sea-cucumbers,

Seagrass Cymodocea rotundata

seaweeds and several species of seagrasses, which are themselves food for fish at high tide.

Along the east coast of Unguja (and the east coasts of the other islands and the mainland) shallow lagoons occur, extending to the reef crest. The lagoons support assorted coral, seagrass and seaweed communities and often great selections of **starfish** and beautiful **nudibranch** (sea hares and their relatives).

Seagrass Thalassodendron ciliatum

Blue starfish

Coral reefs

Corals are not plants, but animals belonging to the *Coelenterata* group (which also includes sea anemones and jellyfish). Corals exist in clean, clear, shallow, warm water, and so are only found in the tropical regions. A coral begins life as a soft many-tentacled 'polyp' around 1mm in size, and then produces a hard calcium carbonate skeleton around itself for protection. These types of coral are called **'hard corals'**. A coral colony develops from a single polyp by a process called 'budding' (where a new polyp grows out of an existing one). When polyps die, their hard skeletons remain, and the colony expands as new polyps form on the skeletons of old dead polyps. In this way colonies grow, and the growth rate varies from about 1cm to 5cm per year depending on species, depth and water conditions. Groups of colonies together make up the coral reefs found fringing the islands.

Staghorn coral

Different types of hard coral form their colonies in different shapes; the commonly known varieties include stag-horn coral, plate coral, mushroom coral, table corals and brain corals – all abundant in shallow water.

Coral also uses a form of sexual reproduction where sperm and eggs are mixed (either internally with a coral embryo or larvae later being released, or by 'spawning' where eggs and sperm are released by polyps to mix in the water). In both ways the corals can colonise new areas.

Within the polyps exist microscopic algae-type organisms called *zooxanthellae*, which trap the sunlight needed to power the chemical reactions which produce the coral's hard calcium skeleton. It is the *zooxanthellae* which give the coral its colour – usually pink or pale brown in a variety of shades – as the coral polyps themselves are virtually transparent. Thus when coral is picked, and taken out of the water, the corals and the *zooxanthella* die and lose colour, leaving only the pale 'bleached' chalky white skeletons.

During daylight hours, the coral colonies use sunlight in much the same way as plants do, but at night-time on a reef, most hard coral species are busy, with polyps extending their tentacles to catch planktonic foods.

Crown-of-thorns starfish feeding on brain coral

Soft corals, on the other hand, do not have a hard external skeleton and do not form reefs. They are far more colourful than hard corals, although they also require light to build the tiny crystal fibres embedded in their soft pink, lilac or cream-coloured tissues. The daytime feeding of the eight-tentacled polyps, a feature of this group, is clearly visible on soft corals which can, in places, dominate underwater scenes.

On the east coasts of Unguja and Pemba typical fringing reefs are marked by a continuous line of surf resulting from Indian Ocean swells. At low tide the reef crest dries out revealing pink algal-rock and boulders – the coral itself usually only becoming prolific on the seaward slope below 5m. On Unguja, the coral-covered reef slopes dip down to about 20m, after which a fairly bare sandy seabed continues down a further 4km to the ocean bottom. On the more sheltered west coasts of the Zanzibar Channel smaller, isolated patch reefs with sandbars, and island reefs (around Chapwani, Changuu, Bawe and Chumbi islands), provide coral gardens in the relatively shallow waters. In contrast, parts of the reef around Pemba Island drop down over 50m or more offering spectacular vertical coral walls. Some of the most dramatic dive sites along the Tanzanian coast are found on the steep slopes of Pemba Island.

On any of these coral reefs you will immediately note the amazing variety of colourful fish of all sizes and shapes, incredible in their patterns and forms: **butterfly-fish**, **parrot-fish**, **surgeon-fish**, **damselfish**, **emperors**, **goatfish**, **pufferfish**, **angel-fish**, **triggerfish**, **groupers** and **grunts** to name a few. Most of these typical coral reef fish are territorial and reside over small areas of reef, rarely leaving their patch and aggressively protecting it from others of their own species. Some, like the butterfly-fish, pair up for life and occupy a patch the size of a tennis

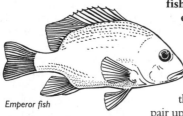

Emperor fish

court; others, such as the blue-lined **yellow snappers**, roam around the reefs in schools of a few hundred.

Because of the rich diversity of life forms, coral reefs have been compared to tropical rainforests. With Zanzibar's waters containing more than 700 fish species associated with coral reefs, over 100 species of hard corals, 150-odd species of seaweed and 300-plus species of seashells, to mention just a few of the more obvious sea creatures, the comparison is certainly a valid one. Then there are sponges, anemones, brittlestars, sea-cucumbers, sea-squirts, feather-stars and crustaceans, all forming a seemingly chaotic, mind-boggling complexity which has fascinated scientists since Darwin's time.

The loss of the microscopic *zooxanthellae* from the coral, resulting in bleaching, was a major feature of the reefs around Zanzibar and elsewhere in the tropics in 1998, as the region experienced increased sea water temperatures (up to 32°C) associated with a severe, and much publicised, shift in global climate conditions called El Niño. Although coral bleaching had occurred in the past, this event was on a scale not witnessed before. Much coral (both hard and soft) bleached and failed to regain its *zooxanthellae*. Within about five months vast areas of previously rich and diverse coral communities died. In many reef areas since then, new, small colonies have begun to emerge from settlement of coral larvae, and the coral component of these reefs

Grouper

is beginning to return to that prior to 1998. In other areas, total recovery to pre-1998 conditions may take decades or centuries. For reasons that are still unclear, much more coral around Pemba eventually died, whereas on Unguja corals recovered after bleaching.

For the visitor, access to good snorkelling or dive sites (including a selection of generally shallow patch reefs, ideal for night dives) is easily gained from Zanzibar Town. In addition, there are numerous dive operators based at hotels on the north and east coasts of Unguja. On Pemba a few shore-based dive operators exist in Mkoani and Chake Chake. Live-aboard charters are also available, and highly recommended. More details are given in the *Diving* section in *Chapter 4 – Practical Information*, on page 108.

Open waters

The open waters, though mostly empty at first glance, can be very busy at times. They are home to vast schools of small, plankton-feeding, pelagic fish species such as **sardines**, **silver-sides** and **Indian mackerel**, continuously on the move and relentlessly pursued by larger pelagic fish, like **skipjack**, **yellowfin tuna**, **kingfish**, **sailfish** and **marlin**. Out at sea, in the Pemba Channel or off the east coast, flocks of hundreds of white terns identify tuna feeding frenzies as they dart into the shoals of small pelagic fish forced up to the surface by the tuna below.

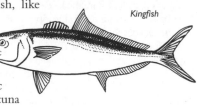

Kingfish

Also feeding out at sea for most of their lives are **turtles**, coming into shallow waters when looking for a mate. Green and hawksbill turtles are the most common. (See the *Sea turtles* section, page 71.)

Yellowfin tuna

Both the friendly **bottlenose dolphin** and the less bold **humpback dolphin** can be seen in small groups, or pods, quite close to the shore. (See the *Kizimkazi dolphins* box, page 222.) Around Unguja there appear to be a few pods of 10–15 members, each with its own territory. One area where they are commonly seen is off Kizimkazi in southwest Unguja (viewing is easily arranged with a local boat), or around Mnemba Island in the northeast, or, with a bit of luck, even off Zanzibar Town. (Watching dolphins is especially enjoyable if you're also sipping a cool beer on Africa House Hotel terrace at sunset.) At Kizimkazi and Mnemba it's also sometimes possible to see groups of hundreds of **spinner dolphins**, providing an unforgettable memory.

Sailfish

Less common are whales, though **humpback whales** have been spotted several times around October–November in the Zanzibar Channel and off Nungwi in the north, leading their recently born young back to the summer feeding grounds in Antarctica.

Tides and weather

Tides, the daily rise and fall of sea level, are a noticeable feature along the east coast of Africa. Tides are dictated mostly by the moon (and to a lesser extent the sun) and there are two main types. The smaller tides, known as neap tides, occur during the half-moon phases and result in a tidal range (the difference between high and low water) of only 1.5m. From this period onwards the tidal range increases, until a full or new moon (ie: every two weeks), when spring tides occur. These result in the largest tidal range, of about 4m between high tide and low tide. Spring tide low water always occurs at around 10.00–11.00, for about three days, twice every lunar cycle (at full moon and new moon). Through the rest of the lunar cycle, the time of each tide changes from one day to the next by an average of 50 minutes (about 30 minutes during springs). So if high tide is at 15.00 on one day it will be about 15.50 on the following day.

During spring low tides the low-water mark can be a couple of kilometres out and these days are ideal for walking out on the intertidal flats and reef crest to explore the kaleidoscope of life. Take care to avoid trampling on living coral and on sea-urchins or blue-spotted stingrays. Good footwear (trainers, plastic sandals or neoprene booties) is strongly recommended. Even the tiniest cut or graze can flare up into a nasty tropical ulcer which will keep you out of the sea for days recovering. Be aware, also, of the

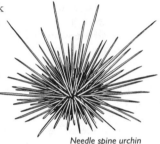

Needle spine urchin

speed with which the tide comes in and don't be caught out on the reef crest of the east coast with the incoming tide around your waist – you'll have an exhausting swim back to the beach if you do. And remember, tidal currents are strongest during spring tides so be careful not to swim too far out, or into tidal channels.

Prevailing weather also greatly influences sea conditions and travellers should be aware of the main seasons. These are described in more detail under *When to visit* in *Chapter 4*.

Local people and marine life

It won't take you long to realise that a great number of Zanzibaris are dependent on the surrounding seas and shallows for their variety of foods. Various fishing methods are used to catch this vital source of protein which contributes over 70% of the needs of the local population. On dark new-moon nights in the Zanzibar Channel, sardine boats with lights attract and net vast shoals; on the same nights gill-netting boats, with 15cm-mesh nets, are after the large pelagic species (tuna, kingfish and billfish) in the southern Pemba Channel, operating mostly from Nungwi. Conventional hook-and-line fishing and passive fish-trapping using baited basket-traps (*Madema*) are still practised all around the islands.

Octopus

During the low spring tides thousands of women and children collect octopus, shells, sea-cucumbers and moray eels from the intertidal flats, whilst other women tend to their seaweed (*Mwani*) farm patches in the lagoons on the east coast. The lines of sticks protruding out of the water at low tide can't be missed (for details see the box on *Seaweed farming*, page 71).

Mangroves are also harvested: the wood has been used for building poles for centuries, because of its resistance to rotting and insect infestation. However, the rapid increase in demand over the last few years, with overcutting in places, has led to deterioration of the forests and the marine life which relies on them. Recently, the felling of planted casuarina (Australian pine, though not actually a true pine) has produced, so far, acceptable insect-resistant poles, easing some of the pressure on the mangroves.

Conservation

Due to the rapid increase in population (at present doubling every 20 years), the availability of new fishing materials, the development of a number of destructive fishing methods and the inability of the government to enforce fisheries regulations, the delicate balance of life in the shallow seas (and therefore this vital source of food) is beginning to be destroyed. Spear-fishing is on the increase and due to its effectiveness can quickly strip the reefs of the larger fish, and even of small species such as butterfly-fish. Not only does it reduce fish numbers and make them wary of snorkellers, such as around the shallow reefs close to Zanzibar Town or in the lagoon on the east, but by removing these vital predators the balance within the ecosystem is being lost. Netting around reefs, and the type of fishing known locally as *Kigumi* where corals are broken deliberately to force fish out into the surrounding net, are also practised and extremely destructive. Dynamite-fishing is also very destructive, but mostly restricted to the mainland coast. Also restricted to the mainland and Mafia coasts, fortunately for Zanzibar, is the collecting of shallow live coral (mainly of the genus *Porites*) for baking on open kilns into lime. On Unguja at least, quarried coral rock is used instead.

Careless anchoring of boats on coral reefs can also, over a short time, cause considerable localised damage. In 1994 a project funded by the Dutch Embassy of Dar es Salaam through the Institute of Marine Sciences established, in conjunction with the tourist boat operators who use the reefs, 15 permanent moorings for the islands and reefs close to Zanzibar Town, thus reducing tourism-related damage. Although these have since deteriorated and are no longer functional, the project did serve to increase the awareness of the importance and needs of living coral reefs, and in general boat operators around Zanzibar Town are careful when dropping anchor, attempting to set it in sand or rubble. Perhaps in the future the shallow coral gardens around Bawe Island and the sandbanks off Stone Town will come under some form of management to conserve their productivity and attractiveness to visitors. The main threat to these shallow coral reefs, some of which have superb hard coral communities, remain the *Kigumi* fishermen.

The local demand for marine curios (shells, dead coral and turtle products) has increased with the growing number of tourists, further adding to the over-exploitation of the marine resources. The collection of large, colourful, attractive mollusc shells like the giant triton (*Charonia tritonis*) and the bull-mouth helmet shell (*Cypraecassis rufa*) have secondary effects which are not that obvious. These feed on the crown-of-thorns starfish (*Acanthaster planci*) and sea-urchins respectively. Absence of the molluscs again upsets the balance, and populations of these

crimson-red

Bull-mouth helmet shell

echinoderms can increase alarmingly, furthering the destruction of the coral reefs. Collection of live hard corals is, of course, extremely damaging to the reef ecosystem. A colony the size of a football can take over 20 years to grow and the implications of mass removal for sale to tourists or export needs no further explanation. Don't buy the stuff!

Some steps are being taken to try and address the problems. With the involvement of donor organisations, and conservation bodies such as the Worldwide Fund for Nature, private enterprise, the Institute of Marine Sciences, and the Zanzibar authorities (Department of Fisheries, Commission of Environment and Department of Tourism), plans to create marine protected areas have made some progress. On Pemba the only marine protected area is Misali Island Conservation Area which involves local fishermen in conservation and charges fees to visiting divers and snorkellers. On Unguja, a few miles south of Zanzibar Town, Chumbe Island Coral Park (CHICOP), a private investment, includes a protected forest and coral reef on its western shores. Chumbe can be visited for a day, or you can stay overnight, and funds generated contribute to raising awareness of marine issues through the educational centre used by local school pupils. Further south the Menai Bay Conservation Area brings fisheries and mangrove issues to local community groups supported by the government in an attempt to manage the resources for the long term. The only other marine protected area is a zone 200m wide around Mnemba Island, an exclusive private island resort off the northeast coast. However, the spectacular turquoise waters around Mnemba Island extend beyond this boundary and the 20km of fringing reefs are accessible to divers and snorkellers from several beach hotels operating from the north and east coasts of Unguja.

Giant triton shell

Tourism development, now a rapidly growing industry, also has a role to play in marine conservation. By acknowledging that the marine resources on which it depends are finite and also vital to the neighbouring coastal villages, and by attempting to come up with methods which assist all the users, tourism can contribute to a healthy future for all concerned. Survival of both may be in the balance.

So, when bobbing around over a coral garden, or simply sitting on the seabed, 10m down, watching the coral reef world around you, or wading through the dark mud in a mangrove forest, think about it ... and enjoy it. There's a whole lot going on: between individuals, between species, between habitats and between the ecosystem and the people who use it. This section has touched on some of the more salient issues and examples of life in the seas and on the shores of Zanzibar. Many more exist to be discovered and pondered upon; whilst doing so, the following are a few points to remember:

- Don't touch living coral. There's no need to and it is more sensitive than it looks. Be careful when reef walking and snorkelling or diving. Be aware of what your flippers are doing and avoid landing on coral when entering into the water. Maintain good buoyancy control at all times.
- Help prevent anchor damage. Insist on the use of permanent moorings, if available, or anchor only in sand.
- Don't buy shells, turtle products or corals.

● Spread the word. Explain what you now know about the local marine ecosystems to other visitors and locals.

Sea turtles of Zanzibar

Original text by Fiona Clark,
updated by Lorna Slade, ecologist, Zanzibar Sea Turtle Survival Project
Five types of sea turtle occur in the western Indian Ocean: the **green turtle** (*Chelonia mydas*), the **hawksbill turtle** (*Eretmochelys imbricata*), the **loggerhead turtle** (*Caretta caretta*), the **olive ridley turtle** (*Lepidochelys olivacea*) and the **leatherback turtle** (*Dermochhelys coriacea*). All are endangered species. The most

SEAWEED FARMING

Seaweed farming was introduced to Zanzibar at the end of the 1980s, and the practice now extends from Paje in the southeast to Nungwi on the north coast of Unguja (Zanzibar Island). The seaweed species are *Euchema spinosum* and *E. cottoni*, and seaweed plots can be recognised by rectangular patterns of sticks in the sand, just below the low-tide mark. Plots are tended by the local villagers who tie young seaweed cuttings on to strings which run between the sticks. Each plot has up to 50 rows of strings between 25cm and 35cm apart, and each string carries 10 to 15 cuttings.

The seaweed grows at a rate of 7% per day, and the local people regularly tend their plots, removing algae from the strings to prevent the seaweed from breaking off. After two weeks the cuttings have increased tenfold in weight and are harvested. The wet seaweed is laid out in the sun or hung on racks to dry, and loses 80% of its weight. It is then sold to dealers who export the seaweed to countries such as Denmark and the Philippines, where it is used as a thickening agent in cosmetics, medicines, food, ice-cream and even beer. Each plot yields about 5–8kg per harvest, and the full 8kg can be sold for $1 by the farmer, although when the dealers sell it on to the users, the value can be 30 times higher.

Over 3,000 tonnes of seaweed are exported each year and, despite the relatively low prices that the villagers receive, the additional income from seaweed farming has improved their standard of living considerably. In common with many other parts of Africa, farming has been traditionally regarded as women's work, and this is the case with seaweed farming on Zanzibar. The drying and selling is also women's responsibility, so much of the money earned from the seaweed stays in their hands. Normally, rural women would not have their own source of income, so the advent of seaweed farming has given them a certain degree of freedom and empowerment. Money is used for house improvements, kitchenware or even luxuries like radios and cassette players. Many people use the money to pay for school fees, and the villagers of Paje have built two day-care centres for their children.

The success and growth of seaweed farming led to conflict on the east coast between the villagers and the owners of hotels. The latter claim that seaweed farms are unsightly (somewhat unfair, considering the size and style of some hotels), and deter visitors from swimming. This may be true, but it is also worth remembering that thanks to the all-inclusive nature of many big hotels, the local people may benefit more from a beach full of seaweed than a beach full of tourists.

commonly found turtle in Zanzibar is the green turtle, followed by the hawksbill. Both nest in Zanzibar. Leatherback and loggerhead are sometimes seen, but don't nest. There have been no records for the olive ridley since 1975.

Zanzibar is not a major turtle nesting site, but appears to be a feeding ground for sea turtles from other areas. Conservationists have recovered tags from captured turtles showing that green turtles come to Zanzibar from Aldabra Island, in the Seychelles, and from Europa and Tromelin islands. Loggerheads that nest in KwaZulu-Natal (South Africa) also feed in Tanzania – one loggerhead was captured in Tanzania just 66 days after being tagged in South Africa.

The bad news

The sea turtle population is decreasing in Zanzibar. This is bad because turtles are part of a food web which includes sea-grasses, sponges, jelly fish and tiger sharks, and also because living turtles are attractive to tourists and (like dolphins) can sometimes be a way for local people to earn money.

The number of nesting sites has been reduced dramatically, and turtles are hunted and trapped by more efficient means than previously. Local fishermen tell how, 20 or 30 years ago, some beaches would contain 100 or more turtle nests every year. But these days the same beaches only contain two or three nests. Places where nests can still be found include Mnemba Island, the beaches north of Matemwe Bungalows, and around Kizimkazi. Pemba is home to the most important nesting beaches; turtles nest on Misali Island, at Ras Kiuyuand and on the beaches near Ngezi Forest – especially Vumawimbi. Unfortunately, except for the island sites, few of these nests are successful: many eggs are taken by people, while others are lost to the sea when erosion has formed steps on some beaches forcing turtles to nest in places that are vulnerable to the high tide.

The burgeoning tourist industry also has its costs. In the last ten years many hotels have been built on turtle nesting beaches. Buildings often extend right to the beach, vegetation is cleared and the beach lit up at night, disturbing any turtles coming up to nest and disorienting any hatchlings. For example, Kiwengwa Beach on the east coast of Unguja (Zanzibar Island) is now wall-to-wall hotel with no space or peace for turtles.

Turtle hunting in Zanzibar only became illegal in October 1993. Although penalties are quite severe (a large fine, or two years in prison, or both) enforcement of the new law is unlikely. The Fisheries Department is under-resourced and has many other problems to deal with (such as dynamite fishing).

Turtles are usually captured with gill nets, which are set on the sea bed, while others are caught with spear guns. They are brought ashore and have their flippers and shell removed, often while still alive. The number of turtles caught increased dramatically in the 1960s when gill nets, snorkelling gear and spear guns were introduced. Some local fishermen claim that their increased catch proves the population is increasing too, but the same fishermen also agree that nesting turtles have all but disappeared. Uroa on the east coast of Unguja is a renowned area for turtle hunting and the beach sometimes looks like a turtle graveyard.

In March 1996 there were two incidents of poisoning in Pemba through the consumption of turtlemeat, resulting in the death of 37 people. Hawksbill turtles, in particular, are known on occasion to harbour toxins thought to originate from toxic algae in the food chain. These toxins do not harm the turtle, but have disastrous effects on any humans eating the meat. These unfortunate incidents helped reduce turtle slaughter, but apparently only for a short while.

The good news

Since 1992, there have been several small-scale turtle protection projects run with volunteer help through the government of Zanzibar's Department of the Environment. These include the following:

- A Swahili-language education package for schools and other youth groups, emphasising the plight of sea turtles, and their need to be protected. A poster carrying the same message has also been produced both in English, aimed at visitors, and in Swahili, aimed at locals.
- A nest protection scheme, run by Matemwe Bungalows, a hotel on the east coast. Local villagers are paid a small fee if they report an intact nest, and a further bonus for each successful hatching. To avoid the problems of beach erosion, some nests are moved to safer sites.
- A survey and protection scheme carried out by the management of the exclusive lodge on the private Mnemba Island. This is an ideal site for turtles, with safe beaches (no local fishermen are allowed to land) and deep water access.
- A nest protection and monitoring scheme on the protected Misali Island, off Pemba, now a marine conservation area, patrolled by local rangers. (Misali is one of the best turtle nesting areas in Zanzibar, with over 65 nests recorded in 1999.)
- From 1995 to 1998 there was a community education and nest-recording programme in both Pemba and Unguja, including the successful production of an educational drama and video.
- Mnarani Aquarium at Nungwi, a local initiative set up by a group of local fishermen, in a large tidal-fed rock pool. The pool has been stocked with several species of fish and around ten green and hawksbill turtles. The Department of Environment has allowed this group (only) to keep a maximum of eight turtles for educational purposes and any excess brought in by fishermen are periodically tagged and released. Although generally keeping turtles in captivity is not to be encouraged, in this case the local community benefit, and the educational value to locals (school children are allowed in free) and tourists is judged to be worth it. The aquarium does not keep mature female turtles.

Turtle-shell products

Zanzibar used to be a major centre for turtle-shell, usually called 'tortoiseshell', and at the height of the trade (the early 20th century) some 3,300kg were exported every year from the islands and nearby mainland coast. Demand dropped, but has recently been revived by the growth of tourism. A survey showed that the amount of turtle-shell jewellery went up five times between early 1993 and late 1994. Less than half the tourists who bought turtle-shell items knew what it was, or that turtles were endangered. However, local conservationists and aware tourists complained to such a degree that many shops now refuse to stock turtle-shell products. Tourists are asked by conservation organisations to boycott any shops that continue to sell turtle products.

Local police and customs officials are now also aware that turtle-shell products are illegal. In 1995, a tourist who bought a whole shell from a hawker on the east coast was stopped at a road block on the way back to Zanzibar Town after hotel staff tipped off the police. The tourist was reprimanded, and the shell was confiscated.

Local perspectives

Lest we get too self-righteous about all this, we should perhaps remember that Zanzibar is a poor country and that a large sea turtle is worth about a month's wages for an office worker, and considerably more than that to a fisherman or farmer. Turtlemeat is also held traditionally to have healing properties. Stopping the local people from catching turtles will inevitably make some of them poorer, yet if the turtle hunting continues there will soon be none left anyway. But many Zanzibaris can't afford the luxury of thinking ahead. Life is hand to mouth and the 'if I don't catch it someone else will' attitude is of course understandable.

Having said that, there does need to be a halt to turtle killing as populations are in danger of extinction. In addition to finding alternative food and income sources for local communities, it is also essential that continued education, improved law enforcement and government protection for important nesting beaches is maintained, to ensure that the turtle has a place in Zanzibar's future.

Practical Information

4

WHEN TO VISIT

The climate of Zanzibar is dominated by the movements of the Indian Ocean monsoons, and characterised by wet and dry seasons. The northeast monsoon winds (known locally as the *kaskazi*) blow from November/December to February/March, and the southwest monsoon winds (the *kusi*) blow from June to September/October. The main rains (the *masika*) fall from mid-March to the end of May, and there is a short rainy season (the *vuli*) in November.

The best time to visit Zanzibar is during the dry seasons, from December to February and June to October. Generally speaking, from December to February if the wind gets up, it comes from the northeast, so beaches on the southern and western parts of the islands are more sheltered. Conversely, from June to October, any wind tends to come from the southwest, so northern and eastern coasts are more sheltered. Wherever you go, though, it's worth remembering that Zanzibar is an oceanic island and subject to unpredictable weather patterns at any time of year. Even during the 'dry' seasons, afternoon showers are not unknown, although they tend to be short and have a pleasant cooling effect.

Throughout the year, humidity is generally quite high (less so in the rainy season), although this can be relieved by winds and sea breezes. Temperatures do not vary greatly throughout the year, with daytime averages around 26°C (80°F) on Zanzibar Island from June to October, and around 28°C from December to February, although in this latter period the humidity is often higher, so temperatures feel hotter. Pemba tends to be cooler and get slightly more rain than Zanzibar Island.

It is also possible to visit Zanzibar during the rainy season. At this period, there are fewer visitors and you are more likely to get good bargains for hotel rooms, car and bike hire, boat trips, and so on. Rain is heavy, but not constant. Sunsets during this time are magnificent on the west coast, and another bonus is that pineapples are in season. Travel can be more difficult at this time, as roads can be damaged and buses delayed, but most places can still be reached eventually.

READING UP BEFORE YOU GO

A very important part of your preparation for a visit should be to find out as much as you can about the history, geography and culture of Zanzibar before you arrive. If text books and encyclopaedias put you off, read a few novels or travelogues to get yourself in the mood, or dip into some of the early explorers' accounts (see the books listed in the *Further Information* appendix). Also, scan the foreign pages of newspapers, or magazines specialising in developing countries, to familiarise yourself with politics and current affairs. You could even try learning a few phrases of Swahili. All this will make your trip much more rewarding.

CLIMATE

Month	Temp (°C) Av min	Av max	Hrs of sun daily	Rainfall, mm	Av days of rain
January	25	31	8	80	7
February	25	31	8	70	6
March	24	31	7	140	12
April	23	30	5	390	19
May	22	29	6	250	14
June	20	29	8	60	4
July	19	28	7	45	5
August	19	28	8	40	6
September	19	28	8	50	6
October	21	29	8	90	7
November	22	30	8	220	14
December	24	31	8	160	12

At holiday times, such as Christmas and Easter, as well as being favoured by overseas visitors, Zanzibar is a popular short-break destination for expatriate workers from Dar es Salaam and Nairobi. This can mean fully booked flights and surcharges in some hotels.

During the Islamic fasting period of Ramadan many restaurants, snack bars and shops are closed during the day, and life on the island runs at a generally slower pace. (For details on Ramadan and other important dates in Zanzibar, see the *Public holidays* section on page 105.) The information on local festivals on page 50 may also help you plan your visit. Sports fans may like to tie in their visit with the Zanzibar International Marathon, held every year in early November. If you've come specifically for scuba diving or game fishing, see the *Zanzibar diving and fishing seasons* box, page 111.

GETTING TO ZANZIBAR
Flights from Europe

There are no non-stop flights to Zanzibar from Europe. When this book was being researched (2002) all flights had at least one stopover requiring a change of plane. However, the choice of routes and airlines is increasing every year, and reaching Zanzibar is now more straightforward than it's ever been.

Airlines flying from Europe to Zanzibar include KLM in conjunction with Kenya Airways (changing planes in Amsterdam, and at Nairobi on some flights), with flights about four times a week. Another option is on Ethiopian Airlines (changing in Addis Ababa), with flights twice a week, also including a touch-down at Kilimanjaro International. With connections to/from various European cities, and good fares (although sometimes long connections) this is an increasingly popular way to reach Zanzibar from Europe. Note that if you come by Ethiopian Airlines, you only transit in Addis and go through customs and immigration facilities only once – on arrival in Zanzibar. However, on Kenya Airways, travellers have reported that it is necessary to go through Kenyan customs and immigration at both Nairobi and/or Mombasa (even though these are only transit stops) and then again at Zanzibar.

Your other alternative – and the option taken by most visitors to Zanzibar these days – is to fly to Dar es Salaam (on the Tanzanian mainland, near Zanzibar) then take a regional service to Zanzibar (such as Air Tanzania, Precision Air, Coastal or

ZanAir) to Zanzibar. You can also take a private charter plane to fly from Dar to Zanzibar. As the regional carriers (especially Coastal and ZanAir) offer reliable flights that tie in with the international arrivals, this option can sometimes be quicker and easier than taking the flights to Zanzibar via Nairobi or Addis. Details of these options are given below, and a good specialist travel agent will be able to help you with these arrangements.

The main airlines with services to Dar es Salaam from Europe are:

British Airways, from London, direct to Dar, with about three flights a week;
KLM, from Amsterdam, direct to Dar, about five times a week, sometimes in partnership with Kenya Airways, via Nairobi;
Swiss, from Zurich, direct to Dar, about four times a week;
Kenya Airways, from London, via Nairobi, to Dar, four times a week;
Emirates, from London, via Dubai, to Dar;
Gulf Air, from London, via Muscat or Abu Dhabi, to Dar.

Although BA's, KLM's and Swiss's main hubs are London, Amsterdam and Zurich respectively, they all have regional connecting flights to/from most cities in Europe, so you can use their services wherever you happen to be.

As an alternative to flying all the way to Zanzibar, once you've flown into Dar es Salaam, you can travel on to Zanzibar by ship (details are given below). Another option for keen travellers is to fly from Europe into Nairobi, then go overland to Dar es Salaam, and take a plane or a ship to Zanzibar from there.

Britain is one of the cheapest places in Europe to buy scheduled flights to Zanzibar, Dar, Mombasa or Nairobi. Specialist travel agencies can also arrange regional flights to/from Zanzibar, and make other arrangements if you need them, such as hotel and tour bookings. To give you an idea of costs, return flights from London to Zanzibar in the low season start at UK£400 (about US$600), and are around UK£500 to UK£600 in the high season, although by shopping around and buying long in advance you can get some good bargains. On Gulf Air particularly, fares can be very reasonable but connections can be poor on this route.

The best way to find out about travel agents selling flights to Zanzibar or anywhere else in East Africa, is to look through the advertisements in travel magazines or newspaper travel supplements. Simply compare prices and give the agents a call to check availability and other details, although be prepared to find out that many of the bargain fares offered in ads are rarely actually available when you phone. Nevertheless you can still find some good deals. Prices tend to vary widely, and usually reflect the quality of airline, the flight duration and the number of stops en route, so it's well worth shopping around.

For visitors from Europe, another option to consider is holiday charter flights. There are also increasing numbers of holiday charter flights straight into Zanzibar from Europe (particularly from Italy, Switzerland and France), although by 2002 there was none from the UK. Although usually sold as part of a package with accommodation, many tour operators sell 'flight only' deals, which is often cheaper than the scheduled flight fares. These are often advertised in the travel pages of national newspapers or in travel agents' windows.

Flights from the USA, South Africa and elsewhere

There are no direct flights to Zanzibar from the USA. You must fly to Europe and then take one of the flights mentioned above. Travel agents specialising in flights to Africa advertise in travel magazines and travel sections of major newspapers.

From South Africa, there are no direct flights, but South African Airways flies between Johannesburg and Dar es Salaam twice-weekly, from where you can take a plane to Zanzibar, as described above, or a ship as described below. Another option to consider is the Gulf Air flight from Durban to Dar es Salaam.

If you want to reach Zanzibar from somewhere else in the world other than the countries mentioned above, it is usual to fly to Europe, to East Africa, or to the Gulf states and pick up a connecting flight from there. For example, from many parts of Asia you could fly on Gulf Air to Muscat then take another plane to Dar es Salaam.

By organised tour

An organised tour is ideal if you don't have the time and inclination to travel to and around Zanzibar making your own arrangements. Various companies based in the UK, USA, South Africa or elsewhere include Zanzibar in their Tanzania or East Africa itineraries, and a few specialist agents offer dedicated trips to Zanzibar alone.

Tours are either scheduled (ie: you join a group and keep to pre-set departure dates and itineraries) or tailor-made (prepared to fit in exactly with what you want to do). The main advantage of an organised tour is its all-inclusive nature – you usually pay one price which includes your flight, transfers, accommodation, meals, excursions and the services of a guide or tour leader. Once your plane takes off you can sit back and enjoy the trip; there's nothing more to plan or arrange. The main disadvantage is, of course, the fixed itinerary: you cannot change your plans to spend more or less time at a particular place. If you're having a tour tailor-made for you then of course you can specify just how organised you want to be. For example you might have the tour company arrange your flights, a few hotel nights and a hire car, and make your own arrangements for the rest of the trip.

Organised tours range from the very luxurious to the very simple, catering for various interests (such as diving, history, cultural experiences or simply relaxing), and may be based either at a hotel on the beach or in Zanzibar Town. Prices and lengths of stay vary too. Several travel agents offer a choice of scheduled trips run by other operators and can also organise a tailor-made itinerary especially for you. The best way to find a trip that suits your own interest and pocket is to phone the companies direct, ask for a brochure or website details, and then discuss your ideas with them.

As with the flight agents, the best way to find out about companies arranging tours to Zanzibar is to look through the advertisements in any travel magazine or newspaper travel supplement.

Travel agents and tour companies

If you're travelling **from the UK**, the following travel agents and tour companies specialise in East Africa, including Zanzibar, and are worth contacting for flights and/or tours. Although those listed below are all based in Britain, those marked with an asterisk (*) are also represented **in the USA** and in various other countries by local specialist travel agencies. Alternatively, from outside Britain, the companies can be contacted direct.

Abercrombie and Kent★ Tel: 020 7559 8500, fax: 020 7730 9376; email: info@abercrombiekent.co.uk; website www.abercrombiekent.com. Upmarket tour and safari specialists, covering Africa and destinations worldwide.
Africa Travel Centre Tel: 020 7387 1211; fax: 020 7387 7512; email: africatravel@easynet.co.uk; web: www.africatravel.co.uk. Long-standing and experienced tour and flight agency, covering the whole continent of Africa.
Art of Travel Tel: 020 7738 2038; fax: 020 7738 1893; email: safari@artoftravel.co.uk; web: www.artoftravel.co.uk. Experienced agency, specialising in upmarket tailor-made

Previous page Traditional dhow at Nungwi (AZ)
Above Rooftop view of Stone Town and the House of Wonders (AZ)
Right Fukuchani Ruins, dating from the 16th century (DE)
Below Maharubi Palace, built in 1882 (AZ)

holidays.

Explore Worldwide★ Tel: 01252 760100, fax: 01252 343170; email: res@exploreworldwide.com; web: www.exploreworldwide.com. Adventure tours for groups across the globe, including Zanzibar visits, which can be combined with safaris in northern or southern mainland Tanzania.

Footloose Adventure Travel Tel: 01943 604030; fax: 01943 604070; email: info@footlooseadventure.co.uk; web: www.footlooseadventure.co.uk. Experienced travel agency, with flights, safaris, group tours and individual tailor-made holidays, specialising in Zanzibar and mainland Tanzania, with good local contacts and detailed knowledge of on-the-ground options for a range of budgets.

Gane and Marshall International Tel: 020 8441 9592; fax: 020 8441 7376; email: holidays@ganeandmarshall.co.uk; web: ganeandmarshall.co.uk. Attractive range of tours and tailor-made trips all over the world, including Zanzibar and mainland Tanzania.

Hayes and Jarvis★ Tel: 0870 8989890; email: res@hayes-jarvis.com

Okavango Tours and Safaris★ Tel: 020 8343 3283; fax: 020 8343 3287; email: info@okavango.com; web: www.okavango.com. Africa specialists, with options in Zanzibar.

Partnership Travel Tel: 020 8343 3446; fax: 020 8349 3439; email: info@partnershiptravel.co.uk; web: www.partnershiptravel.co.uk

Somak Holidays Tel: 020 8423 3000; fax: 020 8423 7700; email: holidays@somak.co.uk; web: www.somak.co.uk. Package tours in middle range, including some in Zanzibar.

Sunvil Africa Tel: 020 8232 9777; fax: 020 8568 8330; email: info@sunvil.co.uk; web: www.sunvil.co.uk. Award-winning and good-value tour operator with specialist programmes to Tanzania, the islands and southern Africa. Their operations in southern and western Tanzania, Zanzibar and Mafia are run personally by Africa expert Heather Tyrrell – co-author of this guide – who can help plan your trip.

Tanzania Odyssey Tel: 020 7471 8780; fax: 020 7384 9549; web: www.tanzaniaodyssey.com. Tanzania specialists, with tours and safaris in the national parks on the mainland which can all be combined with visits to Zanzibar.

Travelbag Adventures★ Tel: 01420 541007; fax: 01420 541022; email: mail@travelbag-adventures.co.uk; web: www.travelbag-adventures.co.uk. Reasonably priced, good-value adventure holidays for small groups, including dedicated tours for families, cover all parts of the world, including Zanzibar and the Selous Game Reserve in southern Tanzania.

Tribes Travel Tel: 01728 685971; fax: 01728 685973; email: bradt@tribes.co.uk. web: www.tribes.co.uk. Small award-winning operator of exciting and imaginative tours around the world, with many options in Tanzania, run on fair-trade principles, avoiding exploitation of destinations and native peoples.

Zanzibar Travel Tel/fax: 01242 222027; email: info@zanzibartravel.co.uk; web: www.zanzibartravel.co.uk. You can't get more specialised than this! Tours, flights and holidays to Zanzibar, with expert knowledge built up over many years.

If you're coming **from South Africa**, travel companies include:

Unusual Destinations Tel: 011 706 1991; fax: 011 463 1469; email: info@unusualdestinations.com; web: www.unusualdestinations.com

Getting to Zanzibar from Kenya
By air
Air Kenya flies between Nairobi and Zanzibar most days; the fare is US$188 one-way, and the flight takes 60–90 minutes. Flights used to go from Mombasa direct to Zanzibar, but now frustratingly go via Nairobi. Although flying this way takes much longer, and involves a change of plane in Nairobi, the fare is slightly less than the Nairobi–Zanzibar sector. Agents in Nairobi or Mombasa can arrange these flights. More details are given under Air travel companies in *Chapter 5, Zanzibar Town*.

Another option for flying from Kenya to Zanzibar is by private charter. Several of the local air companies listed below offer services from Mombasa, Nairobi or the Kenyan national parks direct to Zanzibar. A travel agent in Mombasa or elsewhere can make the arrangements for you.

By sea
Ships
Several of the large passenger ships which run between Dar es Salaam (Tanzania) and Zanzibar used to serve Mombasa as well, but at the time of research (mid-2002) there were no services on the Mombasa–Zanzibar route. As Kenya's tourism picks up again (after a slump in late 2001 and early 2002), these services may resume.

Dhows
Dhows taking tourists from Kenya to Zanzibar Island are very rare. However, although tourists cannot legally travel by dhow from Dar es Salaam to Zanzibar, it is still permitted from Mombasa. Dhows go more frequently between Mombasa and Pemba (see page 234) and some hardy budget travellers go first to Pemba then travel on to Zanzibar Island from there, although it's getting more unusual and increasingly difficult to go this way, as other easier (and almost as cheap) methods become available.

Before deciding to travel by dhow, read the *To Zanzibar by dhow* box on page 82. If that doesn't put you off, you can find a dhow to Zanzibar by asking around in the old port area of Mombasa. There is usually a boat twice a week, going to Wete or Mkoani on Pemba, although times and days are variable. A one-way trip costs about US$10 to US$15, payable in Kenyan shillings or hard currency.

Getting to Zanzibar from mainland Tanzania
The two main methods for reaching Zanzibar from mainland Tanzania are by air or sea from Dar es Salaam.

By air
Scheduled flights
The number of scheduled flights from the mainland to Zanzibar, and especially from Dar as Salaam to Zanzibar, has increased markedly in the last few years. At the same time, fares have dropped, or remained little changed, and this method of reaching Zanzibar is becoming increasingly common for all tourists.

Air Tanzania (ATC) ATC Building, Ohio St, Dar es Salaam; Tel: 022 211 0245–8. Flies daily between Dar es Salaam and Zanzibar. Fares are US$43 one-way, US$86 return, and flights can be booked at travel agents in Dar. Officially, flights take about 20–30 minutes, but the service is not very reliable (with frequent delays and cancelled reservations), so if you don't want to chance your luck with Air Tanzania, some local regional air companies offer regular scheduled flights from Dar to Zanzibar. These include:

Coastal Travels Tel: Dar es Salaam 022 2117 959; fax: 022 2118 647; email: aviation@coastal.cc; web: www.coastal.cc. This company flies between Dar and Zanzibar for US$55, between Arusha and Zanzibar for US$190, and between Selous National Park and Zanzibar for US$130.

Precisionair Flight Services Tel: Arusha 027 6903, 2818; fax: 8204; Tel: Dar es Salaam 022 213 0800; email: info@precisionairtz.com or precision-dar@twiga.com; web: www.precisionairtz.com. This company has daily flights between Zanzibar and Dar and other destinations in East Africa. Fares to Zanzibar are US$55 from Dar and US$165 from Arusha.

ZanAir PO Box 2113; main office: Malawi Rd, Zanzibar Town; Tel: 024 2233670, 0742 750478, 0747 410077; fax: 233768; branch office, Zanzibar Airport, Tel: 024 232993, 0742 750476; email: zanair@zitec.org; web: wwwzanair.com. This is the main air company based on Zanzibar – with offices in Zanzibar Town and at the airport. There's at least one service from Dar es Salaam to Zanzibar each day, which usually ties in with the timetables of long-haul flights to/from Europe. Flights are US$45 each way.

Private charter flights

If you're in a hurry, or all the scheduled flights are full, you can charter your own aircraft to get from the Tanzanian mainland to Zanzibar. Most tourists arrange charters from Dar to Zanzibar, but you can also fly from Arusha, Tanga, Kilimanjaro International or from air strips in the national parks, especially Selous and Ruaha in the south. The charter planes are small, from three to eight seats, and if you're in a small group chartering can sometimes work out only slightly more expensive per person than taking a scheduled flight.

Private charters can be arranged with Precision, Coastal or ZanAir (listed above). Rates vary, but to give you an idea, the cost for a five-seater plane between Dar and Zanzibar starts at about US$260. You can contact the companies direct, or visit any travel agent in Dar, Arusha or Moshi and they will make the arrangements for you.

If you're on Zanzibar Island and need to fly to the mainland, more details on air services are given in the *Zanzibar Town* chapter on page 141.

By sea
Ships
Several large passenger ships run between Dar es Salaam, Zanzibar and Pemba, and – occasionally – other points on the mainland. As the number of flights between Dar and Zanzibar increases, and airfares become increasingly competitive compared to boat fares, the number of services has reduced over the years. Also, the timetables produced by the shipping companies are notoriously subject to change, although the ships themselves generally do arrive and depart when they're supposed to.

The ships used by most tourists are listed below. In Dar, all the ship booking offices are at the main passenger port, very near the city centre. Schedules and prices are chalked up on boards outside each office, and you can buy tickets on the spot very easily. Reservations are not essential but if you are in Dar a day or two (or even an hour or two) before you want to travel, you should buy a ticket in advance to make sure. Non-Tanzanians usually have to pay in US dollars and prices are quoted in this currency. Tanzanian residents enjoy cheaper rates, and can pay in Tanzanian shillings.

Note that all non-Tanzanian passengers leaving Dar must pay a port departure tax of US$5. The departure tax office is near the ship booking offices, and tickets are carefully checked before you board. Most of the shipping companies include this charge in the ticket price, so check very carefully whether this is included to avoid paying again unnecessarily at the port tax office.

Also beware of hustlers who loiter around the passenger port, offering to help you buy tickets and port tax, carry luggage, or simply show you the way. It's best to decline assistance politely, as some of these men are experts at currency con-tricks or may simply run off with your bag.

The main ships used by visitors between Dar es Salaam and Zanzibar are:

Flying Horse This is a large catamaran, with a capacity of more than 400 passengers, running once every day in each direction between Zanzibar and Dar. The daytime service

TO ZANZIBAR BY DHOW

Until the end of the 1980s, for anyone who couldn't afford the airfare, the usual way to reach Zanzibar from Dar was to go by dhow, one of the traditional wooden boats widely used around the coasts of Arabia and East Africa. This was a romantic way to travel, although most of the boats used motors, rather than sails, to make the voyage. Unfortunately, it is now illegal for tourists to travel between Dar and Zanzibar Town in this way (and the port police are strict), although we have heard from a few intrepid travellers who found dhow captains willing to take them from Zanzibar Town back to Dar. Details are given on page 144.

However, if you really want to go by dhow, it is still possible to reach Zanzibar by sailing from Tanga, a port on the mainland about 250km (156 miles) north of Dar. Some dhows also occasionally go from Bagamoyo, in between Dar and Tanga. Many of the dhows from Tanga and Bagamoyo actually go to Pemba Island, rather than Zanzibar Island (Unguja), but once on Pemba you can easily get to Zanzibar Town on one of the regular ships. More details are given on page 234.

Whichever way you go, if you are searching for that authentic East African sailing-boat experience, this is where you'll find it, although these days passengers (tourists and locals) are not allowed on any dhow travelling under sail, only on boats with motors. The lack of sails may shatter your romantic illusions but, for many people, 'the dhow experience' is still a bit too authentic and not an option for the faint-hearted. Many dhows tend to be dangerously overloaded, and a small boat riding low in a rough sea can be very frightening. The roll is considerable and many people suffer from seasickness. On top of this, motors are installed with no exhaust outlet pipes, and the stench of fumes coming up through the floorboards doesn't do much to calm weak stomachs. And, for when things get really bad, the toilet is a 'captain's chair' hanging out over the rail, usually in full view of the rest of the passengers.

Journeys between the mainland and Zanzibar can take more than two days. You need to bring all your own food and water. Horror stories, involving leaky boats, engine failures, drunken sailors and even shipwrecks, are regularly told on the travellers' grapevine.

from Dar to Zanzibar departs at 12.30 and arrives at 15.30. The trip from Zanzibar departs at 22.00 and arrives in Dar at 06.00 – the boat runs deliberately slowly on this overnight journey so passengers don't have to board or leave the boat in the middle of the night. All tickets cost US$20, and include a mattress for the overnight service. The seating areas are air conditioned, and an 'in-flight' video is usually shown. The ship also has a small bar and restaurant. It's possible to travel on the deck, which has a few seats and an awning to keep off the sun, but little else. However, it is a very pleasant way to travel, especially when you come into Zanzibar port at sunset.

Sea Express A large hydrofoil with a capacity of 150 passengers, travels between Dar and Zanzibar once per day in each direction. The journey takes 90 minutes. Departures from Dar are at 07.30, from Zanzibar 16.00. Tickets are US$30 plus tax. These boats are reported to be unsteady in rough seas, and seasick-bags are not provided! There is no deck-space either.

Azizah I and *Azizah II* Pride of the fleet is *Azizah I*, which sails five times weekly between Dar and Zanzibar. On the Dar to Zanzibar leg this boat departs in the morning and arrives in the evening. Going the other way it's an overnight trip. The journey time is between five and eight hours. Each week, usually over the weekend, the service is extended to Pemba, and *Azizah II* is brought into service at busy times. The fares are: Dar–Zanzibar US$15, Zanzibar–Dar US$15; Zanzibar–Pemba US$15; all plus port tax.

Seastar This large catamaran runs between Dar and Zanzibar. It departs Zanzibar at 07.00, arrives Dar at 09.00. Then departs Dar at 10.30 and arrives back at 12.30. The timetable is the same every day, except Sunday, when the captain has a lie-in and all times are an hour later. Tickets cost US$30 plus tax.

Seabus I and **Seabus II** These are two large Australian-built high-speed boats, running once per day between Zanzibar and Dar (with an extra service in high season), taking about two hours to make the crossing. Departures from Zanzibar are 13.30, arriving Dar at 15.30. From Dar, departure is at 16.00, arriving Zanzibar at 18.00. First-class tickets cost US$40, second-class US$35, children US$20, including tax.

Mapinduzi Zanzibar Shipping Corporation (ZSC), the state-owned line, run the *Mapinduzi* ('Revolution'), an old cargo-passenger ship, between Dar and Zanzibar, and also between Zanzibar and Pemba, and Dar and Mtwara on the southern coast of mainland Tanzania. These services are used by local people because they are cheap, and some travellers on a tight budget also travel this way. The fare is around US$5 for a place on the deck, US$10 for a bed in a shared cabin, and US$12 for a bed in a private cabin. Although the boats are slow, the cabins are quite airy and comfortable, and this is a pleasant way to travel if you're in no hurry. The official schedule, which follows a two-week pattern, is as follows:

Depart Zanzibar Fri pm, arrive Pemba Sat am;
Depart Pemba Sun am, arrive Zanzibar Sun pm;
Depart Zanzibar Sun pm, arrive Dar Mon am;
Depart Dar Wed pm, arrive Mtwara Thu am;
Depart Mtwara Fri pm, arrive Dar Sat am;
Depart Dar Sat pm, arrive Zanzibar Mon am

This timetable, admittedly, looks vague. In reality, the actual service is even worse. The *Mapinduzi* is notoriously unreliable and often runs many hours, or even days, late. Even the booking clerks in the ZSC office in Dar advise visitors to take one of the other ships to Zanzibar.

Canadian Spirit A final option for reaching Zanzibar might be the *Canadian Spirit* – a large cargo ship which sometimes steams up and down the Tanzania coast between Dar and Mtwara (in southern Tanzania) about once a week, via Zanzibar and Mafia Island. When we were researching this book, the service had been suspended. It may recommence though, or another ship might start covering the same route, but it's only worth persevering with this if you want to reach Mafia without flying or get to/from the far south of Tanzania while avoiding the cost of a plane fare or the long bus journey.

Local boats
Intrepid travellers have managed to reach Pemba Island by dhow from the port of Tanga, on the Tanzanian coast, in between Dar es Salaam and Mombasa (Kenya). For more details see the *Getting there* section of *Chapter 7 – Pemba Island* (page 231).

Another option is to get to the small town of Pangani, about 50km south of Tanga. Here, you can hire the motorised boat belonging to a boatman associated with the New River View Lodge in Pangani. To Nungwi on the north of Zanzibar Island, a trip of roughly three hours, will cost about US$60 for a private charter.

ARRIVING AND LEAVING
Arrival at Zanzibar
If you fly into Zanzibar, the main airport is on the outskirts of Zanzibar Town. If you travel by ship from Dar you arrive at the main port in Zanzibar Town. The

customs and immigration officials on Zanzibar used to have a reputation for toughness. Today, at the airport and main port, arrival formalities are fairly quick and not too strenuous, although they are somewhat disorganised.

You will be required to complete an immigration card and you may have to show your yellow fever certificate (for more details see *Entry regulations* – next section). You will also have to show your passport and Tanzanian visa. These formalities are required even if you have arrived from mainland Tanzania (remember that Zanzibar is a separate state within Tanzania). The same applies if you come into Zanzibar Town by ship from Pemba, although if you arrive from Pemba by air there are usually no formalities to worry about.

Arriving from Europe, Kenya or elsewhere, you will be asked how long you want to stay (two to four weeks is usual, and creates no problem), and then given a Zanzibar stamp in your passport. The customs officials may want to check your bag, but a detailed search is unlikely.

You are not allowed to import or export Tanzanian shillings, unless you are travelling to or from mainland Tanzania. There are no other currency regulations at present, which means you can import or export as much foreign ('hard') currency as you like.

Leaving Zanzibar

All the planes and ships to Zanzibar described in the sections above of course go the other way, and can be used to leave Zanzibar as well. Single fares on most routes are the same in either direction. For more details on the airlines, shipping companies and travel agents, see the *Zanzibar Town* chapter, pages 141–3.

If you are including Pemba in your visit, you may be able to leave this island and get to Mombasa or Tanga by ship or dhow, without having to come back to Zanzibar Island (see page 234).

When you leave Zanzibar Town, by air or sea, formalities at the airport and port are fairly straightforward. You will be given a departure card, which you need to fill in, even if you are going to mainland Tanzania. You must also show your passport to prove you have not overstayed, and your bags may be checked. Some travellers have reported that the customs officials may ask for 'presents' while checking through your belongings. If this happens to you, a polite but firm (and maybe loud and indignant) refusal is all that's required to fend off such unwanted interest.

Many travellers report problems at the port from the porters eager to carry your bags, and from touts who try to persuade you to buy ship tickets from one of the four or five different shipping company ticket booths. The way to get round hassle with buying tickets is to come the day before you travel (or even earlier) and buy your ticket without having to worry about watching your bags or hurrying for a boat. You could also use the services of a tour company to buy the ticket for you. Avoiding the porters (unless of course you want their help) is harder. If you walk in through the port gates already carrying your own backpack you're unlikely to be bothered by porters. But if you drive in by taxi, it will instantly be surrounded by a crowd of eager hopefuls all begging for work. You might want to ask your taxi driver to act as porter too, for an extra tip. Alternatively, you might just employ the services of a porter – it will cost no more than US$1.50.

Also watch out at the port for con tricks involving tickets – see the box for more information.

A small problem about leaving Zanzibar by air on a large international flight is the check-in system at the airport. Even though there is a large departure hall behind the check-in desks, passengers are required to queue outside the hall, under the African sun. The queues tend to be long and the check-in process slow, so be

TICKET SCAMS

Some shoestring travellers have been approached by baggage porters at the ferry port, and been tempted into buying ferry tickets at the (cheaper) residents' rate, rather than the foreigners' rate. The porter offers to buy the ticket for you, then accompanies you on to the boat, explaining to 'their friend' the ticket collector about your temporary residential status. Then, once you're on board the porter asks for (or demands) a tip – which is often more than the foreigners' ticket price. If you resist, you get reported to the no-longer-friendly ticket collector, who demands that you pay a costly fine. Resist that, and they'll call the police, who will no doubt be keen to extract their own, even more costly, fine. So you end up paying the porter more than the normal ferry price, and feeling cheap and embarrassed into the bargain.

Now it's our turn for a tip: always pay the correct fare.

prepared for a hot and frustrating wait. If you use the services of a good tour company, they can usually arrange for a member of staff to handle check-in for you, so at least you can wait in the shade.

If you're leaving Zanzibar by air for Kenya, or elsewhere beyond Tanzania, the airport has a pleasant little terrace restaurant where you can spend the last of your Tanzanian shillings as you wait for your flight.

Departure taxes

Warning All passengers have to pay a departure tax of US$20 when flying out of Zanzibar airport on international flights. This is payable in US dollars, cash; local currency is not acceptable. Travellers' cheques and other hard currencies are also not accepted, although you can change these into cash dollars at the airport bureau de change. Many departing tourists get caught by this rule, and often end up changing more than they need at a poor rate, just before departing. Even if all the rest of your money is in travellers' cheques, pounds or any other currency, it is well worth keeping a US$20 bill specifically to pay the airport tax.

For domestic flights, from Zanzibar to Dar or Pemba, the airport tax is around US$3 to US$5, payable in Tanzanian shillings.

Before you pay anything, especially if you've come to Zanzibar on an international return flight, check that the US$20 tax payment isn't already included in your ticket price (even better, check what taxes are included when you buy your ticket). If you are flying to Dar to pick up an international flight, you need only pay the international departure tax once (probably at Dar), and pay the domestic flight rate at Zanzibar.

Even ship passengers cannot escape departure tax! All tourists leaving by boat from Zanzibar are charged a US$5 'seaport departure service charge'. This is also payable in dollars only, but many of the ship companies include this tax in the ticket price. Check this carefully to avoid paying port tax twice.

ENTRY REGULATIONS

All non-Tanzanian visitors to Zanzibar need a passport, valid for the duration of their stay. Zanzibar is part of Tanzania and most foreigners entering the country need a visa or visitor's pass, depending on their own nationality. Visas and visitors' passes cannot always be issued at a point of entry, so you may need to apply in advance to your nearest Tanzanian Embassy or High Commission. A charge is usually made for issuing a visa. Costs range from US$20 to US$50 (£38 in the UK) depending on your nationality. If you are planning to reach Zanzibar via Nairobi or Mombasa, you may also need a visa or visitor's pass for Kenya. Again, this depends on your own nationality.

Officially, to visit Zanzibar, there is no need for a yellow fever vaccination and the certificate to prove you've had it. This requirement was dropped by Tanzanian health authorities in 2001, and strictly covers the whole country. (This vaccination is now only required if you come from a country where yellow fever is endemic.) However, in reality, tourists arriving by air at Zanzibar in 2002 were still being asked to show yellow fever certificates. The reasons for this are unclear. It could be that the immigration staff at the airport had not been informed about the new regulations, or it could be a way for Zanzibar to partake in a little gentle muscle-flexing to show it's a separate state from the mainland, and will make its own decisions when it comes to entry requirements. That said, the vaccination is strongly advised for travel to Zanzibar anyway. More details on vaccinations are given in the following *Health* section.

You may also need a return ticket out of Tanzania or Kenya, or be required to show that you have sufficient funds to cover your stay. (Other currency matters are covered on pages 98–100.)

Entry regulations are always liable to change, so you should make enquiries at your nearest Tanzania diplomatic representative (embassy or high commission) or tourist office before you leave. As visas can take several weeks to issue, you should do this well in advance of your planned travel date.

Visitors from the UK can make enquiries at:
Tanzania High Commission 43 Hertford St, London W1Y 7FF; tel: 020 7499 8951; fax: 020 7491 9321; web: www.tanzania-online.gov.uk. You can download a visa application form from this website, and send it off to the High Commission along with your fee, two passport photos, and an envelope for return. The process takes a week by post. If you want to visit the High Commission in London in person, you can pay for the visa only in cash; cards, cheques or postal orders are not accepted.
Tanzania Tourist Board Tanzania Trade Centre, 78–80 Borough High St, London SE1; tel: 020 7407 0566; fax: 7403 2003.
Zanzibar Travel Reynards House, Selkirk Gardens, Cheltenham GL52 5LY; tel/fax: 01242 222027; email: info@zanzibartravel.co.uk; web: www.zanzibartravel.co.uk. This commercial organisation works with the Zanzibar Commission for Tourism, and can deal with general tourism enquiries, as well as help you make booking for hotels, tours, etc.

Visitors from the USA should contact:
Tanzanian Embassy 2139 R St, NW, Washington DC 20008; tel: (202) 939 6125.
Tanzania Tourist Board The Bradford Group, 347 Fifth Av (suite 610), New York, NY 10016; tel: (212) 447-0027; fax: (212) 725-8253; email: tanzania@bradfordmarketing.org; web: www.tanzania-web.com. The Bradford Group is the marketing and public relations arm for Tanzania in the USA. This company stocks brochures on Tanzania that include a few pages on Zanzibar, and may be able to help with enquiries. This is not a travel agency or tour operator.

HEALTH
with Dr Felicity Nicholson and Dr Jane Wilson-Howarth
Before you go
Immunisations
All visitors to Tanzania (including Zanzibar) must be vaccinated against **yellow fever** provided that it is deemed suitable. If the vaccine is contraindicated then you are advised to carry an exemption certificate, which can be obtained from a

travel clinic. You will almost always be required to show a yellow fever certificate (or exemption certificate) when you enter the country. The certificate is not valid until ten days after your vaccination. Vaccinations for typhoid, **tetanus**, **diphtheria**, **polio**, meningitis and hepatitis A are also generally recommended.

The majority of travellers are advised to have immunisation against **hepatitis A** with hepatitis A vaccine (eg: Havrix Monodose, Avaxim). One dose of vaccine lasts for one year and can be boosted to give protection for up to ten years. The course of two injections costs about £100. It is now felt that the vaccine can be used even close to the time of departure and has replaced the old-fashioned gamma globulin. The newer **typhoid** vaccines last for three years and are about 85% effective. They should be encouraged unless the traveller is leaving within a few days for a trip of a week or less when the vaccine would not be effective in time.

Meningitis vaccine (containing strains ACW and Y) is also recommended, especially for trips of more than four weeks (see *Meningitis*).

Immunisation against **cholera** is considered ineffective in the UK, but a cholera exemption certificate is in theory mandatory for Zanzibar, and should be obtained before departure (you do not have a vaccination for this). Vaccinations for **rabies** are advised for travellers visiting more remote areas (see *Rabies*, page 91). **Hepatitis B** vaccination should be considered for longer trips (two months or more) or for those working in situations where the chance of contact with blood is increased, or with children. Three injections are preferred and can be given over a four-week period prior to travel. Longer schedules are preferred if you go to your doctor in plenty of time. A BCG vaccination against **tuberculosis** (TB) is also advised for trips of two months or more. Ideally, then, you should visit your own doctor or a specialist travel clinic (see below) to discuss your requirements about eight weeks before you plan to travel.

Malaria prevention

There is no vaccine against malaria, but using prophylactic drugs and preventing mosquito bites will considerably reduce the risk of contracting it. Seek professional advice for the best anti-malarial drugs to take. Mefloquine (Lariam) is still the most effective prophylactic agent for Tanzania and Zanzibar. If this drug is suggested and you have never tried it before then you should start at least two and a half weeks before departure to check that it suits you. Stop immediately if it seems to cause depression or anxiety, visual or hearing disturbances, severe headaches or changes in heart rhythm. Anyone who is pregnant, has been treated for depression or psychiatric problems, has diabetes controlled by oral therapy, or who is epileptic (or who has suffered fits in the past) or has a close blood relative who is epileptic should not take mefloquine.

Malarone (proguanil and atovaquone) is a new drug that is almost as effective as mefloquine. It has the advantage of having few side effects and need only be continued for one week after returning. However, it is expensive and because of this tends to be reserved for shorter trips. Malarone may not be suitable for everybody so advice should be taken from a doctor. The antibiotic doxycycline (100mg daily) should be considered when either mefloquine or Malarone are not considered suitable for whatever reason. Like Malarone, it need only be started one day before arrival. It may also be used by travellers with epilepsy, unlike mefloquine, although the anti-epileptic therapy may make it less effective. Users must be warned about the possibility of allergic skin reactions developing in sunlight which can occur in about 3% of people. The drug should be stopped if this happens. Women using the oral contraceptive should use an additional method of protection for the first four weeks when using doxycycline.

Chloroquine and proguanil are no longer considered to be very effective for this area. However, they may still be recommended if no other regime is suitable. All prophylactic agents should be taken with or after the evening meal, washed down with plenty of fluid and, with the exception of Malarone (see above), continued for four weeks after leaving Tanzania/Zanzibar.

Travellers to remote parts may wish to consider carrying a course of malaria treatment. Presently quinine and Fansidar is the favoured regime but check for up-to-date advice on the current recommended treatment. Self-treatment is not without risks and diagnosing malaria may not be easy which is why consulting a doctor as soon as possible is important. Assume that any high fever lasting more than a few hours is malaria regardless of any other symptoms. And remember malaria may occur anything from seven days into the trip to up to one year after leaving Africa. Zanzibar's hospitals and medical centres are listed in the *Zanzibar Town* chapter, page 157.

It's a good idea to have a dental check-up before you go, as local dentists can be painful, expensive, or both.

Travel clinics and health information

A full list of current travel clinic websites worldwide is available on www.istm.org. For other journey preparation information, consult web: ftp://ftp.shoreland.com/pub/shorecg.rtf or www.tripprep.com.

UK

British Airways Travel Clinic and Immunisation Service There are now only three BA clinics, all in London: 156 Regent St, W1B 5LB (no appointments); 101 Cheapside, EC1V6DT (tel: 020 7606 2977); 115 Buckingham Palace Rd, SW1W 9SJ (Victoria Station; tel: 020 7233 6661); see also www.britishairways.com/travelclinics. All sell a variety of health-related goods.

Fleet Street Travel Clinic 29 Fleet St, London EC4Y 1AA; tel: 020 7353 5678

Hospital for Tropical Diseases Travel Clinic Capper St (off Tottenham Ct Rd), London WC1; tel: 020 7388 9600; web: www.thhtd.org. Offers consultations and advice, and is able to provide all necessary drugs and vaccines for travellers. Runs a healthline (tel: 09061 337733) for country-specific information and health hazards. Also stocks nets, water purification equipment and personal protection measures.

MASTA (Medical Advisory Service for Travellers Abroad) Keppel St, London WC1 7HT; tel: 09068 224100. This is a premium-line number, charged at 50p per minute.

NHS travel website www.fitfortravel.scot.nhs.uk provides country-by-country advice on immunisation and malaria, plus details of recent developments, and a list of relevant health organisations.

Nomad Travel Pharmacy and Vaccination Centre 3–4 Wellington Terrace, Turnpike Lane, London N8 0PX; tel: 020 8889 7014; email: sales@nomadtravel.co.uk; web: www.nomadtravel.co.uk. As well as dispensing health advice, Nomad stocks mosquito nets and other anti-bug devices, and an excellent range of adventure travel gear.

Thames Medical 157 Waterloo Rd, London SE1 8US; tel: 020 7902 9000. Competitively priced, one-stop travel health service. All profits go to their affiliated company, InterHealth, which provides health care for overseas workers on Christian projects.

Trailfinders Immunisation Centre 194 Kensington High St, London W8 7RG; tel: 020 7938 3999. Also at 254–284 Sauchiehall St, Glasgow G2 3EH; tel: 0141 353 0066.

Travelpharm The Travelpharm website, www.travelpharm.com, offers up-to-date guidance on travel-related health and has a range of medications available through their online mini-pharmacy.

Irish Republic
Tropical Medical Bureau Grafton Street Medical Centre, Grafton Buildings, 34 Grafton St, Dublin 2; tel: 1 671 9200. Has a useful website specific to tropical destinations: www.tmb.ie

USA
Centers for Disease Control 1600 Clifton Rd, Atlanta, GA 30333; tel: 877 FYI TRIP; 800 311 3435; web: www.cdc.gov/travel. The central source of travel information in the USA. Each summer they publish the invaluable *Health Information for International Travel*, available from the Division of Quarantine at the above address.
Connaught Laboratories PO Box 187, Swiftwater, PA 18370; tel: 800 822 2463. They will send a free list of specialist tropical-medicine physicians in your state.
IAMAT (International Association for Medical Assistance to Travelers) 736 Center St, Lewiston, NY 14092; tel: 716 754 4883. A non-profit organisation that provides lists of English-speaking doctors abroad.

Canada
IAMAT (International Association for Medical Assistance to Travellers) Suite 1, 1287 St Clair Av W, Toronto, Ontario M6E 1B8; tel: 416 652 0137; web: www.sentex.net/~iamat
TMVC (Travel Doctors Group) Sulphur Springs Rd, Ancaster, Ontario; tel: 905 648 1112; web: www.tmvc.com.au

Australia, New Zealand, Thailand
TMVC Tel: 1300 65 88 44; web: www.tmvc.com.au. 20 clinics in Australia, New Zealand and Thailand, including:
Auckland Canterbury Arcade, 170 Queen Street, Auckland City; tel: 373 3531
Brisbane Dr Deborah Mills, Qantas Domestic Building, 6th floor, 247 Adelaide St, Brisbane, QLD 4000; tel: 7 3221 9066; fax: 7 3321 7076
Melbourne Dr Sonny Lau, 393 Little Bourke St, 2nd floor, Melbourne, VIC 3000; tel: 3 9602 5788; fax: 3 9670 8394
Sydney Dr Mandy Hu, Dymocks Building, 7th Floor, 428 George St, Sydney, NSW2000; tel: 2 221 7133; fax: 2 221 8401

South Africa
SAA-Netcare Travel Clinics PO Box 786692, Sandton 2146; fax: 011 883 6152; web: www.travelclinic.co.za or www.malaria.co.za. Clinics throughout South Africa.
TMVC (Travel Doctor Group) 113 DF Malan Dr, Roosevelt Pk, Johannesburg; tel: 011 888 7488; web: www.tmvc.com.au. Consult the website for details of clinics in South Africa.

Switzerland
IAMAT (International Association for Medical Assistance to Travellers) 57 Voirets, 1212 Grand Lancy, Geneva; web: www.sentex.net/~iamat

Common medical problems
When travelling around Zanzibar or East Africa, the different climatic and social conditions mean visitors are exposed to diseases not normally encountered at home. Although you will have received all the vaccinations recommended in the *Before you go* section, this does not mean you will be free of all illness during your travels: certain precautions still have to be taken.

You should read a good book on travel medicine (see *Appendix 1*) and be aware of the causes, symptoms and treatments of the more serious diseases. But don't let these colourful descriptions put you off – with a little care and attention most of these illnesses can be avoided.

Travellers diarrhoea

'What with bad water and worse liquor, the Briton finds it hard to live on Zanzibar.'

Richard Burton, British explorer (1857)

At least half of those travelling to the tropics will suffer from a bout of travellers' diarrhoea during their trip; the newer you are to exotic travel, the more likely you will be to suffer. By taking precautions against travellers' diarrhoea you will also avoid typhoid, cholera, dysentery, worms, etc. Travellers' diarrhoea and the other faeco-oral diseases come from getting other people's faeces in your mouth. This most often happens from cooks not washing their hands after a trip to the toilet. Even if the restaurant cook does not understand basic hygiene you will be safe if your food has been properly cooked and arrives piping hot. The maxim to remind you what you can safely eat is:

PEEL IT, BOIL IT, COOK IT OR FORGET IT.

This means that fruit you have washed and peeled yourself, and hot foods, should be safe, but raw foods, cold cooked foods, salads, fruit salads which have been prepared by others, ice-cream, and ice are all risky. Foods kept lukewarm in hotel buffets are usually dangerous. It is also important to maintain a high standard of personal hygiene: wash your hands after going to the toilet and before eating. It is a good idea to carry antiseptic wipes for the times when water or soap are hard to find.

Water sterilisation

It is much rarer to get sick from drinking contaminated water but it happens, so try to drink from safe sources. At good hotels, clean drinking water will be available. You can also buy bottled water in Zanzibar Town and some other tourist places. If you're off the beaten track or staying in smaller hotels, supplies are not always reliable. Therefore you may need to purify your own water by adding purification tablets (or solution); these are available from any outdoor or travel shop, but not in Zanzibar so get some before you leave home. Before adding the purifying chemicals it might also be worth using a filter bag/bottle to take out larger particles so the tablets or solutions work more effectively. Alternatively, several makes of mini filter pumps are available which do this whole process quickly and easily. Again, these are not available in Zanzibar and should be bought from a good outdoor shop before you leave.

When buying bottled water, you should check the seal around the cap as it is not unknown for discarded bottles to be filled with tap water and sold again. (Don't become nervous and avoid drinking altogether. It is very important to keep up your liquid intake in the hot climate to avoid the headaches caused by mild dehydration. Drink at least three litres a day.)

Treating travellers' diarrhoea

It is dehydration that makes you feel awful during a bout of diarrhoea and the most important part of treatment is drinking lots of clear fluids. Sachets of oral rehydration salts give the perfect biochemical mix to replace all that is pouring out of your bottom! However, any dilute mixture of sugar and salt in water will do you good, so if you like coke or orange squash, drink that with a three-finger pinch of salt added to each glass. Otherwise make a solution of a four-finger scoop of sugar with a three-finger pinch of salt in a glass of water. Alternatively add eight level teaspoons of sugar (18g) and one level teaspoon of salt (3g) to one litre (5 cups) of safe water. A squeeze of lemon or orange juice improves the taste and adds potassium, which is also lost during a bout of diarrhoea. Drink two large glasses after every bowel action and more if you are thirsty. You need to drink three litres a day plus whatever is pouring into the toilet.

It is best to avoid food for 24 hours then eat bland, non-fatty foods for the next two or three days. Also avoid the use of blocking agents such as Lomotil or Imodium, unless you have no access to toilet facilities.

If the diarrhoea is bad, or you are passing blood or slime, or you have a fever, you will probably need antibiotics in addition to the fluid replacement. Try to seek medical advice before starting antibiotics. If this is not possible then a single dose of ciprofloxacin (500mg) repeated after 12 hours may be appropriate. If the diarrhoea is greasy and bulky and is accompanied by sulphurous (eggy) burps the likely cause is giardia. This is best treated with tinidazole (2g in one dose repeated seven days later if symptoms persist).

Meningitis

This is a particularly nasty disease as it can kill within hours of the first symptoms appearing. The telltale symptoms are a combination of a blinding headache (light sensitivity), a blotchy rash and a high fever. Immunisation protects against the most serious bacterial form of meningitis and the tetravalent vaccine (ACWY) is recommended for Tanzania and Zanzibar. Other forms of meningitis exist (usually viral) but there are no vaccines for these. Local papers normally report outbreaks. If you show symptoms go immediately to a doctor.

Rabies

Rabies is carried by all mammals (beware the village dogs and small monkeys that are used to being fed in the parks) and is passed on to man through a bite or a lick of an open wound. You must always assume any animal is rabid (unless personally known to you) and seek medical help as soon as possible.

In the interim, scrub the wound with soap and bottled/boiled water then pour on a strong iodine or alcohol solution. This helps stop the rabies virus entering the body and will guard against wound infections including tetanus.

If you intend to have contact with animals and/or are likely to be more than 24 hours away from medical help, then pre-exposure vaccination is advised. Ideally three doses should be taken over four weeks. Contrary to popular belief, these vaccinations are relatively painless!

If you are exposed as described, then treatment should be given as soon as possible, but it is never too late to seek help as the incubation period for rabies can be very long. Those who have not been immunised will need a full course of injections together with rabies immunoglobulin (RIG), but this product is expensive (around US$800) and may be hard to come by. Another reason why pre-exposure vaccination should be encouraged in travellers who are planning to visit more remote areas!

Tell the doctor if you have had pre-exposure vaccine, as this will change the treatment you receive. Remember if you contract rabies, mortality is 100% and death from rabies is probably one of the worst ways to go.

Malaria

As anti-malaria drugs do not provide complete protection, you should also take steps to avoid being bitten by a mosquito: wear long-sleeved shirts and long trousers, covering wrists and ankles, in the evening when mosquitoes are active. Most hotels have mosquito nets and these should always be used. In cheaper hotels

LONG-HAUL FLIGHTS
Felicity Nicholson
There is growing evidence, albeit circumstantial, that long-haul air travel increases the risk of developing deep vein thrombosis. This condition is potentially life threatening, but it should be stressed that the danger to the average traveller is slight.

Certain risk factors specific to air travel have been identified. These include immobility, compression of the veins at the back of the knee by the edge of the seat, the decreased air pressure and slightly reduced oxygen in the cabin, and dehydration. Consuming alcohol may exacerbate the situation by increasing fluid loss and encouraging immobility.

In theory everyone is at risk, but those at highest risk are shown below:

- Passengers on journeys of longer than eight hours duration
- People over 40
- People with heart disease
- People with cancer
- People with clotting disorders
- People who have had recent surgery, especially on the legs
- Women on the pill or other oestrogen therapy
- Pregnancy
- People who are very tall (over 6ft/1.8m) or short (under 5ft/1.5m)

Deep vein thrombosis (DVT) is a clot of blood that forms in the leg veins. Symptoms include swelling and pain in the calf or thigh. The skin may feel hot

some nets may be broken, so a needle and thread for quick repairs is useful. Or carry your own (see *What to take*, page 94). The nets should also be impregnated with permethrin – if in doubt carry an impregnation kit bought before you leave.

Insect sprays and mosquito coils, which burn slowly through the night, can be bought in shops in Zanzibar Town, but the tubes of repellent to rub on your skin which tend to be very effective (eg: the Repel range containing 50% DEET) are not available. If you need medical attention, there are several hospitals and medical centres in Zanzibar Town. These are listed in the *Zanzibar Town* chapter.

Dengue fever
This mosquito-borne disease may mimic malaria but there is no prophylactic available to deal with it. The mosquitoes that carry this virus bite during the daytime, so it is worth applying repellent if you see them around. Symptoms include strong headaches, rashes and excruciating joint and muscle pains and high fever. Dengue fever only lasts for a week or so and is not usually fatal. Complete rest and paracetamol are the usual treatments. Plenty of fluids also help. Some patients are given an intravenous drip to keep them from dehydrating.

Bilharzia
Bilharzia or schistosomiasis is a common debilitating disease afflicting perhaps 200 million people worldwide. Those most affected are the rural poor of the tropics who repeatedly acquire infections. Infected travellers and expatriates generally suffer fewer problems because symptoms will encourage them to seek prompt treatment and they are also exposed to fewer parasites. But it is still an unpleasant problem, and worth avoiding.

to touch and becomes discoloured (light blue-red). A DVT is not dangerous in itself, but if a clot breaks down then it may travel to the lungs (pulmonary embolus). Symptoms of a pulmonary embolus (PE) include chest pain, shortness of breath and coughing up small amounts of blood.

Symptoms of a DVT rarely occur during the flight, and typically occur within three days of arrival, although symptoms of a DVT or PE have been reported up to two weeks later.

Anyone who suspects that they have these symptoms should see a doctor immediately as anticoagulation (blood thinning) treatment can be given.

Prevention of DVT

General measures to reduce the risk of thrombosis are shown below. This advice also applies to long train or bus journeys.

- Whilst waiting to board the plane, try to walk around rather than sit.
- During the flight drink plenty of water (at least two small glasses every hour).
- Avoid excessive tea, coffee and alcohol.
- Perform leg-stretching exercises, such as pointing the toes up and down.
- Move around the cabin when practicable.

If you fit into the high-risk category (see above) ask your doctor if it is safe to travel. Additional protective measures such as graded compression stockings, aspirin or low molecular weight heparin can be given. No matter how tall you are, where possible request a seat with extra legroom.

When someone with bilharzia excretes into fresh water, the eggs hatch and swim off to find a pond snail to infest. They develop inside the snail to emerge as torpedo-shaped cercariae, barely visible to the naked eye but able to digest their way through human or animal skin. This is the stage at which it attacks people as they wade, bathe or shower in infested water. The snails which harbour bilharzia are a centimetre or more long and live in still or slow-moving fresh water which is well oxygenated and contains edible vegetation (water-weed, reeds). The risk is greatest where local people use the water, bearing in mind that wind can disperse cercariae a few hundred metres from where they entered the water. Wading in slow-moving, reed-fringed water near a village thus carries a very high risk of acquiring bilharzia, while swimming in a rocky pool below a waterfall in a forest carries a negligible one.

Water that has been filtered or stored snail-free for two days is safe, as is water that has been boiled or treated with Cresol or Dettol. Some protection is afforded by applying an oily insect repellent like DEET to your skin before swimming or paddling.

Cercariae live for up to 30 hours after they have been shed by snails, but the older they are, the less vigorous they are, and the less capable they are of penetrating skin. Cercariae are shed in the greatest numbers between 11.00 and 15.00 hours. If water to be used for bathing is pumped early in the morning from deep in the lake (cercariae are sun-loving) or from a site far from where people excrete there will be less risk of infestation. Swimming in the afternoon is riskier than in the early morning. Since cercariae take perhaps ten to 15 minutes to penetrate, a quick shower or a splash across a river followed by thorough drying with a towel should be safe. Even if you are in risky water longer, towelling off vigorously after bathing will kill any cercariae in the process of penetrating your skin. Only a proportion of those cercariae which penetrate the skin survive to cause disease. The absence of early symptoms does not necessarily mean there is no infection, but symptoms usually appear two or more weeks after penetration: typically a fever and wheezy cough. A blood test, which should be taken six weeks or more after likely exposure, will determine whether or not parasites are going to cause problems. Treatment is generally effective, but failures occur and re-treatment is often necessary for reasons that aren't fully understood, but which may imply some drug resistance. Since bilharzia can be a nasty illness, avoidance is better than waiting to be cured and it is wise to avoid bathing in high-risk areas.

Jiggers or sandfleas

These latch on if you walk barefoot in contaminated places, and set up home under the skin of the foot, usually at the side of a toenail, where they cause a painful, boil-like swelling. They need picking out by a local expert; if the distended flea bursts during eviction, the wound should be dowsed in spirit, alcohol or kerosene, or more jiggers will infest you.

SAFETY

Crime of any sort is rare in the rural areas of Zanzibar Island and on Pemba Island, but unfortunately it is on the increase in some parts of Zanzibar Town. A few pickpockets operate in the main market, and some tourists have had bags and cameras snatched while walking around the narrow streets of the Old Town. (For more specific details on places to be careful, see the *Zanzibar Town* chapter.) There have also been attacks and robberies on some of the beaches around Zanzibar Town; it is better not to go there alone, especially at night. There will always be a large financial gap between tourists and local people, but you can reduce the chances of having anything stolen by not displaying your wealth. Keep your valuables secure and out of sight in a pouch under your shirt or inside your trousers. Keep most of your money there too, and do not peel off notes from a huge wad for every small purchase. Wandering around the town with a camera or personal stereo casually slung over your shoulder is insensitive and simply asking for trouble. A simple, dull-looking bag is much less attractive than something brightly coloured and fashionable. Theft from hotel rooms is unusual. Most hotels have safes, where valuables can be stored, but in a few small hotels there have been reports of stuff disappearing even from the safe. For more details see the *Zanzibar Town* chapter.

WHAT TO TAKE
Clothing

You are unlikely to experience great extremes of temperature on Zanzibar, although days can be very warm and some nights chilly. Clothing should be light and loose-fitting for daytime, and you may need something slightly more substantial for evenings. Even in the dry seasons, a rain jacket is a good idea (though you may not need it). Umbrellas (should you need them) are available locally. You'll need a good pair of shoes for sightseeing, and a pair of sandals for relaxing. A hat to keep off sun and rain completes the outfit.

Plastic beach shoes, rafting sandals, or something similar to avoid the spiky sea-urchins, are useful for walking out into the sea across old coral beds. (Remember, though, never to tread on live coral. In a few seconds you can break off chunks which will take several decades to re-grow.)

Dress codes are very relaxed, even in the smartest hotels and restaurants, so you won't need black tie or ball gown. However, for wandering around towns and villages you should be aware of local Muslim sensibilities and not expose too much bare flesh. As visitors, we have absolutely no right to impose our attitudes on the local people, who are always dressed modestly. Remember that walking around a Zanzibar town with your shoulders and most of your legs bare is almost like being naked in your own high street back home.

Of course, tourists don't need to don robes, veils and turbans, but around town it is important for women to have knees and shoulders covered. This is recommended for men too. Therefore, for men and women, long trousers are better than shorts, although baggy surf-shorts or culottes are acceptable. Many women find skirts more comfortable than trousers. For men and women, long-sleeved shirts and blouses are better than vests and skimpy T-shirts. For the beach, normal swimming gear is fine, although going into local fishing villages in briefs or bikinis shows a complete lack of sensitivity.

Equipment

If you're planning to base yourself in one place during your stay, or have all your transfers arranged, then carrying your stuff in a **suitcase** or **kitbag** is absolutely fine. If you're likely to have to carry your own luggage, particularly if you're travelling or backpacking and visiting Zanzibar as part of a longer trip, then it is usually easier to carry all your clothing and equipment in a **rucksack.**

Old-fashioned rucksacks with external frames are bulky, and liable to break on planes and buses, and thus not recommended. Much better are rucksacks with internal frames, or the rucksacks that turn neatly into travel bags, with a zipped flap to enclose the straps and waist-belt. These convertible bags are ideal if you've got to carry your kit for any distance, but also look smart enough to be acceptable in up-market hotels. Another advantage is that with the straps zipped away, they don't get damaged on bus roof-racks or airport carousels.

If you're staying in the cheaper hotels, sheets are not always very clean, so a light **sheet sleeping bag** is useful. It's unlikely you'll need a sleeping bag, and if you do hit Zanzibar in a cold patch, most smaller hotels provide blankets. Most of the larger hotels have good facilities including clean bed linen and blankets or bed covers which you'll need if the air conditioning is full on.

It is important to protect yourself from mosquitoes, to avoid getting malaria. Most hotels provide nets over the beds, but in the smaller cheaper hotels some nets are in bad condition, with holes big enough to let small birds through, let alone the odd mosquito. Either take your own **mosquito net** (some excellent portable models are available in good outdoor equipment shops), or take safety pins or needle and cotton to make running repairs. For more protection take a roll-on **insect repellent** or use mosquito coils (available locally) in your room at night. Remember, it only takes one pesky mozzie to spoil your night's sleep and maybe spoil your whole holiday by giving you malaria.

For budget travellers, or those who prefer the outdoor life, camping on Zanzibar is not really an option, so it's probably not worth bringing a tent. There are no official campsites anywhere on Zanzibar. Although camping is possible on the beaches, near the low-budget hotels, this is not the general practice as the hotels are cheap anyway and security for campers cannot always be guaranteed.

Personal items include toiletries, lipsalve, sun protection cream and sunglasses. Soap, toothpaste and medicines can be bought locally if you run out. Suncream is also available in some hotel shops, but it's expensive, so bring all you need. All but the cheapest hotels provide towels.

You'll almost certainly be bringing a **camera**. Make sure you bring spare batteries and enough film (although straightforward print film can be bought in

PHOTOGRAPHIC TIPS
Ariadne Van Zandbergen
Zanzibar doesn't offer the possibilities for wildlife photography that exist on mainland Tanzania, but the Swahili culture combined with the idyllic Indian Ocean beach scenes create some stunning photographic opportunities.

Equipment
The simpler the camera, the less there is to go wrong. For landscapes and portraits, a solidly built manual-focus camera will be adequate and can be bought cheaply secondhand. An auto-focus camera will, however, focus with greater precision than any person can hope to, and is particularly useful for moving objects. If you carry only one lens in Zanzibar, a 28–70 or similar zoom should be ideal. For a second lens, a lightweight 80–200 or 70–300 or similar will be excellent for candid shots, monkeys and varying your composition.

Film
Print film is the preference of most casual photographers; slide film of professionals and some serious amateurs. You should definitely use slide film if you hope to have anything published. Slide film is more expensive than print film, but development costs are cheaper.

Most serious photographers working outdoors in Africa favour Fujichrome slide film, in particular Sensia 100, Provia 100 (the professional equivalent to Sensia) or Velvia 50. Slow films (ie: those with a low ASA or ISO rating) produce less grainy and sharper images than fast films, but can be tricky without a tripod in low light. Velvia 50 is extremely fine-grained and shows stunning colour saturation; it is a good film to use in soft, even light or overcast weather. Sensia or Provia may be preferable in low light, since 100 ASA allows you to work at a faster shutter speed than 50 ASA. Because 100 ASA is more tolerant of contrast, it is also preferable in harsh light.

For print photography, a combination of 100 or 200 ASA film should be ideal. For the best results, stick to recognised brands. Fujicolor produces excellent print films, with the Superia 100 and 200 recommended.

Some basics
The automatic programmes provided with many cameras are limited in the sense that the camera cannot think, but only make calculations. A better investment than any amount of electronic wizardry would be to buy or borrow a photographic manual for beginners and get to grips with such basics as the relationship between aperture and shutter speed.

Beginners should note that a low shutter speed can result in camera shake and a blurred image. For hand-held photographs of static subjects using a low magnification lens (eg: 28–70), select a shutter speed of at least 1/60th of a second. For lenses of higher magnification, the shutter speed should be at least the inverse of the magnification (eg: a speed of 1/300 or faster on a 300 magnification lens). You can use lower shutter speeds with a tripod.

Zanzibar Town, and from some big hotels on the coast). For more information on cameras and photography, see above.

A **first-aid and medical kit** is recommended, but what you need depends on your type of holiday, the amount of travel, and how far you plan to get off the

Most modern cameras include a built-in light meter, with the choice of three types of metering: matrix, centre-weighted or spot metering. Built-in light meters are usually reliable, but in uneven light, or where there is a lot of sky, you may want to take your metering selectively, perhaps by taking a spot reading on the main subject. As the meter will tend to under- or overexpose when pointed at an almost white or black subject, take a reading against an 18% grey card, or a substitute such as grass or light grey rocks – basically anything that isn't almost black, almost white or highly reflective.

Auto focus is more reliable than manual focus, but can instil a tendency to place the subject at the centre of the frame. A more interesting image will normally be obtained if the subject is at least slightly off-centre; this can be achieved by focusing on the main subject, then holding the focus down while moving the camera to adjust the framing.

Dust and heat
Dust and heat are constant problems in Africa. Keep your equipment in a sealed bag, stow films in an airtight container (such as a small cooler bag), leave used films in your hotel room, and avoid changing film in dusty conditions. On rough roads, carry your equipment on your lap to protect against vibration and bumps. Never stow camera equipment or film in a car boot/trunk (where it will bake), or let it stand in direct sunlight.

Light
The light in Africa is much harsher than in Europe or North America, so the most striking outdoor photographs are often taken during the hour or two of 'golden light' after dawn and before sunset. Shooting in low light may enforce the use of very low shutter speeds, in which case a tripod (ideally) or monopod (lighter) will be required. Be alert to the long shadows cast by a low sun; these show up more on photographs than to the naked eye.

Although side lighting and backlighting can produce stunning effects, it is generally best to shoot with the sun behind you. Most buildings and landscapes are therefore a 'morning' or 'afternoon shot', depending on the direction in which they face, so time your shots accordingly.

In the harsh midday sun, images taken in light but even shade are likely to look nicer than those taken in direct sunlight or patchy shade, but do avoid photographing a shaded subject against a sunlit background, which also creates severe contrast. Fill-in flash is almost essential if you want to capture the facial detail of dark-skinned people in harsh or contrasty light.

Protocol
Except in general streets, do not photograph the Swahili people without permission. Many traditionally dressed people will refuse to be photographed; others will agree for a payment. Even the most willing subject may pose stiffly when a camera is pointed at them; relax them by making a joke, and take a few shots in quick succession to improve the odds of capturing a natural pose.

beaten track. Whatever, you should include sticking plasters (some waterproof), antiseptic cream, antihistamine, tubigrip bandages, aspirin or paracetamol and anti-diarrhoea pills. Oil of cloves for toothache is useful, or you can just chew on a local clove bud. More elaborate medicines, if you need them, are available from the private hospitals in Zanzibar (see page 157). Remember to bring adequate supplies of any personal medication you may need. Many travellers also carry an 'anti-AIDS' kit (a pack of needles, syringes and other items which come into contact with blood) for use in an emergency. Your doctor or a vaccination centre can provide more information.

If you're staying in the smaller cheaper hotels, the following items will be useful:

Torch/flashlight Power cuts are not infrequent in the towns, and the smaller beach hotels have generators that only run for a few hours each night.

Water bottle and purification tablets Water supplies in towns are not always drinkable, and wells at the beach and in rural areas are shallow and can often be contaminated (purification works more effectively if you filter the water first).

Universal sink plug Plugs always seem to be missing from all but the best hotels.

Snorkelling gear Some readers have written to us complaining about the expense of hiring snorkelling gear, and about the poor quality of many of the masks available. If you're keen on snorkelling (and Zanzibar offers some of the best in the world) it might be worth taking your own snorkelling mask, or even a full set of gear, with you.

Documents

As well as your **passport** and **visa** (see page 85), you *may* need a **health certificate** to show you've been vaccinated against yellow fever (see page 86) and a cholera-exemption certificate. If you intend hiring a car or motorbike, you'll also need an **International Driving Permit** (IDP), as ordinary national driving licences are not recognised in Zanzibar. It's easy to get an IDP from your national motoring association (in Britain contact the AA); you just need to show your current national licence. The cost is minimal, but you need two passport photos.

MONEY AND BANKING
Currency

Tanzania's unit of currency is the Tanzania shilling (TSh), and this is used throughout Zanzibar. Exchange rates given on page 5 are likely to fluctuate, and prices generally are likely to increase as Zanzibar becomes a more popular tourist destination and the number of visitors to the islands grows.

Non-Tanzanians in Zanzibar have to pay for some items, such as air flights, ship tickets and hotels, in foreign currency. US dollars are most readily accepted and the easiest to deal with. The prices of many other items, such as tours or rental cars, are often quoted in dollars, although these are also payable in TSh at the current rate. In this book, the prices of many items are quoted in US dollars, as these prices are less likely to become out of date.

For visitors to Zanzibar, without doubt the most convenient currency to use is US dollars (as it is in most parts of eastern or southern Africa). Ideally, this should be carried in a combination of cash and travellers' cheques (TCs), and a mix of high and low denominations. Cash is handy as it can be used almost anywhere, and gets you better rates at bureaux de change. TCs are more secure (as they can be replaced if stolen), and well-known brands are more readily accepted and tend to be processed faster. However, in Zanzibar, TCs often attract very poor rates compared to cash, or may not be accepted by some hotels, and so for convenience many visitors prefer to carry US dollars only. You have to weigh up the risk over the convenience, and decide what's best for your own type of travel. (Note also that if you want to change US dollar TCs into US dollars cash, you have to go into TSh and out again, at poor rates both ways!)

Changing money

Many of Zanzibar's currency regulations that restricted visitors in the past were lifted in the mid-1990s. Currency declaration forms are not used, and it is no longer necessary to change a certain amount of money for each day of your visit. Basically, you only have to change as much as you need.

In Zanzibar, the easiest place to change money is Zanzibar Town, where there are banks and many bureaux de change (see *Chapter 5*). It is also possible to change money in Chake Chake on Pemba (see *Chapter 7*). Around Zanzibar Island, money can also be changed at most large and medium sized hotels – although sometimes here the rates are not so good. Several tour companies are also licensed to change money.

Both banks and bureaux de change offer tourists 'free market rates', which means the rates are not artificially fixed (and therefore usually good for tourists). Generally, the banks offer better rates for travellers' cheques and the private bureaux offer better rates for cash, particularly for large denomination bills. The change bureaux also tend to have a faster service. Banks and bureaux accept most foreign currencies, but staff are most familiar with US dollars, and these get relatively higher rates than other hard currencies. You may want to shop around if you've got the time and inclination.

Try not to change more than you need into Tanzanian shillings (TSh), as it can sometimes be difficult changing this back into hard currency. The bank often just refuses to do it (or will only accept money that you have already exchanged at the People's Bank of Zanzibar, not money changed at banks on the Tanzanian mainland), and private change bureaux may offer poor rates or not have foreign currency available. When calculating the amount of money you need to change into TSh, remember that many items, such as the larger hotels, car hire and air tickets, are payable in hard currency only (usually US dollars). Many other items, such as bike hire, boat trips and souvenirs, can also be paid for with US dollars.

Credit cards

You can pay for many items such as tours, mid-range and upmarket hotels and air tickets with a credit card (or with a debit card), but you may be charged a high commission (usually 10–20%). Drawing cash may also be possible through hotels and tour companies, but once again high commissions are charged, or poor rates given. The official reason for the charges is that Zanzibar is not hooked up to any international electronic card validation process, and staff have to make telephone calls (sometimes to the card's country of origin) to get authorisation before the card can be accepted. In reality, it's because plastic is still pretty new on Zanzibar, and most people still prefer to deal in tangible cash! (More information on credit and debit cards is given under *Payments and reservations* in *Accommodation*, page 102). For Visa card holders there's an Assistance Point at the office of Coastal Travels and Mtoni Marine Centre near the Serena Hotel in Zanzibar Town. This is not a bank or bureau, though: it issues only relatively small amounts of cash against a card in cases of emergency, and the exchange rates are still poor compared to cash or travellers' cheques.

The black market

It is possible to change money on the black market, ie: unofficially. There used to be a very high demand for US dollars in Zanzibar, and visitors could get several times more than the official bank rate by changing 'on the black'. However, since currency forms were abolished and free market exchange rates introduced, the black market demand has diminished considerably, and almost disappeared, although some black market dealers will still give you more than the bank or bureau rate.

If you do decide to change on the black market, remember that you are depriving a developing country of its income. Remember, too, that unofficial dealing is highly illegal. Never change in the open, and beware of con-artists and police informers.

Costs

The cost of a visit to Zanzibar depends very much on your standard of travel. At the bottom line, the cheapest hotels cost between US$5 and US$10 a night, per person. If you have meals in local eating-houses, supplemented by lunches of fruit and bread from the market, plus tea or soft drinks, food will cost another US$5 to US$10 a day. Hotels in the middle range cost between US$20 and US$50 for a double, and meals in smarter restaurants cost the equivalent of around US$10 per person. Towards the top of the range, good quality hotels are upwards of US$60 to US$100 for a double, with meals in the best establishments from around US$20.

You also need to take into account the costs of getting around. Buses are very cheap, costing the equivalent of only a few dollars to cross the island. For independent travel, you can hire bicycles for around US$5 per day, motor-scooters for US$25 or cars from around US$40.

Organised tours of the spice plantations or boat trips out to the smaller islands start from about US$10 per person for a small group. If you want a vehicle or boat to yourself this can go up to about US$50 for a day's outing. Entry to most of the historical sites and ruins on the island is free, as is lying on the beach!

GETTING AROUND

This section gives a general impression of what you can expect. It was correct when we went to press, but remember that road conditions and transport facilities are likely to have changed by the time you get to Zanzibar. New bus services may have been introduced, and new car hire facilities opened. Some roads will have been repaired or newly surfaced, while others will have fallen into disrepair. Be ready for these changes when using this information and your visit will go more smoothly.

Bus and dala-dala

For independent travellers, local buses, minibuses and small pick-up vans called dala-dalas link Zanzibar Town with several of the smaller towns and villages around Zanzibar Island. On Pemba, minibuses and dala-dalas link Chake Chake to the towns of Wete and Mkoani, and also serve outlying villages. Minibuses and dala-dalas are faster than buses, and gradually replacing them on the roads. Fares are cheap: it costs around US$1 to cross Zanzibar Island.

Buses and dalas-dalas from outlying villages heading for Zanzibar Town tend to leave very early in the morning but, apart from that, there are no fixed timetables: most vehicles simply leave when they're full. At any bus or dala-dala station, don't expect an information board: you will need to ask around to find the transport you need.

Tourist minibus

Most independent travellers go from Zanzibar Town to one of the beaches in a minibus organised by the papaasi (touts) who meet incoming ships and lurk at budget hotels looking for custom. A ride in one of these vehicles is much quicker than the bus and costs US$3–5. They usually pick you up from your hotel and drop you at any of the hotels on the southern part of the east coast, or at Nungwi. As other parts of the coast become more popular, similar services may start operating there.

If dealing with the *papaasi* is not your scene, most tour companies can arrange private transfers from Zanzibar Town to any point on the island. Rates start at about US$50 for a car or minibus.

Rental car, motorbike or bicycle

It is possible to tour Zanzibar Island by rented car, motorbike or motor-scooter: there are several hotels and agencies in Zanzibar Town where this can be arranged. Bicycles can also be hired in Zanzibar Town, on the east coast beaches and in a few places on Pemba.

Warning If you hire a car, scooter or motorbike it is essential that you have an International Driving Permit (IDP), valid for cars and/or motorcycles as appropriate. Your own national driving licence is not enough. There are several police checkpoints on the roads between Zanzibar Town and the north and east coasts, which are normally no problem at all, but the officers are very hot on checking for IDPs. Beware of eager tour companies who are keen to rent you a car and say that IDPs are not essential. Also watch out for a scam where local *papaasi* rent you a motorbike without an IDP on the pretext that they are not required, then grass you to the police, who then find you and fine you, and split the proceeds with the informant!

ACCOMMODATION

For tourists in Zanzibar, the accommodation and food available are probably the most important aspects of a visit. This section describes briefly what you can expect, but at the time of writing (2002), Zanzibar is going through a great period of change so these aspects, more than any others, are likely to be different by the time you arrive. Several more hotels will have been built, new cafés and restaurants opened, and much more. Be ready for these changes when using information from this book and your visit will go more smoothly.

Hotels and guesthouses
Zanzibar Town

At the upper end of the range, Zanzibar Town's only large, international-standard hotel is the Serena Inn, part of a chain with other properties in Tanzania and Kenya. Double rooms cost around US$200. Other hotels of the same quality and in the same price bracket are planned – but things move slowly in Zanzibar. Several grand old buildings in Zanzibar Town have been renovated and opened as hotels, combining good quality with a local atmosphere. Prices range from US$75 to US$150 for a double room. In this price bracket, most hotels offer air-conditioned rooms, fridges, TVs and telephones; however, some of the more interesting places make a deliberate selling point of the fact that they offer none of these!

Zanzibar Town has a wide choice of mid-range hotels, costing between US$20 and US$50 for a double, where rooms are en suite, clean and comfortable, but may not be air conditioned.

At the lower end of the price range there are several small hotels and guesthouses which offer good-value service for between US$8 and US$12 per person. Rooms may not be spotless, and are not usually en suite, but these smaller places are generally friendly, and popular with independent travellers on a tight budget.

Several hotels have been opened on the outer edges of Zanzibar Town, around 5km from the centre, on the south side of town nearer the airport, and on the north side of town towards the village of Bububu. These range from top-quality hotels to basic guesthouses.

All hotels in Zanzibar include breakfast in the room price, unless otherwise stated.

Zanzibar Island

Around Zanzibar Island, away from Zanzibar Town, nearly all the hotels and guesthouses are built on or very near the coast. This is where you find idyllic tropical beaches with palm trees, clean white sand, and the warm blue waters of the Indian Ocean. Some travellers come here for a couple of days, just to relax after seeing the sights of Zanzibar Town, and linger for a couple of weeks instead. Visitors on tighter time restrictions always wish they could stay for longer...

On the coast there are several different kinds of place to stay, ranging from large hotels and resorts with many facilities, through small but comfortable lodges and bungalows, to local-style guesthouses which are basic but adequate. Some places deal almost exclusively with package tourists who fly in from Europe (particularly Italy) and spend most or all of their time on Zanzibar within the confines of their hotel. These hotels may not even be able to take guests who simply 'walk-in' and want a room. At the middle and lower end of the range there are many places which normally deal with walk-in guests, although reservations at busy times are recommended. For budget backpackers there's a huge choice, and even if you could reserve a room (if they had a phone, and if it was working) it would be a very unusual thing to do.

As the number of tourists visiting Zanzibar continues to grow, the number of hotels on the coast increases also. The following list describes a wide selection, but cannot hope to be complete. You should expect to find more new places by the time you arrive, and also expect a few other places to have disappeared or been renamed.

Most of the hotels and guesthouses have restaurants, where the food and prices reflect the quality of the hotel itself. In some villages there are also local restaurants where you can buy basic food and drinks.

Pemba

On Pemba Island there is relatively little in the way of tourist accommodation. Each of the three main towns has a plain and dilapidated government-run ZTC hotel, and a couple of local guesthouses which are less impersonal and better value. Chake Chake has a guesthouse attached to a dive centre, catering specifically for independent travellers; on the coast there are a few more upmarket hotels and several more are planned to be finished over the next few years.

Self-catering

Cooking for yourself is not usually possible at any of the larger, more expensive hotels in Zanzibar Town or on the coast, as Western-style self-catering apartments are not available. At some cheaper hotels and guesthouses, you may be allowed to use the kitchen, but, again, this is not usual. Where places do allow self-catering this is mentioned in the various hotel listings.

Camping

As yet, there are no official campsites in Zanzibar. Camping is permitted in the grounds of some budget hotels on the coast, but this is not usual as the hotels are so cheap anyway. On the most popular beaches, there have been occasional incidents of theft from unoccupied tents.

Payments and reservations

Officially, all non-Tanzanian visitors must pay hotel bills in hard currency, usually US dollars, so all prices are quoted in this currency. Residents and citizens are charged lower rates (between 50% and 80% of the visitor rate), and can usually pay in Tanzanian shillings (TSh). In many places foreigners can also pay in TSh – at the current rate of exchange so it makes no difference to the price – but dollars are usually easier to carry and deal with. Smaller hotels accept only cash. In larger hotels you can pay with US dollar travellers' cheques, although the hotel will usually make a surcharge (to cover its own bank charges), so you might be better off changing into local currency or cash dollars to pay your bill – although there won't be much in it. Some of the hotels, mostly in the US$50-plus bracket, accept credit cards – mainly Visa, Mastercard and American Express – but a surcharge of between 10% and 20% (again to cover bank charges) is usually added to your bill. Some hotels proudly display 'Visa welcomed here' and similar little notices on their reception desk or front door, but in reality don't actually accept credit cards – or only sporadically. To save any surprises, you should check this when reserving a room, or at least well in advance of checking out. Despite ambitious claims made in some tourist promotional literature about the ease of using credit cards, Zanzibar is still essentially a cash economy.

The prices quoted in this book are mostly for double rooms, with some single and triple rates. Single rooms are normally about 60% to 75% of the double room price, and triple rooms about 125%. All prices quoted are high-season rates. You can normally get discounts of 25% to 50% in the low season, and there may be additional premiums at the Christmas and New Year peaks. At any time of year, rates may be negotiable if you're in a small group, or plan to stay several nights. All hotels include breakfast in the room price – although this varies from a full buffet in the more expensive places, down to tea, bread and fruit in the cheaper establishments.

If you intend staying in one of the cheaper places it is usually possible simply to arrive and get a room on the spot. However, advance reservations may be necessary for some of the smarter hotels, or at very busy periods. You can use phone, fax or email. Or you can use good old-fashioned post and write direct to the hotel, although allow between three and five weeks for a reply. Whichever method you use, if you can't book in advance don't worry – except at seasonal peaks you're very unlikely to get completely stuck with nowhere to stay.

FOOD AND DRINK
Restaurants
In Zanzibar Town, there are several good restaurants catering specifically for the tourist trade, specialising in local dishes, seafood or curries (remember that Zanzibar is on the shores of the Indian Ocean). Meals in such places usually cost between US$7 and US$12 per person. There are also smarter restaurants, and restaurants attached to large hotels, where prices are higher.

Zanzibar Town also has restaurants where meals and snacks are less elaborate and prices around US$5. There are also some small eating-houses catering mainly for local people where you can eat for around US$2. They usually only have one or two types of food available, such as stew and rice, but they also serve chapatis, samosas and other snacks.

THE FRUIT SEASONS
Between December and March is the main mango time on Zanzibar, and the markets are full of these tasty green-to-yellow fruits. From March to mid-June it's the wet season (*Masika*), when pineapples are plentiful, and July to September is when oranges are in abundance.

Outside Zanzibar Town, in the smaller towns and villages, there are very few places to eat. Local people tend to eat in their own houses and there are not enough tourists around yet to create a market for cafés and restaurants. On the coast, hotels and guesthouses usually have restaurants attached, where food and service generally reflect the overall standard of the accommodation. A few small restaurants have opened by the most popular beaches, catering for the growing influx of visitors.

On Pemba, Chake Chake and Wete have a couple of local restaurants, but there is little else in the other towns on the island. More details are given in the relevant chapters.

Cafés and bars

In Zanzibar Town, many places serve drinks as well as food, although at busy times you may be required to buy a meal rather than have a drink on its own. You can buy international and Tanzanian brands of fizzy drink, plus local and imported beers. Prices vary greatly according to where you drink: a bottle of Coke from a shop or small backstreet café costs US$0.25, and may cost four times this in a smarter café or restaurant. A bottle of local beer (including Safari, Tusker or Kilimanjaro) costs US$1 in a local bar, and at least double this in smarter places.

At larger hotels and restaurants in Zanzibar Town or on the coast you can also buy imported beers, wines (mostly from South Africa) and spirits.

Self-catering

If you plan to provide for yourself, in Zanzibar Town there are several shops selling locally produced bread and cakes, plus a reasonable choice of food in tins and packets imported from Kenya or other parts of the world. Zanzibar Town has a very good market where you can buy all sorts of fruit and vegetables, plus fresh meat and fish if you have a means of cooking it. Other towns on Zanzibar and Pemba also have small markets where you can buy meat, fish, fruit and vegetables, and shops with a limited but adequate supply of tinned food.

THINGS TO BUY

If you're looking for souvenirs, collectables or gifts for the folks back home, Zanzibar has a lot to offer. Most of the shops and stalls are in Zanzibar Town (see *Shopping*, in the *Zanzibar Town* chapter, page 152), but you can also buy things at the larger hotels along the coast.

Zanzibar Town has a huge collection of shops and pavement stalls selling souvenirs. In the market, and various shops, you can also buy some of the many different sorts of aromatic spices that make Zanzibar so famous. Other popular items are carvings and models made from wood, paintings (particularly in the Tingatinga style – see page 47 – but also in other styles), jewellery in stone, gold and silver, and models or mobiles made from coconut shells in the shapes of dolphins, dhows or fish.

Zanzibar Town also has several curio shops selling antiques, all sorts of hand-crafted pieces, and a lot of genuine junk. Some of the antique items have been brought to the islands by Arab or Indian traders in the last couple of centuries. The unique Zanzibar clocks, originally used by Zanzibari merchants, are often bought by collectors. Carpets, rugs and mats, made in the Persian or Arab style, are sold in some shops. Most curio shops also sell wood carvings: boxes inlaid with shells, or decorated with hammered brass, are very popular. Traditional Zanzibar furniture, such as tables, beds and wardrobes decorated with stained glass and mirrors, can be found but these are hard to carry home!

POINTERS FOR RESPONSIBLE TOURISM ON ZANZIBAR

- Dress and act sensitively: locals consider revealing clothing or public displays of affection offensive. Keep swimwear for the beach, and in towns or villages keep your upper legs and shoulders covered. Sporting bare chests or bikini tops as you stroll around the market is the height of rudeness and arrogance.
- Support locally owned, small-scale shops and businesses. This is the best way for your money to benefit the grass-roots economy.
- Buy locally made crafts, but avoid wildlife products, such as ivory, skins, coral, shells from turtles or any other kind of marine animal, and even wooden carvings, unless the material comes from a sustainable renewable source.
- Always ask permission before photographing local people. And accept refusals.
- Non-Muslims should not enter mosques without permission.
- During the holy month of Ramadan, local people fast, and you can show understanding for this tradition by not eating or drinking in public places. (Eating in tourist restaurants is fine.)

Some shops sell shells and coral, taken from the reefs and beaches around the islands. This trade encourages local people to catch live molluscs, rather than simply collect empty shells from the beach, and to break off live coral from a reef which will take many years (or even decades) to re-grow. If you buy any of these items you are helping to degrade, and eventually destroy, the islands' fascinating marine life.

You may also see turtle shells, or items made from turtle-shell such as bracelets or earrings, but you should avoid buying these things as turtles are an endangered species in Zanzibar. (For more details, see the *Sea turtles* section on page 71.) You should also avoid buying carvings and other products made from ivory; in this part of the world it's likely to have come from a poached elephant. In an effort to sell their wares, some traders will tell you turtle-shell or ivory products are made from horn or bone, but if you're in any doubt – don't buy.

PUBLIC HOLIDAYS

Zanzibar shares most public holidays with the rest of Tanzania. Offices and businesses are usually closed on these days, although some tour companies remain open. Public holidays include:

January 12	Mapinduzi (Revolution) Day
April 26	Union Day
May 1	Workers' Day
July 7	Peasants' and Farmers' Day (called *Saba Saba* – Seven Seven)
December 9	Independence Day

Christmas Day, New Year's Day and Easter are also public holidays, although many tour companies stay open, and celebrations are low-key on this largely Muslim island.

The Muslim feasts of Idd il Fitri – the end of Ramadan – and Idd il Maulidi (also called Maulidi ya Mfunguo Sita) – Mohammed's birthday – are celebrated by many people and are effectively public holidays. Dates of these holidays depend on the lunar calendar, and fall 11 or 12 days earlier every year. Approximate dates for Ramadan for the next few years are as follows:

2003   Oct 27 to Nov 21
2004   Oct 16 to Nov 10
2005   Oct 5 to Oct 30
2006   Sep 24 to Oct 19

On Revolution Day (January 12), don't be surprised if you hear gunfire (live) from the army barracks or even heavy anti-aircraft artillery (also live) from warships moored off Zanzibar Town, particularly at night (when the tracer makes a nice arc through the sky). It's just the military celebrating – not another revolution.

BUSINESS HOURS
Most shops and travel company offices in Zanzibar Town are open every day, although some close on Fridays, the Muslim holy day, or on Sundays, the official day off. Normal business hours are from between 08.00 and 09.00 until noon, then from 13.00 or 14.00 until 17.00 or 18.00. Some private shops and tour agencies take a longer break at midday and stay open later in the evening. In the low season, some souvenir shops stay closed, while others open mornings only. Government offices and banks are closed on Saturdays and Sundays. Post offices are closed on Saturday afternoons and Sundays.

COMMUNICATIONS
Post
Most towns and large villages on Zanzibar and Pemba islands have post offices, but it's best to send all your mail from Zanzibar Town. The main poste restante service for Zanzibar is also in Zanzibar Town (see page 155). The post service is reliable, with letters taking about a week to ten days to reach destinations in Europe and North America (Australia takes a bit longer). Letters to destinations inside Tanzania cost about US$0.20, while postcards to countries outside Africa are about US$0.50 (slightly more for letters).

Telephone and fax
By far the best place to make international calls is in Zanzibar Town, where there's a public call office next to the old post office, and several private phone bureaux. International calls to Europe or the USA cost between US$2.50 and US$5 per minute, depending on where you go. Note that all places charge per full minute; go over by one second and you might as well speak for the next 59. More details are given in the *Zanzibar Town* chapter, on page 156. Elsewhere on the islands some hotels allow guests to make international calls, although rates are at a premium.

Zanzibar has at least three mobile phone (cell phone) service providers, and these phones can be used around Zanzibar Town and in some parts of Zanzibar Island as network coverage increases. They also work in and around Chake Chake and Mkoani on Pemba Island.

If you're bringing a mobile/cell phone from home, phones with GSM capability work in Zanzibar, although this depends on whether your own service provider has a reciprocal agreement with local providers.

Email
Of course, very few travellers use fax or *poste restante* these days, as web-based email is the most popular way to stay in touch with family and friends at home or around

NEW TELEPHONE CODES
In January 2000 telephone dialling codes and numbers across Tanzania were changed.

- For emergency calls dial 112 (replacing 999).
- For directory enquiries dial 118 (replacing 991).
- Mobile phone (cell phone) codes have also changed:
    the old 0811 is now 0741;
    the old 0812 is now 0742;
    the old 0821 is now 0761.
- The area code for Zanzibar is now 024 (replacing 054). This covers the islands of Unguja and Pemba.
- Individual numbers have also changed. On Zanzibar Island and Pemba, all phone numbers should have seven figures. On Zanzibar, add 2 to the front of old six-figure numbers. On Pemba, add 24 to the front of old five-figure numbers.
- Area codes on the Tanzanian mainland that have changed include:

Area	Old code	New code
Dar es Salaam	051	022
Tanga	053	027
Arusha	057	027
Kilimanjaro	055	027
Mtwara	059	023
Dodoma	061	026
Tabora	062	026
Mwanza	068	028

the world. Most of the phone bureaux in Zanzibar Town also offer internet services, and there are also many dedicated internet bureaux. More details are given in the *Zanzibar Town* chapter, on page 156.

EMBASSIES AND CONSULS
Countries with diplomatic representation on Zanzibar include China, Egypt and Oman. Of more use to British tourists in case of emergency, is the British Consular Correspondent, Mr Carl Salisbury at ZanAir (listed under *Regional and local air companies* on page 143). The equivalent for visitors from the USA is the American Warden, Mr Emerson Skeens at the Emerson & Green Hotel (listed on page 121). The German Honorary Consul is Mrs Angelica Sapetu, at the International School (tel: 024 2233691, 024 2234062, 0747 410045). These people have limited powers and are unable to assist with visas or with simple problems such as illness or theft of belongings, but they will try to help in more serious cases such as *wrongful* arrest or imprisonment. Most countries have embassies or high commissions in Dar es Salaam or Nairobi.

If you do lose your passport in Zanzibar, you can get an Emergency Travel Document from the Ministry of the Interior. This will allow you to leave Zanzibar, and either go directly back to your own country, or reach Dar where most countries have representation and you should be able to get a replacement.

MAPS
A straightforward tourist map of *Zanzibar Town & Zanzibar Island* is available from the Zanzibar Tourist Corporation offices, and from some bookshops and hotels in

the town. It costs around US$2. Better than this is the excellent hand-drawn map of *Zanzibar Stone Town & Zanzibar Island* produced by local artist Giovanni, which is widely available. The Zanzibar Island map on the reverse is at a scale of about 1:100,000. This is part of a wider series of maps, including many of the national parks and mountains of mainland Tanzania.

The *Gallery Map of Zanzibar* is available in the bookshop of the same name. The map of Zanzibar Island is not as clear to read as the Giovanni map, but the map of Stone Town is clear and useful.

A map called *Pemba the Clove Island* is available in some book and gift shops, and is well researched at a scale of 1:100,000. There are two versions however: one from 1992, and a better one from 1995. The date is on the back cover.

Most commercially produced maps of Tanzania also include Zanzibar. One of the best is the *Tanzania Travellers Map* published by Macmillan, which shows the mainland at a scale of 1:2,000,000 and has more detailed maps of Zanzibar Island (1:500,000) and Pemba Island (1:830,000) on the back, although even these contain a few errors.

Good-quality maps of Zanzibar and Pemba islands (produced by the British Directorate of Overseas Surveys at scales of 1:50,000 and 1:10,000) are available in Zanzibar Town from the Map Office in the Commission of Lands and Planning, part of the Ministry of Environment, near the People's Bank of Zanzibar and the Fort. Maps cost about US$2.

DIVING AND FISHING

Zanzibar has many riches to offer diving, fishing and watersports enthusiasts. People come to dive and fish here from all over the world, and even if you're only a casual snorkeller or angler, there's still plenty to attract. Some diving and fishing companies are based in Zanzibar Town (on the west coast of Zanzibar Island), while others operate from hotels on the north or east coast, or from Pemba. Details on the best seasons for diving and fishing are given in the box on page 111.

Diving

The seas around the islands of Zanzibar offer some of the best diving conditions in the Indian Ocean. As well as coral reefs, the marine life is also a major attraction. All around the islands many types of colourful tropical fish are easily seen, while encounters with larger fish such as groupers, barracudas, sharks, rays and mantas, plus turtles, dolphins and even whales, are possible – particularly on the northern and eastern sides of the island.

Off the west coast, and within easy reach of Zanzibar Town, are numerous small islands, sandbanks and reefs where divers can experience amazingly varied coral, spectacular slopes and drop-offs. This area is favoured by beginners, because access is straightforward. There are also some good sites for experienced divers, including a couple of wrecks. (There are no wrecks on the east coast.)

Off the north coast and northern part of the east coast are many more reefs. There's also Mnemba Island (sometimes more fancifully termed Mnemba Atoll) – promoted as one of the finest dive-sites in and around Zanzibar and along the whole East African coast, although these days its popularity means it can get busy, and there are other, more rewarding and challenging dives, elsewhere on Zanzibar and Pemba islands. The southern part of Zanzibar Island's east coast is more specialised and noticeably less crowded than Mnemba and some of the popular islands off the west coast.

The main diving seasons are outlined in the box on page 111, but it's worth noting that at any time of year, the east coast areas are exposed to the Indian Ocean swell, while the west coast tends to be more sheltered.

There are two dive schools based in Zanzibar Town, and several more based at hotels on the north and east coast of Zanzibar Island and on Pemba Island. If you're only here for a short visit, the places in Zanzibar Town are convenient, but many holidaymakers prefer the places outside Zanzibar Town as there are also beaches and other water activities for non-divers.

Prices for open-water dives vary slightly between the companies, and are listed below. In general, the prices for diving can fluctuate up and down a bit, depending how busy the centres are, but even so there's often a similarity between rates at places in the same area. Thus, it's harder to decide which company to go with based on price. It's far more important to choose on quality.

You might be able to negotiate deals if you plan to do a lot of diving with just one company. Generally, the dive centres include hire of equipment in their rates, and some make a reduction if you bring all or some of your own gear. Reductions are also often available for groups of four or more, so if you're on your own it might be worth teaming up with some other people before arranging anything. Most of the dive centres also offer night dives, underwater photography courses, special training sessions, tank filling, snorkel trips, and so on.

When deciding which dive company to go with, it is very important to note that some of the companies are very experienced, professional and reputable, while others seem to operate in a more relaxed manner. When making bookings or enquiries you should ask about the equipment they use: What type is it? How old is it? How often is it serviced? When was it last serviced? Ask about safety equipment too: Do they have access to medical oxygen? Do the boats have spare outboard motors, radios, flares, life jackets and so on? You might also want to know about the boats the dive centres use; some have traditional dhows or wooden boats, others use more modern 'ribs' (rigid-hulled inflatable boats). The former are more spacious and absolutely fine for visiting local reefs, while ribs are generally smaller and faster, and used for reaching more distant dive-sites.

As with so many things on Zanzibar, the best thing to do is shop around on the spot (or in advance by writing, faxing or emailing) between the various dive centres, and also to get recommendations from other divers if you can.

Dive companies in Zanzibar Town

The Zanzibar Dive Centre – One Ocean Ltd PO Box 608, Zanzibar; tel/fax: 024 2238374, 0742 750161; email: oneocean@zanlink.com; web: www.zanzibaroneocean.com. Based near the beach to the west of Forodhani Gardens, at the junction of Shangani and Kenyatta roads, this is the only PADI five-star instructor development centre in Zanzibar, with efficient management, modern gear and keen staff. The base is open 08.00 to 18.30 daily. Most of the diving is done on the islands, reefs and wrecks off Zanzibar Town, using traditional dhows fitted with diesel engines, but they also have faster boats so that some of the more distant and rarely visited sites, such as Boribu Reef, can also be reached. Single dives are US$40, double dives US$70 (a day trip, including lunch). Four dives are US$130, and night dives US$45. A Discover Scuba for total beginners is US$50, an open-water course (over four or five days) is US$320 and an advanced course is US$240. A 10% discount is given if you have your own gear. Confined water training is done in the Serena swimming pool. Snorkelling trips and dhow cruises are also arranged from Zanzibar Town. This company also has bases on the east coast of Zanzibar Island at Matemwe Beach Bungalows and at Bluebay Beach Resort, which gives divers access to the reefs in this area, which includes Mnemba Island. Diving tours to Pemba can also be arranged.

Bahari Divers PO Box 204, Zanzibar; tel: 0742 750293; email: baharidivers@hotmail.com; web: www.zanzibar-diving.com. This small, friendly and well-organised operation has an office near the northern end of Kenyatta Road. The main dive sites are Bawe Island, Fungu Reef and Pange Sandbank, all within easy reach of Zanzibar Town. One dive is US$40, two dives US$70 (including lunch) and four dives US$120. Night dives are US$45. A discovery dive for complete beginners is US$50, and a four-day open-water course is US$320.

Dive companies around Zanzibar Island

Nearly all the dive centres around the coast of Zanzibar are based at hotels, and can be contacted either directly or through the hotel. You do not need to be staying at a hotel to use the dive centre facilities, although some places give a discount to guests.

Ras Nungwi Beach Hotel Tel: 024 2232512, 2233767; fax 2233039; email: rasnungwi@zanzibar.net; web: www.zanzibar.net/nungwi. This good-quality hotel at Nungwi, at the northern tip of Zanzibar, has its own fully equipped dive centre. A single dive is US$45, double US$80, five dives US$200 and ten dives US$360. To visit the best sites at Mnemba Island and Leven Bank costs a small extra supplement. The hotel also arranges various PADI courses including open-water (US$350) and advanced (US$300). **Divemaxx** Tel 024 2240014, 0741 324744; email: divemaxx@zanlink.com; web: www.divemax.com. Based at Sazani Beach Hotel in Nungwi, local dives are US$40, and two-dive excursions US$75. A two-dive trip to Mnemba or Leven Bank is US$90. If you plan to dive all week, packages of five dives are US$175, and ten dives US$330. Courses include introductory Discover Scuba (US$80), and PADI open-water (US$350). Snorkel trips to Mnemba are also available.

Sensation Divers Tel: 0747 418453, 0741 602747; email: sensationdivers@yahoo.com; web: www.sensationdivers.com. This dive outfit is based at Amaan Bungalows in Nungwi, and uses dhows and fibreglass boats to reach dive sites. Single dives cost US$35 locally, US$45 on Leveb Bank or US$60 on Mnemba. A day out (two dives plus lunch) on Mnemba costs US$80. A five-dive package is US$145. A single-day Discover Scuba course is US$60, and a four-day PADI open-water course is US$350.

Dive Zanzibar Tel: 0747 410535, 0741 326574, 0747 416616; email: divezanzibar@hotmail.com; web: www.divezanzibar.net. Based at Paradise Beach Club in Nungwi, this company offers single dives in the local area for US$35, single dives at Leven Bank for US$45 and two dives off Mnemba Island for US$80. A four-day PADI open-water course is US$350. Various multi-dive packages are also available.

East Africa Diving Centre PO Box 2750, Zanzibar; tel: 0747 416425, 0747 420588; email: eadc@zitec.org; web: www.sansibar-tauchen.de. Based at Jambo Brothers Guesthouse in Nungwi, with a dhow and a speedboat to reach dive sites. The experienced owner-managers speak English, German and Afrikaans. One dive is US$35 ($40 to Leven Bank), two dives US$65 ($80 to Mnemba), four dives US$120 and ten dives US$230. A four-day PADI open-water course is US$350, and a three-day advanced is US$260.

Zanzibar Sail Tel: 0747 418378; email: zanzibarsail@yahoo.de; web: www.zanzibarsail.com. Based on a yacht moored off Nungwi, this company offers sailing trips (see the Nungwi section) as well as diving. A combination of sailing (or just cruising) and live-aboard diving would be delightful. Single dives cost US$35, or US$30 for more than five dives. A PADI open-water course is US$350. Boat charter costs US$125 per 24 hours full board. More details are available at the Zanzibar Sail booking office at Amaan Bungalows in Nungwi.

Scuba Do Tel: 0747 417157; email: info@scubado.demon.co.uk; web: www.scubado.net. This new but very professional and well-equipped dive centre is based at Sunset Bungalows in Kendwa, just south of Nungwi. There's plenty of good equipment, two smart boats, and dive sites include all the favourites (Leven Bank, Mnemba, etc) plus some more unusual places like Tumbatu Island. Single dives are US$35, but this company concentrates on full days and double dives for US$60. PADI open-water courses are US$350.

Previous page Zanzibar red colobus monkey, *Colobus badius kirkii*, also called Kirk's red colobus (AZ)

Above left Masked booby, *Sula dactylatra*, Latham Island (MR)

Above right Zanzibar road sign (HT)

Below left Starfish at Chumbe Island (HT)

Below right Coconut crab, the world's largest land crab, on Chumbe Island (DE)

ZANZIBAR DIVING AND FISHING SEASONS
If you are coming to Zanzibar specifically for scuba diving, there are some points you need to know. Diving is possible at any time of year, and divers visit different parts of the archipelago according to conditions. Having said that, most people avoid the main rainy season from March/April to May, even though during this period there can be some very good days. The weather is especially changeable at this time, and in less than an hour can switch from beautifully calm and sunny conditions to a full-blown tropical rainstorm, reducing visibility on the surface to a few hundred metres.

Generally speaking, from June/July to October, when the winds come from the south, the northern coasts of Zanzibar Island and Pemba Island are better, although during August some days can offer perfect conditions, while on other days the sea may be rough. September–December is usually the calmest time, and from November to February/March, the southern coasts are preferred, as the winds come from the north. Pemba enjoys some of the best visibility of the year in February.

At any time of year the western sides are more sheltered, while the eastern sides (the ocean side) are more prone to swells and rough days. As in many other parts of the world, the weather and sea conditions on Zanzibar are unpredictable and there's always a chance of a bad day during the 'good' times, and perfect conditions at the heart of the 'bad' times.

If you're seriously into game fishing, the best time is August–March, although conditions are also reasonable from July to September. August–November is reckoned to be the best time for yellowfin tuna, while November–March is the best season for billfish, especially marlin.

Dhow Divers PO Box 3275; tel 024 236535; fax 236536; email: matemwe-znz@twiga.com. Based at Matemwe Bungalows, a good small hotel near Matemwe village on the northern part of the east coast (see *Chapter 6*), with standard dives and courses run in the same sensitive and responsible manner. A single dive is US$45, double dive US$80, four-day open-water course US$450, all including equipment. Dive sites include the nearby Mnemba Island. The resident fully-qualified dive instructor is also a marine biologist and offers fish identification courses, and a unique reef ecology course. Night dives ($55) and other special courses are also available. You can also hire underwater cameras and whacky motorised devices to propel divers effortlessly through the water. Snorkelling and traditional sailing are also available. Using dhows to reach dive sites, a full day often involves motoring out to the reef, and sailing back.

The Zanzibar Dive Centre – One Ocean Ltd Email: onceocean@zanlink.com; web: www.zanzibaroneocean.com. As well as a base in Zanzibar Town (listed above) this experienced and highly regarded company has a base at Matemwe Beach Village, a hotel near Matemwe, (tel: 0747 417250, 0742 750161; email: matemwebeachvillage@zitec.org) and at Blue Bay Resort on the east coast (tel: 024 2241240, 0747 414332; email: mail@bluebayzanzibar.com). Motor-dhows are used at Matemwe and custom-built dive-boats serve Bluebay Beach Resort. At Matemwe Beach Village, single dives are US$50, double dives US$70, six dives US$180, and a PADI open-water course is US$350. At Blue Bay single dives are US$55, double dives US$90, four dives US$160, six dives US$210, and a four-day PADI open-water course US$385. At all One Ocean bases, night dives, simple snorkelling and various courses are available.

Mawimbi Watersports – based at Zanzibar Safari Resort. Small fleet of dhows and motorboats, dives in local area.

Paje East Coast Diving Tel: 024 2240191, 0741 607436; email: pajediving@zanzinet.com. Based at the village of Paje, between Bwejuu and Jambiani on the southern part of the east coast. Single dives cost US$40 and double dives US$65 for qualified divers. Snorkelling gear and kayaks can be hired.

Rising Sun Dive Centre PO Box 479, Zanzibar; tel/fax: 0747 417594, 0741 326595; email breezes@africaonline.co.tz; web: www.risingsun-zanzibar.com. This company is based at Breezes Beach Club near Bwejuu. (The dive centre can also be contacted through the hotel.) The enthusiastic manager speaks (and can instruct) in several European languages, and is a great east coast fan, willing to cater for beginners or to show experienced divers some 'hidden treasures' which are very rarely visited by other companies. With GPS and echosounder, several brand new sites have been discovered. A single dive is US$40, and a five-dive deal US$175. Ten dives are US$300. On to these rates add equipment hire: wetsuit, regulator, BCD, mask and fins, all for US$20 per day. An open-water course costs US$310, plus US$80 certification.

Some of the other big hotels on the east coast have dive centres. These include the Karafuu Hotel north of Bwejuu, and some of the resorts at Kiwengwa. Although aimed mostly at hotel guests, visitors can also arrange dives here. Additionally, some companies from Dar es Salaam and the Tanzanian mainland dive around Kizimkazi at the southern end of Zanzibar Island, and some companies from Kenya dive around the northern end of Pemba.

Dive companies on Pemba

Swahili Divers PO Box 146, Chake Chake; tel: 024 2452786; fax: 024 2452768; email: swahilidivers@intafrica.com, web: www.swahilidivers.com. This company is the main dive operator on Pemba, run by a well-travelled and larger-than-life character called Raf (a Brit of Turkish origin, who used to run his own dive centre in India). The Swahili Divers base is in Chake Chake (see details on the Old Mission Lodge in the Chake Chake section of *Chapter 7 – Pemba Island*). Swahili Divers uses a motor-dhow and two fast ribs (all with safety equipment and radio) to reach a very wide range of dive sites, and promises live-aboard conditions at land-based prices. But if you want to be on the water all the time, a live-aboard dhow is under construction and should be ready by 2003. Snorkelling is also on offer, and dhow sailing can be arranged with a day's notice. The people at Swahili Divers are also very keen on showing visitors more than just the surrounding ocean, and arrange forest walks and historical tours, and encourage cultural encounters. A full day's diving with two tanks costs US$95. A four- or five-day PADI open-water course is US$295. A package of six nights' full board accommodation plus five days of diving (ten dives) is US$600.

Fundu Lagoon Tel: 024 2232926, 0741 326551; fax 024 2232937; email fundu@africaonline.co.za; website: www.fundulagoon.com. A smart hotel near Mkoani, with a fully equipped dive centre. One-off dives or combined accommodation and diving packages are available. (More details are given in the Mkoani section of the *Pemba Island* chapter.)

Pemba Afloat Tel: 0741 330900, 0748 341459, 0741 330904; web: www.pembaisland.com or www.pembaafloat.com. This company runs three 20ft yachts which are normally moored in the lagoons of northern Pemba, near Wete, and together form a live-aboard base for divers. The mooring is an idyllic spot, in a calm bay sheltered from the sea by Njao Island, with just enough breeze to keep the mozzies and sandflies off. From the nearby village, fisherman sail or canoe past – it's a scene unchanged for centuries. One of the boats is mainly for daytime use, with a dining area under shade on the deck, while another has cabins (for eight people) and showers. Near the main mooring is a small reef where beginners learn, and two fast ribs with twin engines and radios take experienced divers to the various sites in the area. It costs US$50 to US$70 per person per day all inclusive to live on the boats, plus US$35 per dive, all equipment included. To reach the boats from Wete is usually a 45-minute drive and a 10-minute boat ride, and advance bookings are usually required.

Aristos Email: aristos@africaonline.co.ke. A 56ft ketch called *Aristos* based at Kalifi in Kenya makes regular sailing trips around Pemba and Zanzibar Island, fully equipped with diving and fishing gear, with three crew and berths for six passengers. The cost for a seven-night cruise is about US$1,200, including full board and unlimited diving.

Manta Reef Hotel is on the northwestern tip of the island and effectively the diving base for the Mombasa Reef Hotel and Shimoni Reef Lodge on the Kenya coast. This hotel is totally geared up to receive guests from Kenya rather than from Zanzibar. You can get more information on diving here from their Kenya office (tel +254 11 471771; email: onearth@africaonline.co.ke; web: www.africa-direct.com). For details on the lodge itself, see the Ngezi section of the *Pemba Island* chapter.

Fishing companies

The waters around Zanzibar and Pemba islands are reckoned by experts to offer some of the best fishing in the world, especially the Pemba Channel, between Zanzibar and Pemba islands, or around Mafia Island, south of Zanzibar. Big game fish include barracuda, kingfish, sailfish, billfish, wahoo, dorado and blue marlin.

There are several fishing companies based on Zanzibar, but it is important to note that while most are very experienced and reputable, some others seem less so. When making bookings or enquiries you should ask about the equipment they use: What type is it? How suitable is it for big game fishing? How old is it? How often is it serviced? Ask about safety equipment too: Are the boats fitted with radios? Do they carry spare outboard motors, life jackets and so on?

One of the best game fishing operations is **Ras Nungwi Beach Hotel** (tel: 024 2232512, 2233767; fax: 2233039; email: rasnungwi@zanzibar.net; web: www.zanzibar.net/nungwi), which runs a fully equipped deep sea fishing operation in association with the Pemba Channel Fishing Club. Modern purpose-built game fishing boats have experienced skippers, echo sounders and fishfinders, plus GPS and other safety equipment, while all the tackle is international quality, although clients can bring their own if required. To hire a boat for six hours (with skipper, tackle, bait and lunch) costs US$400. A full day is US$600. Night rates are also available.

Some of the diving and sailing centres listed above also organise fishing trips on request. **Mtoni Marine Centre** (listed under *Hotels* in the *Zanzibar Town* chapter, on page 129) can also put you in touch with game fishing operators on the north coast and east coast.

Part Two

The Guide

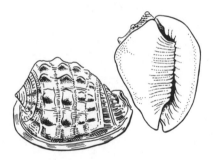

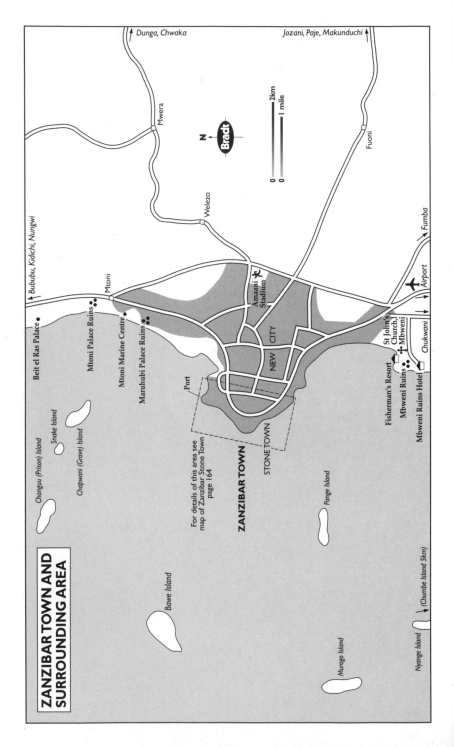

ZANZIBAR TOWN AND
SURROUNDING AREA

Dunga, Chwaka

Jozani, Paje, Makunduchi

Mwera

N

Bradt

2km
1 mile
0
0

Welezo

Fuoni

Bububu, Kidichi, Nungwi

Mtoni

Beit el Ras Palace

Mtoni Palace Ruins

Mtoni Marine Centre

Maruhubi Palace Ruins

Port

Amaani Stadium

NEW CITY

Fumba

Airport

St John's Church

Mbweni

Fisherman's Resort

Mbweni Ruins

Mbweni Ruins Hotel

Chukwani

For details of this area see
map of Zanzibar Stone Town
page 164

ZANZIBAR TOWN

STONE TOWN

Changuu (Prison) Island

Snake Island

Chapwani (Grave) Island

Bawe Island

Pange Island

Murogo Island

Nyange Island

(Chumbe Island 5km)

Zanzibar Town

'The streets are, as they should be under such a sky, deep and winding alleys, hardly twenty feet broad, and travellers compare them to the threads of a tangled skein.'

Richard Burton, British explorer (1857)

Zanzibar Town (sometimes called Zanzibar City) is situated about halfway along the west coast of Zanzibar Island. It has a population estimated at more than 100,000 which makes it by far the largest settlement on the islands of Zanzibar, and one of the five largest in Tanzania. Before the development of towns such as Dar es Salaam, Nairobi and Mombasa during the colonial period, Zanzibar Town was the largest settlement in the whole of East Africa.

Zanzibar Town is divided into two sections by Creek Road. (The creek itself has now been reclaimed.) On the west side lies the 'heart' of Zanzibar Town: the old quarter, usually called Stone Town. This is the most interesting section for visitors: many of the buildings here were constructed during the 19th century (although some date from before this time), when Zanzibar was a major trading centre and at the height of its power. The trade created wealth which in turn led to the construction of palaces, mosques and many fine houses. A further fascination for visitors is the tortuous maze of narrow streets and alleyways that winds between the buildings of Stone Town – virtually unchanged since the mid-19th century, when it was described by Burton in the quotation above.

On the east side of Creek Road is the part of town which used to be called Ng'ambo (literally 'the other side') but is now called Michenzani, or the 'New City'. This is an extended area of mainly one-storey houses and other buildings, covering a much wider area than Stone Town. This used to be where the poorer African and Swahili people lived, while more wealthy Arabs, Indians and Europeans lived in Stone Town. To a large extent this rich–poor division still exists today. Some attempt has been made to 'modernise' this area: at the centre of Michenzani are some ugly blocks of flats (apartment buildings) which were built in the late 1960s by East German engineers as part of an international aid scheme. Few visitors go to this eastern part of Zanzibar Town, as there is little in the way of 'sights'. But it helps to broaden your perception if you realise that outside the 'touristy' areas of Stone Town is a place where many thousands of real people live and work in much less exotic, but no less authentic, surroundings.

The best way to explore Stone Town is on foot, but the maze of streets can be very disorientating. To help you get your bearings, it is useful to think of Stone Town as a triangle, bounded on two sides by sea, and along the third by Creek Road (see the Zanzibar Stone Town map on page 164). If you get lost, it is always possible to aim in one direction until you reach the outer edge of the town where you should find a recognisable landmark.

Although most of the streets in Stone Town are too narrow for cars, when walking you should watch out for bikes and scooters being ridden around at breakneck speed! It's also useful to realise that thoroughfares which are wide enough for cars are usually called roads. Hence, you can drive along New Mkunazini Road or Kenyatta Road, but to visit a place on Kiponda Street or Mkunazini Street you have to walk. When looking for hotels or places of interest, you should also note that most areas of Stone Town are named after the main street in that area. But sometimes the area is referred to as Kiponda Street or Malindi Street, instead of simply Kiponda or Malindi. This can be confusing, as you may not be on the street of that name. But don't worry: at least you're near!

TRAVEL AROUND ZANZIBAR TOWN
Most visitors and locals get around the town on foot (and in Stone Town this is the best way), but there are other means of transport available.

Taxi
Private taxis for hire wait at taxi ranks around town – they do not usually cruise for business, although if you see a taxi in the street you can always flag it down. The main taxi ranks are near the BP petrol station on Creek Road, outside the ZanAir office just east of the Port Gates, beside the House of Wonders and at the northern end of Kenyatta Road.

There are no meters. Wherever you go, you should check the fare with the driver *before* starting your journey. A short ride through town costs US$1.50 to

GUIDES AND THE 'PAPAASI'
Nearly all tourists who come to Zanzibar Town use the services of a guide at some stage during their visit. If you come on an organised tour arranged at home, this will of course include the services of a guide. Even if you arrange something simple through a tour company on the spot, like a trip to the spice plantations, the price always includes a guide to show you around. Guides from reputable companies have to be registered with the Tourism Commission, and these carry identity cards.

There are also many other guides in Zanzibar who are not registered. Most of these are not really guides at all, but touts and hustlers who make their money showing tourists to hotels and souvenir shops, arranging transport or getting groups together to share boat rides. These touts are known locally as beach-boys or *papaasi* – literally meaning 'ticks' (ie: parasites or irritating blood-suckers).

When a ship comes into Zanzibar from Dar, there is usually a group of *papaasi* on the dockside. Some can be quite aggressive, but a few are not too unpleasant and will help you find a place to stay (which may be useful, as the labyrinth of alleys in Stone Town is disorientating at first). Tell them exactly what you want in terms of standard and price. It should not cost you any more money (the *papaasi* get a commission from the hotel) and could save you a lot of walking.

Unfortunately, this plan does not always work, as some hotels pay more commission than others, and some do not pay at all, so the *papaasi* will only take you to the places where they get a decent cut. We have heard from several travellers who arrived on Zanzibar, aiming to stay in a certain hotel only to be told by the *papaasi* that it was 'full' or 'closed', or even 'burnt down'. If you're

US$2. All the way across town costs US$2 to US$3. A longer ride, from town out to Mtoni Marine Centre or Mbweni Ruins Hotel will be about US$3–5. From town to the airport is around US$10, and it should be the same the other way, but from the airport into town, taxi drivers may quote fares of US$20 or higher.

One last thing to remember: If there is a petrol shortage, taxi fares go up.

Dala-dala

Pick-up vans called *dala-dalas* (or *dalas* for short) carry passengers on local runs around town and to outlying suburbs. There are several routes, all starting at the Darajani Bus Station on Creek Road. The most useful routes for visitors are:

Route A, to Amaani Stadium and the eastern part of the New Town, via the Main Post Office;
Route B, along the coast road north of Zanzibar Town, to Bububu, near Fuji Beach;
Route U, along the main road south of Zanzibar Town, to the airport (Uwanje ya Ndege).

If you go the whole way, *dala-dala* fares are about US$0.20 on Route A, and about US$0.25 on Routes B and U. If you travel only part of the route, the fare is slightly cheaper.

Bicycle

For getting around Zanzibar Town and the surrounding area, a bike is very handy. Bikes can be hired from several of the tour companies listed in this chapter. They are either sturdy steel Chinese-made models, or more modern looking (though

in any doubt, it is best to be polite but firm with the *papaasi* (or simply ignore them completely), and find your own hotel. Even better, make a phone call or send an email from Dar es Salaam or your home country to reserve a room in advance. Some hotels even give discounts for advance bookings.

After arranging your hotel, most *papaasi* will want to be your 'guide', offering to show you around the sights or souvenir shops of Stone Town, find companions for dive trips or boat excursions, or arrange transport to the east coast. Use these services if you need them but be prepared to pay if necessary, or be aware that the owners of the souvenir shops, boats and dive centres will have to pay commission to the *papaasi*, a charge which will of course be passed on to you.

Some *papaasi* are outright crooks, and involved in robberies and other crimes like drug dealing. Others are con-men, and some travellers have been stung arranging budget hire cars where a *papaasi* has taken a deposit then simply disappeared. Others offer to change money at very good rates then pull sleight -of-hand tricks or just run off with your cash. Some budget travellers have reported having drugs planted on them by *papaasi* they befriended, who then reported them to the police; any fines (official or unofficial) paid out included a kickback to the informant.

If you deal only with reputable tour companies (whether low or high budget) you'll have none of these problems. Although reputable guides have identity cards, some *papaasi* have managed to get some too (they could be fakes, or simply stolen – it's hard to tell). This of course is confusing for tourists. There is a need for legitimate guides on Zanzibar, who can help tourists without hassling them, and it is hoped that the government department responsible for tourism will apply itself to this matter in the near future.

almost as heavy) mountain bikes. Prices for Chinese bikes are about US$10 per day. Mountain bikes are US$15 per day. A deposit of around US$50 may be required.

Car and motorbike

A car or motorbike is not really necessary for getting around Zanzibar Town as distances are short, but they can be hired from various tour companies listed in this chapter. Prices vary, but are generally around US$25 to US$30 per day for a scooter, US$35 to US$40 per day for a motorbike, between US$45 and US$60 per day for a small car (eg: a Suzuki 'jeep') and around US$100 per day for a larger car (eg: a Toyota Landcruiser). Petrol costs about US$0.50 per litre. Diesel is slightly cheaper. For more details on car and motorbike hire see page 101.

WHERE TO STAY IN ZANZIBAR TOWN

The following section is a selection of places to stay in and around Zanzibar Town. The list is not complete, as the number of hotels increases every year, and there are frequent name and location changes, but certainly indicates the range of accommodation available.

If you are coming from the airport (or elsewhere on the island) by taxi, and don't have a reservation, be firm about which hotel you want to go to, otherwise the driver may take you to a place where he gets the best commission. Also, remember that many hotels in the older part of Zanzibar Town cannot be reached by vehicle, and you may have to walk some distance through the narrow streets. If the driver shows you the way (and he'll also probably help with your luggage), it's usual to give a fair tip for this extra service.

Hotels in Zanzibar Town

Many hotels are in, or very near, Stone Town, and this is the best area for atmosphere and ease of getting around. The places to stay are arranged in this section roughly in descending order of price and standard (ie: the best or most expensive first, the cheapest last) although you should note that some of the more costly hotels may be overpriced, while some of the cheaper guesthouses offer remarkably good value for money. Many of the budget hotels are happy to negotiate on prices, especially if you're in a group or want to stay for two nights or more.

Please note that many hotels do not have exact street addresses, or if they do these are not used, as many streets and house numbers, if they do exist, are often unmarked. For more general information about hotels in Zanzibar, and paying for them (including an important reminder about credit and debit cards), see *Chapter 4*, pages 101–3. See also the Zanzibar Stone Town map, page 164.

TELEPHONING ZANZIBAR

If you are telephoning a hotel to make a room reservation, note that the area code for all of Zanzibar (Zanzibar Island and Pemba Island) is 024, if you are calling from elsewhere in Tanzania, Kenya or Uganda. Within Zanzibar you do not need to use the 024 code. For calls from other countries, the international code for Tanzania is +255, then 24 for Zanzibar. Mobile phones have six-digit numbers and have a code of either 0741, 0742 or 0747; you do need to prefix any mobile number with a code, wherever you're phoning from.

THE SERENA INN

The Zanzibar Serena Inn is in the Shangani part of Stone Town. The main building was originally the External Communications ('Extelcoms') headquarters, built in the early 20th century by the British colonial administration. The next-door house is much older and was originally known as the Chinese Doctor's Residence. The explorer David Livingstone stayed here before one of his journeys to the African mainland. It later became the private home of the British consul.

The Extelcoms building had been empty for many years, and the Chinese Doctor's Residence had fallen into a bad state of repair. Restoration of these two buildings, and their conversion into a hotel, has been sensitive and appropriate. The design reflects Zanzibar's mixed heritage, and includes Indian, Arabic and colonial styles. Restoration was completed in 1997. Big 'chain' hotels of this nature often appear bland and anonymous, but the architects and local craftsmen who worked here have done a very good job.

The walls of the hotel are decorated with historic prints and some contemporary paintings, but perhaps the most interesting 'decorations' are the old telecommunications equipment that were discovered in the basement, where they'd been dumped and forgotten by colonial staff almost 100 years ago. Most of this equipment was hand-made in wood and brass, and several items have also been restored to their original condition.

The Serena's restoration goes beyond façades and decorations. It is the first hotel in Zanzibar to install a sewage plant, so that waste discharges are treated to international standards. (Most other waste from Stone Town gets pumped out to sea in its raw state.) Although dumping sewage at sea, in whatever state, is never an ideal solution, the hotel owners should be congratulated for this positive step.

In early 2000, the Serena was planning an extension; it is hoped the new buildings will be constructed in the same style and in the same spirit as the rest of the hotel.

Zanzibar Serena Inn Shangani Rd; tel: 024 2233587; fax: 2233019; email: zserena@zanzinet.com; web: www.serenahotels.com. Part of the internationally renowned Serena chain, which has lodges all over East Africa, this large hotel is in the Shangani area of Stone Town, overlooking the sea. The hotel has been converted from two historic buildings, and restored at great expense (see box). All rooms are en suite and air conditioned, with all the facilities visitors expect of an international-class hotel, including a large swimming pool, fine restaurant and coffee shop. If you happen not to be on holiday here, there's a business centre with fax, photocopying and email services (although rates are high), and conference facilities. Rates for walk-in visitors are US$190 single, US$240 double. Half board is an extra US$20 per person, full board an extra US$35. The hotel also has state, executive, honeymoon and business rooms. Generous discounts are available in the low season and sometimes also during quiet midweek periods. Cheaper rates are also sometimes available if you book through a travel agent rather than direct.

Emerson & Green Hotel Hurumzi St, PO Box 3417; tel: 024 2231038, 0747 423266; fax: 024 2231038; email: emerson&green@zitec.org, emegre@zanzibar.org; web: www.zanzibar.org/emegre. This hotel grew out of the now sadly closed Emerson's House – listed by the British *Sunday Times* newspaper as one of the 'great little hotels of the world'. The new Emerson & Green Hotel is in a grand old building which dates from the 1840 to

ELECTRICITY IN ZANZIBAR TOWN

Zanzibar Town gets occasional cuts in the electrical supply. To overcome this, most of the larger hotels have generators, but some of the small budget places don't, which can mean no lights and no fans. If the lights go out, kerosene lamps may be provided but it's best to have a torch or candles handy just in case. When the fans stop working there's not much you can do, and inside rooms can get unbearable during Zanzibar's hot season. Bear this in mind when choosing a place to stay. Hotels that have been built recently rely on a constant electrical supply to work the fans or air conditioning. Older hotels have been built to withstand the hot weather using designs that date from before the invention of electricity. If you can't find a genuine old hotel, look for one built in traditional style – with large windows, thick walls, high ceilings, courtyards, wide verandas and even a double roof, not just a pseudo-oriental façade. If all the new hotels were built using genuine traditional designs, fans and air conditioning would be unnecessary, Zanzibar would not need to burn so much imported oil, and tourists would be more comfortable during power cuts!

1870 period, once the home of a prominent Ismaili Indian merchant called Tharia Topan who also built the Dispensary (now called the Zanzibar Cultural Centre, see page 161). Run by Emerson Skeens and Tom Green, the house has been completely restored and tastefully decorated, with antique Zanzibar furniture and carpets, and has a peaceful and slightly bohemian atmosphere. There are seven rooms, each different in character, including the vast Ball Room and the airy island South Room – reached by a small bridge! Each room, very deliberately, has no phone, no TV and no fridge. Some rooms have AC, others rely on natural cooling – shutters, shades, deep balconies and a sea breeze. Breakfast is taken in the hotel's Tower Top Restaurant, the second highest building in Zanzibar Town, with some of the finest views on the whole island. Dinners are also served here; you don't have to be resident to eat, but reservations are essential (for more details see page 133). All rooms cost US$150 (single or double), and can be turned into triples for families on request.

Shangani House Tel 024 223 0171; fax: 024 223 1038; email: emegre@zanzibar.org: web: www.zanzibar org/emegre. Not to be confused with the Shangani Hotel, this atmospheric old four-bedroom house stands on the western side of Stone Town, draped in vines and surrounded by an overgrown garden that creates a 'lost city' feel. Managed by Emerson's & Green, the whole house can be rented at US$250 per night, making it great value for groups of 5–8 people. The rate includes breakfast.

Tembo Hotel Shangani Rd, PO Box 3974; tel: 024 2233005, 2232069; fax 2233777; email: tembo@zitec.org. This hotel is in a great location, just west of Forodhani Gardens. Part of the hotel was a grand old house, and there's a more recent extension, so that the hotel now has a new wing and old wing, both overlooking the ocean and decorated in a mixture of traditional and modern styles. A notable feature is the upstairs landing separated from a balcony by a huge stained-glass window which fills the room with coloured light. All rooms are en suite, with AC, fridge, telephone and TV. Most have a sea view, or overlook the large swimming pool, but some don't – so choose carefully, or specify a view when booking. Although this hotel bills itself as one of the best in town, some guests report that the standard of management, rooms and the food in the restaurant has slipped just a bit over the years. It wouldn't take much to get it all up to scratch, so this hotel is still worth trying in case things change. It's also worth noting that alcohol is not served in this hotel. Singles cost US$80, doubles US$90–100. Deluxe rooms with seafront balconies are US$125–150. It's an extra US$25 for half board or US$40 for full board. Non-guests can use the pool for US$4.

Chavda Hotel Baghani St, PO Box 540; tel: 024 2232115; fax 231931, email: chavda@zanzinet.com. Just off Kenyatta Rd in the Shangani area, this fairly new hotel is decorated with lots of antique-style Indian furniture and Persian carpets, but it's still a little dark and uninspiring. Rooms are fine, although some are a bit small, but all have a large en-suite bathroom, and some doubles have a separate lounge. Originally, with just 24 rooms this hotel had a nice feel, although a new wing under construction may change this. Upstairs is a restaurant and a very pleasant rooftop bar. Free collections from the port or airport are available for guests. Singles are US$70, doubles are US$90 (or US$110 if you want a balcony).

Mazsons Hotel Kenyatta Rd, PO Box 3367; tel: 024 2233062, 2233694, 0741 340042; fax: 2233695; email: mazsons@zenjcom.com. This hotel in the Shangani area has an interesting history: old records show it was built in the mid-19th century by one Said bin Dhanin, who is thought to have settled here about the time Sultan Said moved his court to Zanzibar from Muscat. Ownership changed hands several times, and during the early part of the 20th century the building was a Greek-run hotel before becoming a private dwelling once again. After the revolution the house, along with many others, fell into disrepair. Today, it is once more a hotel. Most rooms are self-contained, air conditioned and well-appointed, but all are a little soulless. The hotel has a good restaurant, satellite TV, a business centre and bureau de change. Although power supplies are pretty good on Zanzibar these days, this hotel has its own generator in case of cuts – so big it supplies many surrounding buildings as well. A 'moderate' single is US$45. Standard singles are US$60; doubles are US$80.

Dhow Palace Hotel off Kenyatta Rd, PO Box 3974; tel: 024 2233012, 2230304; fax: 2233008; email: dhowpalace@zanzibar.net; web: www.zanzibar.net/dhow. In the Shangani area, just off Kenyatta Rd, this is an excellent and frequently recommended hotel, in a renovated old house built around a cool central courtyard, complete with tinkling fountain. Rooms all have en-suite bathroom (complete with Persian baths) and lead off long balconies which overlook the courtyard. The hotel is furnished with real antiques and antique-style items (apart from the TV in the lounge and the table football upstairs, which both look a bit out of place but seem hardly used). The whole place is spotlessly clean and the atmosphere is very peaceful and tranquil. It lacks only a sea view, although if it had this the rates would be higher, so you get luxury at a very fair price. Breakfast and other meals are served in the lovely rooftop restaurant. Guests from the Dhow Palace can use the swimming pool at the Tembo Hotel free of charge – ask for a voucher at reception. Single rooms are US$55, and doubles US$85.

Hotel International Ukatani, PO Box 3784; tel: 024 2233182; fax: 2236248; email: hotelinter@zanzibar.net; web: www.zanzibar.net/hotelinternational. In the Ukatani area, this hotel is a large old house, built around a central roofed courtyard. Although the rooms are all spacious and well-equipped (air conditioned and completely self-contained with its bathroom, dining area, fridge, satellite TV and video) they all seem a bit dilapidated and uncared-for, which makes the hotel rather soulless and uninspiring. Additionally, rooms on the lower floors have no view, so are worth avoiding, while the upstairs rooms are better, although the very steep stairs might put some people off going up further than they need to. Credit cards are accepted, and the hotel has an efficient bureau de change. Out the front is a shady café serving pizzas for US$3, local dishes for US$3.50 and other meals from US$4, and upstairs is a restaurant serving meals around US$7.50. Room rates are US$50 for singles, US$70 doubles and US$80 for triples.

Hotel Marine Mizingani Rd; tel: 2232088, 0747 411102; fax: 233082; email: hotelmarine@africaonline.co.tz. This hotel is in a large old renovated house overlooking the roundabout near the port gates. Inside, a grand staircase winds around an inner courtyard to the rooms on two upper floors, but the splendid potential here has been totally wasted, with threadbare purple carpets and dark brown paint on the walls making the whole place very gloomy. The rooms are all en suite, and fair quality, furnished with

SAFETY IN AND AROUND ZANZIBAR TOWN

Theft from hotel rooms is very unusual, but we've heard from some readers of a scam played by staff in one of the less reputable hotels in Zanzibar Town. Apparently, the guests left a small bag of valuables (passport, air tickets, money, etc) in the hotel safe, only to find items missing when they returned to collect it. It seems that a member of staff had a duplicate key to the safe and removed a few US$20 bills in the hope that the theft wouldn't be noticed. The only way to prevent this happening to you is to store your valuables in a lockable bag or pouch, to prevent tampering when it's out of your hands, or count and write down everything you have in the presence of the receptionist (although this can be embarrassing and possibly a bit too tempting ...). This is not a problem at hotels in the middle and upper price ranges, because most offer individual safe deposit boxes, either at reception, or in the rooms. Several of the budget hotels in Zanzibar Town now run an organised system with a book for guests to write in exactly what they leave.

More serious robberies (sometimes with violence) have occurred on some of the beaches in and around Zanzibar Town. You should not walk here alone, particularly after dark. Other notorious parts of town include the port, and the area around the Garage Club and the Bashasha Bar, especially late at night when drunken youths wander the streets looking for kicks (just as they do in many other parts of the world). Another time to be wary is the hour or two just after sunset during the period of Ramadan, when everybody is inside breaking their fast, and the streets are absolutely deserted.

Zanzibar beds, but those assumed essential facilities (fridge and TV) make things cramped. Bathrooms are tiny – having a shower without falling down the loo is tricky. On the plus side, the staff are great, and free transfers to/from the port or airport are available. Singles are US$55, doubles US$60, plus US$5 if you want a room with a balcony. Pay another US$10 for a room on the upper floor (better views), slightly less for a room on the ground floor (not worth having).

Shangani Hotel Kenyatta Road, PO Box 4222; tel/fax: 2233688; email: shanganihotel@hotmail.com. On busy Kenyatta Rd, near the old post office, this hotel is an adequate choice in the middle range. Rooms have AC, fridge, telephone and satellite TV. Breakfast and other meals are taken in the rooftop restaurant. En-suite doubles are US$65 (US$50 with shared bathroom).

Baghani House Hotel off Kenyatta Rd, PO Box 609; tel: 024 2235654; fax: 2233030; email: baghani@zanzinet.com. In the Shangani area, almost next door to the Dhow Palace Hotel, this is a friendly place, immaculately kept, with just eight rooms – all with simple but pleasant decor, TV, AC and big, clean, spacious bathrooms. Rates include full breakfast served in a small open-air courtyard (there's no restaurant) and – a nice touch – afternoon tea. Singles are US$45, doubles US$50–55.

Coco de Mer Hotel off Kenyatta Rd, PO Box 2363; tel: 024 2230852, 0741 224074; email: cocodemer_znz@yahoo.com, wild-footprints@africaonline.co.tz. In Shangani, off Kenyatta Rd, this is a straightforward, but clean and friendly place with rooms set around a very pleasant airy courtyard, decorated with potted plants. The rooms downstairs are a bit dark, but those upstairs are bright and cheerful. The restaurant does tasty good-value food. A good choice in this range. En-suite singles are US$35, doubles US$50 and triples US$60.

Kid's Play Annexe Hotel Tel: 024 2236315. This strangely named establishment is in the northeast corner of Stone Town, south of Malindi police station. The title could come from the age of the reception staff, and their attitude to service. Whatever, it's uninspiring, with dark cramped rooms, and not good value, so probably worth considering only if others are full. Singles are US$35, and doubles US$50. There are also dormitories where a bed costs US$15.

Narrow Street Hotel Malindi St; tel: 024 2223263; email:narrow22@yahoo.com. In an interesting bit of town, this old hotel has been recently renovated. There are just eight rooms, all neat and tidy, but quite small, so ideally you should know your room-mate well. The en-suite bathrooms are also small and simple but clean. The staff are a bit sleepy, but this is a fair choice in the low-to-middle range. Rates are US$30 per single, US$40 per double, US$50 per triple.

Narrow Street Hotel Annex II PO Box 3784; tel: 024 2233006. This place is off the western end of Kiponda St, and despite the name, is not directly connected to the Narrow Street Hotel. Rooms have en-suite bathrooms, fridge (broken), AC and Zanzibar-style beds, but are all a bit shabby and dreary, and not good value at US$25 for singles, US$35 for doubles.

Blue Ocean Hotel off Kenyatta Road, PO Box 4052; tel: 024 2233566. Just off Kenyatta Rd, near the Dolphin Restaurant, this hotel is pleasant enough, in a big rambling old house full of ladder-stairways and verandas, although overall, it's nothing special and a touch expensive in this bracket. Definitely worth the money however is the Seaview Room, right at the top of the house, with views in all directions over the whole of Stone Town and out across the bay towards the islands. At reception, you also can't miss the rules ('no unmarried couples, no alcohol, no visitors, no credit cards, payment in advance'). All rooms have bathrooms; singles are US$20, doubles US$38 and triples US$55, although rates may be negotiable.

Kokoni Hotel Kokoni, PO Box 1256; tel: 0747 421515. In the Kokoni area between Malindi St and Creek Rd, a short walk behind the BP petrol station, this is the former Hotel Karwan Sarai. It's a big old house and has a range of rooms; some are large and airy with old wooden shutters leading onto a small balcony overlooking the square, while others are small and dark with no view. Most rooms have en-suite bathroom, all have fans, and some also have TV, while the rooftop lounge has great views across Stone Town. It's a quiet place but veering towards soulless. Some more light, some cheery staff and an all-round makeover wouldn't go amiss at all. Singles are US$20, doubles US$35.

Hotel Kiponda Nyumba ya Moto St, PO Box 3446; tel: 024 2233052; fax: 2233020; email: hotelkiponda@email.com, samatours@zitec.org. In the Kiponda area, not far from the main seafront, this is a small, quiet hotel in a building which used to house part of a sultan's harem. It has been renovated in local style and still has an original carved wooden entrance door. The Dutch-Australian-Zanzibari management team have given the place a relaxed and friendly atmosphere: we've received several letters from travellers recommending this hotel. A touch more expensive than the budget hotels with which it is sometimes compared, this place is cleaner, quieter and much better value. All prices are discountable for long stays and for groups, with extra reductions in low season. There's a rooftop restaurant specialising in Zanzibari and seafood dishes. The hotel also has good connections with the local Kenya Airways office and can help with flights and reservations. Single rooms are US$18, doubles US$35, and triples US$45. En-suite doubles are US$45.

Spice Inn Changa Bazaar, PO Box 1029; tel: 0747 415048; fax: 232174. This is one of the town's oldest hotels, with a very impressive façade of balconies overlooking a small square. Inside, on the wide wooden stairway and in the lounge, are several antique pieces of furniture, and the place has a feel of faded elegance, although way past its best. Rooms are basic and mostly quite plain, although some of the ones at the front of the building are spacious. Not all beds have mosquito nets, and the bathrooms are old and rusty. The only reason to stay here is to be at the heart of Stone Town and experience the musty feel of bygone days. Double en-suite rooms range from US$25 to US$30. Smaller rooms with shared facilities are US$20–25.

Clove Hotel Hurumzi St, PO Box 1117; tel: 2236724. This old stalwart stands about halfway along Hurumzi St, but has definitely seen better days. Rooms are plain but clean and would be adequate, but have no mosquito nets. The en-suite bathrooms are aging but functioning. Rates are US$18 single, US$25 double.

Malindi Guesthouse Malindi, PO Box 609; tel: 024 2230165. In the northern part of Stone Town, near the port, this place has been consistently popular with travellers for many years. It's clean and nicely decorated, with a lot of character and a fine collection of old photographs from Arab-ruled and British colonial times and the early years of independence. There's also a bar and restaurant. Rooms with shared bathrooms cost US$15 per person, and rooms with en suite are US$20 per person. Small groups like the room for six, which costs US$60.

Stone Town Inn Shangani Rd, PO Box 3530; tel: 024 2233101, 0741 334872; fax: 2233060. In the Shangani area, next to the Fisherman Restaurant, this small place has clean, straightforward rooms for US$15 per person, or en-suite doubles with AC and hot shower for US$50.

Mzuri Guesthouse Malawi Rd; tel: 024 2230463. In the Malindi area near the port, opposite the Passing Show Restaurant, this is a definite budget place, used mainly by locals and a few backpackers. Rooms are quite small and have a fridge, TV and AC (noisy), and bathroom (small and a bit tired). Singles are US$15, doubles US$30.

Garden Lodge Kaunda St, PO Box 3413; tel: 024 2233298. Near the People's Gardens and the main hospital, this place is simple but neat and friendly, and good value in this range. Upstairs rooms are clean and bright and airy; downstairs they're still spacious and adequate but darker. All rooms have en-suite bathroom, the showers are warm, the breakfast filling and there's a nice little garden terrace out the front. When choosing a room, try to get one at the back as those overlooking Kaunda Rd are noisy. Downstairs singles are US$15, doubles US$20, triples US$30. Add an extra US$10 per person for the upstairs rooms.

Warere Guesthouse PO Box 1298; tel: 024 2231187. In the northern part of Stone Town, very near the port, this is another place which has been popular for many years with travellers on a tight budget. When we were researching this guidebook, a major rebuild was underway, and when finished, rooms with bathroom will be around US$25–30.

Karibu Inn Shangani, PO Box 3428; tel/fax: 024 2233058; email: karibuinn@zanzinet.com. On a narrow street, parallel with Kenyatta Rd, in the Shangani part of town, this very simple, hostel-like place caters mainly for backpackers, budget tour groups or people off overland trucks. The friendly and helpful management can set you up with budget tours, and also run a very well organised safe-deposit scheme. Clean but basic double rooms cost US$25, en-suite doubles are US$30 and en-suite triples US$40. For groups, the inn also has some small dormitories (sleeping between four to seven people – in very saggy beds! – each with its own bathroom) at US$10 per person. If you come alone, a single bed in the dorm costs US$20.

St Monica's Hostel Sultan Ahmed Mugheiri Rd (formerly New Mkunazini Rd); tel: 024 2235348; fax: 2236772; email: cathedral@zanzinet.com. Very near the Anglican Cathedral, on Sultan Ahmed Mugheiri Rd (which everyone still calls New Mkunazini Rd), this hostel is mainly for church guests, but it is also open to the public. The hostel was built in the 1890s and formerly housed teachers and nurses working at the UMCA mission. The reverential atmosphere remains but this place really has an aura, with thick walls, wide staircases, sweeping arches and rooms with balconies (some have views of the cathedral). Rooms are simple and very clean. In the same building is a restaurant, with simple good-value meals. No alcohol is allowed. On the lower floor is a small art workshop where you can buy paintings and hand-printed T-shirts. Straightforward rooms cost US$12 per person, en-suite single are US$28 and en-suite doubles US$32.

Pyramid Hotel Kokoni St, PO Box 254; tel: 024 2233000; fax: 2230045, email: pyramidhotel@yahoo.com. On Kokoni St, between the Malindi and Kiponda areas, this long-standing hotel is just behind the Ijumaa Mosque, a short walk back from the seafront. It's been a budget travellers' favourite for many years – deservedly so – and gets it name from the very steep and narrow staircases (almost ladders) that lead to the upper floors. The rooms all have fans and are cleaned daily, but vary in atmosphere: some are large and bright, others small and dark, so choose carefully. Like the rooms, the shared bathrooms vary – some are spotless, others need attention (though all have hot water). The staff are very friendly, and the rooftop restaurant does good cheap food. Overall, it's a good budget choice. Standard single, double and triple rooms are all US$10 per person. En-suite rooms are US$15 for singles, US$25 for doubles, US$35 for triples.

Jambo Guesthouse PO Box 635; tel: 024 2233779, 0747 414585; email: jamboguest@hotmail.com. In a quiet and peaceful quarter of the Mkunazini area, near the Anglican Cathedral and opposite the Green Garden Restaurant, this straightforward little hotel has a range of rooms, and is a good budget place, which has been justifiably popular with backpackers for many years. The rooms are simple and bright, though can get a bit hot, and the shared bathrooms are OK. Book in advance to arrange a pick up from the port. Singles are US$15, doubles US$20 and triples US$30.

Malindi Lodge Malawi Rd, PO Box 3546; tel: 024 2232359; fax: 024 2233030. In a handy position if you're coming by boat, near the port gates and next to the Ciné Afrique, the Malindi Lodge (not to be confused with the Malindi Guesthouse, see below) is a good choice in the budget range. There are just eight rooms, which are all very simple but clean and light and absolutely spotless. There are no fans, just noisy AC. The shared bathrooms are also basic but clean. This place has links with Sunset Bungalows at Kendwa near Nungwi and can arrange bargain transport there and back. The rate is US$10 per person.

Victoria House Vuga St, PO Box 4137; tel: 024 2232861. Near the People's Gardens, this place is old (in fact, back in the early 1980s it was just about the only budget option on the whole island) and is nothing special, in a fairly modern but dilapidated building, but it's in a nice position and worth checking in case of improvements. Rooms are very spacious but beds and other facilities are decades old. Some rooms have shared bathrooms, others are en suite. The official charge is US$10 per person, but this is reported to be negotiable.

Haven Hotel PO Box 3746; tel: 024 2235677; fax: 2238426; email: havenghouse@hotmail.com. This is a very friendly place, in the southern part of Stone Town between Soko Muhugo Street and Vuga Road, and many budget travellers have written to recommend it. Makame the manager knows what backpackers want, and offers very simple but clean bedrooms and bathrooms, hot water, and a big breakfast with as much tea and coffee as you like. There's a generator in case of power cuts, an organised safe-deposit system, luggage storage, a kitchen for self-catering (free) and travel information boards about Tanzania and other parts of East Africa. The staff can arrange cheap transfers to the coast, boat trips and tours, and they also have bikes for hire. At US$10 per person this is very good value.

Manch Lodge tel: 024 2231918; email moddybest@yahoo.com. Just up the street from the Haven Hotel, this is another friendly budget place, although their penchant for heavy brown furniture makes things a bit cramped. Phone in advance for a pick-up from the port (free), or from the airport (US$2.50). The rate is US$10 per person in singles, doubles or triples, all with an en-suite bathroom.

Florida Guesthouse Vuga Rd, PO Box 1876; tel: 024 2233136. Set back slightly from Vuga Rd, near the Culture Musical Club, this is another low-budget regular. The downstairs rooms are dark and cramped; upstairs ones are a bit brighter. Straightforward singles are US$10, doubles US$20. A smarter double with TV and AC is US$40. There's also a room with four beds and its own (surprisingly nice) bathroom which costs US$40 and is a good budget option for a small group.

Bottoms Up Guesthouse Named after the attached – and very disreputable – bar, this place is hard to find in the narrow alleys between the Spice Inn and the House of Wonders, and might not be worth the effort anyway. Facilities are basic, bathrooms are dilapidated and the atmosphere at night is not pleasant, but with rooms at US$10 per person the guesthouse remains popular with budget travellers. Another attraction is the roof terrace where people relax, sunbathe and swap travel tales.

Flamingo Guest House Mkunazini St, off New Mkunazini Rd, PO Box 4279; tel: 024 2232850; fax: 024 2233144; email: flamingoguesthouse@hotmail.com. The surrounding area is a bit noisy, but this no-frills place is friendly, with simple but clean rooms and bathrooms, and popular with budget travellers. Facilities include TV and video lounge, book-swap service and sale of cold drinks. From the terrace upstairs you get great views of the Anglican Cathedral. Rates are US$8 per person (US$10 per person in en-suite rooms).

Riverman Hotel off Tharia St; tel: 024 2233188; email: rivermanhotel@hotmail.com. Located at the back of the Anglican Cathedral, well signposted off Tharia St, this is a basic guesthouse and definite budget option. Rooms have seen better days but are adequate. This hotel is an agent for the Tazara train on the Tanzanian mainland, and you can buy tickets here.

Pearl Guesthouse Kiponda St; PO Box 4201; tel: 024 2237661. At the eastern end of Kiponda St, this has basic and dirty rooms with dingy shared bathrooms. It's cheap at US$8 per person, but not good value. The en-suite rooms cost twice this price and are even worse value as the bathrooms are grubby and in need of maintenance.

Hotels near Zanzibar Town

The hotels in the outer suburbs of Zanzibar Town are not so convenient for sightseeing, shopping or visiting restaurants, although most run free shuttle services for guests to/from the centre. You can also hire a car or bike to get around town, or use taxis. On the plus side, hotels outside town are generally quieter, often with gardens, or on the beach, and may be the only places with rooms during busy times, such as Christmas or Easter. Those on the south side of town are also handy for reaching the airport, and for people on business trips, as some government and NGO offices are also in this area.

Protea Hotel Mbweni Ruins PO Box 2542; tel: 024 2235478, 2231832, 0741 320855; fax: 024 2230536; email: hotel@mbweni.com; web: www.mbweni.com. South of town, in the Mbweni area, a few kilometres off the airport road, this hotel is in the grounds of Mbweni Ruins, originally built in the 1870s as a school for the children of freed slaves. Today, many visitors rate this as one of the best hotels of its type in and around Zanzibar Town. There are just 13 rooms, all spacious and very comfortable, each with large bathroom, AC, canopy beds, tasteful furniture and small private balcony. The hotel is set in extensive well-maintained grounds with a lush botanical garden (with a nature trail) and a swimming pool overlooking the beach. The food in the terrace restaurant overlooking the sea is recommended, with many visitors staying in Zanzibar Town coming here for lunch or dinner, combined with a swim or a walk in the grounds. Lunches are between US$5 and US$10, and a full evening meal is US$10–25. There is a free shuttle service to and from town, and transfers to/from the port or airport cost US$10 for four people. The ruins are open to visitors, and sometimes the hotel arranges atmospheric open-air dinners amongst the pillars and arches of the school chapel. Also nearby and worth a visit is St John's Anglican Church (see page 170). Nearby mangroves provide good birding, and the hotel has its own list of birds and butterflies seen in the grounds and further afield. The staff are keen naturalists, and can advise visitors on all aspects of local natural history. B&B is US$170 per double, or US$95 per single. Half board is an extra US$15, and full board an extra US$25 per person.

Zanzibar Beach Resort PO Box 2586; tel; 024 2230208; fax 024 2230556; email: zanzbeachresort@zanlink.com. This hotel (formerly the Fisherman's Resort, and before that the Zanzibar Reef) is about 7km from Zanzibar Town and 3km from the airport, between the areas of Mazizini and Mbweni. The hotel is set in landscaped grounds overlooking the sea, with 60 en-suite rooms, and aimed more at groups (discounts are available), although individual tourists stay here as well. The rooms are in large two-storey chalets with whitewashed walls and thatched roofs. There are four rooms in each chalet, two larger ones at the front with sea views, and two smaller ones at the back. All rooms have canopy beds, big bathrooms and a nice veranda, although the furniture seems unnecessarily heavy and dark. The hotel has a restaurant, bar and disco, squash court, gym, swimming pool, conference room, and facilities for fishing and watersports. Single rooms are US$100, doubles US$130. Add US$20 per person if you want a sea view. Half board is an extra US$10 per person; full board is an extra US$18 per person.

Mtoni Marine Centre PO Box 992; tel: 024 2250140, 0741 323226; fax: 024 2250496; email: mtoni@zanzibar.cc; web: www.zanzibar.cc. Situated in Mtoni, on the north side of Zanzibar Town, about 4km from the port, this marine activities centre is also a very good hotel, in extensive gardens overlooking the bay and a large stretch of beach. The management style is relaxed and efficient – a perfect combination. There's a range of rooms: the best rooms in the house, roomy and decorated to a high standard, are in a small two-storey building with views over the ocean, and cost US$60 per person in a double, or US$100 per single. There are also 'club' rooms at US$40 per person in a double, and standard rooms at US$30, single or double. As well as the rooms, Mtoni also offers straightforward self-contained two-bedroomed bungalows for four people at US$100, and a three-bedroomed bungalow for six at US$150, for the whole bungalow. All these options include bathroom, AC and breakfast. The food in the restaurant at Mtoni is very highly rated (one reader said it was Michelin Star quality), and many people come from Zanzibar Town to eat here, even if they're not staying. Snacks start at US$3–5, and you can enjoy an excellent meal for US$10–20. The twice-weekly beach buffet barbecues (US$12) are particularly popular. At the other end of the gardens, Mtoni also has the Mcheza Bar, a more casual place, overlooking the beach, where straightforward items such as sandwiches and burgers (US$3.50) are served. Mtoni is also well known for its popular sunset dhow cruises, which offer great views of Stone Town in the evening light (US$10 per person, including snacks and soft drinks). All-day dhow cruises are also arranged, at US$40 including lunch, drinks and snorkel gear, with discounts for hotel guests. If you want to stay nearer your room, the hotel also has a swimming pool. The staff can also arrange tours, car hire, boat trips and so on. Mtoni Marine is also the official Visa International assistance agent for Zanzibar. A taxi from town to the hotel is US$4, and from the hotel to the airport US$10.

Imani Beach Villa PO Box 3248; tel: 024 2250050, 0741 333731; email: info@imani.it This small and delightful hotel sits right on the beach outside Bububu, about 10km from Stone Town. There are about ten rooms, all decorated in local style. Meals in the Arab-style restaurant, with low tables, cushions and carpets on the floor, are around US$20. A taxi to/from town is US$6.50, and the hotel also has bikes for hire which are free for guests. 'Comfort rooms' with huge beds and en-suite bathroom are US$90 double, or US$45 per single. Simpler rooms in a separate wing are US$25 single, US$50 double.

Salme's Garden Located next to Imani Beach Villa, with the same contact details – or book direct through an agent called House of Wonders, email info@houseofwonders.com; web: www.houseofwonders.com. On the edge of the beach, this beautiful old house – once owned by the sultan and occupied by Princess Salme – is set in lush gardens surrounded by a high wall. It's a private and exclusive place, with just four airy bedrooms, wide verandas and shady balconies, and is a perfect place for hire by small groups (which means you get cheaper rates too). With the lovely old furniture and historical links it's amazing this place isn't a museum; staying is a unique and privileged experience. The only disadvantage is that, like the Imani next door, the high wall doesn't stop the noise of music drifting over when there's a disco at Fuji Beach Bar, a short distance along the sand. Rooms cost US$120–150, and include the services of a cook and housekeeper. You can buy food for the cook to prepare, or use the restaurant at the Imani next door.

Mawimbini Club Village Tel: 024 2231163. Near the village of Chuini, about 20km outside Stone Town, this is an international-style resort complex, part of the Italian VentaClub chain, catering almost exclusively for fly-in package tourists. The hotel consists of bungalows set in a large garden around a central area with swimming pool, restaurant and bar. A theatre has regular dancing and cabaret shows. Doubles cost between US$100 and US$200 per person, full board, depending on the season. To stay here, it is easier to make arrangements through one of the tour companies in Zanzibar Town, as they can phone and check availability for you.

Star Hotel PO Box 2221; tel: 024 2234982. This place is very near the Zanzibar Beach Resort (described below), although not on the coast. Rooms are all en suite and very clean but uninspiring, and although equipped with TV, phone, fan, AC and fridge, are not especially good value. Singles cost US$55, doubles US$60–70.

Island View Hotel Kaunda Rd, Kilimani, PO Box 6; tel: 024 2234605, 2235222; email: islandview@africamail.com. About 2km south of Zanzibar Town, at Kilimani, this is a small and welcoming B&B, run by the friendly Mitha family. Other meals can be ordered, and tea or coffee is available all day free of charge. All rooms are spacious, clean and tidy, with en-suite bathroom, and some have AC, TV and telephone. This hotel is very handy for the airport, and only a few minutes drive from town (transport can be provided). Island View is loosely linked with Chit Chat Restaurant (see page 137), and if you eat at the restaurant you get a discount at the hotel. Rates are good value with singles at US$20, doubles US$30 and triples US$40. AC is an extra US$3.

Coconut Beach Inn PO Box 3587; tel: 024 2235897, 0742 740030; email: coconutbeachinn@hotmail.com. This quiet and simple place is about 9km south of Zanzibar Town, on the road towards Chukwani, about 4km from where the road to Mbweni turns off the main airport road. The owner-managers are relaxed and friendly, and the setting is perfect, with six little cottages around a swimming pool overlooking the beach, with views straight out to Chumbe Island. Evening meals (lots of seafood, around US$4) and lunches are available. Rooms cost US$30 per person.

Bububu Guesthouse PO Box 1929; tel: 024 2250110; email: bububu@zanzinet.com. In Bububu village, about 9km from the centre of town and 5km beyond Mtoni, this guesthouse is a simple place but clean, friendly, very relaxed, and good value. Meals are available, and the guesthouse is very near Fuji Beach (more details on page 184), which has a bar and restaurant. The guesthouse can also arrange spice tours, rental cars and motorbikes. There's a free transfer service to/from town twice a day, or you can catch a *dala-dala*: those on Route B run regularly between Bububu village and Zanzibar Town. From the *dala-dala* stop on the main road in Bububu village, it's a short walk down a dirt track towards the beach to reach the hotel. The tariff here is US$10 per person in en-suite rooms.

Hotels offshore

The following hotels are all on small islands off the west coast of Zanzibar Island, a short distance from Zanzibar Town.

Chunguu Island Guesthouse Changuu Island (more commonly called Prison Island) is about 5km offshore from Zanzibar Town, and many people take boat trips here just for the day (see page 185). It would be nice to stay for a night or two, but unfortunately the government-run guesthouse is not very inspiring – a group of wooden bungalows set back from the main beach – and poor value at US$20 per double, with breakfast. Other meals are available from the island restaurant, or you can bring picnic food from Zanzibar Town. You can book a room in advance at the ZTC office on Creek Rd, or at Livingstone House. There's a chance this place will be privatised and spruced up in the future.

Chapwani Private Island Tel: 024 2233360; email: chapwani@zitec.org or chapwani@houseofwonders.com; web: www.houseofwonders.com. Long, thin and tiny, Chapwani Island (more commonly called Grave Island) is between Changuu Island and Zanzibar Town. There's a small patch of tropical forest, some poignant old graves from the colonial period (for details see page 186), and this small exclusive hotel. There are five bungalows, each with two airy rooms, where the décor is simple but pretty. The rooms themselves might be a bit close together, but there's space on the island for guests to spread out: small paths wind through the forest and mangroves, there's a beach where you can swim all day, and sea-kayaking equipment or snorkelling gear is also available. There's also a shuttle boat to take you to Zanzibar Town, or to Mtoni Marine Centre (which has a noted restaurant), just 20 minutes away. Other boats and ships coming and going to Zanzibar Town also pass the island, so it doesn't quite live up to its 'island hideaway' billing, but it's still unusual and delightful, and well worth consideration. Full board is US$80–100 per person. All shuttle-boat transfers are US$10 each way.

Chumbe Island Lodge Chumbe Island Coral Park (CHICOP), PO Box 3203; tel: 0747 413 582; tel/fax: 024 231040; email: chumbe@zitec.org; web: www.chumbeisland.com. Chumbe Island Lodge is on Chumbe Island, some 12km to the south of Zanzibar Town, and has by far the most interesting offshore accommodation. The island and surrounding reefs are a marine sanctuary called Chumbe Island Coral Park (see page 187), and day trips to the island are available (US$50), but visitors are encouraged to stay overnight in the reserve to get a full appreciation of their surroundings. The lodge has about eight bungalows – all very comfortable and described as 'eco-friendly', and for once this term is used in a genuine manner. Each bungalow has two storeys and is made mostly from local materials, with a lounge-terrace downstairs and a bedroom upstairs. At the rear of the ground floor is a bathroom. More importantly, they are completely self-sufficient with solar panels to provide electricity, funnel-shaped roofs to catch and collect rainwater, and even 'compost toilets' to avoid septic tanks and the pollutants they often produce. Grey water from the showers goes on to flowerbeds where specially chosen plants absorb salts and minerals before the water drains into the ground. This accommodation is unique in Zanzibar, and very unusual in the whole of Africa. Unfortunately, genuine eco-friendliness is not cheap, and it costs US$200 per person per night to stay here in the high season. This includes full board, soft drinks, guides, transfers and all activities. This is on a par with other top-notch wildlife lodges elsewhere in Africa, so if you've got the money a visit here is highly recommended. Chumbe Island Coral Park is recognised internationally as a site of major significance. It is hoped that the Zanzibari government also recognises the island's importance and its potential as a tourism attraction and flagship environmental project.

New hotels in Zanzibar Town

Although the list of hotels above is quite comprehensive, tourism development is growing rapidly on Zanzibar, and you should expect to see several new hotels in and around Zanzibar Town by the time you arrive.

In town itself, the famous old **Africa House Hotel** was undergoing renovation during our research trip and due to open some time in the future under the management of an international hotel group. When the renovations are complete, the hotel will have 13 rooms, at around US$150 a double. In the colonial days this building was the English Club, and after the 1964 revolution it was turned into a hotel by the Zanzibar Tourist Corporation and, it seems, run completely into the ground. At the end of the 1990s, there was still a marble floor, panelled rooms and dusty old hunting trophies on the walls, but the rooms were shabby, the toilets disgusting and the restaurant empty of food. For many years, the only thing that kept running was the terrace bar overlooking the sea – a popular place for sundowners, and one of the best meeting spots in the whole of East Africa, although a large crowd and a small fridge meant the beer wasn't always cold, and many travellers remember the famously surly barman. Although the rooms weren't ready when we visited in 2002, the restaurant was open again, and the famous sundowner terrace was going great guns, now with significant improvements – a big new fridge and two friendly helpful bartenders!

Near the Africa House, the old **Zanzibar Hotel** has been taken over by the same company, and great improvements are also planned here. Expect double rooms in the US$100 range, but changes may be a long way in the future.

On the edge of town, the **Bwawani Hotel** was still run by the government on our research trip, with double rooms from US$52. But this place is well worth avoiding – it's a drab monstrosity on the outside, and abysmally dreary inside, more like a prison than a hotel and spectacularly bad value for money. Non-guests can use the swimming pool for US$1, but it's a third-full of green slimy water – great if you're a mosquito larvae, but not much fun as a tourist. However, reports have been circulating for years that it may be taken over and completely altered (possibly demolished and rebuilt) by an international hotel chain, so look out for major changes and possibly a new name here.

Another international hotel group intends to transform the large building between the Customs House and the Palace Museum on the main seafront. In colonial times this was the **Grand Hotel**, and the name may be used again for the planned 48-room, five-star, US$250-a-night place that is due to open some time in the future.

Further up the coast, between Bububu and Mawimbini, several more new places are planned or under construction, including a big new **Serena Hotel** and several smaller hotels and guesthouses.

MEMORIES OF THE ENGLISH CLUB

We received these reminiscences from a former member of the English Club (now the Africa House Hotel) who served in the colonial government before Zanzibar's independence:

'The English Club, Zanzibar, was the oldest expatriate club in East Africa. The Rules and Regulations of 1888 – the year of its foundation – state that "it is established for the association of an unlimited number of English Residents, together with officers of the Royal Navy stationed in these waters". At this date the RN officers from no fewer than six warships outnumbered the other members.

'By the 1950s eligibility for membership was widened to include "any British subject or American citizen of European extraction". Extraordinary members could also be elected from other residents such as the representatives of European trading companies. Honorary membership was extended to resident members of the Universities Mission to Central Africa, the Catholic Mission to Zanzibar, Armed Forces officers, officers of any British Cable or Merchant Ship or Civil Aircraft, and so on. There was also reciprocity with similar clubs in Nairobi, Dar es Salaam and Mombasa, which was a bonus when travelling in East Africa.

PLACES TO EAT AND DRINK IN ZANZIBAR TOWN

This section lists restaurants, cafés, snack bars, eating-houses and all other places that serve primarily food – or food and drink in equal measures. Bars, and other places which serve primarily drinks, are listed along with music venues in the *Bars, clubs and entertainment* section on page 140.

Some restaurants and cafés in Zanzibar Town are simple and aimed at locals; others are smarter and cater specifically for tourists, expatriates and more well-off residents. The following list, arranged very loosely in order of quality and price, cannot hope to be complete, but it will give you an idea of the type and range of places available. Nearly all the establishments included here are open in the evenings for dinner, and most also open for lunch. Some are open all day. At busy times reservations may be necessary in some of the smarter restaurants.

Tower Top Restaurant Emerson & Green Hotel, Hurumzi St; tel: 024 2230171, 0747 423266. Up on the roof of the well-known and highly rated Emerson & Green Hotel (see the hotel listing) this restaurant has a superb view, which the management modestly claims to be the 'best on the island'. Most visitors seem to agree that it is. The hotel is in a house built in the 19th century by Tharia Topan, financial advisor to Sultan Barghash. As the second-wealthiest man on Zanzibar at the time, he built his home as the second-highest in town, lower only than the sultan's House of Wonders palace. A century later, he would be impressed by the feast still enjoyed by guests every evening. Meals here are relaxed affairs, starting with sunset drinks and cocktails, listening to the sound of the muezzins calling from the minarets around town. Guests sit local style on cushions and carpets, working slowly through starters and several courses of a top quality Arabic-Swahili meal and ending with Arabic coffee. Numbers are limited, so that guests can stay for the whole evening, and reservations are essential. The cost is US$25. At weekends it's US$30, and includes performances by local dancers and musicians.

Kidude Restaurant Emerson & Green Hotel, Hurumzi St; tel: 024 2230171, 0747 423266 Attached to the Emerson & Green Hotel (see the hotel listing) this place was originally set up as a café, but it is now also a more elaborate – and very impressive – restaurant. The ambience is delightful; the room has massive high ceilings, wall-hangings of rich fabrics, oil

'Bedrooms were available for visitors, and for use by members when departing or arriving from home leave. A Dining Room provided meals for single members, if required, and was popular for entertaining. After garages were built at ground level, their roof formed an attractive terrace – which remained one of the most popular meeting spots in Zanzibar Town, especially for drinks at sunset. There was a Billiard Room and a quite extensive Library. Sporting facilities were available at a separate site at the far end of Mnazi Mmoja Road, where tennis and golf were popular, together with squash, cricket and hockey.

'In the latter years of the Club's existence, the fancy dress dance on New Year's Eve was a well-attended event. Among the other communities it was known that the *wazungu* (Europeans) would be walking through Stone Town, or arriving by car at the Club about 8.00pm, dressed in weird costumes, and there was always a sizeable gathering of local people to look with amusement at these strange antics.

'The reader may be of the opinion that this all smacked of a monopoly of club life, but this was not so. There were Goan, Parsee, Bohora, Hindu, Ismaili, Ithnashery and other clubs, each used by a single community, whilst preserving an easy-going and relaxed contact among the various communities resident in the Island.'

paintings, brass urns, antique furniture and ornaments. During the day, you can enjoy great cakes and coffees, or take lunch (the fixed menu changes every day; US$12). In the evenings there's also a fixed menu (US$25), with a vast and impressive range of dishes similar to those offered in Emerson & Green's Tower Top Restaurant (see page 133). On Friday evenings, a buffet is served (US$15). Reservations are usually required at busy times.

Baharia Restaurant Serena Hotel, Shangani Rd; tel: 024 2233587. Not quite as flamboyant as the restaurants at Emerson & Green, but as this is a good quality place nonetheless. The food is a mix of Asian, African and European. Starters like salads or mini kebabs are US$5, while main courses include curries for around US$10, fish in garlic and ginger for US$12.50, chicken in coconut for US$15, and lobster for US$25. In the coffee shop and patisserie, snacks and light meals start from around US$5, and you can have coffee and cakes for US$4.

Mtoni Marine Restaurant Tel: 024 2250117. At Mtoni Marine Centre, just a few kilometres north of Zanzibar Town, this restaurant is too far to reach by foot (and not a pleasant walk anyway) but very well worth the taxi ride. The food is an imaginative mix of European and Swahili techniques and ingredients, and gets many good reports, and – although it's not cheap – it's good value. More details are given in the hotel listings, see page 129.

Dhow Restaurant Tel: 024 2250117, 0742 740336. Floating in the bay, just a short distance offshore from Forodhani Gardens, this traditional Zanzibari boat has been converted into a delightful restaurant, open for lunch and dinner. On the deck are about ten low tables, while guests sit on big cushions resting against the polished woodwork, enjoying lovely views of Stone Town as well as the excellent food. It's a magical Zanzibari experience, especially in the evenings, when you can watch the sunset, and then see the town at night. If there's a bit too much of a sea breeze, starters and cocktails are taken on deck, and the main meal eaten inside. Most evenings there's live traditional music or dance as well. You need to reserve ahead, either at the small booking desk in Forodhani Gardens (open 13.00–21.00) or at the Mtoni Marine and Visa Assistance office next to the Serena Hotel. Meals are set menus, but with lots of choice: predominantly seafood and traditional Zanzibar specialities, with great salads, soups and desserts too. Lunch is US$15, dinner US$25, which includes a welcome cocktail and transfer by smaller boat from the town to the Dhow Restaurant itself.

Monsoon Restaurant Fordhani Gardens; tel: 0747 411362; email: monsoon@zanzinet.com. Near the Fort and the sea-front, this is a smart French-run place serving a good and interesting selection of Mediterranean and Zanzibari food. There are two parts to Monsoon: one is a bar, while the other is a massive open space covered in rugs and cushions. You leave your shoes at the door and lounge around kasbah-style. Thick walls and good ventilation mean it's always cool, and so are most of the clients.

If you want to relax even more, you can even enjoy a hubble-bubble pipe with your Arabic coffee or cocktail. There are also a few seats outside, but so near the road they're hot and noisy. It's far better inside. Main courses cost US$4.50–9.

La Fenice Shangani Rd; tel: 0747 411868; email: fenice@zanzinet.com. Very near the seafront in the Shangani area, near the Africa House Hotel, this is a smart new place with a big open courtyard, serving Italian and Swahili food. As well as the restaurant, it's a cocktail bar and ice-cream parlour. It's not cheap but you get excellent food and a warm welcome here. Starters are US$3–4, and main courses (such as lobster risotto) are US$4–7.

Blues Forodhani Gardens, Mizingani Rd; tel: 0741 328509, email:znz@halcyontz.com. On a pier jutting out above the water, easily reached from Forodhani Gardens and the Old Fort, Blues is a bar and restaurant transported straight from the Cape Town waterfront. This place is popular, open all day, and a breezy haven of peace and tranquillity, although some people might find the unavoidable detachment from the lively and very local-style Gardens a touch uncomfortable. After a reportedly stormy start, the quality now seems good, although the menu isn't especially imaginative. Meals include Swahili-style linefish for US$7.50, Swahili seafood curry (US$12), prawns (US$10) and lobster (US$20). Widely recommended are the pizzas (from US$6), while steaks (US$9), burgers (US$7) and salads (US$2.50) are also served. The bar serves a wide range of drinks, including cocktails – try the shark-bite (US$3.80).

Sweet Easy Restaurant & Lounge Shangani Rd; tel: 0747 416736; email: sweeteasy@retom.com. At the east end of Shangani Rd, between the Tembo Hotel and Forodhani Gardens, several adjectives spring to mind when describing this place: new, cool, smart, relaxed, spacious and trendy. There are two big rooms with rough-hewn walls, electric blue-floor, Tingatinga decorations, copious pot plants and wooden chairs with painted covers. One of these rooms is a bar, with a pool table; a very popular hang-out. The other room is the main restaurant, and there's also a small garden outside. The bar has a good range of drinks, including cocktails for US$2–3. In the restaurant, the food is mostly Thai (thanks to the specialist chef, from Dar!), and there are some good veggie options. Starters cost US$3–3.50, main courses are US$5–7.50. The waiters are friendly and the management have ambitious plans for pan-African meals (from Uganda, Ethiopia, etc) in the future. On Fridays there's live music or a disco, and on Sunday the all-you-can-eat buffets (US$8) are very good indeed. Later in the evening this is where it's at for locals and visitors alike, and in the relaxed atmosphere, single men need not be lonely. Open 11.00 to midnight at least.

Pagoda Chinese Restaurant off Kenyatta Rd; tel: 024 2234688; email: pagoda888@hotmail.com. The Pagoda is just off Kenyatta Rd, near the Africa House Hotel, and run by Mr Chung, who has lived on Zanzibar for many years and used to run a diving outfit, along with his son George and other members of the family. They proudly and justifiably claim to serve the only genuine Chinese food in Zanzibar. The restaurant is open for lunch and dinner, and is highly rated, with good service, immaculate tables, nice surrounds, generous servings and excellent food. Chinese agricultural technicians from projects around the island often come here – so it must be good! Starters range from five spring rolls for US$1 to crispy deep fried squid for US$1.50, and main courses include sweet and sour fish, prawns piripiri, chicken in oyster sauce and satay beef, all around US$5. Roast duck is US$9, and the menu also includes a few specialities, such as Chinese curried crab, for US$6. There are also a lot of vegetarian options, and meals including crisp, fresh vegetables specially flown in from Kenya. Rice and noodles are around US$2. Open daily 11.30–14.30 and 18.00–11.00.

Fisherman Restaurant Shangani Rd; tel: 024 2233658, 0747 414254. Opposite the Tembo Hotel, a small old Zanzibari door leads into a dark building with thick white walls and blue tables, decorated in hybrid Zanzibari-Mediterranean style with fishing nets, crab boxes and other aquatic paraphernalia on the walls. Naturally, the menu is dominated by seafood. Starters such as fish kebabs are US$2.50, simple dishes around US$4–6, and larger dishes such as crab masala or grilled lobster for around US$12, with specials around US$20, and a three-course *menu de jour* (prawns or crab starter, lobster, prawns, crayfish and rice, plus dessert) for US$19. Open 11.00–midnight.

Zi-Bar Victoria Rd; tel: 0747 410410. At the far end of Stone Town, this is a European-style café-bar, with stone floor and stylish wrought iron furniture, serving coffees, beers and wines, ice-cream, sandwiches for US$2.50, pizzas from US$3, big salads for US$3.50. In the attached restaurant, the same meals are also available plus pastas and larger Swahili and seafood dishes in the US$4–5 range. Open evenings until 20.00, and some lunchtimes and afternoons.

Old Fort Restaurant Mzingani Rd; tel: 0744 278737, 0741 630206. Opposite the Forodhani Gardens, Zanzibar's old Arab Fort (known locally as *Ngome Kongwe*) has been here for centuries, and was renovated in the early 1990s. As well as a historical landmark it's now a very impressive cultural centre, with a semi-circular open-air theatre, several smart

FREDDIE MERCURY

The late Freddie Mercury, former lead singer and front man for the rock band Queen, was born in Zanzibar on September 5 1946. His name then was Farouk Bulsara, and his father was an accountant working for the British government in the House of Wonders in Zanzibar Town. His family had immigrated to Zanzibar from India but were originally of Persian extraction. When he was nine, Farouk was sent to boarding school in India, and never returned to Zanzibar. He later went to a college in London, and in the 1970s formed Queen with three other former students.

The current inhabitants of various houses around Zanzibar Town will tell visitors 'Freddie lived here', but his father moved house several times so the claims could all be genuine. Local historians confirm that the Bulsara family lived in the house now occupied by Camlur's Restaurant, and in at least one other house near the post office, either on Kenyatta Road or the small square just behind the post office.

souvenir shops, and this shady outdoor café-restaurant – a very good place to meet friends or take a break from sightseeing in the heat of the day. There's a good selection of snacks for around US$2, local dishes such as chicken and *ugali* (maize meal) or octopus and chips for around US$3, plus coffees, beers and chilled wine. Open for lunch and dinner daily. Every Tue, Thu and Sat, there's an evening of entertainment (*taarab* music, African dance, etc) and a barbeque, which costs US$9 – you may need to book ahead.

Mercury's Bar & Rest Mizingani Rd; tel: 024 2233076. Named after Zanzibar's most famous son (see the Freddie Mercury box), and formerly called Pychi's (pronounced 'peaches', and still often known by that name) this place is in a fine setting on the seafront, overlooking a small beach, the bay, and part of the new port. It's popular, and has a good atmosphere. Wooden tables, director's chairs, and big sunshades are set out on the large wooden deck, and you can enjoy choosing from the menu which unashamedly cashes in on the former Queen-man's apparent dietary preferences – Freddie's Favourite Salad (US$3.50), Mercury's Special Pizza (US$5.20), etc, etc; but despite this corniness the food is very good. Other options include pizzas (margaritas from US$5 up to prawn, beef, tuna and mushroom for US$7), a mixed plate of grilled seafood (US$10), smaller dishes of octopus, grilled fish, pastas (all for around US$5) and a huge range of cocktails from US$2.50–3. It's open daily (with happy hour 17.00–20.00) and there's live traditional music or other entertainment three evenings a week.

Le Spices Rendezvous Kenyatta Rd; tel: 0747 410707; email: les.spices@zitec.org. This was formerly the Maharaja Restaurant, and still serves mainly Indian food, with starters around US$2–3, and main courses such as crab masala, chicken tikka, lamb biriyani or various tandooris for US$5–6. Vegetarian dishes are available, and specials, such as prawn curry, are US$7–8. This place also offers Chinese, French and seafood dishes in the same price range. Credit cards are accepted.

Sea View Indian Restaurant Mizingani Rd; tel: 024 2232132. On the seafront near the People's Palace, this is one of the oldest tourist-orientated restaurants in Zanzibar Town, founded way back in the 1980s and still going strong. With tables on an upstairs balcony and a beautiful view across the bay, it's ideal for breakfasts, lunches and evening meals. During the day (until 18.00) you can enjoy spicy snacks with your drinks – a plate of spring rolls, samosas and bhajis is about US$2 – plus toasted sandwiches for US$2.50, and omelette and chips from US$4. For larger lunches or evening meals the choice is very small, but the quality consistently good. Vegetarian *thalis* (a mixture of dishes) cost

US$7.50, and fish, chicken, squid or octopus in coconut sauce with popadums, plus snacks for starter, a fruit dessert and tea or coffee costs US$7. Open all day from 07.00 until 22.00 or later.

Sambusa Two Tables Restaurant, Victoria St; tel: 024 231979, 0747 416601. Usually called simply Two Tables, this place is particularly worthy of mention, because it's good and because for a long time there was nothing else quite like it on Zanzibar. This is a small place (it really does have only two tables – although one seats about eight people), on the balcony of a private house. It's set back off Victoria St, near the junction with Kaunda Rd, but clearly signposted. The entrance is round the back. Food is cooked by husband-and-wife team Salim and Hidaya, with help from the rest of the family. It's best to phone or call in the afternoon to tell Salim you'll be coming in the evening. A full meal with a variety of local dishes costs US$7. It's highly rated by all who go here, although we heard from some travellers who said pacing themselves was tricky – not knowing how many courses to expect, they filled up on snacks and starters and couldn't do justice to the main course when it arrived!

Nyumbani between Soko Muhugo St and Vuga Rd; email: amir@artlover.com. Nyumbani is similar to Two Tables (described above), in that you eat in someone's house, although the dining-room here is a bit larger. *Nyumbani* means 'at home', and it's most appropriate here, as you're welcomed into the home of Amir, a local artist, and his wife Khadija. They do the cooking, helped by Amir's sister Moulid. We think this place is wonderful, but if you need any more persuading, have a look at the visitors' book. For US$5 you get a set menu of Swahili specialities, with soup and spicy snacks as starters, a main course with local styles of rice, fish and vegetables, and a dessert of dates, fruit and numerous sweets made from nuts, sugar and spices. (Don't forget to check out the works of art while you're there too.) This place is opposite the Haven Hotel, in the southern part of Stone Town between Soko Muhugo St and Vuga Rd. It's open in the evenings only from 19.30, and you need to make arrangements by around noon if you want to eat later that day. You can also book a few days in advance. Unfortunately in the past some people have made reservations then not turned up, so Amir very apologetically asks for a deposit. For more details or reservations it's easiest to visit the house. Alternatively, speak to Amir on the phone (tel: 024 2238170, office – he has a day job!) or leave a message via Manch Lodge (tel: 024 2231918, 0747 413622).

Chit-Chat Restaurant Cathedral St; tel: 024 2239156, 0747 410088. This friendly, family-run place attracts a mix of locals and tourists on all budgets, with very good Indian food and excellent Zanzibari specialities, such as fish in coconut, or garlic prawns, in the US$2 to US$5 range. At the same price are Goan specialities such as *sor potal* (spicy pork) and beef *xachuti* (in spiced coconut sauce), although these sometimes have to be ordered a few hours in advance. Favourable reviews from various newspapers, magazines and guidebooks are proudly pasted to the wall. If you book a table in advance you get a discount – during the day you have to knock on the door. The restaurant is near St Joseph's Cathedral. The owner refuses to pay commission to local touts, so ignore those who tell you this place is closed. Open every evening, except Mon, 18.00–22.00 – even during power cuts as they have a small generator.

Paracuda Restaurant Kenyatta Rd; tel 024 2235871. Despite an initial unappealing ambience, this place has food good and friendly management. Snacks are US$1, burgers or pizzas around US$2.50 and main courses (eg: kingfish in dill butter or periperi prawns) around US$3.50–4.

Radha Food House off Kenyatta Rd; tel: 024 2234808. Tucked away up the narrow street which runs parallel to Kenyatta Rd near the Karibu Inn, Radha Food House is a small and simple place, proudly serving pure vegetarian Indian food. This place is deservedly popular and at busy times it's wise to book a table in advance. A *thali* consisting of dal, rice, lentil and vegetable curries, okra, roti, popadum and lassi costs US$4. You can also get savoury snacks (US$1 for four pieces), cakes and sweets, fresh juices and beers.

Dolphin Restaurant Kenyatta Rd. The staff at the Dolphin have been serving tasty, unfussy Zanzibari, vegetarian and seafood meals for many years. It remains popular, and is open for lunch and dinner, with meals from US$2–3, and specials for around US$3.50.

Fanny's Green Restaurant Kenyatta Road; tel: 2233918. Next to the long-standing Dolphin, this relative newcomer offers a very different atmosphere, with tables inside or outside overlooking busy Kenyatta Rd. Open from 06.30, you can get breakfast (traditional English or traditional Zanzibari) here until 10.00. Lunches and dinners are mainly fish and pizza, with main course US$3.50–4.50.

Namaste Restaurant off Kenyatta Rd; tel: 0741 343322. Near the Dolphin Restaurant and Ocean View Hotel, just off Kenyatta Rd, this long-standing place is clearly signposted upstairs in an old building. It's bright and cheerful with attentive staff, and the large menu contains mainly Indian dishes, but Swahili, European and Chinese specials are also available; main courses around US$3.50–4.50. Open daily for lunch and dinner until 21.00.

Camlur's Kenyatta Road; tel: 024 2231919. A very long-standing favourite, this small and friendly place serves delicious Goan specialities, such as fish and coconut curry, starting from about US$3. Open every evening, except Sunday.

Sunrise Restaurant and Pub Kenyatta Rd; tel: 2239142. Almost opposite Mazson's Hotel, the Sunrise is a simple, friendly, locally owned place serving cheap meals, snacks and drinks in an open-air courtyard above the road. It opens in time for coffee or breakfast and in the daytime it has more of a café feel, while in the evening it's more of a bar, open until late every night. Fish dishes are around US$4–6, chicken and chips is US$2.50. Open 09.00–late.

Green Garden Restaurant, off Mkunazini St. In the southern part of town, near the Jambo and Flamingo guesthouses, this nice, quiet little open-air place offers snacks (around US$3) and meals (US$4–6), served by friendly staff in peaceful and unpretentious surroundings.

Wings Fast Food Shangani. Opposite Tembo Hotel, this is the KFC or McDonalds of Zanzibar, complete with plastic tables, staff in red caps, burgers for US$2.50 and other takeaway favourites.

Spicers Changa Bazaar. Under the venerable old Spice Hotel (see the hotel listings), this is a little street café with straightforward décor, good coffee and cakes at very reasonable prices, and recommended for its people-watching vantage point. They also do omelettes and 'quick lunch' sandwiches for US$1–1.50.

Clove Restaurant Hurumzi St. This is a nice, local, open-air place in a small and shady garden-square opposite the Clove Hotel, run by a friendly group of Swahili women. Their busy times seem to be breakfast and lunch, and you should check in advance if you plan eating here in the evening. Local dishes such as meat and *ugali* (maize meal), rice and fish, or curry and chapati cost US$1–2.

Sea View Forodhani Gardens. This is a simple booth in the park, serving cold drinks and local snacks, with tables and chairs under trees nearby, and a good place to rest after museum visits. At the other end of the Gardens is another similar booth, also selling drinks, snacks and ice-cream.

Passing Show Hotel Malindi Rd. Despite the name, not a hotel, but a Zanzibar institution nonetheless, serving bowls of rice and vegetable sauce or beans for around US$1, or larger plates of rice and meat or chicken for up to US$2. The food is good, and the service quick. This place caters mainly for local people, although visitors are always welcomed, but if you come in a group to eat here please don't move the tables around so you can all sit together – it really annoys the waiters and the other diners who have come for a quiet bite. Open lunchtime only.

Café de Zenj Vuga Rd. This place is worth a mention only because it claims to specialise in 'the selling of fast food', and we heard from some travellers who waited over an hour for hamburger and chips. At least they got something; when we were researching here the kitchen was bare, and the staff politely referred us to another place which actually had food!

Local restaurants

For a real local flavour, the **Tropicana Restaurant**, next to the High Court on Kaunda Road, caters for office workers, serving cheap meals of fish and rice for around US$1. Similar is **Café Kelele** on Shangani Road – a tiny place run by two nice old ladies. At both, only Swahili is spoken.

Near the Masumo Bookshop in the Mkunazini area, just back from the market, are several local teashops, also selling snacks and cakes, including the **Sinai Restaurant**, the **Utamanduni Restaurant**, the **SB Café**, the **Baobab Restaurant** and **Bakan's Restaurant**.

Some readers wrote to recommend a restaurant called **Kawaida** which caters for locals and tourists, in the new part of Zanzibar Town near the roundabout close to Michenzani flats. The staff serve up good Swahili food in a pleasant setting at reasonable prices.

There are many other, seemingly nameless, basic eating houses which you may just stumble across as you walk around the streets of Zanzibar Town. Menus are rare in these simple establishments, and some of the very small places may only have one meal available (sometimes called *chakula leo* – food of the day): you'll have to ask what they've got.

If you're leaving Zanzibar by air, the **airport restaurant** does surprisingly good snacks and meals, including our favourite: squid and chips for US$3.

Hotel restaurants

Several smart hotels in Zanzibar Town, such as those at Emerson & Greens and the Serena, deserve a mention in their own right, and are listed above.

Among the mid-range hotels, the restaurant at **Mazsons Hotel** has good main courses in the US$4–10 range. The rooftop restaurant at the **Shangani Hotel**, on Kenyatta Road, has also been recommended, with simple main courses around US$4 and fine views. More recommendations come for the rooftop restaurant at the **Chavda Hotel**, just off Kenyatta Road, where good Indian meals are in the US$5–9 bracket.

Cheaper, but very good value, the restaurant at the **Hotel Kiponda** serves speciality Zanzibari and seafood dishes for US$3–5, but you may need to order some time in advance. The restaurant at the **Coco de Mer Hotel** is friendly and offers good food: beef escalope, masala jeera and chicken Chinese are all US$4.50, and vegetarian options go for US$3.

Food stalls

For very cheap eats, and a wonderful taste of the local atmosphere, by far the best place to eat in the evening is at **Forodhani Gardens**, on the seafront opposite the House of Wonders. This is a gathering place for local people and tourists, and as the sun goes down, a long line of stalls fire up their braziers and hurricane lamps, and serve food such as fish and meat kebabs, grilled squid and octopus, chips, fishcakes, samosas, chapatis and 'Zanzibar pizzas' – more like a filled savoury pancake. Most of the food is grilled on hot coals in front of you, and served on a paper plate. Prices are very reasonable, and a filling plate will cost between US$1 and US$2. You can simply stroll along the line of stalls, seeing what takes your fancy, asking the price and buying a few items at each, or get a whole plate put together at one stall. Other stalls sell water, sugar-cane juice, ice-cream and cold drinks, and there are also lots of souvenir sellers. All in all, an evening at Forodhani Gardens is one of the highlights of a trip to Zanzibar.

Another place for snacks is the street outside the Ciné Afrique cinema in the Malindi area, or outside the Majestic Cinema on Vuga Road. As crowds gather for the evening films, stalls do a brisk trade in peanuts, crisps, chips, cakes, chapatis and samosas.

Food shopping

If you are self-catering, or just going on a picnic for the day, Zanzibar Town has a large market selling many types of fruit and vegetables, plus fresh fish and meat. You can also buy fresh bread in the market from the salesmen who ride in from the bakeries in the suburbs with large baskets on the backs of their bicycles. Dotted around the town are many small shops with a supply of basics, such as bread, biscuits, some fruit and vegetables, and maybe a few tinned items. As these foods are mainly for local people, prices are low. For more choice go to the 'container stores' (they're built in converted shipping containers) along Creek Road or to the shops in the street near the Ciné Afrique, where you'll find a good range of food in tins and packets, imported mainly from Kenya, but also from other parts of the Indian Ocean. Most items are reasonably priced, only slightly more than if bought in Dar or Mombasa. The best supermarket with the widest stock in Stone Town is the Shamshuddin Cash & Carry Supermarket, off Creek Road, near the market.

BARS, CLUBS AND ENTERTAINMENT

The number of bars in Zanzibar Town grows steadily each year as visitors continue to come in ever-increasing numbers. Some bars cater almost exclusively to tourists, others mainly to locals (mostly Tanzanians who have migrated to Zanzibar from the mainland, as indigenous Zanzibaris are generally Muslim and don't drink). Usually available are Tanzanian, Kenyan, South African and international beers and soft drinks, plus local and imported spirits. Wines are mostly South African.

Many of the larger hotels have separate bars, open to non-guests, and many of the restaurants and cafés mentioned in the section above also serve drinks.

Africa House Hotel Shangani. No visit to Zanzibar is complete without a visit to the terrace bar at the Africa House Hotel (see page 131) in Shangani, where people have been meeting up for drinks at sunset since colonial days. You can order snacks and meals (US$2–5) to enjoy on the terrace, and a smarter inside restaurant is promised. Especially popular among locals and the more adventurous visitors are the traditional pipes (also knows as hubble-bubble pipes, water pipes or, correctly, *shisha* pipes).

Mercury's Mizingani Rd. As well as the Africa House Hotel, also good for sundowners is Mercury's (listed under restaurants), which serves drinks and food all day and long into the evening. This place is noted for its happy hour – out of high season running generously

---

DAFU

A delicious Zanzibari snack is one of the young coconuts that can be found all over the island when they are in season. Locally they are called *dafu*. Around town, they are displayed at the side of the road or in the market, like a pile of rough, light brown footballs. You choose your coconut and the salesman will chop off its top with a knife so that you can drink the milk inside. It is very refreshing. After that, he will carve a makeshift spoon from part of the coconut shell, so that you can scoop out the fresh tender 'meat' from inside.

from 17.00 to 20.00 – and its excellent range of cocktails. *Shisha* pipes are also available (and popular). If you're here for the scenery more than the beer, in the May–September period the angle of the sun means the sunsets are easier to appreciate at Mercury's than at the Africa House (which is better from October to April).

Starehe Club Shangani. Just 50m down Shangani Rd from the Tembo Hotel, the Starehe is a low-key and peaceful place with a terrace overlooking the bay. The staff are friendly and the beer (reasonably priced) is nearly always cold. Don't be put off by the wire mesh between the customers, the barman and the sea, nor by the souvenir stall at the entrance. This is the sort of place where you'll almost certainly end up chatting with the locals – and we don't mean fishermen! This place is due for renovation soon which might alter things, as a restaurant, ice-cream parlour and marine sports centre are planned.

New Happy Bar Shangani. Next to the Africa House Hotel, this joint has a very strong local flavour, which lurches dangerously towards the dire and disreputable, and is frequented mainly by off-duty hookers and tour touts rapidly spending their ill-gotten gains. The attached New Happy Lodge seems to cater for the same clientele, and is best avoided.

Garage Club Shangani. Almost opposite the Starehe is the vastly different Garage Club, a fully air-conditioned and (fortunately) fully soundproofed disco, where the music is a loud and eclectic mix of house, hip-hop and reggae, and African and European pop. You can't miss this place – with outside walls painted in black and white zebra stripes. Entry is US$2, although often free for women. It rocks till dawn at weekends.

Bwawani Disco Bwawani Plaza Hotel. There are discos most nights at the dire Bwawani Plaza Hotel (see the hotel listings), in a dark and equally seedy room under the swimming pool. Weekends are the most popular, entry is US$1.25 and evenings don't usually warm up until about midnight. (If this hotel is renovated, the disco might also get a lick of paint and some decent furniture too, but don't hold your breath. Or rather, do, if you visit the loos here.)

Live music

For live music, there is no one particular venue in Zanzibar Town, but local artists – from traditional *taarab* to Afro-pop and rap – often perform at bars such as Sweet Easy, Mercury's or the Starehe Club. To find out what's going on, ask at your hotel or look for posters around town advertising special events. The Arab Fort is another good venue for live music – mostly traditional musicians and dancers, but sometimes contemporary performances too. A couple of times each week a 'Night at the Fort' evening is organised, which includes at least two performances plus a barbecue dinner. There are often performances on other nights too. The best thing to do is call in at the Fort during the day, and ask the staff at the desk what's happening in the evening.

AIR TRAVEL COMPANIES

For travel by air *away* from Zanzibar Island, to either Pemba, mainland Tanzania, or elsewhere in Africa, you have several choices, depending mainly on your budget and the way you want to go. These are outlined below. Getting *to* Zanzibar by air is covered on pages 76–80.

International airlines

Air Tanzania Vuga Road, near junction with Creek Rd; PO Box 773; tel: 024 2230297; fax: 2230213. Planes of the Air Tanzania Corporation (ATC) fly between Zanzibar and Dar es Salaam, where you can connect to any other destination on the Air Tanzania network or transfer to a flight on another airline. Air Tanzania has a reputation for being very unreliable (locals say ATC means Any Time Cancel), and when we were researching this book the staff were not very helpful and the phones didn't work. According to the timetable, however, there are daily flights between Zanzibar and Dar, taking about 20–30 minutes and costing US$43 one way. A twice-weekly flight from Zanzibar to Kilimanjaro International (between Moshi and Arusha), via Dar, costs US$123.

Kenya Airways Vuga Rd; PO Box 3840; tel: 024 2235775, 2232042; fax: 2237536; email kenyaair@zanlink.com. Air Kenya's regional service includes flights between Zanzibar, Mombasa and Nairobi, from where you connect with any other airline. There are flights to Nairobi five times per week in the low season, and daily in the high season. The one-way fare Zanzibar–Nairobi is US$188. At the time of research, flights between Zanzibar and Mombasa were in a state of flux. Some flights were going via Nairobi (which involved a change of plane), although the ticket cost was less than the normal Zanzibar–Nairobi flight. Air Kenya also has direct flights from Zanzibar to Mombasa, four times per week, for around US$100 one-way. Bizarre but true. In Nairobi you can connect to international flights to Europe and elsewhere. Kenya Airways is part owned by the Dutch airline KLM and shares many of its routes between Africa and Europe.

Ethiopian Airlines Kaunda Rd; tel: 024 2230458, 2239466. With twice-weekly flights from Zanzibar to Addis Ababa, connections to Europe, and good fares (although sometimes long connections), this is an increasingly popular way to go between Zanzibar and Europe.

Gulf Air Mizingani Rd; PO Box 3197; tel: 024 2232824, 2233772/3. Technically, this place is called Salama Tours, but they have a large Gulf Air sign, wear Gulf Air uniforms, can confirm Gulf Air reservations and can issue Gulf Air tickets, so that will do for most customers. At the time of research, however, Gulf Air flights were not landing at Zanzibar. There are three flights a week between Dar es Salaam and Abu Dhabi or Muscat, with connections to other destinations in Arabia and the Indian Ocean, but connections to Europe are not good and may involve overnight stops or long waits.

Regional and local air companies

As comparatively few international flights land at Zanzibar Airport, and so many arrive at Dar, several local and regional air companies fly regularly between Dar and Zanzibar. Flights take just 20–30 minutes, and most tie in with long-haul international arrivals and departures. They are also reasonably priced and reliable, making this air hop an increasingly attractive alternative to a transfer by ship (which until recently has been the most usual way to go).

The regional air companies fly from Zanzibar Town to Pemba Island, Dar es Salaam, Mombasa and to other places on the mainland, such as the national parks of Selous and Ruaha in southern Tanzania, or even direct to the northern attractions such as Serengeti and Kilimanjaro.

Coastal Travels Zanzibar airport; tel: 024 2233112; email: aviation@coastal.cc; web: www.coastal.cc. This company is based in Dar es Salaam and also has an office at Zanzibar airport. Coastal operates regular flights between Dar, Zanzibar, Mafia Island, and the Selous and Ruaha national parks in southern Tanzania. Between Zanzibar and Dar there are two or three flights each day in each direction. Flights also go to Arusha, Pemba and Tanga daily. Fares are: Zanzibar–Dar US$55, Zanzibar–Arusha US$190, Zanzibar–Selous US$130. Coastal also offers two-day all-inclusive safaris to Selous for US$480 per person.

Precisionair Flight Services Kenyatta Rd; tel: 024 2234521; fax: 2234520; email: pwznz@africaonline.co.tz; web: www.precisionairtz.com. This company is based in Arusha, with another main office in Dar, and a branch in Zanzibar. There are daily flights between Zanzibar and Dar, flights most days between Zanzibar and Arusha, and twice weekly between Zanzibar and Kilimanjaro International Airport, plus other services to many other destinations all over East Africa. Precision's office in Zanzibar Town is next to Mazson's Hotel, but their flights are also sold by several travel agents around town. Some sample fares from Zanzibar: to Dar US$55; Arusha US$165; Kilimanjaro International US$146. At the time of research, Precisionair were about to commence operating direct flights between Zanzibar and Mombasa, which may provide a handy alternative to Air Kenya's service.

ZanAir PO Box 2113; main office, Malawi Rd, Malindi; tel: 024 2233670, 0742 750478, 0747 410077; fax: 233768; branch office, Zanzibar airport; tel: 024 232993, 0742 750476; email: zanair@zitec.org; web: wwwzanair.com. The largest air charter company in Zanzibar, ZanAir runs several regular services including between Zanzibar and Dar, and between Zanzibar and Pemba. Flights between Zanzibar and Dar are US$45 each way, and go at least once daily, leaving around 07.00, with afternoon flights about three times per week. Between Zanzibar and Pemba costs US$65 each way (for more details on the Pemba flights see the *Getting there* section of the *Pemba* chapter on page 231). If you want a safari on the Tanzanian mainland, ZanAir runs daily flights to and from Selous National Park, via Dar, for US$120 each way. ZanAir also runs an air charter service, and on some charter flights, spare seats are sold to individuals. Charter rates vary according to the aircraft and destination, so you should contact the company direct for details; as an example, a seven-seater between Zanzibar and Dar is US$340, Zanzibar–Pemba US$570, Zanzibar–Mombasa US$1070, and Zanzibar–Arusha US$1700.

Air travel agents

If you need a long-haul air ticket, it's usually easier to use the services of a specialist agent, rather than trawling around all the different offices. The following companies offer a good service.

United Travel Agency Gizenga St; PO Box 122; tel: 024 2232258, 2230874; fax: 2232391; email: uta@zitec.org. This is one of very few specialist airline agents in Zanzibar, dealing in international flights rather than local tours, and are one of only three IATA-approved agents in Zanzibar. They represent all airlines (with flights departing from Zanzibar and from Dar es Salaam) and can issue tickets. Their office is on Gizenga St behind the Arab Fort. Visa card payments are possible.

Maha Travel and Tours Vuga Rd, PO Box 1511; tel: 024 230029, 0747 418344; email: mahatravel@zanlink.com. This company represents several carriers, and specialises in flights to Europe, mainland Africa and some other parts of the world. Approved IATA agent.

SHIPPING COMPANIES

Several shipping companies operate large passenger ferryboats between Zanzibar, Pemba, Dar es Salaam and other points on the mainland. As the number of flights between Dar and Zanzibar increases, and airfares become increasingly competitive compared to boat fares, the number of services has reduced markedly over the years. Also, the timetables produced by the shipping companies are notoriously subject to change, but the boats themselves generally do arrive and depart when they're supposed to.

The services used by most tourists are operated by the companies listed below, which all (apart from the Zanzibar Shipping Corporation) have their offices just inside the gates of the new port in Zanzibar Town. Schedules and prices are usually chalked up on a board outside each office. You can buy a ticket on the day, up to an hour or so before the boat departure but, if possible, it's safer to reserve a seat in advance. Touts and hustlers often hang around the boat ticket offices, encouraging you to go to one company instead of another. This can be disconcerting, and as an alternative you can buy your ticket through one of the tour companies listed above. This can often save time and hassle, as the tour companies should be up-to-date on the latest timetables, and it usually does not cost you any more money (as the tour company gets a commission from the shipping company); however, some tour companies do charge extra for this service, so check before you make arrangements.

The companies and boats are outlined here; schedules and fares (and more details on getting *to* Zanzibar by sea) are given in *Chapter 4 – Practical Information* on page 76.

Africa Shipping Corporation Tel: 0741 610884. This company operates the *Flying Horse*, a fast catamaran which runs once daily in each direction between Zanzibar and Dar.
Azam Marine Ltd Tel: 024 2231655, 0741 334884. This company operates the *Seabus* high-speed ships between Zanzibar and Dar es Salaam. It also operates the *Serengeti* ship between Zanzibar and Pemba.
Sea Express Ltd Tel: 0744 278692. A large hydrofoil called *Sea Express* runs daily between Zanzibar and Dar. This company also runs a boat called *Sepideh* which runs erratically about twice per week between Dar es Salaam, Zanzibar and Pemba.
Sea Star Services Tel: 0747 411505. This company runs a fast catamaran called *Sea Star* between Dar and Zanzibar.
Zanzibar Shipping Corporation Tel: 024 2230302, 2232578. This state-owned line operates the *Mapinduzi* between Zanzibar, Pemba and Dar. This is primarily a cargo ship with deck space, and the service is used by local people as it is cheap: about US$3 for Zanzibar to Dar. Some travellers on a tight budget also use it but the service is irregular and unreliable. The company's main office is in the Mambo Msiige Building in the Shangani part of Zanzibar Town, but you can also get information and tickets from an 'office' (a hole in the wall) at the Marine Studies Institute, opposite the Zanzibar Cultural Centre (formerly the Old Dispensary). A noticeboard outside the office shows details (in Swahili) of the next departures and arrivals.

Other shipping companies
You might also look out for the *Canadian Spirit* – a large cargo ship going between Dar and Mtwara (in southern Tanzania) once per week, via Zanzibar and Mafia Island, although when we were researching this book the service had been suspended. It may recommence, or another ship might start covering the same route, although it's only worth persevering with this if you want to reach Mafia or the far south of Tanzania without flying.

Travel by dhow
Non-Tanzanians are not allowed to travel by dhow in any direction between Dar and Zanzibar, although a few intrepid travellers do find dhow captains willing to take them on board. It is also illegal for tourists to travel by dhow from Zanzibar to Pemba, but again some travellers have reported finding captains who are willing to take them, and the price includes 'fees' paid to encourage port officials to turn a blind eye. Most of these boats are motorised, but you may find a few still travelling under sail. There is no set procedure; the best way to do things seems to be to go to the port at low tide, and find a boat which may be sailing in the next few hours. You may be lucky, but remember that it is against the law, so you may not have much luck in finding a boat that will take you. Also remember that although it may appear to be a romantic way to travel, dhow voyages are not for the faint-hearted (see page 82). If you get into any trouble (some dhows are notoriously overloaded and unseaworthy), you'll be completely on your own.

The rules concerning dhow travel between Pemba and Tanga or Mombasa seem to be a bit more relaxed (see page 231).

TOUR COMPANIES
In Zanzibar Town, it seems that every other shop or office is a tour company, and it's always easy to find someone to arrange/organise tours within Zanzibar. The

TELEPHONING ZANZIBAR

If you are telephoning a hotel to make a room reservation from elsewhere in Tanzania, and Kenya or Uganda, note that the area code for all of Zanzibar (Zanzibar Island and Pemba Island) is 024. Within Zanzibar you do not need to use the 024 code. For calls from other countries, the international code for Tanzania is +255, then 24 for Zanzibar. Mobile phones have six-digit numbers and have a code of either 0741, 0742 or 0747; you do need to prefix any mobile number with a code, wherever you're phoning from.

problem is finding a *good* tour company, and the following section should help you find something suitable.

The most popular tours organised from Zanzibar Town are boat excursions to Prison Island and the trips around the plantations called 'spice tours'. (For more information, see the *Spices and spice tours* box on page 146) Most companies also arrange tours to the Jozani Forest Reserve to see the monkeys, trips to Kizimkazi to see the dolphins (details on these places are given in the *Zanzibar Island* chapter), and visits to old palaces and other ruins in the Zanzibar Town area or elsewhere on the island. You can also usually arrange transport to the beaches on the north or east coasts and other parts of Zanzibar with a tour company.

Many tour companies can also make hotel and ship reservations, flight bookings, car hire arrangements, and so on. Check the arrangement before organising this, though. Some companies make no charge for the service (they get a commission from the transport company or hotel they arrange for you), some charge a small fee (which is probably fair enough), but others charge a pretty hefty fee for the service, which can sometimes be for no more than making a couple of phone calls on your behalf.

Tour prices are usually quoted in US dollars (although they can be paid for in TSh or other currencies), and tend to vary considerably between the different companies. A lot depends on the quality you're looking for. At one end of the scale, budget outfits offer cheap and cheerful tours, where you'll be sharing a basic minibus or *dala-dala* with several other tourists, and the quality or knowledge of your guide may be poor. At the other end of the scale, you can arrange a private tour for just two or three people, in a good quality vehicle (air-conditioned if you want it) with a knowledgeable guide. Good companies can provide guides who conduct the tour in French, German, Italian and some other languages.

This is not to knock the cheaper outfits: many tourists go on budget tours and have an excellent time. In the same way, some of the so-called upmarket companies may rest on their laurels a bit and not be up to scratch. It is therefore worth comparing a few tour companies before finally arranging your tour, and when comparing prices it is also very important to compare exactly what you get for your money. Your best source of recommendations (good or bad) is always other tourists and travellers, so talk to some of them if you can before signing up for anything. All the companies listed here have been recommended by readers of previous editions of this book.

To get an idea of prices, budget companies – running tours which you share with other people – offer the following rates: Prison Island Tour US$5; Spice Tour US$10; City Tour US$10; Dolphin Tour US$25; Jozani Forest Tour US$15. All these rates are per person, but for the tour only, and do not include extras like entrance fees (for the Palace Museum this is US$2, for Prison Island US$4, for Jozani Forest US$4).

SPICES AND SPICE TOURS
Gemma Pitcher

Sooner or later every visitor to Zanzibar Island (Unguja) will be offered a 'spice tour' – a trip to the farmlands just outside Stone Town to see aromatic plants and herbs growing wild or cultivated in kitchen-gardens. Even if you decline a tour, the array of spices on offer in the souvenir shops or heaped in baskets in the local markets will tell you that spice is central to Zanzibar's history and economy.

The history of spices in Zanzibar begins early in the 16th century, when the 'spice race' between the major European powers to control the lucrative trading routes to the Far East was at its height. Portuguese traders gained a toehold on Zanzibar as part of their plan to rule the coast of East Africa and imported various plants, including spices, from their colonies in South America and India. Some land was cleared for plantations, but the Portuguese never really developed their presence on Zanzibar beyond a military one.

It was left to the Omani Arabs, who ruled Zanzibar from the early 19th century, to develop Zanzibar economically as a spice-producing entity. Sultan Seyyid Said, the first Omani sultan to govern Zanzibar, quickly realised the potential of his new dominion, with its hot climate and regular rainfall, as a location for spice farming. With the demise of the slave trade in the late 19th century, spices became Zanzibar's main source of income.

When the era of the sultans ended and the long arm of the British Empire reached Zanzibar, the island's new colonial administrators encouraged the farming of spices and other useful plants, bringing European scientists to establish experimental agricultural stations and government farms such as those

If you want a private tour with a mid-range or top-quality tour company, the rates are more likely to be around the following: Prison Island US$20–40; City Tour US$20–45; Jozani Forest US$35–45; Spice Tour (half day) US$25–35, (full day) US$45–55; Dolphin Tour US$45–75; Nungwi US$45–65. These prices are per person, for a minimum of two passengers, and usually include all entrance fees, although you should check this when booking or comparing prices.

While in Zanzibar you can also use tour companies to set you up with tours to Pemba, to the Tanzanian mainland, or to Kenya and even further afield. In recent years there's been significant growth in the number of companies offering fly-in safaris to the national parks of Selous and Ruaha in southern Tanzania. Logistically it's easier to get there than to the northern parks of Serengeti and Ngorongoro, although many companies offer this option too.

All tour companies have to be licensed by the government of Zanzibar and, if you have a reason to be dissatisfied, you can complain to the Ministry of Tourism who may take action against the company on your behalf, although in reality there's little control. It is, therefore, best to use only registered companies. If you decide to use unofficial operators, take care. We heard of a group of travellers who arranged things with a company which turned out to be bogus, and were then attacked and robbed when their minibus was on a remote stretch of road. The whole thing appeared to be a scam set up between the driver and the robbers, but don't let it worry you too much – it was an isolated event.

Most of the companies listed here can arrange tours on the spot (or with a day's notice), but you can also make prior arrangements by phoning, faxing or emailing in advance. At a push, you could try writing, but these days it's unusual;

at Kizimbani and Kindichi. Today these areas still contain spice plantations controlled by the modern Tanzanian government.

But spices in Zanzibar today are by no means simply the preserve of governments keen to produce cash-rich export products or a useful tourist attraction. For the ordinary people of Zanzibar, spices and useful plants are a vital part of everyday life and a rich element in the island's strong and vibrant culture. The spices grown in village kitchen-gardens give their flavour to the distinctive cuisine of Zanzibar, provide innumerable cures for everyday ailments, and yield the dyes and cosmetic products needed to celebrate weddings and festivals.

A spice tour is probably the best way of seeing the countryside around Stone Town and meeting rural communities. Guides take you on a walking tour of the villages and plantations at Kizimbani or Kindichi, picking bunches of leaves, fruit and twigs from bushes and inviting you to smell or taste them to guess what they are. Pretty much all the ingredients of the average kitchen spice rack are represented – cinnamon, turmeric, ginger, garlic, chillies, black pepper, nutmeg and vanilla among many others. Local children follow you all the way round, making baskets of palm leaves and filling them with flowers to give to you. At lunchtime, you'll stop in a local house for a meal of pilau rice and curry, followed by sweet Arabic coffee and perhaps a slice of lemongrass cake. Many spice tours include a visit to the Persian baths built by Sultan Said for his harem, and stop at Fuji or Mangapwani beaches just outside Stone Town for a swim on the way back.

All in all, even if horticulture isn't one of your interests, a spice tour is still an excellent way of gaining an insight into one of the most important aspects of rural life in Zanzibar.

include the PO Box number in the address and allow between three and five weeks for a reply.

Recommended tour companies based in Zanzibar Town include the following (listed alphabetically):

Asko Travel & Tours Kenyatta Rd, next to the old Post Office; tel: 0747 411392. A small and rather informal outfit, but with very friendly and helpful management. Just three straightforward tours are offered, and bike, scooter and car hire can also be arranged.

Eco & Culture Tours Hurumzi St, opposite Emerson & Green Hotel; tel 024 36808; email:ecoculture@gmx.net; web: www.ecoculture-zanzibar.org. Relatively new on the scene, this tour company is deliberately not trying to do what all the other companies do. For example, instead of the ubiquitous 'standard' spice tour, this company takes guests to plantations and gardens guided by a local herbalist, and as well as a visit to Jozani Forest, walks in the community forest at Ufufuma are arranged. Village tours are another option – a good opportunity to meet local people, whereas dolphin trips are particularly avoided. Trips are slightly more expensive than those arranged by some other tour companies in Zanzibar but they are refreshingly different. The eventual plan is for profits from tours to be put back into various community schemes around the island.

Fernandes Tours & Safaris Vuga Rd; PO Box 647; tel: 024 2230666; tel/fax: 024 2233102; email: fts@zanlink.com. This small, friendly and well-connected company used to work mainly with incoming tour groups from Britain, South Africa and elsewhere, but is now branching out to provide good-quality tailor-made trips around Zanzibar for groups and individuals in the mid-range price bracket. You can arrange things on the spot, or in advance.

UNDER SAIL ON ZANZIBAR

Then I'll go sailing far,
Off to Zanzibar,
Though my dream places seem,
Better than they really are.

Popular song (1950s)

In Zanzibar, of course, things can seem even better than your dreams, although if you're keen on serious yachting, the opportunities here are (perhaps surprisingly) limited. The only operator offering sailing excursions with a modern yacht is **Zanzibar Sail**, based in Nungwi (see that section in *Chapter 6 – Zanzibar Island* for more details.

For a wonderful taste of sailing in traditional Zanzibari fashion, several operators have wooden dhows and run excursions for a few hours or a day. These are very relaxing affairs, and you certainly don't have to be a sailor to take part. The experienced crew members do all the hoisting of ropes and so on, while you lounge on the deck, drink in hand, with the skyline of Zanzibar town or the palm-lined coast on one side, and the endless clear blue ocean on the other...

The Zanzibar Dive Centre – One Ocean Ltd (details under *Dive companies* in *Chapter 4*, see page 109) offers a classical dhow cruise most evenings from 17.30 to

Fisherman Tours Vuga Rd; PO Box 3537; tel: 024 2238791/2, 0747 412996/7; fax: 024 228790; email: reservation@fishermantours.com; web: www.zanzibar-tours.com. This well-established and experienced company has skilled and efficient staff, and caters for overseas tour groups, as well as individuals and small parties, offering a total guided and escorted service. They have their own fleet of vehicles, and most drivers are equipped with mobile phones. Other services include the organisation of wildlife safaris on mainland Tanzania, as well as the usual tours around Zanzibar, plus car hire, hotel bookings, ground transfers and so on. In 1999 Fisherman Tours received quality awards from two business organisations based in Europe and America. The office is on Vuga Rd, near Air Tanzania. They also have full credit card facilities.

Jasfa Tours Shangani; PO Box 4203; tel: 0741 340035, 024 2234027; email: jasfatours@yahoo.com. A well-established company, Jasfa has an office near the Africa House Hotel, catering for groups from overseas, and for individuals arranging things on the spot. Any budget level is catered for. The management is calm and collected, and can also arrange car hire, chauffeur-driven transport, a wide range of excursions such as spice tours and boat trips, plus guides (English-, French-, Italian-, Spanish- or Arabic-speaking) for tours of Stone Town or any of the ruins elsewhere on Zanzibar Island. They also arrange safaris on the Tanzanian mainland, plus plane and ship tickets.

Madeira Tours Opposite Baghani House Hotel; PO Box 251; tel/fax: 024 2230406; email: madeira@zenjcom.com. All the usual tours are offered by this switched-on and efficient company, plus air ticket reservations, safaris on the mainland, and car, motorbike and bicycle hire.

Mreh Tours, Baghani St, near the Chavda Hotel; PO Box 3769; tel: 024 2233476; email: mrehtours@zanzinet.com. This company offers all the usual tours, and is especially keen on bicycle hire and tours by bike. One itinerary is a nine-day trip around the island (no doddle even on Zanzibar's flat roads, as the bikes are the traditional steel Chinese type, not tip-top lightweight jobs) but shorter variations are possible. Costs are around US$50 a day

19.30. This costs US$20 per person, including drinks, and there's a minimum of only two people required. For US$40, you can go on a longer sailing trip, which leaves Zanzibar Town in the afternoon, and ends at Mtoni Marine Centre, where a fine dinner (included in the price) is served.

Mtoni Marine Centre based at Mtoni, 4km north of Zanzibar Town, has two dhows, and offers evening or all-day cruises and sailing trips to smaller islands. For more details see the Mtoni listing in *Hotels near Zanzibar Town*, page 129.

Adventures Afloat (tel: 0747 423162, 024 2239101; email: adventure@zanlink.com; web: www.safariblue.net) has a fleet of nine motorised traditional wooden dhows, and offers full-day 'Safari Blue' excursions in the bays around the southern end of Zanzibar Island. The trip is a luxurious experience, and includes a huge buffet lunch, served at tables under shade on a 'desert-island' sandbank, as well as stops for swimming and snorkelling (equipment included). In the fleet is a traditional *ngwala* sailing boat, which you can have a go at sailing. There's also a good chance of seeing dolphins. At the end of the day, the dhows return to Zanzibar under sail, wind permitting. Each dhow takes around 12 passengers, and the main business for Adventures Afloat are large groups of holidaymakers from the big resort-hotels on the east coast. However, smaller groups and individuals are welcome, and if you phone in advance the friendly owner-manager will let you know if it's a quiet day, when you may join just a few other visitors, or if it's a busy day when your companions may be a much larger (and louder) party. The cost is US$90 per person.

including bike, food, drink and back-up vehicle. Basically, if you have the slightest interest in cycling, call in and discuss the options with Saleh Mreh Salum, the energetic and friendly owner.

Ocean Tours, Shangani, near the Serena Hotel; PO Box 3075; tel: 024 2233642; email: asaid@oceantourszanzibar.com. This experienced company is the local rep for Abercrombie & Kent, but can also arrange tours for individual clients looking for a top-quality service. Clients report that they are professional and helpful.

Sama Tours Gizenga St; PO Box 2276; tel/fax: 024 2233543; tel: 0741 608576, 0747 430385, 0747 431665; email: samatours@zitec.org; web: www.samatours.com. As well as spice tours, boat trips and all the usual services, the friendly and helpful team at Sama Tours arranges cultural tours, giving visitors an opportunity to meet local people, and recommended by clients as a great opportunity for photos. Guides speak English, French, German and Italian. Sama Tours also offers 'special' spice tours, organised by one of the owners, Salim Abdullah, who is very knowledgeable about the spices and fruits grown on Zanzibar. He knows their names in several languages (ideal for visitors who do not use English as a first language themselves). As well as being a knowledgeable naturalist, Salim is a bit of a small-screen star, having appeared on several TV travel programmes – his company also provides logistical back-up for visiting camera crews. Sama Tours also caters for groups (anything from cruise ships to overland trucks), and offers complete tailor-made tours for individuals, which include pick-ups from the port or airport (or from Dar), hotels, excursions, transfers, car hire, and so on. Prices depend on the length of the tour, the services required and the number in the group. This company has an office on Gizenga St, behind the House of Wonders.

Sun N Fun Safaris Mizingani Rd; PO Box 666; tel: 024 2237381, 024 2237665, 0741 600206; email: zanzibarsun@hotmail.com. In the same building as the Sea View Indian Restaurant, and with the same enthusiastic management, this company can set you up with absolutely anything, usually at a very reasonable price. It runs tours of Zanzibar Town and the island, provides transfer services to the airport or east coast, and can help with general tourist information regarding Zanzibar and elsewhere in Africa. They can also assist with visas, car and bike hire, boat trips, flight tickets and bus tickets, in Zanzibar and on the mainland. The office sells postcards, stamps (it has a mailbox), maps and souvenirs of the 'I love Zanzibar' sticker variety.

Suna Tours Forodhani; PO Box 2213; tel: 024 2237344. This company represents some mid-range hotels on the east coast and can assist with reservations for any other hotel on the coast, plus arrange transport and tours to that side of the island. Suna also organises good-quality spice tours and trips to the islands. They have to be good: the company is run by the formidable Naila Majid Jiddawi, a leading figure in Zanzibar politics and the promotion of Zanzibar tourism. The company office is in a small white building at the end of Forodhani Gardens, near the Arab Fort, and the staff here are very happy to provide general tourist information, even if you don't take one of their tours.

Tropical Tours Kenyatta Rd, opposite Mazsons Hotel; PO Box 325; tel: 024 2230868, 0747 413454; email: tropicalts@hotmail.com. From a small but highly efficient office, this straightforward and friendly budget company has been recommended by several travellers, and offers the usual range of tours (a spice tour, dolphins, Jozani Forest, Nungwi and Prison Island trips), plus car hire, and ferry and air ticket reservations.

ZanTours off Malawi Rd; PO Box 2560; tel: 0741 335832; tel/fax: 024 2233116; email: zantours@zitec.org; web: www.zantours.com. This company confidently entered the tourist scene in 1997, and is now one of the largest operators in Zanzibar, if not the largest, with a smart office in the Malindi area, trained, efficient staff, a fleet of modern vehicles and an impressive range of tours, transfers, excursions and safaris. They cater for groups of any size (from several hundred to just a few) including individuals wanting tailor-made services. You can walk in and they'll set something up on the spot, although most of their clients arrange things in advance by email. ZanTours is closely allied to ZanAir (see page 143) and some tours utilise their fleet of planes. One of their most popular tours is a short fly-in excursion from Zanzibar direct to the Selous National Park in southern Tanzania, which many other agents sell. For more details see the *Southern Tanzania Safaris* chapter.

Zanzibar Tourist Corporation Creek Rd; PO Box 216; tel: 024 2238630, 2233417; email: ztc@zanzinet.com. ZTC is the state travel service, mainly handling transport, tours and reservations for groups from overseas. For individuals, ZTC offers the standard range of island tours and handles reservations for the ZTC bungalows on Changuu Island and the east coast. The main office is in Livingstone House, on the northeast side of town on the main road north towards Bububu. For general tourist information, ZTC also has an office on Creek Rd (open Mon–Fri 07.30–15.30, Sat 10.00–noon), where you can also buy postcards and maps.

Zenith Tours, behind the Fort, PO Box 3643; tel: 2232320, 0747 413084; fax: 024 2233973; email: zenithtours@zitec.com; web: www.zenithtours.net. This very professional and efficient organisation offers transfers, accommodation and excursions in the mid-range price bracket, including safaris to the mainland.

As well as those tour companies listed above, there are many more to choose from in Zanzibar. In fact, the number is growing fast, although for every two that open another closes just as quickly. As with so many things, your best source of information is always other visitors. We have heard from readers who recommended:

Jojoba Travel & Tours Shangani, PO Box 3889; tel: 0747 410346; email: hassanjojoba@hotmail.com

Maya Tours, behind ZanAir; PO Box 3508; tel: 024 230986; fax: 233021; email: maya@twiga.com

Marlin Tours, Shangani; PO Box 3435; tel: 024 231283; fax: 232378; email: marlin@zanzinet.com

GUIDES AROUND ZANZIBAR STONE TOWN

Although the narrow streets of Zanzibar are like a labyrinth, guides are unnecessary as Stone Town is not very large, and getting seriously lost is unlikely. (If you don't know where you are, just keep walking and you'll soon come out on to Creek Road or one of the streets alongside the sea.) In fact, for many visitors getting lost in the maze of narrow streets and alleys is all part of the fun.

However, if your time is limited, or you prefer not to become disorientated, or want to find some specific sites of interest, you may want to hire a guide to take you from place to place. Most local tour companies can arrange city tours, with a knowledgeable guide who will take you to many of the major places of interest. You can go by their suggestions, or use the places listed in this book to work out which places you would find most interesting.

If you'd prefer not to have a formal tour, but would still like to be accompanied by a local, you could engage the services of the *papaasi* (see box, page 118), although generally they will be more interested in taking you to souvenir shops than to museums. It might be better to ask your hotel or a reputable tour company to put you in touch with someone who will happily walk with you through the streets, and show you the way if you get lost. We have heard from readers who employed a local schoolboy, who was also very happy to practise his English, and this seems an excellent idea. About US$3–5 (in TSh) for a day's work would be a suitable fee.

If you are seriously interested in the history of Zanzibar, a local artist and historian, John da Silva, is very occasionally available for private guided tours around Stone Town. John knows the history of every public building and every house (and literally every balcony and door) in the town. His rates are US$20 for a tour lasting two to three hours. You can contact John through Sama Tours (listed under *Tour companies*).

Independent guides

If you prefer not to use a tour company, it is possible to arrange a tour of the spice plantations, a boat trip to the islands or transport to the east coast with an independent guide. Many double as taxi drivers. In fact many are taxi drivers first, and guides second. One driver, a Mr Mitu, has been doing these tours for many years and has been recommended by many visitors, although sometimes he subcontracts work to other drivers. These days he's so popular that instead of Mr Mitu in his taxi you might find yourself joining a large group touring the island in a fleet of minibuses. He's even got his own office (tel: 024 2234636) – a tiny room tucked away behind the Ciné Afrique with the walls covered in photos. Mr Mitu's tours leave from outside the Ciné Afrique every morning at 09.30, returning about 15.00, cost US$10 per person and are still highly recommended by those who have been.

There are several other taxi drivers who also organise their own spice tours. Most will undercut the tour companies (about US$30 for the car seems average), although you may not get the same degree of information that you'd get with a specialist guide. We've also been told about a driver called Saleh Mreh, who organises 'eco' tours around the island, concentrating on environmental aspects.

You are almost certain to meet some of the local independent 'guides' who are in fact just hustlers (see the box on the *Papaasi*, page 118) who tout for business outside hotels and restaurants, or along the streets of Stone Town. For spice tours, prices are often cheaper than those offered by regular companies; but the tours are usually shorter and do not include a proper guide, which usually makes the whole thing pointless unless you are a fairly skilled botanist.

For boat trips to the island it doesn't usually make much difference if you go with the *papaasi* or a regular company, although if you deal with the *papaasi* and things go wrong, it is very difficult to complain or get your money back.

For more details on local guides see the *Places to visit* section later in this chapter.

SHOPPING

Zanzibar Town has a huge number of shops to cater for the ever-growing tourist numbers, and we have listed a selection of favourites here. Even die-hard deal-hunters will be hard pushed to visit them all, and there are bound to be more by the time you visit.

One of the best places to start any shopping trip is the **Zanzibar Gallery.** The main shop is on Kenyatta Road, and there's a branch on Gizenga Street, behind the Fort. Both shops sell an excellent range of carvings, paintings, jewellery, materials, maps, clothes, rugs, postcards, antiques and real pieces of art from all over Africa. You can also buy local spices, herbs, pickles and honey, and locally made oils such as pineapple bath oil or banana-scented bubble bath – all made naturally from Zanzibar fruit. Each shop also has a very good selection of guidebooks and coffee-table books on Zanzibar and other parts of Africa, animal and bird field guides, maps, histories and general novels. The Zanzibar Gallery is run by local photographer and publisher Javed Jafferji; his own books (signed) are also for sale here, including some beautiful large-format photo books, plus diaries and address books lavishly illustrated with photos from Zanzibar and Tanzania.

Another good place on Kenyatta Road is **Memories of Zanzibar**, opposite the

---

THE DANGERS OF LEMON GRASS OIL AND SPICES

The exotic herbs and spices of Zanzibar can be dangerous. We heard from a rather impulsive traveller who sent us the following warning:

> In Zanzibar I bought some lemon grass oil, which smelt wonderful! I decided to spoil myself and applied a liberal coating to my face. Having rubbed it all in well it started to burn. It was worse than the very very hottest curry in your mouth. My skin went red and I thought blisters would appear, it hurt so much. Cold water and other plain oils helped after about 20 minutes, but any longer and I would have gone to hospital. Only later did I find a tiny slip of paper in the bottom of the packet which warned of skin and eye irritation. I strongly urge all other spice enthusiasts not to exceed the recommended dose!'

We also heard from some other travellers who bought back several little baskets of spice from a Stone Town souvenir shop, which languished in a cupboard once they'd got home. A little while later, some 'seeds' in the little baskets came alive and whole rooms were infested with exotic insects. If you buy spice in Zanzibar, it's best to buy it fresh, not pre-packaged, ideally from the market where there's a quicker turn-over of goods. You should also keep spices in sealed containers once you get home (it keeps it fresh that way too), and to use it up fairly quickly. It's also worth noting that some countries have strict regulations about tourists bringing back natural products from overseas – precisely because such products can come alive!

KHANGAS AND KIKOIS

A *khanga*, the traditional coloured wrap worn by local women, makes an ideal souvenir. You can wear it, use it as a beach mat on the coast or a sheet to cover bare mattresses in cheap hotels, and then hang it on your wall, throw it over your sofa or turn it into cushion covers when you get home. A *khanga* normally comes as a large rectangle which the women then cut into two pieces, each about a metre square. One half is worn as a wrap-over skirt and the other is worn as a head scarf. (A knot is usually tied in one corner and used for keeping money in.) Prices for a *khanga*, from the market or local cloth shop, start at about US$3.

On Zanzibar, and elsewhere on the coast, men traditionally wear a *kikoi*, a wrap-around 'kilt' of woven cotton, usually striped, and usually thicker than a *khanga*. Once again, a *kikoi* also has many practical travel uses before you take it home to use as a seat cover. Prices start at US$8.

If you want to combine African and Western clothing, you could even have a local tailor make up a shirt or pair of baggy shorts from a *kikoi*. For more ideas see the excellent little book *101 Uses for a Khanga*, by David Bygott, available in Zanzibar bookshops.

post office. This shop sells everything from beaded flip-flops and silver bracelets to carpets and gourd-lamps. Also worth a look is the **Pan African Gallery**, on Kenyatta Road next to the Paracuda Restaurant, where the owner, Mr Baraka, carves soapstone plates, bowls and other ornaments, then paints them with African designs.

There are many more shops on Kenyatta Road, and along Gizenga Street, and its continuations, Hurumzi Street and Changa Bazaar, all the way to the Spice Inn. As well as shops, along these streets many sellers offer carvings and paintings from pavement stalls. Most of the shops and stalls stock contemporary carvings and older traditional statues and artefacts from mainland Tanzania and elsewhere in Africa: paintings, on canvas or wooden trays, particularly in the Tingatinga style (see page 47), but also in other styles; jewellery of all sorts, in stone, gold and silver; packets of spices in various forms – some just in plastic bags, others in decorative containers made from palm leaves; and mobiles made from coconut shells in the shapes of dolphins, dhows or tropical fish.

Some of the paintings and craftwork stocked in the souvenir and craft shops is bashed out and of very poor quality, but occasionally, if you search hard enough, you'll find real works of art which have been more carefully made. It's worth spending a bit more money (if indeed the stallholder charges more for better quality – some don't seem to) to get something that will still look good when you get it home, away from the glaring sunlight of Zanzibar, which sometimes seems to cloud judgement! One of the best shops we found for good quality Tingatinga work was **Jambo Souvenirs**, next to the Sunrise Bar on Kenyatta Road.

Another place for good quality crafts is **Hurumzi Art & Craft Gallery** next to the Emerson & Green Hotel on Hurumzi Street. The same owner has another fine shop called **Kibriti** on Gizenga Street, just off Kenyatta Road, near the post office, selling arts and crafts and a good selection of antiques and curios.

Around Zanzibar Town there are also several shops selling antiques from Arabia and India, dating from Omani and British colonial times. **Coast Antique Shop** on Gizenga Street has a particularly good selection of Zanzibar clocks. There are several more antique shops on the street between St Joseph's Cathedral and Soko Muhogo crossroads.

Other places to buy paintings and pieces of art include **Paul's Gallery** at St Monica's Hostel near the Anglican Cathedral (where you can also buy hand-painted T-shirts) and the **Tower Workshop** at the Old Fort, where the resident artists deliberately don't stock Tingatinga stuff and concentrate on water colours and some beautiful batik-like works 'painted' with different coloured candle wax. In the main part of the Fort is another cluster of spice and craft shops, including **Namaan Art Gallery**, which has Tingatinga works, some watercolours and some some superb oil paintings.

Outside the Fort, in **Forodhani Gardens**, are several more stalls selling carvings and jewellery – especially in the evening when nearby food stalls attract the crowds. Nearby, outside the House of Wonders, Tingatinga painting salesmen hang their works on the railings, and you can also watch some of the artists (all men) working here. In the same area, local weavers (all women) make mats and baskets from grass and palm leaves. This area is also a good place to find local colourful fabrics and clothing.

For a different medium, visit the **Capital Art Studio** on Kenyatta Road, near the Dolphin Restaurant, which has a good selection of old photographic prints, most from the 1950s and 1960s, and a few earlier ones. (The shop itself seems unchanged since colonial times.) They also sell camera film and batteries, and offer a one-day developing service.

Local craftwork can also be found in the **Orphanage Shop**, near the Fort. The orphanage is a large building on the main seafront road (Mizingani Road) with a tunnel passing right through the middle of it. The shop is on the side nearest the sea. Here, blind craft-workers weave a good range baskets, rugs and other items.

At **Sasik Shop** on Gizenga Street, you can buy very beautiful and intricate patchwork cushion-covers and wall-hangings, made on the spot by a local women's cooperative. Also on Gizenga Street, the tailor at **Mnazi Boutique** can copy any shirt, skirt or trousers you like, from material you buy in the shop or elsewhere in town. Prices start at US$8, and go up to US$25 for a complicated dress. If you prefer traditional African clothing, consider a *khanga* or a *kikoi* (see box, page 153). On Kenyatta Road, the very smart and fancy **One Way** boutique also sells piles and piles of T-shirts embroidered with giraffes and elephants or emblazoned with Kenyan and Tanzanian slogans and logos. If you want a lurid T-shirt, this is the place. If not, it's a bit limited.

For postcards you can't go wrong at **Angi's Postcards & Maps**, on Mizingani Road, near the Big Tree; there's a truly massive selection here, all at good prices.

LOCAL SERVICES

This section covers local services in Zanzibar Town that tourists may require during their visit. For more general matters covering the whole of Zanzibar Island and Pemba see *Chapters 4, 6* and 7.

Tourist information

The Zanzibar Tourist Corporation (ZTC) is the state travel service. It has offices in Livingstone House, on the northeast side of town on the main road towards Bububu, where you can make reservations for the ZTC bungalows on the east coast. For general tourist enquiries, you're better off asking at the ZTC office on Creek Road, where the members of staff are a bit more helpful. You can also buy postcards and maps here.

For general information, some tour companies are happy to help, even if you don't end up buying a tour from them. Try Sun N Fun Safaris, Sama Tours and Suna Tours, listed on pages 149 and 150.

Also worth visiting is the information desk at the Arab Fort, which has details of local musical, cultural and sporting events. For less formalised (but equally useful) information, check the noticeboard at the open-air restaurant inside the Fort. Local events are advertised here, and you'll find details of companies selling tours or spare seats on charter flights, and local residents selling cars or motorbikes. This is also a good place to leave messages for those people you last saw in Cairo or Cape Town and are trying to contact again. (The best notice and message board used to be at the Africa House Hotel, but this hotel is undergoing renovation, and it's uncertain if the famous board will remain in place.)

Banks and money-changing

Some general points on banks and change bureaux are given in *Chapter 4*, page 98. In Zanzibar Town, the best bank for changing money is the branch of the People's Bank of Zanzibar, near the Fort. Make sure you go to the foreign exchange department which is across the other side of a narrow alley from the main building (which is guarded by soldiers). Do not change money at the Commercial Bank of Zanzibar: this is mainly for business transactions, and the rates are bad.

Getting cash on a debit or credit card is virtually impossible, although when we were researching this book, there was a possibility that Barclays would be opening a branch (with change facilities and an ATM) at the northern end of Kenyatta Road. Alternatively, Jojoba Travel & Tours (see the list of *Tour companies* on page 150) will issue cash on a card.

Good change bureaux include the Shangani Bureau de Change (at the northern end of Kenyatta Road, near the Tembo Hotel), and Malindi Bureau de Change (next to the ZanAir office, east of the port gates). Most large hotels will also change money (although some deal only with their own guests). One of the best is the bureau at the Hotel International (in the Ukatani area), which welcomes everyone and usually offers some of the best rates in town. There are also change bureaux at the port and airport.

For Visa and Mastercard holders there's an assistance point at the office of Coastal Travels and Mtoni Marine Centre near the Serena Hotel. This is not a bank or bureau, though, and only issues relatively small amounts of cash against a card in cases of emergency.

Post

Some general points on post services and costs are given in *Chapter 4*, page 106. Although letters can be sent from other post offices around Zanzibar Island, it's best if you can to send all your mail from Zanzibar Town. The service is reliable, with letters taking about a week to ten days to reach destinations in Europe and North America (Australia takes a bit longer).

Zanzibar Town's main post office (GPO) is a large building in the new part of town on the road towards the Amaani Stadium. It is open from 08.00 to 12.30, then 14.00 to 16.30 every day, except Sunday when it closes at 12.30. However, for tourists the old post office on Kenyatta Road, in the Shangani area, is much more convenient. You can buy stamps here, and this is also the place to collect letters sent to you by poste restante (although some items may get sent to the main post office by mistake – so make sure anyone writing to you writes 'Old Post Office, Kenyatta Road, Shangani' on the envelope). The old post office hours are: Monday to Thursday, 08.00 to 13.00, then 14.00 to 16.30; Friday 08.00 to 12.00, then 14.00 to 17.00; Saturday 09.00 to 12.00; Sunday closed.

Telephone and fax

Zanzibar Town has a very wide choice of places where you can make calls or send faxes. Some are properly equipped bureaux, others are just a dusty phone in the corner of someone's shop which is nevertheless proudly touted as an 'international communication centre'.

One of the best phone centres is the Tanzanian Telecommunications international telephone office, next to the old post office on Kenyatta Road. Calls cost US$1 for ten minutes inside Zanzibar, US$1 for three minutes elsewhere in Tanzania, US$1 for about one-and-a-half minutes to other parts of Africa, and US$2.50–3 for one minute to Europe, the USA and other international destinations. This office is open 08.00 to 21.00 daily. The office is large, cool and quiet, and the staff members are very friendly and helpful – so much better than some of the privately owned booths, where they put a stopwatch in your face and there's no privacy at all.

Another option for international calls is to buy a phonecard from the international telephone office (they are also sold at some shops and hotels) and use this in the direct-dial phone booth outside. A 150-unit card costs US$7.50 and gives you two minutes to Europe or the USA. A 500-unit card costs US$20. For local calls a 10-unit card is US$1.25, and a 100-unit card is US$5.

If the international telephone office is closed, local boys loiter by the phone booths outside with cards and will charge you to use them per unit. There's even one young entrepreneur with a mobile phone who allows international calls at negotiable rates. It makes you wonder who is really paying the bill.

At the private phone bureaux around Zanzibar Town, international calls are around the same price as those charged by the Tanzanian Telecommunications office, although a few places manage to undercut this rate, and some can be considerably more, so it's worth checking if you've got a lot of calls to make. For example, at Asko Tours, next to the old post office, local calls are US$0.40 per minute, calls to Africa are US$1.50 per minute, and international calls cost US$3 per full minute. Opposite the international phone office a souvenir shop offers international calls to Europe for US$2.60 per minute. At Next Step Services on Hurumzi Street, international calls cost US$5 per minute. For cheap international calls, worth seeking out is Asad Secretarial Services, near the Clove Hotel, which offers phone calls via the internet for US$2 per minute. There's a delay of a second or two while you're speaking, but once you're used to that, it's fine.

Email and internet

Since 2001, internet bureaux have sprung up everywhere in Zanzibar Stone Town. Like the phone offices (indeed, many are also phone offices), some internet bureaux are large and air conditioned with several terminals, while others are in the corner of someone's shop and you connect to the outside world crammed between boxes of soap. In general, most hotels do not offer public email services.

There's a pretty standardised cost across town of US$1 per hour, although a couple of places offer rates cheaper than this. Most charge per 30-minute increment, and if you go over this by a few seconds you'll be charged for the next 30 minutes. The minimum time is usually 30 minutes, but if you only have one or two quick lines to send, you can find some bureaux which charge per message, but this normally works out the same as the minimum charge anyway.

Internet bureaux include:

Shangani Internet Café, Kenyatta Rd; tel 2232925. This is one of the best places in Zanzibar Town. It has long opening hours, fast connections, about 15 computers, a fridge full of ice-cream and cold drinks, and charges US$1 per hour.

Sanjay Internet Café, just off Gizenga St, behind the House of Wonders. This small place has about five terminals, and normally charges US$1 per hour, but sometimes offers special rates of half this price.
Asad Secretarial Services, near the Clove Hotel, is a small place with good connections, charging US$1 per hour.
Zanzibar Cybercafé, on Changa Bazaar, not far from the Spice Inn, and connected to the Macrosoft computer shop nextdoor, this place is open every day from 09.30–22.30, charging US$1 per hour, but often with special offers of half this price. If you've only got a few quick messages to send, and can find someone in the same position, this place doesn't mind groups of two or three people sharing a slot for only a slightly higher price.

Other bureaux include: **Green Garden Internet Service**, opposite the Green Garden Restaurant (charging US$0.50 for 45 minutes); **New Net Services**, Hurumzi Street (US$1 per hour); and **Next Step Services**, Hurumzi Street, a rather small and cramped place, but with good rates (US$0.50 per hour, plus cheap international calls) and also offering photocopying and secretarial services.

Hospitals, doctors and pharmacies
The main public hospital for all of Zanzibar Island is at Mnazi Moja, on the south side of Stone Town. (During the island's revolutionary heyday it was called the Lenin Hospital, but this title has now been dropped.) Like many hospitals in developing countries, the staff are dedicated but the wards are badly under-funded and under-supplied, and in very poor condition. More worrying is the pile of rubbish (including drip-feeds and needles) simply dumped on the beach behind the hospital.

Most tourists go to one of the private medical centres where staff speak English and the service is usually better. Of course, this has to be paid for, and costs around US$50 per consultation, but all fees should be covered by your travel insurance. The medical centres also have pharmacies selling medicines and other supplies.

Zanzibar Medical and Diagnostic Centre (PO Box 1043; tel: 024 233113, 24-hour emergency no: 0747 413714), just off Vuga Road, near the Majestic Cinema, is recommend by most expatriates. This fully equipped centre is run to European standards and the staff members speak several European languages. **Zanzibar Medical Group** on Kenyatta Road (tel: 024 2233134) is another good-quality private clinic, charging US$30 per consultation.

If your insurance covers only major medical problems, and you want to keep costs down for something minor, you could go to one of Zanzibar's other medical centres. **Afya Medical Hospital** (tel: 024 223 2570, 0747 411934), off Vuga Road at the southern end of Stone Town, is large and well-stocked, with friendly staff; consultations cost US$2, blood or urine tests are available, and there's also a pharmacy.

Other places include **Dr Mehta's Hospital** (tel: 024 2230194, 0741 612889), on Vuga Road. At the very basic **Fahaud Health Centre** near St Joseph's Cathedral, consultations cost US$1 and a malaria blood test is US$0.50. Should your test prove positive, they also sell Fansidar at US$0.50 per tablet.

In case of real emergency, the nearest major hospital, fully staffed and equipped, is the Aga Khan Hospital in Mombasa. You may even need to fly there (by charter plane if necessary) if things are really serious, but this should be covered by your insurance.

If you need to buy medicines, Zanzibar Town has several pharmacies stocking drugs which are mostly imported from Europe and India, and other items such as

> ### TELEPHONING FROM ZANZIBAR
> For information on making calls to Zanzibar, see the box on page 145. Within Zanzibar (Zanzibar Island and Pemba Island), there are no area codes – you just dial the number you want. (Note that all five-figure numbers changed to six-figure numbers in early 2000 and all six-figure numbers went up to seven figures in 2002.) Phoning out of Zanzibar to mainland Tanzania, Kenya or Uganda you just need the city or area code, followed by the individual number. For all other countries you need to dial the international access code (tel: 000), plus the country code (eg: 1 for America, 44 for Britain), followed by city or area code (minus the 0), then the individual number.

toiletries and tampons. Stocks are not always reliable, so if you know you're likely to need a specific drug during your visit it's best to bring a sufficient supply with you. There are pharmacies near the Musoma Bookshop, next to the Emerson & Green Hotel, and another on Creek Road near the market. Straightforward medicines, toiletries and tampons are also available at the 'container stores' on Creek Road.

Police
In case of emergency in Zanzibar Town, the main police station is in the Malindi area, on the north side of Stone Town. This is also the central police station for the whole of Zanzibar. Robberies can be reported here (travel insurance companies usually require you to prove you have notified the local police), but you should not expect any real action to be taken as the police are not particularly well motivated.

Zanzibar also has a platoon of Tourist Police, supposedly to assist and protect Zanzibar's foreign visitors, although many people question their effectiveness. They are mostly seen driving around town in fancy new patrol cars, while touts continue to hassle tourists unimpeded.

Newspaper and bookshops
Newspapers from Kenya and mainland Tanzania, some international magazines, and a reasonable range of books, are available from the Masumo Bookshop, off Creek Road, near the market, and from some of the souvenir shops along Kenyatta Road, near the old post office.

One of the best bookshops is the Zanzibar Gallery, with branches on Kenyatta Road and Gizenga Street behind the Fort. Although primarily a souvenir shop, they have a very good selection of guidebooks and coffee-table books on Zanzibar and other parts of Africa, animal and bird field guides, maps, histories and general novels.

Film and camera supplies
Slide and print film for cameras is available in several souvenir shops in Zanzibar Town (the ones along Kenyatta Road have the best stock). The Shamshuddin Cash & Carry Supermarket, near the Musoma Bookshop, also has a good stock. The best place to buy film is Majestic Quick Foto, on the east side of Creek Road, opposite the BP petrol station.

Cinemas
The main cinema in Zanzibar Town is the Ciné Afrique on Malawi Road, in the Malindi area, near the Port Gates. There is also the Majestic Cinema on Vuga

Road. Tickets are around US$0.25. Films are almost exclusively kung fu or action flicks, or Hindi melodramas, but mainstream Hollywood movies are also shown a few times a week.

Swimming

The swimming pool at the Tembo Hotel is open to non-guests for US$3, all day. At the Bwawani Hotel, swimming costs less than US$1, but the pool is only half full, of green and slimy water, so this is not at all recommended. (The hotel is due for redevelopment, so this may change.) There's also a pool at the Serena Hotel.

Swahili lessons

If you would like to learn a few words (or even more) of the local language, the Taasisi Kiswahili Institute (PO Box 146; tel: 024 2230724) inside the State University on Vuga Road offers lessons. Classes are normally 08.00 to noon and cost US$4 per hour, or US$80 for a week's course.

Single lessons away from the institute, and longer courses, which include lodgings in the house of a teacher or local family, are also available.

PLACES TO VISIT IN ZANZIBAR TOWN

In the old Stone Town of Zanzibar you can spend many idle hours and days just wandering through the fascinating labyrinth of narrow streets and alleyways. One writer has compared the town to a tropical forest with tall houses instead of trees rising up towards the sky, and overhanging balconies instead of foliage to block out the sun. Most visitors agree that Stone Town is certainly an exotic and fascinating place.

Stone Town was originally built on a peninsula which has probably been inhabited since the first people arrived on Zanzibar (although the creek that separated its eastern edge from the rest of the island has now been reclaimed). Ras Shangani, at the western tip of the peninsula, is thought to have been the site of a fishing village for many centuries, and at least one of Zanzibar's early Swahili rulers, the Mwinyi Mkuu, had a palace here.

In the 16th century, Portuguese navigators built a church and trading station on the peninsula as it had a good harbour and was easy to defend. When the Omani Arabs began to settle on the island in the 18th century, they built a fort on the site of the church, and today's Stone Town grew up around the Fort.

Most of the houses that can be seen today were built in the 19th century when Zanzibar was one of the most important trading centres in the Indian Ocean region. The coralline rock of Zanzibar Island was easy to quarry for use as a construction material, so that many of the houses were built in grand style with three or four storeys. Until this time most of the houses on Zanzibar had been much smaller, built with mangrove poles and palm thatch, so the fine white buildings of Stone Town were even more exceptional.

Today, nearly all of these old houses are still inhabited, although many are in a very bad state of repair. The coralline rock was a good building material but it is also soft, and easily eroded if not maintained. Crumbling masonry, along with dilapidated woodwork, is an all too familiar sight in Stone Town.

However, since the end of the 1980s and through the 1990s, several buildings in Stone Town have been renovated. The Zanzibar government, with assistance from the United Nations Centre for Human Settlements (the Habitat Fund), plans to preserve many more, eventually restoring the whole Stone Town to something like its original magnificence. The Stone Town Conservation and Development

Authority has been established to coordinate this work, although it is sometimes hampered by a lack of coordination with the local government authorities.

During the 19th century many of the people living in Stone Town were wealthy Arabs and Indians. Consequently, the houses were built in two main styles: the Arab style, with plain outer walls and a large front door, leading to an inner courtyard; and the Indian style, with a more open façade and large balconies decorated with ornate railings and balustrades, designed to catch sea breezes and dispel the humid atmosphere.

Many of the buildings have doors with elaborately carved frames and panels, decorated with brass studs and heavy locks. The size of the door, and the intricacies of its decoration, were signs of the family's wealth and status. Today the Zanzibar door has become a well-recognised symbol of the town and island's history and cultural background, and many new buildings incorporate a Zanzibar door in the design – either a genuine one removed from an old building, or a reproduction. (For more on doors see box on page 48.)

As you walk through the town, between the houses, you will come across mosques, churches and other public buildings, almost hidden in the maze. Stone Town also has a few streets of shops, some of which are still called bazaars. Some of the shops are very small, no more than a kiosk, with a few dusty food tins or a couple of jars of sweets on the shelf; others are larger, catering for locals and visitors, with a wider range of foods, books, fabrics, furniture or electrical goods. There are also antique and curio shops, and an increasing number of places selling locally produced arts and crafts, aimed specially at the growing tourist market.

When walking around the narrow streets, you should remember that Zanzibar Town is very much a real community, where people live and work. It is not a museum piece created for tourists. You should show respect for local sensibilities (see *Clothing*, page 94) and should not enter any private house or courtyard unless expressly invited to do so. Mosques are not usually open to non-Muslim visitors. Taking photos of buildings is generally acceptable, but you should never take photos of people without their permission. (See also *Mosques* on page 176.)

The market

The market is about halfway along Creek Road and a good place to visit even if you don't want to buy anything. The long market-hall is surrounded by traders selling from stalls, or with their wares simply spread out on the ground. It's a very vibrant place where everything, from fish and bread to sewing machines and secondhand car spares, is bought and sold. People bring their produce here from all over the island, and other people come to buy things they can't get in their own villages.

Towards the end of the 19th century, the town's marketplace was inside the Old Fort. Today's market-hall was built in 1904. Some very early photographs of the market displayed in the museum show that very little has changed since then.

On some evenings, a public auction is held in the street behind the market where furniture, household goods, old bikes, and all sorts of other junk is sold. It is very entertaining to watch, but make sure you don't bid for anything by mistake. Keep your hands still!

Livingstone House

On the northeast side of the town, this old building is now the main office of the Zanzibar Tourist Corporation (ZTC). It was built around 1860 for Sultan Majid (sultan from 1856 to 1870). At this time Zanzibar was used as a starting point by many of the European missionaries and pioneers who explored eastern and Central Africa during the second half of the 19th century. David Livingstone, probably the most famous explorer of them all (see box, page 162), stayed in this house before sailing to the mainland to begin his last expedition in 1866. Other explorers, such as Burton, Speke, Cameron and Stanley, also stayed here while preparing for their own expeditions. The house was later used by members of the island's Indian community, and in 1947 it was bought by the colonial government for use as a scientific laboratory for research into clove diseases. After independence and the revolution it became the Zanzibar headquarters of the Tanzania Friendship Tourist Bureau, the forerunner of today's ZTC.

The Old Dispensary

Opposite the new port buildings, on Mizingani Road, this is a grand four-storey building with a set of particularly decorative balconies. It is also called the Ithnasheri Dispensary, and lettering at the top of the front wall reads 'Khoja Haji Nasser Nur Mohammed Charitable Dispensary'. The dispensary was originally built in the 1890s as a private house for a prominent Ismaili Indian merchant called Tharia Topan, who was a customs advisor to the sultans, and one of the wealthiest individuals on Zanzibar at the time. In 1899 he gave the house up to be used as a dispensary, also funding the medicine and other services. Topan also provided money (with the Aga Khan and Sultan Ali) for a non-denominational school which opened in Zanzibar in 1891. The dispensary fell into disrepair during the 1970s and 1980s, but was renovated in 1995 with funding from the Aga Khan Charitable Trust. A few years later it opened as the Stone Town Cultural Centre. There is a small exhibition (free) of historical photographs, but most of the building is now used as offices. More businesses are due to open here in the future.

The Old Customs House

On Mizingani Road (the main seafront), overlooking the sea, this large building has a plain façade and is fairly featureless apart from the beautiful set of carved wooden doors. These have been decorated in the Arab style with fish, lotus and anchor chain motifs. Hamoud, grandson of Sultan Said, was proclaimed sultan here in 1896. In 1995 the Customs House was renovated with funds provided by Unesco, the United Nations cultural organisation. (The equally large building next door to the Customs House was formerly Le Grand Hotel and then became a private house before being abandoned. A group of developers have long-term plans to convert it into a hotel once again.)

The Palace Museum

This is a large white building with castellated battlements situated on Mizingani Road, where the latter runs very close to the sea. Originally called the Sultan's Palace, it was built in the late 1890s for members of the sultan's family. From 1911, it was used as the sultan of Zanzibar's official residence. It was renamed the People's Palace after the 1964 Revolution, when Sultan Jamshid was overthrown, and was used as government offices until the early 1990s.

In 1994 the palace was turned into a museum dedicated to the history of the sultans of Zanzibar. Remarkably, much of their furniture and other possessions survived the revolutionary years and can now be seen by the public for the first time. The museum is well organised and informative: the ground floor is dedicated to the early years of the sultanate (1828 to 1870), while the upper floors contain exhibits from the later, more affluent period of 1870 to 1896. These exhibits include thrones, banqueting tables and ceremonial furniture, and also more personal items such as beds and the sultan's personal water-closet. There is also a

DAVID LIVINGSTONE

David Livingstone is the best-known of all the European explorers who travelled in Africa in the 19th century. Many of his journeys began and ended in Zanzibar.

David Livingstone was born on March 19 1813 in the village of Blantyre, near Glasgow, in Scotland. In 1841 he went to South Africa as a missionary doctor. There he married Mary Moffat, a missionary's daughter. On his early expeditions in southern Africa he crossed the Kalahari Desert and, in November 1855, became the first European to see Mosi oa Tunya ('the smoke that thunders') which he renamed the Victoria Falls. Livingstone made his fourth major expedition from 1858 to 1864 in the area around the Lower Zambezi and Lake Nyasa (present-day Lake Malawi). He was accompanied by Dr John Kirk, another Scot, who joined the expedition as medical officer and naturalist. After the expedition, in April 1864, Livingstone spent a week in Zanzibar before travelling back to Britain.

Livingstone returned to Zanzibar in January 1866. He had been asked by the Royal Geographical Society to explore the country between Lake Nyasa and Lake Tanganyika and solve the dispute over the location of the source of the Nile. He left for the mainland on March 19 1866, and travelled around the southern end of Lake Nyasa.

After several years of exploring the region, during which time little news of his travels had reached the outside world, Livingstone met with journalist Henry Stanley at Ujiji on Lake Tanganyika on November 10 1871 – the famous 'Dr Livingstone, I presume' incident described in more detail in the *Henry Morton Stanley* box on page 26.

room devoted to Princess Salme, the daughter of Sultan Said who eloped to Hamburg with a German merchant in 1866 (see the *Princess Salme* boxes on pages 180–1.) In the palace garden are the graves of sultans Said, Barghash, Majid, Khaled, Khalifa and Abdullah.

The museum is open 09.00–18.00 Monday to Friday, and 09.00–15.00 Saturdays/Sundays and holidays. Entrance is US$3. An excellent little leaflet is available containing a clear, concise historical background with plans and descriptions of all the palace rooms. Guides are also available to show you around and describe the exhibits in detail; their fee is open to negotiation, but should be agreed beforehand. About US$3–5 is fair.

The House of Wonders

This large, white building dominates the waterfront area of Zanzibar Town, and is one if its best-known landmarks. A perfect rectangle, it has several storeys, surrounded by tiers of pillars and balconies, and topped by a large clocktower. After more than a century of use as a palace and government offices, the House of Wonders was opened in 2002 as the Museum of History and Culture.

When we were researching this book, the museum was still under development, but if the management's plans are realised, there will be a huge and fascinating range of exhibits here. These will cover: dhows and the maritime history of Zanzibar; the history of Stone Town; the industrial heritage of Zanzibar; historical displays covering the era of the Swahili civilisations; the Portuguese period; and the Omani and British colonial times. Exhibits will be brought here from many sources, including from the Peace Museum (the former historical museum, which

At this meeting, Livingstone was suffering terribly from foot ulcers, fever and dysentery, and had only a few days' supply of cotton with which to buy food. But two weeks later his strength had returned sufficiently for him to set out on a small expedition with Stanley. They explored the northern shores of Lake Tanganyika, establishing that the River Ruzizi flowed into (not out of) the lake, and could not therefore be a headwater of the Nile.

Livingstone and Stanley left Ujiji on December 27 1871 and reached Kazeh, halfway to the coast, in February the following year. Livingstone was in good health, so Stanley continued on alone and arrived in Zanzibar in May 1872.

Livingstone stayed at Kazeh until August 1872, then set out on a short expedition around the southern shores of Lake Tanganyika. He was still looking for the source of the Nile when he became ill again with dysentery. He died at the village of Chitambo, a few miles south of Lake Bangweulu (in present-day Zambia) on May 2 1873. Two of his loyal companions, called Susi and Chumah, removed his heart and buried it under a tree at the spot where he died. They dried his body in the sun for two weeks, then carried it to Zanzibar, wrapped in bark and cloth, where it was identified by a broken bone in the left arm, once crushed in the jaws of a lion. Livingstone's body rested at the British Consulate before being taken to London for burial. Stanley and Kirk were among the pall bearers at his funeral in Westminster Abbey on April 18 1874.

The tree under which Livingstone's heart was buried eventually fell down, and a stone monument now stands in its place. However, some of the wood from the tree was made into a cross, and this now hangs in the Anglican Cathedral in Zanzibar Town.

will become an environmental museum), and more improvements are planned for the future, including a library and conference centre.

As well as the items on show, the House of Wonders building itself is a fascinating exhibit, and now the museum has opened, it means the public can enter officially for the first time in decades. The ground floor was empty when we visited (apart from four old cars from the 1960s used by President Karume) but seemed all the more vast for this, with great views up through the central courtyard to the top of the building. On the next level, the floor is covered with marble tiles. Currently a bit dusty and cracked, with a good polish they'd be amazing. On each floor are four massive wooden carved doors. On the next floor up, from the exhibition room you can walk out on to the upper balcony and walk all the way around the outside of the House of Wonders. Needless to say, the views over Stone Town and the bay are spectacular.

Outside the House of Wonders are two old bronze cannons which have Portuguese inscriptions. It is thought that these cannons were made in Portugal some time in the early 16th century, but they were probably brought to Zanzibar by the Omanis, after taking them from Persian forces who had originally captured the guns from the Portuguese in 1622.

History

The House of Wonders was built in 1883 as a ceremonial palace for Sultan Barghash (sultan from 1870 to 1888), and was designed by a marine engineer, hence the great use of steel pillars and girders in the construction. It was built on the site of an older palace used by Queen Fatima, the Mwinyi Mkuu (ruler of Zanzibar) in the 17th century.

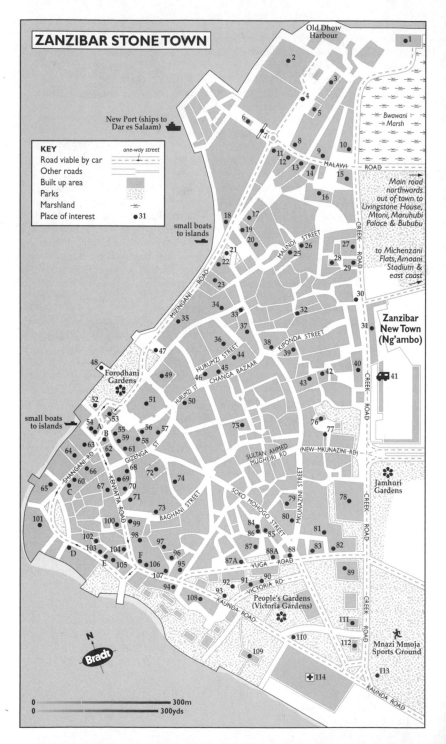

ZANZIBAR STONE TOWN

Old Dhow Harbour

New Port (ships to Dar es Salaam)

Bwawani Marsh

KEY
one-way street
Road viable by car
Other roads
Built up area
Parks
Marshland
Place of interest ●31

small boats to islands

Main road northwards out of town to Livingstone House, Mtoni, Maruhubi Palace & Bububu

to Michenzani Flats, Amaani Stadium & east coast

MALAWI ROAD

CREEK ROAD

MIZINGANI ROAD

MALINDI STREET

KIPONDA STREET

Zanzibar New Town (Ng'ambo)

small boats to islands

Forodhani Gardens

HURUMZI STREET

HURUMZI ST

CHANGA BAZAAR

GIZENGA ST

SHANGANI RD

KENYATTA ROAD

BAGHANI STREET

SULTAN AHMED MUGHEIRI RD

(NEW MKUNAZINI RD)

SOKO MOHOGO STREET

MKUNAZINI STREET

Jamhuri Gardens

VUGA ROAD

VICTORIA RD

KAUNDA ROAD

People's Gardens (Victoria Gardens)

KAUNDA ROAD

Mnazi Mmoja Sports Ground

N

Bradt

0 ———— 300m
0 ———— 300yds

Numerical key to Zanzibar Stone Town map opposite

1 Bwawani Hotel	65 Starehe Club
2 Clove Distillery	66 Fisherman Restaurant, Bashasha Bar
3 Malindi Guesthouse	67 Shangani Hotel & Shangani Internet Café
4 Fish market	68 Namaste Indian Restaurant
5 Warere Guesthouse	69 Post office & telephone office
6 Shipping company ticket offices	70 Blue Ocean Hotel
7 Port gates	71 Dolphin Restaurant & Fanny's Green
8 Ciné Afrique	Restaurant
9 Mzuri Guesthouse	72 St Joseph's Catholic Cathedral
10 Petrol station	73 Chavda Hotel
11 Hotel Marine	74 Chit-Chat Restaurant
12 Malindi Bureau de Change	75 Hamamni Baths
13 Zan Air	76 Anglican Cathedral
14 Passing Show Restaurant	77 St Monica's Hostel
15 Police station (main)	78 Haile Selassie School
16 Zan Tours	79 Jambo Guesthouse
17 Old Dispensary (Stone Town Cultural	80 Flamingo Guesthouse
Centre)	81 Zanzibar Medical & Diagnostic Centre
18 Mercury's Restaurant	82 Kiswahili Language Institute
19 Gulf Air	83 Air Tanzania
20 Ijumaa Mosque	84 Manch Lodge (guesthouse)
21 The Big Tree	85 Nyumbani Restaurant
22 Sea View Indian Restaurant	86 Haven Hotel
23 Old Customs House	87 Florida Guesthouse
25 Pyramid Hotel	87A Kenya Airways
26 Narrow Street Hotel	88 Fisherman Tours, Fernandes Tours
27 Zanzibar Tourism Corporation	88A Maha Travel & Tours
28 Kokoni Hotel	89 Ben Bella School
29 BP petrol station	90 Victoria House (guesthouse)
30 Taxi rank	91 Zi-Bar & Restaurant
31 Container shops	92 Two Tables Restaurant
32 Narrow Street Annexe Hotel	93 Garden Lodge
33 Palace Restaurant	94 Zanzibar Medical Group
34 Hotel Kiponda	95 Dr Mehta's Hospital
35 Palace Museum	96 Afya Medical Hospital
36 Hindu Temple	97 Zanzibar Hotel
37 Aga Khan Mosque	98 Dhow Palace Hotel, Baghani House Hotel
38 Spice Inn	99 Sunrise Restaurant & Pub
39 Hotel International, Bureau de change	100 Mazsons Hotel
40 Market	101 Serena Inn
41 Bus & dala-dala station	102 Tippu Tip's House
42 Masumo Bookshop	103 Jasfa Tours
43 Shamshuddin Cash & Carry Supermarket	104 Pagoda Chinese Restaurant
44 Emerson & Green Hotel	105 Africa House Hotel
45 Bottoms Up Guesthouse	106 Camlur's Restaurant
46 Clove Hotel	107 Rendezvous Les Spices Restaurant
47 Taxi rank	108 High Court
48 Blues (restaurant)	109 State House
49 House of Wonders	110 Zanzibar Milestone
50 Sama Tours	111 Museum Annexe
51 Arab Fort	112 Peace Memorial Museum
52 Suna	113 Old Cricket Pavilion
53 Orphanage	114 Mnazi Moja Hospital
54 Zanzibar Dive Centre	A Sweet Easy Restaurant
55 Radha Food House	B National Bank of Commerce
56 People's Bank of Zanzibar	C Wings Fast Food
57 The Zanzibar Gallery	D Jojoba Tours
58 People's Bank of Zanzibar (Foreign Exchange)	E La Fenice
59 Karibu Inn	F Paracuda Restaurant & Pan African
60 Stone Town Inn, Garage Club	Gallery
61 Coco de Mer Hotel	
62 The Zanzibar Gallery	
63 Old British Consulate	
64 Tembo Hotel	*For alphabetical key see next page*

Alphabetical key to Zanzibar Stone Town map, page 164

105 Africa House Hotel
96 Afya Medical Hospital
37 Aga Khan Mosque
83 Air Tanzania
76 Anglican Cathedral
51 Arab Fort
98 Baghani House Hotel
66 Bashasha Bar
89 Ben Bella School
21 Big Tree, The
70 Blue Ocean Hotel
48 Blues (restaurant)
45 Bottoms Up Guesthouse
29 Petrol station, BP
39 Bureau de change
41 Bus & dala-dala station
1 Bwawani Hotel
106 Camlur's Restaurant
73 Chavda Hotel
74 Chit-Chat Restaurant
8 Ciné Afrique
2 Clove Distillery
46 Clove Hotel
61 Coco de Mer Hotel
31 Container shops
98 Dhow Palace Hotel
95 Dr Mehta's Hospital
71 Dolphin Restaurant
44 Emerson & Green Hotel
71 Fanny's Green Restaurant
88 Fernandes Tours
4 Fish market
66 Fisherman Restaurant
88 Fisherman Tours
80 Flamingo Guesthouse
87 Florida Guesthouse
60 Garage Club
93 Garden Lodge
19 Gulf Air
78 Haile Selassie School
75 Hamamni Baths
86 Haven Hotel
108 High Court
36 Hindu Temple
49 House of Wonders
20 Ijumaa Mosque
39 International, Hotel
79 Jambo Guesthouse
103 Jasfa Tours
D Jojoba Tours
59 Karibu Inn
34 Kiponda, Hotel
82 Kiswahili Language Institute
87A Kenya Airways
28 Kokoni Hotel
E La Fenice
88A Maha Travel & Tours
12 Malindi Bureau de Change
3 Malindi Guesthouse
84 Manch Lodge (guesthouse)
11 Marine, Hotel
40 Market
42 Masumo Bookshop
100 Mazsons Hotel
18 Mercury's Restaurant

114 Mnazi Moja Hospital
111 Museum Annexe
9 Mzuri Guesthouse
68 Namaste Indian Restaurant
32 Narrow Street Annexe Hotel
26 Narrow Street Hotel
B National Bank of Commerce
85 Nyumbani Restaurant
63 Old British Consulate
113 Old Cricket Pavilion
23 Old Customs House
17 Old Dispensary (Stone Town Cultural Centre)
53 Orphanage
104 Pagoda Chinese Restaurant
35 Palace Museum
33 Palace Restaurant
F Pan African Gallery
F Paracuda Restaurant
14 Passing Show Restaurant
112 Peace Memorial Museum
56 People's Bank of Zanzibar
58 People's Bank of Zanzibar (foreign exchange)
10 Petrol station
15 Police station (main)
7 Port gates
69 Post office & telephone office
25 Pyramid Hotel
55 Radha Food House
107 Rendezvous Les Spices Restaurant
72 St Joseph's Catholic Cathedral
77 St Monica's Hostel
50 Sama Tours
22 Sea View Indian Restaurant
101 Serena Inn
43 Shamshuddin Cash & Carry Supermarket
67 Shangani Hotel
67 Shangani Internet Café
6 Shipping company ticket offices
38 Spice Inn
65 Starehe Club
109 State House
60 Stone Town Inn
52 Suna
99 Sunrise Restaurant & Pub
A Sweet Easy Restaurant
30, 47 Taxi rank
64 Tembo Hotel
102 Tippu Tip's House
92 Two Tables Restaurant
90 Victoria House (guesthouse)
5 Warere Guesthouse
C Wings Fast Food
13 Zan Air
16 Zan Tours
54 Zanzibar Dive Centre
57, 62 Zanzibar Gallery, The
97 Zanzibar Hotel
81 Zanzibar Medical & Diagnostic Centre
94 Zanzibar Medical Group
110 Zanzibar Milestone
27 Zanzibar Tourism Corporation
91 Zi-Bar & Restaurant

For numerical key see page 165

In its heyday, the interior of the new palace was decorated with a marble floor and panelled walls, and it was the first building on Zanzibar to have electric lighting, and also one of the first in East Africa to have an electric lift – which is why, not surprisingly, the local people called it 'Beit el Ajaib', meaning the 'House of Wonders'. It is still one of the largest buildings on Zanzibar today.

In 1896 the House of Wonders was slightly damaged by naval bombardment during an attempted palace coup, which started when Sultan Hamad died suddenly and his cousin Khaled tried to seize the throne (see *The Shortest War in History* box on page 33). From 1911 it was used as offices by the British colonial government and after the 1964 revolution it was used by the ASP, the ruling political party of Zanzibar. In 1977 it became the headquarters of the CCM (Chapa Cha Mapinduzi, the Party of the Revolution), by that time the sole political party of Tanzania.

In the early 1990s, the House of Wonders was virtually abandoned by the government and the party, and it stood empty for some years, slowly falling into disrepair. By the end of the 1990s, Zanzibar had become a tourist destination, and there were short-lived plans to turn the building into a hotel, but these never materialised. Now the House of Wonders is a museum, suitably covering historical items, with a range of exhibits still worthy of the 'wonder' name.

The Arab Fort

The Arab Fort (also called the Old Fort, and by its local name *Ngome Kongwe*) is next to the House of Wonders. It is a large building, with high, dark brown walls topped by castellated battlements. It was built between 1698 and 1701 by the Busaidi group of Omani Arabs, who had gained control of Zanzibar in 1698, following almost two centuries of Portuguese occupation. The Fort was used as a defence against the Portuguese and against a rival Omani group, the Mazrui, who occupied Mombasa at that time.

The Fort was constructed by the Busaidi Omani Arabs on the site of a church which had been built between 1598 and 1612 by the Portuguese. In the main courtyard, remnants of the old church can still be seen built into the inside wall. In the 19th century the Fort was used as a prison, and criminals were executed or punished here, at a place just outside the east wall. (The Swahili word *gereza*, meaning prison, is thought to be derived from the Portuguese word *ireja*, meaning church.)

In the early 20th century, the Fort was also used as a depot for the railway line which ran from Zanzibar Town to Bububu. In 1949 it was rebuilt and the main courtyard used as a ladies' tennis club. After the 1964 revolution the Fort fell into disuse.

Today, the Fort has been renovated, and is open to visitors. It is possible to reach the top of the battlements and go on to the towers on the western side. In 1994 a section of the Fort was turned into an open-air theatre. The development was imaginative yet sympathetic to the overall design and 'feel' of the original building, with seating in the style of an amphitheatre and the Fort's outer walls and the House of Wonders forming a natural backdrop. The theatre is used for contemporary and traditional music, drama and dance performances. The Fort also houses a tourist information desk, with details on performances in the amphitheatre and other events around town, plus a selection of books for sale and a range of tour company leaflets to browse through.

Also in the Fort are several spice and craft shops and a pleasant café. There are even some very clean public toilets. And don't miss the Tower Workshop in the west tower, where local artists create and display their works (more details are given in the *Shopping* section on page 152). Even if historical ruins don't interest you, it is well worth stopping by at the Fort. With all these attractions and facilities, it's easy to spend quite a few hours here.

Forodhani Gardens

The Forodhani Gardens (also called Jamituri Gardens on some maps) are between the Arab Fort and the sea, overlooked by the House of Wonders. (*Forodhani* actually means 'customs' – the original Customs House was near here.) The gardens were first laid out in 1936 to commemorate the Silver Jubilee of Sultan Khalifa (sultan from 1911 to 1960) and were called Jubilee Gardens until the 1964 Revolution. This is a popular place for local people in the evenings and there are some stalls serving drinks and snacks. In the centre of the gardens is a podium where the band of the sultan's army used to play for the public. Nearer the sea is a white concrete Arabesque arch which was built in 1956 for the visit of Princess Margaret (sister of Queen Elizabeth II of Britain), although this was never officially used, as the princess arrived at the dhow harbour instead. She did visit the gardens, however, and planted the large tree with creepers that can still be seen today.

Saint Joseph's Catholic Cathedral

This large cathedral, with prominent twin spires, is off Kenyatta Road in the Baghani part of town. Although its spires are a major landmark from a distance, the cathedral can be surprisingly hard to find in the narrow streets. It was built between 1893 and 1897 by French missionaries and local converts, who had originally founded a mission here in 1860. The plans were drawn by the same French architect who designed the cathedral in Marseilles, France. The tiles and the stained-glass windows were imported from France, and the murals on the inside walls, painted just after the cathedral was completed, also show a clear French influence. (Some of the murals have been recently – and none too carefully – restored.)

The cathedral is in regular use by the town's Catholic community, a mixture of Zanzibaris, Tanzanians from the mainland, Goans and Europeans. There are several masses each Sunday, and one or two on weekdays too. Outside mass times, the main cathedral doors may be locked, and entrance is via the back door reached through the courtyard of the adjoining convent.

The Hamamni Baths

In the centre of Stone Town, east of St Joseph's Cathedral and northwest of Sultan Ahmed Mugheiri Road (formerly New Mkunazini Road), are the Hamamni Baths. The area is called Hamamni, which means simply 'the place of the baths' from the Arabic *Hamam* (bath-house).

This was the first public bath-house in Zanzibar, commissioned by Sultan Barghash and built by an architect called Haji Gulam Hussein. It is one of the most elaborate on Zanzibar, and is constructed in the Persian style. (Such baths are found in many Arab and Islamic countries, and are commonly known by Europeans as 'Turkish baths'.) Today the baths are no longer functioning, but it is still possible to go in and look around. Inside, the bath-house is surprisingly large, with several sections including the steam room, the cool room and the cool water pool.

The caretaker lives opposite: he will unlock the door, make a small entrance charge, give you a guided tour and sell you an informative leaflet about the baths' history and function.

THE PALACES AT MIZINGANI

The Palace Museum (formerly the People's Palace, and before that the Sultan's Palace) was constructed on part of the site of an even older palace called Beit el Sahel (the House of the Coast), which was originally built for Sultan Said between 1827 and 1834. Contemporary accounts describe Beit el Sahel as a two-storey whitewashed palace, with a roof of green and red tiles, separated from the beach by a high wall, with a grove of pomegranates behind. The accounts go on to describe how Sultan Said spent three days of each week at Beit el Sahel, and the rest of the time at his country palace at Mtoni, about 5km north of Zanzibar Town. He often walked from the town to Mtoni even though his stables were full of Arabian horses. Every morning, the best horses were brought out from the stables and fastened to the seaward side of the wall with long ropes, to roam about and wade in the soft sand at low tide.

Another palace, called Beit el Hukm (the House of Government), was built later behind Beit el Sahel. Then, in 1883, Beit el Ajaib (the House of Wonders) was also built. These three adjoining palaces were connected by a series of covered ways and passages. A lighthouse in front of the palaces was nicknamed the 'Sultan's Christmas tree' by British navy officers, due to its many rows of lamps.

Beit el Sahel, Beit el Hukm and the lighthouse were all destroyed in the bombardment of 1896 (see *The Shortest War in History* box on page 33). The palace that exists today (now the museum) was constructed partly on the site of Beit el Sahel. On the site of Beit el Hukm a private house was built, which is now the offices of Stone Town Conservation and Development Authority, easily seen between the Palace Museum and the House of Wonders, set back from the road. The building has a well-maintained garden with palm trees and shrubs. Outside the main entrance is a pair of cannons, made in Boston, Massachusetts in 1868.

Tippu Tip's House

Tippu Tip (also spelt Tippoo Tib and Toppu Tob) was a slave trader, whose real name was Hamed bin Mohammed el Marjebi. He was born in the 1840s and began to participate in the slave trade at the age of 18. His nickname is thought to come from a local word meaning 'to blink', as he apparently had a nervous twitch affecting his eyes, or because his eyes resembled those of a type of bird called Tippu Tib locally because it had characteristic blinking eyes.

During the mid-19th century, Tippu Tip travelled for many years across the East African mainland, trading in slaves and ivory. He also helped some of the European explorers such as Livingstone and Stanley with their supplies and route-planning.

Contemporary records describe him as tall, bearded, fit and strong, with dark skin, an intelligent face and the air of a well-bred Arab. He reportedly visited his concubines twice a day, and is said to have argued with missionaries that Abraham and Jacob (men of God, who appear in the Bible and the Koran) had both been slave-owners themselves. Tippu Tip became very wealthy and by 1895, after many years of trading on the mainland, he owned seven plantations on Zanzibar and 10,000 slaves. He died in 1905.

The house where Tippu Tip lived is near the Africa House Hotel, behind the offices of Jasfa Tours. Until the 1960s it was a private residence, but after the revolution it was turned into a block of flats and is now occupied by several families. The house has not been maintained since its transformation, and one writer has called it 'the most magnificent squat in all of Africa'. It is not open to visitors. However, the huge carved front door (a sign of Tippu Tip's great wealth) leading into the courtyard can still be seen.

The Anglican Cathedral

The Cathedral Church of Christ, also called the Cathedral of the Universities Mission in Central Africa (UMCA), is near the junction of Creek Road and Sultan Ahmed Mugheiri Rd (formerly New Mkunazini Road) and on the eastern side of Stone Town. It stands on the site of the slave market, used in the 18th and 19th centuries when Zanzibar was a large slaving centre.

A group of UMCA missionaries had originally come to East Africa in 1861, following the call of the explorer David Livingstone to oppose the slave trade and spread Christianity across Africa. In 1864 they settled in Zanzibar, after a number of earlier sites proved unsuccessful. When the slave market was closed by Sultan Barghash in 1873 the missionaries bought the site and almost immediately started building the cathedral. Some adjoining land was donated to the mission by a wealthy Indian merchant called Jairam Senji.

When the first service was held in the cathedral, on Christmas Day 1877, the roof was not finished. It was finally completed in 1880. Tradition has it that the cathedral's altar stands on the site of a tree to which the slaves were tied and then whipped to show their strength and hardiness.

Today, nothing of the old slave market remains, although the cellar of the nearby St Monica's Hostel is reputed to be the remains of a pit where slaves were kept before being sold in the market. The man who was the force and inspiration behind the building of the cathedral was Bishop Edward Steere, who was Bishop of Zanzibar from 1874 to 1882. (He was also the first compiler of an English–Swahili dictionary, using the Roman alphabet; until then Swahili had been written using Arabic script.) He trained local people as masons and used coral stone and cement for building materials. Sultan Barghash is reputed to have asked Bishop Steere not to build the cathedral tower higher than the House of Wonders. When the bishop agreed, the sultan presented the cathedral with its clock. The tower was finished in 1883.

The legacy of David Livingstone lives on in the cathedral: a window is dedicated to his memory, and the church's crucifix is made from the tree that marked the place where his heart was buried at the village of Chitambo, in present-day Zambia.

The mosaic decorations on the altar were given to the cathedral by Miss Caroline Thackeray (a cousin of the famous English novelist William Makepeace Thackeray), who was a teacher at the mission here from 1877 to 1902.

Behind the altar is the bishop's throne and 12 other seats for the canons. They are decorated with copper panels and show the names of several biblical figures, written in Swahili. The window behind the altar has been decorated with pictures of African saints, from Egypt, Carthage and Ethiopia.

Around the church are many plaques, dedicated to the memory of missionaries who died here, and to the sailors and airmen who were killed in action during the East Africa Campaign of World War I.

Today, services are held every Sunday (in Swahili), and an English service is held on the first Sunday of the month. The cathedral is also open to visitors. A small entrance charge is made outside service times.

Outside the cathedral, in a small garden next to the school, is a sculpture of four slaves chained in a pit – an understated yet powerfully emotive work of art that is well worth seeing.

The Peace Memorial Museum

The museum is at the southern end of Stone Town, near the junction of Creek Road and Kaunda Road in the area called Mnazi Moja. It is also known by its local title: Beit el Amani (House of Peace). With its distinctive dome, Arabesque windows and whitewashed walls, the museum looks like a mosque or basilica church. It was designed by the British architect J H Sinclair, who also designed the High Court, the British Residency and several other public buildings around Zanzibar Town.

The museum is informative and quite well organised. The main building has sections on archaeology, early trade, slavery, palaces, mosques, sultans, explorers, missionaries, colonial administrators, traditional crafts and household items, stamps, coins, fishing and clove cultivation. Highlights include Dr Livingstone's medical chest, a section of track from the short-lived Zanzibar Railroad, and some old bicycle lamps customised to run on coconut oil. And be sure not to miss the old lighthouse lamp upstairs.

When we were researching this book in 2002, this museum was undergoing changes. Many of the historical items were being moved to the new Museum of History and Culture at the House of Wonders. The Peace Memorial Museum will become a museum devoted to wildlife and environmental matters.

The museum annexe has a small library and the natural history sections, with some tatty stuffed exhibits, snakes in jars, photos of mutant fish, and the bones of a dodo. A sign invites visitors to 'inspect tortoises behind the building', but in recent years these giant reptiles have become an endangered species and most are kept on Changuu (Prison) Island for safety (see page 185).

The museum is open 08.30–18.00 Monday to Friday, 08.30–15.00 Saturday and Sunday. There is a small entrance charge.

Other places of interest in Zanzibar Town

Although the following places aren't major sights in themselves, you'll probably find yourself walking nearby as you visit some of the more important palaces and museums, and the following background information will be useful.

Mnazi Moja Sports Field

Opposite the museum, on the other side of Creek Road, is Mnazi Moja Sports Field. (Mnazi Moja means 'one coconut tree'.) This area used to be a swamp at the end of the creek that separated the Stone Town peninsula from the rest of the island. The land was reclaimed and converted to a sports field during the colonial period, hence the English-style cricket pavilion in the corner. In the 1920s part of the sportsground was set aside for exclusive use by members of the English Club; it contained tennis courts, a croquet lawn and the only golf course on the island. Today, Mnazi Moja is used mainly for football matches and, although the creek itself has been reclaimed, the sports field is still prone to flooding in the rainy season.

The road leading southeast out of the town (now called Nyerere Road) was originally built as a causeway across the swamp by Bishop Steere of the Universities Mission in Central Africa. Today it is a pleasant avenue lined with giant casuarina trees.

The People's Gardens

The People's Gardens are on Kaunda Road, at the southern end of Stone Town, near the main hospital. They were originally laid out by Sultan Barghash for use

THE EAST AFRICAN SLAVE TRADE

From the earliest times, slaves were one of the many commodities exported from Africa to Arabia, Persia, India and beyond. In the 18th century the demand increased considerably, and Arab trading caravans from Zanzibar penetrated mainland Africa in the search for slaves. Various contemporary accounts describe all aspects of the trade, from the initial capture of the slaves to their sale in the infamous market of Zanzibar Town.

In the interior, the Arab traders would often take advantage of local rivalries and encourage powerful African tribes to capture their enemies and sell them into slavery. In this way, men, women and children were exchanged for beads, corn or lengths of cloth.

When the Arab traders had gathered enough slaves (maybe up to a thousand), they returned to the coast. Although the Koran forbade cruelty to slaves, this was ignored on the long journey to Zanzibar: the slaves were tied together in long lines, with heavy wooden yokes at the neck, or iron chains at the ankles, which remained in place day and night until they reached the coast. The trade in slaves was closely linked to the trade in ivory: the Arab traders also bought tusks from the Africans and some of the captured slaves may have had to carry these on their heads as they marched towards the coast. In addition, women often carried a child on their backs. If they became too weak to carry both child and ivory, the child would be killed or abandoned to make the ivory load easier to carry. Any slaves too weak to march were also killed and left behind for the vultures and hyenas. The passage of a slave caravan was marked by a long line of decaying corpses.

After many weeks or months of marching, the slave caravans reached the coast at ports such as Kilwa and Bagamoyo. Here, the slaves were loaded on to dhows, seldom more than 30m to 35m long, and carried to Zanzibar. Each dhow carried between 200 and 600 slaves, all crammed below decks on specially constructed bamboo shelves with about 1m of headroom. There was not enough room to sit, or kneel or squat, just a crippling combination of the three. Sometimes slaves were closely packed in open boats, their bodies exposed day and night to the sea and the rain. They were thirsty, hungry and seasick and many died of exhaustion. Meals consisted of a daily handful of rice and a cup of stagnant water. Sanitation was non-existent and disease spread

by his harem. Many of the trees and bushes in the garden, including eucalyptus, coffee, tea and cocoa, were added by Sir John Kirk, the British consul on Zanzibar from 1873 to 1887. The gardens were given to the people of Zanzibar by Sultan Hamoud on the occasion of Queen Victoria's Jubilee in 1899 and they were renamed Victoria Gardens. The building in the centre of the gardens was called Victoria Hall. It was built over the baths of the harem and used as the Chamber of the Legislative Council from 1926 to 1964. After the Revolution, the hall and gardens fell into disrepair. They were renovated in 1996, with help from the German government, and Victoria Hall is now rather ignominiously the offices of the Zanzibar Sewerage and Sanitation Project.

The large house opposite the gardens, on the south side of Kaunda Road, was built in 1903 as the official British Residency. After the 1964 Revolution, when the Victoria Gardens were renamed the People's Gardens, the old British Residency became the State House – the official residence of the president. The building next door to the State House was the embassy of the Soviet Union. It is now the offices

rapidly. When any illness was discovered infected slaves were simply thrown overboard.

By the time the slaves reached Zanzibar, they were suffering from starvation and the cramped conditions. It was sometimes a week after landing before they could straighten their legs. The slave traders paid customs duty on all slaves who landed, so any considered too weak to live were thrown overboard as the ship approached the port. Even so, many more slaves died in the Customs House or on the streets between the port and the market.

Before being put on sale, the slaves who did survive were cleaned so that they would fetch a better price. Men and boys had their skins oiled and were given a strip of material to put around their waist. Women and girls were draped in cloth, and sometimes even adorned with necklaces, earrings and bracelets. Generous layers of henna and kohl were smeared onto their foreheads and eyebrows.

The slaves were put on sale in the market in the late afternoon. They were arranged in lines, with the youngest and smallest at the front and the tallest at the rear, and paraded through the market by their owner, who would call out the selling prices. The owner would assure potential buyers that the slaves had no defects in speech or hearing, and that there was no disease present. Buyers would examine the arms, mouths, teeth and eyes of the slaves, and the slaves were often made to walk or run, to prove they were capable of work. Once their suitability had been established, they were sold to the highest bidder.

After being sold to a new owner, slaves were either put to work in the houses and plantations of Zanzibar or else transported again, on a much longer sea voyage, to Oman or elsewhere in the Indian Ocean. However, the slaves were relatively well treated when they arrived at their new homes. They were fed, housed and clothed, and given small plots of land, with time off to tend them. Young mothers were rarely separated from their children, and good slaves were often freed after a few years. Many took paid jobs, such as gardeners and farmers, for their previous masters: some even became leaders of slave caravans or masters of slave ships.

Source: *The Lunatic Express*, Charles Miller,
published by Macmillan (1971)

of the Zanzibar Investment Promotions Agency (ZIPA), a government agency set up to attract foreign business capital to Zanzibar.

The Big Tree

Just west of the Old Dispensary, about 100m along Mizingani Road, is a large tree originally planted by Sultan Khalifa in 1911. Known simply as The Big Tree (or in Swahili as *Mtini* – the place of the tree), it has been a major landmark for many years. It can be seen on numerous old photos and etchings of Zanzibar Town viewed from the sea, and it is still clearly visible on the seafront from ships approaching the port. Today, traditional dhow builders use the tree as a shady 'roof' for their open-air workshop.

The Orphanage

Next to the Fort, the road runs through a tunnel under a large building that is the island's orphanage. Built in the late 19th century, the building was used as a club for English residents until 1896, and then as an Indian school until 1950. There is a small craft shop on the ground floor opposite the gardens.

The Upimaji Building

Between the orphanage and the People's Bank of Zanzibar, this building is now the Commission for Lands and Environment. In the 1860s it was the offices and home of Heinrich Ruete, the German merchant who eloped with Princess Salme (see the *Princess Salme* boxes on pages 180–1.)

The Old British Consulate

This fine old house was used as the British Consulate from 1841 to 1874, after which the consulate was moved to the Mambo Msiige Building (see below). The first consul was Lieutenant-Colonel Atkins Hamerton, posted here to represent the interests of Britain after Sultan Said had moved his capital from Oman to Zanzibar.

Later consuls here played host to several of the well-known British explorers, including Speke, Burton, Grant and Stanley (see page 26), before they set out for their expeditions on the East African mainland. In 1874, the body of David Livingstone was brought here before being taken back to Britain for burial at Westminster Abbey.

From 1874 to 1974 the building was used as offices by the trading company Smith Mackenzie, but it was taken over by the government in the late 1970s. It is still used as government offices today, and visitors are not allowed to enter, but there is not much to see on the inside; most of the building's interest lies in its grand exterior.

The Mambo Msiige Building

This grand house, overlooking the open 'square' at the far western end of Shangani Road, was originally built around 1850 for a wealthy Arab, incorporating a variety of architectural styles. Its name means 'look, but do not imitate'. The building was sold to the British Foreign Office in 1875 and used as the British Consulate until 1913. From 1918 to 1924 it was used as the European hospital, after which it was used as government offices. Today, the Zanzibar Shipping Corporation is based here.

The Zanzibar Milestone

Near the People's Gardens is this octagonal pillar, built with marble taken from the palace at Chukwani, showing the distances from Zanzibar Town to other settlements on the island. For complete accuracy, the distances were measured from this exact point.

The distance to London is also shown: 8,064 miles. This is the distance by sea. (By 1870, ships between Zanzibar and London travelled via the Suez Canal. Before this all voyages were much longer, via the Cape of Good Hope.)

The Zanzibar Archives

For real aficionados, the Zanzibar Archives (*Nyaraka za Taifa* in Swahili) contain some fascinating material. These include many books and manuscripts in Arabic dating from the 17th century, when the Omani sultans took control of Zanzibar; Consular and Protectorate Records from the British colonial times; papers and documents relating to the various European expeditions that started from Zanzibar in the second half of the 19th century; plus a lot of contemporary material such as stamps, newspapers, maps and photographs. If there is something of special interest, the staff

Previous page On the way to Koran school, Zanzibar Stone Town (AZ)

Above left Young boy climbing a palm tree (AZ)

Above right Using a wooden *kinu* in which to pound flour from maize or millet (DE)

Below Local boys meet on Zanzibar Town waterfront at the end of a lazy afternoon (DE)

on duty can help you search through the collections. If you just want to browse there is an exhibition room, where some selected items of interest are on display.

The Archives are open 07.30–15.30 Mondays to Fridays and until 12.00 on Saturdays. Entrance is free. They are situated outside the main town, about 2km along Nyerere Road from the Mnazi Moja Hospital, in an area called Kilimani. To get there take a *dala-dala* on Route U and asked to be dropped at Nyaraka za Taifa, or at the prison. The *dala-dala* will stop at the bottom of Kinuamiguu Hill (the only hill on this road); turn left (north) off Nyerere Road, then take the first road on the right.

More information is available from the Head of the National Archives, PO Box 116, Zanzibar; tel: 024 230342. Or have a look at the (not directly related) website: www.zanzibar-archives.com.

PLACES TO VISIT NEAR ZANZIBAR TOWN

The following places can be reached easily, or without too much difficulty, from Zanzibar Town. They make good day trips by hired scooter, hired bike, or a combination of foot and public transport. (For details on travelling beyond the town see *Getting around Zanzibar Island* on page 189.) If you prefer not to travel independently, visits to any of the places mentioned here can also be arranged with a tour company.

Of the places described below, Mbweni, Chukwani and Fumba lie south and southeast of Zanzibar Town. The palaces of Marahubi and Mtoni, and the Persian Baths of Kidich and Kizimbani lie to the north. Some of the palaces and bath-houses mentioned in this section are included in the 'spice tours' arranged by tour companies and independent guides.

Mbweni

The area of Mbweni is on the coast, about 3km directly south of Zanzibar Town. It was originally a plantation bought by the Universities Mission in Central Africa (UMCA) in 1871. Bishop Tozer (Bishop of Zanzibar from 1863 to 1873) planned to build a mission station here. His successor Bishop Steere (Bishop of Zanzibar from 1874 to 1882) oversaw the building of a church and other mission buildings, and also used the area as a colony for freed slaves.

To reach Mbweni, take the main road out of town going towards the airport. Go uphill through the area called Kinuamiguu ('lift your legs') and another area called Mazizini. After a few kilometres, at a signpost to Mbweni and Chukwani, fork right, then turn right again after 500m on to a smaller road. Continue down this road towards the sea to reach Mbweni. *Dala-dalas* on Route U run between the town and the airport and go past the main Mbweni and Chukwani junction.

St John's Church

At the heart of Mbweni (on the right side of the small road leading towards the sea) is this English-style church, complete with tower and surrounding cemetery. It was opened in 1882 by UMCA missionaries and converts, and consecrated in 1904. Descendants of freed slaves continued to live in the area. Today, the sexton at the church is Peter Sudi, a descendant of John Swedi, one of the first five freed slave boys taken in by the mission.

The church has a marble altar inlaid with mother-of-pearl (colourful shell pieces) and a wooden chair made for Bishop Tozer by sailors from the ship HMS *London*, famous for its slave-dhow captures. Miss Caroline Thackeray (see *Mbweni Ruins* below) is buried in the cemetery here. The nearby building, formerly the Inn by the Sea hotel, was originally the old clergy house.

There are Anglican church services at 09.00 every Sunday.

MOSQUES OF ZANZIBAR TOWN

Most of Zanzibar's population is Muslim and Zanzibar Town has several mosques. The oldest is Malindi Mosque, a small, inconspicuous building near the port, with a minaret which is thought to be several hundred years old. Three of the larger mosques are also in the northern part of Stone Town: the Ijumaa Mosque (Sunni); the Ithnasheri Mosque (Shia); and the Aga Khan Mosque (Ismaili). These were all built in the 19th century. Compared to the large mosques of other Islamic cities, often decorated with domes and tall minarets, the mosques of Zanzibar are relatively plain and unpretentious. However, in 1994 the Ijumaa Mosque (near the Big Tree) was completely renovated in a modern Arabesque style, and the other large mosques may follow this trend.

Non-Muslims are not normally allowed to enter any mosque in Zanzibar Town although, if you have a genuine interest, a good local guide might be able to speak to the mosque's elders on your behalf and arrange an invitation. Men will find this easier than women. There are usually no restrictions on non-Muslims (men or women) visiting the area around a mosque, although photos of local people praying or simply congregating should not be taken without permission.

Sir John Kirk's House

Along the road which passes northwards in front of St John's Church is the house of Sir John Kirk, who was British consul-general in Zanzibar from 1873 to 1887. Kirk first came to Africa as medical officer and naturalist to Livingstone's Zambezi expedition in the 1850s. As consul-general he was very active in the suppression of the slave trade, and is often regarded as the 'power behind the throne' during the rule of Sultan Barghash, his close friend. The house was built as a gift from the sultan and was used by Kirk and his family as a country retreat.

Kirk was an experienced botanist and established a large experimental garden here, which later provided the core species of all the botanical gardens of Zanzibar and mainland Tanzania. He imported many new plant species to the islands, and worked on improved varieties of useful and edible crops. Kirk also collected trees and flowers from the mainland of Africa which formed the basis of the then standard work, *Flora of Tropical Africa*.

In 1887 Kirk left Zanzibar, and sold his house to Miss Caroline Thackeray, the headmistress of the School for Girls at Mbweni (see below). While she lived here, Miss Thackeray opened the grounds of the house for a yearly garden party. She retired in 1902, but continued to live in Kirk's house until her death, aged 83, in 1926.

The house was then sold by the church to a wealthy Arab, who used it until the early 1960s. It is now privately owned and not open to the public.

Mbweni Ruins

If you continue past St John's Church towards the sea, the dirt road leads to the Mbweni Ruins Hotel. Set in the hotel grounds are Mbweni Ruins. These ruins are the remains of St Mary's School for Girls, built between 1871 and 1874 by the missionaries based at Mbweni under the leadership of Bishop Steere. The land, then known as Mbweni Point Shamba, had originally been bought by Bishop Tozer in 1871, when there was an old Arab house on the property which was incorporated into the school entrance.

The school was a large square building, based around a central courtyard. The headteacher from 1877 until 1902 was Caroline Mary Defflis Thackeray (a cousin of the famous English novelist William Makepeace Thackeray). In 1926 she died at Kirk's house (see above) and was buried at St John's Church nearby.

The school educated orphaned girls who had been freed from captured slave-dhows, and daughters of freed slaves who lived at the mission, each with their own house and small garden. Most of the girls were trained as teachers, and were taught reading, writing, arithmetic, geography and sewing. In 1877 Caroline Thackeray had an Industrial Wing built (at her own cost) where vocational training in basketry, stitching, laundry and cooking was given to the girls who were less academically inclined.

St Mary's had its own chapel which is still in good condition today, though without a roof. In 1906 the school became a convent and in 1920 the buildings were sold by the church to a consortium of the Bank of India. They slowly became ruins and were never used or lived in until the present time.

At the the Mbweni Ruins Hotel, and bookshops in town, you can find an informative book called *Zanzibar, History of the Ruins at Mbweni*, by Flo Liebst, which also touches on the general history of Zanzibar and the UMCA missionaries of East Africa.

Chukwani and Fumba

The small village of Chukwani, to the south of Zanzibar Town, is about 5km beyond Mbweni. Southwest of the village, on the coast, is the Chukwani Palace. It was built by Sultan Barghash in 1872 and used mainly as a place to recuperate after illness as the air here was supposed to be particularly healthy. The palace was built as a smaller version of the House of Wonders, without the tower. During the reign of Sultan Ali bin Hamoud (sultan from 1902 to 1911) the palace was used by government officers. Today, most of the palace has been demolished, leaving only the bath-house. The front door of the palace is on display in the Peace Memorial Museum. The new buildings around the ruins are used by the army, so visitors are not allowed to enter, but you can get a good view from the air if you fly out of Zanzibar as the palace lies only a few kilometres southwest of the airport.

Fumba is a village at the end of the peninsula, about 15km southeast of Zanzibar Town, reached by the road that forks left (east) off the airport road, just after a petrol station, then leads down the east side of the airport. To get here, you can take a local bus or *dala-dala*, or hire a car, bike or scooter. From the beach just south of the village, local fishermen take their boats out to the islands of Chumbe, Kwale and Pungume, and to the fishing grounds around the smaller islands in Menai Bay. It's a quiet scenic place, but very few tourists come here. If you want to get a deeper insight, ask around for a local villager called Issa Kibwana, who conducts small tours of the nearby fruit and spice plantations. In Zanzibar Town, the people at Sama Tours can help put you in touch, or arrange a trip to Fumba for you.

The Palaces north of Zanzibar Town

Along to coast from Zanzibar Town, stretching over a distance of about 5km, are several palaces dating from the 19th century built for the various sultans who ruled Zanzibar during this period. Some are in good condition and worth a visit; others will appeal only to keen fans of historical ruins. The entrance price (for the palaces that are open) is very cheap, and the ticket you buy at the first place you visit also allows you to visit many other historical sites on the same day. This includes the baths at Kidichi, the caves at Mangapwani, and several other sites around the island (as described in *Chapter 6*).

Maruhubi Palace

The Maruhubi Palace is on the coast, about 4km north of Zanzibar Town. It was built in 1882 for Sultan Barghash (sultan from 1870 to 1888) and at one time he reputedly kept 100 women here: one official wife and 99 concubines. (The sultan himself lived at the palace in Zanzibar Town.) The palace's name comes from the original owner of the estate who sold the land to Sultan Barghash.

The palace was built with coral stone and wood, and was reported to have been one of the most ornate on the island. Large walls were built around the palace grounds, thought to have been inspired by the park walls seen by Sultan Barghash on his visit to England in 1875. Unfortunately, the palace was destroyed by a fire in 1899. All that remains today are the great pillars which supported the upper storey, and the Persian-style bath-house. The separate bathrooms for the women, and the large bath for the sultan's own use, can still be seen. The original water tanks, now overgrown with lilies, also remain in the grounds of the palace. To the north of the pillars, at the back of the beach, is a small set of arches and steps; this was part of the palace's reception area. (The Peace Memorial Museum in Zanzibar Town contains a photo of the palace taken at the end of the 19th century when it was still in use.)

To reach the palace, take the main road north out of Zanzibar Town towards Bububu. Pass Livingstone House on your right and, after a few kilometres, the Maruhubi Palace is signposted on your left. *Dala-dalas* on Route B run between the town and Bububu village, past the palace entrance gate.

Mtoni Palace

Just north of Maruhubi is the ruined Mtoni Palace, which was built for Sultan Said (sultan from 1804 to 1856) on the site of an older house believed to have belonged to Saleh bin Haramil, the Arab trader who imported the first cloves to Zanzibar (*see Chapter 2, page 15*). Mtoni, which means 'place by the river', is the oldest palace on Zanzibar.

One of Sultan Said's daughters, whose name was Salme, later married a German trader who lived and worked in Zanzibar in the 1860s. She eloped with him to Germany and later wrote a book about her life on Zanzibar (see the *Princess Salme* box on pages 180–1). In her book, Salme describes Mtoni Palace in the 1850s: it had a large courtyard where gazelles, peacocks, ostriches and flamingoes wandered around, a large bath-house at one end and the sultan's quarters at the other, where he lived with his principal wife, an Omani princess whose name was Azze.

Salme records that over 1,000 people were attached to the sultan's court in the palace. She describes how the sultan would pace up and down on a large round tower overlooking the sea, where he could see his fleet anchored off the shore. If visitors came by boat, he would greet them on the steps of his palace as there was no landing pier. Salme and the other princesses were carried out to their boats on chairs.

In her book, Salme also describes her own return visit to Zanzibar in 1885. The palace at Mtoni had been abandoned and was already in ruins. Today, only the main walls and parts of the roof remain. The palace was turned into a warehouse during World War I, and evidence of the alterations can still be seen.

To reach the palace, turn left off the main road on to a dirt track, about 2km north of Maruhubi. There is a small signpost.

Beit el Ras Palace

Further north along the coast, this palace was built for Sultan Said as an 'overflow' house for his children and their servants, when Mtoni Palace became too crowded (see the *Wives and Children of Sultan Said* box on page 179). Building started in 1847 but was not completed by the time of Said's death in 1856. Sultan Majid (Said's

THE WIVES AND CHILDREN OF SULTAN SAID

During his lifetime, Sultan Said (Sultan of Oman and Zanzibar from 1804–56) had three legitimate wives or *harino* (singular *horme*). (Under Islamic law, he was allowed up to four *harino* at a time.)

In 1827, he married Azze binte Seif bin Ahmed, daughter of Seif bin Ahmed and grandchild of Sultan Ahmed, and thus a cousin of Said's. Like any *horme*, Azze was considered to have equal status with her husband. She was reported to be strong willed, and to rule the royal household with a firm hand. Apparently, no act of state was carried out without her advice and approval.

In 1847 Said married his second wife, Binte Irich Mirza, nicknamed Schesade, a beautiful and extravagant princess, and granddaughter of the Shah of Persia. She came to Zanzibar in 1849 and Said built the baths at Kidichi for her in 1850, using stonemasons and plasterers from Persia. Schesade had no children so Said divorced her and sent her back to Persia. By the late 1850s Schesade had become a prominent member of the Persian army, fighting against her former husband.

Said's third wife was Binte Seif bin Ali, of whom little is known. He also possessed a great many concubines. Once they had given birth, they were known as *sarari* (singular *surie*), immediately freed and given equal status with the legal wives.

During his lifetime, Said was credited with 120 children (99 daughters and 21 sons). When he died in 1856, he left a single widow, his first wife Azze binte Seif, and 75 *sarari*. Of his 120 children, only 36 were still alive: 18 sons and 18 daughters. Two of his sons, Thuwaini and Turki, became sultans of Oman. Four more sons, Majid, Barghash, Khalifa and Ali, all became sultans of Zanzibar.

successor) did not continue the project and much of the stone from the palace was used during the construction of the Zanzibar Railroad (described below). The remaining ruins were abandoned and finally demolished in 1947 to make room for a school and teacher training centre. Today, only the giant porch of the original palace remains, with high arches and steps leading up one side. The palace is in the grounds of the training centre, now called the Nkrumah Teacher Training College (*Chuo Cha Ualimu Nkrumah*), and is reached by turning off the main road a few kilometres beyond Mtoni. Beit el Ras means 'the palace on the headland' and from the porch you get good views over this part of the coast and out towards the group of small islands off Zanzibar Town.

Kibweni Palace

North of Beit el Ras, this 'palace' was built in Arabic style by the British authorities in 1915. In the village of Kibweni, its official title was Beit el Kassrusaada (Palace of Happiness), although this name seems to have been forgotten. Sultan Khalifa II (sultan from 1911 to 1960) used the palace as a country residence. After the Revolution it was taken over by the government and is still used as an official residence. It is not open to the public.

Chuini Palace

About 10km north of Zanzibar Town, on the coast near the village of Chuini, lie the ruins of Chuini Palace. (Chuini means 'place of the leopard'.) It was built for

PRINCESS SALME

Salme was a daughter of Sultan Said. She was born at the Mtoni Palace in August 1844. Her mother was a *surie* (secondary wife) from Circassia, in southern Russia. Salme later wrote *Memoirs of an Arabian Princess*, from which we learn many interesting details about life at court and the events of the time (see page 271).

In her book Salme describes her early childhood at the Mtoni Palace, where she lived until she was seven years old. Here she learnt sewing, embroidery and lace-making from her mother. She and her brothers and sisters had a private teacher and lessons were conducted in an open gallery containing just a single large mat and a Koran (Islamic holy book) on a stand. The royal children were taught the Arabic alphabet, reading and a little arithmetic. The boys were also taught to write, using home-made ink, and the well-bleached shoulder blade of a camel for a slate. But Salme was rebellious and taught herself to write in secret.

Twice a day, early in the morning and in the evening, all children above five years old had riding lessons. When they had made sufficient progress, the boys received Arabian horses, while the girls received white donkeys from Muscat. When the princesses rode their donkeys to the clove plantations, slaves ran by the side of each animal with a large parasol to protect the riders from the sun. The children also learnt to swim in the sea at an early age.

Salme was given her own African slaves as personal attendants. At bedtime, one slave would massage her, while another fanned gently, until the princess fell asleep, still fully dressed. Slaves fanned the princess all night. In the morning, her slaves massaged her gently until she awoke. Her bath was filled with fresh spring water. Slaves laid out the day's clothes, on which jasmine and orange blossoms had been strewn overnight, and which were scented with amber and musk before they were worn. Windows and doors were left open throughout the year, even in colder, wetter weather when a charcoal fire was burning. The fresh air helped to disperse the strong scents. Slaves washed the linen daily. It dried in little more than half an hour, was smoothed flat (not ironed) and put away.

As a child, Salme was allowed to mix freely with boys of her own age. After she was nine years old, the only men allowed to see her were her father, close male relatives, and her slaves. She wore trousers, a shirt reaching to her ankles, and a handkerchief for the head. The shirt and trousers were always of a different pattern. On her walks, she wore a *schele*, a large shawl of black silk. When she appeared before a stranger, the law required her to be veiled; part of the face, the neck and chin, and above all, the ankles, had to be completely covered.

In October 1859 Salme became involved in family intrigue between her older brothers, Barghash and Majid. She helped Barghash escape to the Marseilles clove plantation, after his attempt to overthrow Majid failed. (See *The Escape to Marseilles* box on page 24.) Majid never punished Salme for her part in the plot but by siding with Barghash she lost the friendship of many of her other brothers and sisters. When she renewed her friendship with Majid, she isolated herself from her fellow conspirators.

By 1866 Salme was living in Zanzibar Town. Although 22 years old, she was still unmarried. Rejected by her family, she began socialising regularly with many of the foreigners on the island. She became friendly with a young German merchant from Hamburg, called Heinrich Ruete, who was living in a house next to hers. They began a covert relationship, speaking to each other from their balconies across the narrow street, and meeting secretly in the countryside beyond the town.

In July 1866 Salme discovered she was pregnant. Some historians have suggested that she was forced to leave Zanzibar in a hurry, as an illegitimate pregnancy would have brought disgrace to her family and the whole Busaidi dynasty and could have resulted in her death. Others have described her romantic 'elopement' with Heinrich Ruete. However, an analysis by Said el-Gheithy of the Princess Salme Institute presents events in a slightly different light: 'No doubt, her pregnancy sent shock waves through her clan and threatened the position of the European traders, reliant on the goodwill of the sultan. Yet following extensive research, and through a knowledge of her personality from at least one person who knew her, it seems Salme was a very organised and stable individual, with a strength of personality which made her adverse to irrational movements. We must not overlook or underestimate her ability to chose rationally from the options available. The concept of an "elopement" represents her as somewhat flighty. Rather, the move to Germany should be understood as a planned emigration and her departure could be described, to use a Swahili phrase, as "leaving without saying goodbye".'

Salme left Zanzibar on a British warship, and for several months after her departure a wave of anti-European feeling spread through Zanzibar Town. Another British warship was sent to suppress any possible reprisals against Europeans. When Salme reached Aden, she stayed with some European friends, renounced Islam and was baptised into the Anglican Church, with the name Emily. In Zanzibar, Heinrich wound up his affairs, then joined Salme in Aden. They were married immediately and travelled to Heinrich's home in Hamburg.

In the following three years Salme and Heinrich had two daughters and a son. Tragically, in August 1871, Heinrich fell whilst jumping from a tram, and was run over; he died three days later. No longer welcome in Zanzibar, Salme remained in Germany, making one short visit to London in 1875, and two brief returns to Zanzibar in 1885 and 1888, but her attempts at reconciliation were unsuccessful. She lived in exile in Syria until 1914 and died in Germany in 1924. Among the possessions found after her death was a bag of sand from the beach at Zanzibar.

In Zanzibar Town, Princess Salme is remembered at the Palace Museum, which has a room devoted to her life and writings. This was set in place by Said el-Gheithy in collaboration with the Museums of Zanzibar. In London, the Princess Salme Institute was established in 1994 to raise awareness about the life and writings of this remarkable woman, and to promote training and research relevant to Zanzibar. The Institute is based at the Africa Centre (38 King St, London WC2E 8JT, UK; tel: 020 7240 0199), or can be contacted direct by email: sayyidasalme@hotmail.com. The director of the Princess Salme Institute is Said el-Gheithy, who kindly checked the accuracy of the boxed section on pages 24–5, and provided some of the information.

For cultural events in Zanzibar, such as the Zanzibar International Film Festival (ZIFF), the Princess Salme Institute acts as a contact point in Europe. The Institute also mounts an exhibition about Princess Salme at the Festival. Additionally, the Institute's modest resources keep up the enthusiasm for Salme's life, and also provides practical help to academics, researchers, visitors and professionals working on or around Zanzibar. In the future, the Institute hopes to establish a larger base in Zanzibar from where various projects will be administered. These include 'Sayyida Salme tours' where guides will take visitors to the places and palaces lived in and frequented by Princess Salme, while providing a background history of her remarkable story.

Sultan Barghash, added to by Sultan Ali bin Said, and destroyed by fire in 1914. The ruins are on private land and cannot be visited.

The Zanzibar Railroad

In the early 1900s a light railway (36-inch gauge) was built and operated by an American company from a point outside the Arab Fort in Zanzibar Town, along the seafront and up the coast to the village of Bububu. Construction began in 1904 and ended in 1905, and the service was used mainly by local people, but a special first-class coach was joined to the train so that passengers from the steamers that put in to Zanzibar could get a brief glimpse of the island. The line was closed in 1928, but railway buffs can still see the remains of bridges and embankments, as today's main road between Zanzibar Town and Bububu runs parallel to the line (and in some cases over it). A piece of the original track and some old photos of the line can be seen in the Peace Memorial Museum.

In his book *Sketches in Mafeking and East Africa* (published in 1907), Lord Robert Baden-Powell quotes from a description of the Zanzibar train by an American writer called Miss Kirkland. 'Have you ever been to Bu Bu Bu? If not, do not call yourself a travelled person,' she wrote. 'Bu Bu Bu is a settlement in a shady grove on the island of Zanzibar, and is the terminus of a new and important railroad – six and a half miles long.'

It has been suggested that the name Bububu comes from the sound made by the train's hooter, but maps dating from before the building of the railway show the village already had this title. It is more likely that the name was inspired by the sound of the freshwater springs which bubble to the surface just outside the village. (Most of Zanzibar Town's water supply still comes from here.)

Kidichi and Mangapwani

Bububu village has a police station and checkpoint. The main road continues north towards Mahonda and Nunwgi, and a new minor tar road branches off east to reach the agricultural area of Kidichi, where most visitors on spice tours arranged in Zanzibar Town are taken. If you stay on the main road for a few more kilometres, near the village of Chuini (about 10km north of Zanzibar Town) a wide dirt road forks off left (west), signposted to Bumbwini, and this leads to Mangapwani.

Kidichi Persian Baths

The Persian Baths at Kidichi lie to the northeast of Zanzibar Town, about 4km inland from the main coast road, in the island's main clove and coconut plantation area. The baths were built in 1850 for Sultan Said. He owned land in this part of the island, and he and his second wife, Binte Irich Mirza (also called Schesade, more often written Sherazade), would come here for hunting or to oversee the work being done on their plantations. The bath-house was constructed so that they could refresh themselves after the journey from town. Schesade was a granddaughter of the Shah of Persia, so the baths were built in the Persian style, with decorative stucco work. An underground furnace kept the water warm. A small resthouse was also built nearby, but none of this remains.

Today, you can enter the bath-house, and see the changing room, bathing pool and massage tables. Unfortunately, the bath-house has not been especially well maintained, and there is mould growing on much of the stucco. A colony of bats seems to have taken up residence here as well. At the top of the domed ceiling is a circle of small windows: these used to be stained glass, which cast patterns of coloured light over the white walls.

To reach Kidichi, continue up the main road northwards from Zanzibar Town to Bububu. At the police station, turn right on to a new tar road that leads through coconut palms and clove plantations, and past a long row of souvenir stalls selling spices and other goods. After about 4km the bath-house, a domed white building, is seen on the right, just a few metres off the dirt road. There are several more spice-souvenir stalls here, and in the surrounding area several houses where tour groups go for lunch.

Kizimbani Persian Baths

Near Kidichi, these baths were also built in the Persian style for Sultan Said, at about the same time as the baths at Kidichi which they resemble, though there is no interior decoration. The surrounding plantations originally belonged to Saleh bin Haramil, the Arab trader who imported the first cloves to Zanzibar, but they were confiscated by Sultan Said on the grounds that Saleh was a slave smuggler (see *Chapter 2*, page 17). Today the experimental station is the island's centre for agricultural research.

To reach the baths from Kidichi, continue eastwards along the tar road. After about 2km, at a crossroads, there are roads left (north) to Mfenesini and Selem, and right (south) to Mwendo and Mwera. Go straight on, along a dirt road, passing through plantations, to reach the Kizimbani Experimental Station headquarters. The baths are on the right of the track.

Mangapwani Coral Cave

Mangapwani (meaning 'Arab shore') lies on the coast, about 20km north of Zanzibar Town. The Coral Cave is a deep natural cavern in the coralline rock with a narrow entrance and a pool of fresh water at its lowest point. Water was probably collected from here by early inhabitants of this part of the island but at some time in the past vegetation grew across the entrance and the exact position of the cavern was forgotten.

Later, the area became the property of a wealthy Arab landowner called Hamed Salim el Hathy who had many slaves working on his plantations. During this time, the cavern was rediscovered by a young boy searching for a lost goat. Local people were able to use the water again, and Hamed Salim arranged for his slaves to collect the water regularly for his own use. It has been suggested by historians that the cave may have been used as a hiding place for slaves after the trade was officially abolished in 1873.

Most people come here on an organised tour, or by privately hired car or bike. Buses on Route 2 link Zanzibar Town and Mangapwani village, but services are not frequent. To reach the cavern from Zanzibar Town, take the main road through Bububu to Chuini, then fork left towards Bumbwini. After 6km, in Mangapwani village, fork left again and head westwards towards the coast (the Serena Restaurant and Watersports Centre, due to be the site of the new Serena Hotel, is also signposted this way). About 1km from the junction, a narrow dirt road leads off to the left (there's a small signpost). Follow this to reach the cavern. A flight of stone steps leads through the entrance down into the cave itself.

Mangapwani Slave Chamber

The Mangapwani Slave Chamber is a few kilometres further up the coast from the Coral Cave. Although sometimes called the Slave Cave, it is a square-shaped cell that has been cut out of the coralline rock, with a roof on top. It was originally built for storing slaves, and its construction is attributed to one Mohammed bin Nassor Al-

Alwi, an important slave trader. Boats from the mainland would unload their human cargo on the nearby beach, and the slaves would be kept here before being taken to Zanzibar Town for resale, or to plantations on the island. It is thought that some time after 1873, when Sultan Barghash signed the Anglo-Zanzibari treaty which officially abolished the slave trade, the cave was used as a place to hide slaves, as an illicit trade continued for many years.

To reach the Slave Chamber from Zanzibar Town, follow the directions above to the Mangapwani Coral Cave. Instead of turning into the Coral Cave, continue on the dirt road for another 1km to reach the entrance to the Serena Restaurant and Watersports Centre (due to be the site of the new Serena Hotel). Just before you reach the Serena a small dirt track branches off to the right. Follow this for 1km through palm trees and bushes to reach the Slave Chamber. With care, you can reach the steps that lead down on to the chamber floor. Nearby a small path leads to a secluded beach, separated from the main Mangapwani Beach (described below) by some coral-rock outcrops.

Mangapwani Beach
Mangapwani Beach lies a few kilometres west of Mangapwani village. This is the planned site of a new Serena Hotel, but for now it's the site of the Serena Restaurant and Watersports Centre. You can come here for a slap-up seafood lunch (US$30 for three courses), or something less gargantuan like lobster or prawns for US$9, or a pasta dish for US$4. There's also a nice little bar beneath the trees. The beach is exceptionally beautiful at high tide, and a great place to swim or relax. For other activities, the 'watersports' tag is a bit optimistic, as there's only one boat for snorkelling etc (about US$10 per hour) and even that was out of order when we visited.

Transfers by boat and road are arranged by the Serena Hotel in Zanzibar Town (where you can also get more information), and by local tour companies.

Fuji Beach
After an energetic day's sightseeing in the area north of Zanzibar Town, Fuji Beach, near Bububu village, is a nice place to go for a rest before heading back to town. A small dirt road leads down to the beach from near the police station in the centre of Bububu. This is the nearest place to the town where swimming is not inadvisable and it makes a good day-trip destination in its own right if you fancy just relaxing for a while.

Local legend has it that the beach's name was due to one Mr Honda, a Japanese engineer who came to Zanzibar to build roads, but fell in love with a local girl and decided to stay. He built a 'taverna' called Fuji Beach Bar, at the time the best on the island, and the name stuck. Even though Mr Honda is no longer around, his legacy remains. The bar still sells beers and snacks, and the staff will look after your gear while you are swimming. (There have been reports of robberies here, so this is worth arranging.) If you want to stay for more than a day, nearby is the Bububu Guesthouse and Imani Beach Lodge (see pages 129–30).

Islands near Zanzibar Town
A few kilometres from Zanzibar Town are several small islands, some of which are good destinations for a relaxing day's outing. Boat trips to the islands can be arranged with a tour company, or with one of the *papaasi* (touts) who look for business around town and along the seafront, or direct with one of the boat captains. Costs range from US$15 to US$60 for the boat, or from US$5 to US$20 per person, depending on who you deal with, the number of hours

you want, the quality of the boat and whether you're prepared to share with other people or want a boat to yourself. Other factors might be lunch or snorkelling gear included in the price. You can hire a boat for yourself, or reduce costs by getting your own small group together. If you're alone, it's usually easy to link up with other travellers. Boats go across to the islands every morning from the beach by the Big Tree on Mizingani Road (the seafront), from the beach near the Tembo Hotel and the beach opposite the Africa House Hotel.

Changuu Island

This island is also called Prison Island, and was originally owned by a wealthy Arab who used it as a detention centre for disobedient slaves. After the abolition of slavery, in 1873, the island was bought by General Lloyd Mathews, commander of the sultan's army, who built a house here (see the *William Lloyd Mathews* box page 186). In 1893 a prison was built on the island, but it was used instead as a quarantine station for the whole East African region. In the 1920s passengers arriving from India had to spend between one and two weeks on Changuu before proceeding to Zanzibar Town. On some old maps, Changuu is called Kibandiko Island, but this name now seems to be forgotten.

Today, the island is owned by the government and non-Tanzanian visitors must pay a US$4 entry fee (TSh are not acceptable). You can still see the quarantine station, and the house built by General Mathews which is now used as a restaurant. A path leads right round the island (about an hour's easy stroll), also passing some old pits where coral has been dug out to make building stone. Some of these pits fill with water at high tide, and in colonial days they were kept clean and used as swimming pools.

The island's other highlight is the large number of giant tortoises (*Geochelone gigantea*). Four tortoises were brought from the island of Aldabra in the Seychelles in the 18th century, as a gift from the Seychelles governor to his opposite number in Zanzibar. They started to breed, and by 1955 there were 200, but after independence the numbers began to drop, partly because people started to steal them to sell abroad, either as exotic pets, or as food for 'exotic restaurants'. The numbers dropped to 100 in 1988, then 50 in 1990, until by late 1996 there were only seven left. In the same year a group of 80 hatchlings were moved to Zanzibar for protection – and 40 of them disappeared. Today the tortoises are protected in a large sanctuary compound provided by the Zanzibar government with help from the World Society for the Protection of Animals. In 2000 there were 17 adults, 50 juveniles and 90 hatchlings, all individually identified and protected by microchips injected under the skin. You can go into the sanctuary to see the tortoises close up. You can feed them (they delight in fresh mango peel), but please obey the signs and do not lift or sit on the tortoises.

Changuu Island has a small beach, and you can go snorkelling on the nearby reef. Masks and flippers can be hired from the ticket office, but they are not good quality, so you're better off hiring in town. The island also has a small restaurant, with cold drinks and meals like fish and chips for US$4, and a ZTC guesthouse (see the list of hotels on page 130) which costs US$20 a double.

Around the restaurant and on the beach there's a lot of litter, and there seems to be no organised way of collecting or disposing of the rubbish tourists leave behind. There are plans for a tour company to lease the restaurant, and cooperate with ZTC to improve the service and quality, whilst also taking responsibility for maintaining the island itself. There are also long-term plans to lease the guesthouse and improve the quality here as well.

WILLIAM LLOYD MATHEWS

The house on Changuu Island, a short distance offshore from Zanzibar Town, once belonged to William Lloyd Mathews, a military officer and later a government official in Zanzibar in the latter part of the 19th century.

William Lloyd Mathews was a Welshman born in Madeira in 1850. He entered the British navy in 1864, and from 1870 served in the slave patrolling boats of HMS *London*. In August 1877 Mathews was seconded from the navy and appointed to command and organise a European-style army for Sultan Barghash, who wanted to enforce his sovereignty over the interior. Until then, the sultan's army had been composed of Arabs and Persians only, but the new army contained 500 Africans, with a uniform of red caps, short black jackets and white trousers. The Arab officers wore dark blue frock coats and trousers, with gold or silver lace, possibly modelled on uniforms of the British Royal Navy. The British government donated 500 rifles, and by the beginning of the 1880s Mathews had about 1,300 men under his command.

One of the new army's first tasks was to stop the slave smuggling between Pemba and Pangani on the mainland and they were soon successful, capturing several slave smugglers and hindering the illicit trade. Mathews was released from the navy and became Brigadier-General Mathews, commander-in-chief of Zanzibar's army.

A leading slave trader at this time was called Hindi bin Hattam. His dhow was captured by a British navy ship, captained by one Captain C J Brownrigg, between Zanzibar and Pemba. Brownrigg found about 100 slaves on board Hindi bin Hattam's dhow, but before any action could be taken Hindi's men killed Brownrigg, and most of the British crew, and sailed away. In another ship General Mathews pursued Hindi bin Hattam to Wete in Pemba, and took him prisoner after a battle. Hindi died later of gunshot wounds. Brownrigg was buried on Grave Island.

In 1891, when a constitutional government was established in Zanzibar, General Sir Lloyd Mathews was appointed as His Highness's First Minister, and he was awarded a knighthood on March 3 1894. On October 11 1901 Sir William Lloyd Mathews died in Zanzibar, of malaria, at the age of 51. He was buried with full naval and military honours in the English cemetery outside Zanzibar Town.

Chapwani Island

This is also called Grave Island as a small section of it has been used as a Christian cemetery since 1879. Most of the graves belong to British sailors who were killed fighting against Arab slave ships, including Captain Brownrigg – see the *William Lloyd Mathews* box above); others date from World War I when the British ship *Pegasus* was bombarded and sunk by the German ship *Königsberg* in Zanzibar Town harbour. (This latter event is described in detail in the book *Königsberg – an East African Raider* listed in the *Further Information* section.) There is a small beach on the island, and a lovely patch of indigenous forest, with a population of small duikers, some massive coconut crabs and a colony of fruit bats, which every evening do a few circuits of the island then zoom off to Zanzibar Town in a dark cloud. There are about 100 species of bird. You can stay overnight at the small hotel here; see page 131.

Snake Island

This is the popular name for the very small island between Changuu and Chapwani islands. Boats do not usually land here as there is no beach.

Bawe Island

About 6km directly west of Zanzibar Town, this uninhabited island is not as frequently visited as Changuu, although the snorkelling is reported to be of good quality. The same people who run the boats to Changuu will also take you to Bawe, either as part of the same trip, or as a separate out-and-back voyage. Prices to Bawe are a bit higher than those to Changuu.

In the 1870s telegraph cables were brought ashore here, linking Zanzibar with the Seychelles, Aden and South Africa. Another line was run from Bawe Island to the External Telecommunications building in the Shangani area of Zanzibar Town. The old 'Extelcoms' building has now been converted into the Serena Inn, and another hotel is planned for Bawe Island itself. To stay in touch it is thought that they will not use the original phone line...

Chumbe Island

Chumbe lies about 10km south of Zanzibar Town, and is one of the largest of the offshore islands in this area. The coral reef surrounding Chumbe Island is in very good condition (unlike some others off Zanzibar which have been damaged by tourists and the boats that bring them, and by destructive fishing techniques employed by local fishermen), because until recently the island was inside a military area and public access was not allowed. The reefs around Chumbe were officially gazetted as a Marine National Park (the first in Tanzania) in 1994. The island itself has been declared a Forest Reserve, and the island and reef together are known as Chumbe Island Nature Reserve or Chumbe Island Coral Park (CHICOP).

CHICOP's own information publicity states: 'Chumbe Island is a rare example of a still pristine coral island eco-system in an otherwise heavily overfished and overexploited area. It includes a reef sanctuary and a forest and bird sanctuary of exceptional biodiversity.' This has been verified by various global conservation and scientific bodies, including IUCN, WWF and UNESCO. A specialist from the Australian Institute of Marine Sciences called Chumbe 'one of the most spectacular coral gardens to be found anywhere in the world'.

Over 350 species of fish have been identified in the reef and surrounding area. Other marine wildlife usually seen includes turtles, sharks and dolphins. On the island, 60 species of bird have been recorded, including breeding pairs of the rare roseate tern. The island is also home to various lizards and a population of rare giant coconut crabs – the largest terrestrial crab (about 300–400mm across), famed for its ability to climb palm trees and eat young coconuts, sometimes knocking ripe nuts to the ground. Some naturalists believe that Aders' duiker, a small antelope in danger of becoming extinct on Zanzibar Island, used to occur on Chumbe and there are plans to reintroduce this duiker here.

Buildings of historical and cultural interest on Chumbe include a lighthouse built by the British in 1904 (still clearly visible from ships approaching Zanzibar from Dar), now converted into an observation tower, and an old mosque built in an Indian style unique to Tanzania. A cottage originally built for the lighthouse-keepers has been converted into a visitor information centre, including an education room for local schoolchildren who are brought here by the Chumbe management and by other conservation organisations to learn about local environmental issues.

Tourism is being developed on Chumbe in a sensitive and appropriate manner. In conjunction with an environmental organisation called Green Ocean, trails have been established through the forest, along the intertidal section of the beach, and across the reefs. Permanent moorings have been built to allow visitors in boats to reach the coral without needing to drop anchor, and local fishermen have been employed as marine park rangers. Profits from tourists visiting the island are channelled back into education and conservation projects.

For tourists, day trips to the island are available (these cost US$70 including all transfers, snorkelling equipment, guides and lunch), but visitors are encouraged to overnight in the reserve. Accommodation is available in bungalows – using one of the most imaginative construction techniques anywhere in Africa (see page 131). Only authorised tour companies are allowed to bring visitors to Chumbe, as the diversity, quality and management of the island's marine and terrestrial wildlife is of a much higher standard than on many of the other islands around Zanzibar Town.

Chumbe Island's unique situation has been recognised by the World Conservation Monitoring Centre, and CHICOP was chosen to represent Tanzania at Expo2000 in Hanover. CHICOP was also a regional winner (in the Southern Region, which included all of Africa, India and the Middle East) in the British Airways Tourism for Tomorrow Award. The team of people who campaigned to establish Chumbe as a combined tourist attraction and conservation area should be congratulated. And while these aspects continue to be combined with education projects, the people of Zanzibar can also benefit.

For more information, contact Chumbe Island Coral Park (CHICOP), PO Box 3203; tel/fax: 024 231040; tel: 0747 413 582; email: chumbe@zitec.org; web: www.chumbeisland.com. Alternatively, you can make enquiries at any reputable tour company.

Zanzibar Island

After enjoying the unique sights and atmosphere of Zanzibar Town, you can start to explore the rest of Zanzibar Island (or Unguja, to give it its correct local name). This is an ideal place to enjoy travel simply for its own sake; to wander slowly among plantations and farmland, or pass through small towns and fishing villages. Once you move away from the somewhat 'touristy' parts of the island you will find a very different, and more authentic, world where local people continue with their everyday lives in a manner which has changed little over hundreds of years. It is refreshing to see this other side of Zanzibar, but you should not be fooled into regarding the island as some kind of rural paradise created only for tourists to admire. For local people this island is home, where the work in the fields or on the ocean is hard, and where great poverty is not at all unknown. If you remember this, taking the time to see more of the island and its people, and getting beyond the picture-postcard image, your visit to Zanzibar will be greatly enriched.

GETTING AROUND ZANZIBAR ISLAND

You can travel around Zanzibar Island in several different ways: by hire-car, motorbike, scooter, bicycle, tourist minibus, *dala-dala*, bus, taxi, organised tour, walking, hitchhiking, or a combination of all of these. Outside Zanzibar Town, most of the main roads are tarred, although some are in very bad condition, which can make travel by car or bus slow and uncomfortable. The main routes are gradually being resurfaced, which makes travel quicker and easier for tourists and locals. All other roads on the island are dirt or graded gravel which varies in quality. As in the rest of East and southern Africa, traffic drives on the left in Zanzibar.

Car hire

Car hire is best arranged through one of the tour companies listed in *Chapter 5*. Some have their own vehicles, while others will make arrangements with another company on your behalf. Rates vary between the companies, but are generally between US$45 and US$60 per day for a small car (eg: a Suzuki 'jeep') and around US$100 per day for a larger car (eg: a Toyota Landcruiser). However, quality is much more variable than price, and standards on Zanzibar are not always high; you should check your car carefully for defects and even go for a short test drive before agreeing to hire.

The price usually includes unlimited distance, but you pay for the petrol yourself. Petrol costs about US$0.50 per litre. Diesel is slightly cheaper. Insurance is also included in the price, although some tour companies seem a little vague about this, so it is worth checking your exact legal position should you be unfortunate enough to have an accident involving another car or person. Get this in writing.

A deposit and proof of identity are usually asked for. An international driving licence is also required. If you prefer not to drive yourself, most companies provide a driver at little extra charge.

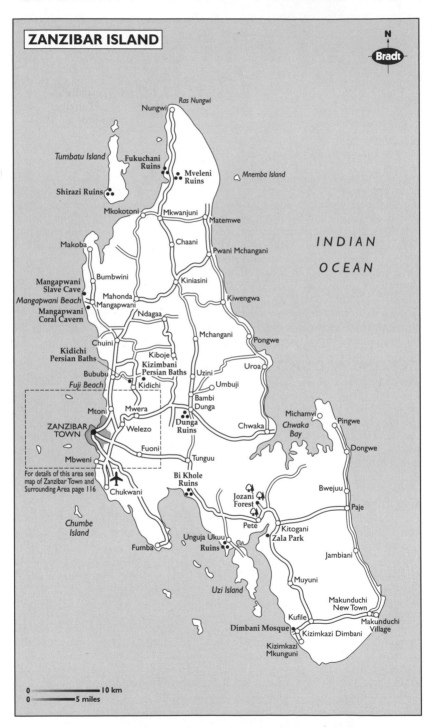

ZANZIBAR ISLAND

N

Bradt

Ras Nungwi

Nungwi

Tumbatu Island

Fukuchani
Ruins

Mveleni
Ruins

Mnemba Island

Shirazi Ruins

Mkokotoni

Mkwanjuni

Matemwe

Makoba

Chaani

Pwani Mchangani

INDIAN

OCEAN

Bumbwini

Kiniasini

Mangapwani
Slave Cave

Mahonda

Kiwengwa

Mangapwani Beach

Mangapwani

Mangapwani
Coral Cavern

Ndagaa

Chuini

Mchangani

Pongwe

Kidichi
Persian Baths

Kiboje

Kizimbani
Persian Baths

Uzini

Uroa

Bububu

Kidichi

Umbuji

Fuji Beach

Bambi

Mtoni

Mwera

Dunga

ZANZIBAR
TOWN

Welezo

Dunga
Ruins

Chwaka

Michamvi

Chwaka
Bay

Pingwe

Fuoni

Dongwe

Mbweni

Tunguu

For details of this area see
map of Zanzibar Town and
Surrounding Area page 116

Chukwani

Bi Khole
Ruins

Bwejuu

Jozani
Forest

Paje

Chumbe
Island

Pete

Kitogani

Unguja Ukuu
Ruins

Zala Park

Fumba

Jambiani

Muyuni

Uzi Island

Makunduchi
New Town

Kufile

Dimbani Mosque

Kizimkazi Dimbani

Makunduchi
Village

Kizimkazi
Mkunguni

0 ————— 10 km

0 ———— 5 miles

Motorbike and scooter hire

It is possible to hire motorbikes (almost all are Honda 125cc or 250cc trail bikes or similar) or scooters (mostly Vespas and Piaggios) from many of the tour companies listed in *Chapter 5*. Prices vary, but are generally around US$25 to US$30 per day for a scooter, US$35 to US$40 per day for a motorbike.

For a cheaper deal, try **Nasor Aly Mussa's Scooter Service**, usually shortened to **Fundi Nasor**, a small garage just off New Mkunazini Road in Zanzibar Town, near the Anglican Cathedral. As with cars, you should take your scooter for a test drive to make sure everything works before agreeing to hire.

Some tourists to Zanzibar hire scooters, imagining them to be similar to Greek-island-style mopeds. However, scooters have larger engines and are harder to handle than mopeds, and there have been a number of accidents and injuries. You should not hire a scooter if you have never ridden one before; the dirt tracks and potholed roads of Zanzibar are not ideal places to start learning.

Petrol is available (usually, but not with total reliability) in Zanzibar Town, and at Kiniasini, on the road to Nungwi, and at Kitogoni, near the junction where the road turns off to Paje.

Bicycle hire

For getting around Zanzibar Town, or going further afield around the island, fit and adventurous visitors will find bicycles ideal. Most bikes are heavy steel Chinese-built roadsters, so you shouldn't plan on covering too many miles (it's too hot to cycle fast anyway). You can also hire mountain bikes, but most of these are pretty basic all-steel models, and only slightly lighter than the Chinese roadsters. They do have gears though, which makes them easier to ride.

Bikes can be hired through several of the tour companies listed in *Chapter 5*. Daily rates start at US$10 for the Chinese roadsters, and US$15 for mountain bikes. Take your bike for a short test ride before hiring to make sure everything works. Unless you plan extensive off-road forays, make sure your tyres are pumped up fairly hard, especially on the mountain bikes where semi-flat fat tyres can make for hard going. Your bike should come with a puncture outfit and pump, but if it doesn't these can be bought from the bicycle *fundi* (mechanic) in the market in Zanzibar Town.

Roads can be rough, but are generally flat, and traffic is very light once you get away from Zanzibar Town. If you get tired, you can put your bike on top of a bus or *dala-dala* and come home the easy way.

Keen cyclists might like to contact Mreh Tours (also listed in Chapter 5) – the only company as far as we know to offer specific cycle tours of Zanzibar.

Tourist minibuses

Several tour companies arrange minibuses for tourists from Zanzibar Town to the popular beaches on the southern part of the east coast, and also to Nungwi on the north coast.

Transport arranged by tour companies is variable. Some of the budget outfits offer fairly straightforward minibuses, which carry up to eight or nine people and can be a bit crowded once you've got all the backpacks inside. These trips cost from around US$5 per person. Other tour companies offer better quality minibuses, which are usually smooth and reliable, and charge from around US$10 per person (if you're happy to share with others – the maximum is normally around six people), or from around US$50 for the private use of the whole vehicle.

Transport to the coasts can also be arranged through 'independent guides' (see *Guides and the Papaasi* box on page 118). This is cheap, but has a slightly rougher edge, and costs between US$3 and US$5 each way to the north or east coast. On top of this cost, sudden mid-trip price rises can occur, so make sure you agree on the fare before travelling. There's a certain degree of cooperation between the *papaasi* outfits, and usually at least one vehicle a day running in each direction, so you can stay on the beach for as long as you like.

Most hotels can also arrange a minibus to the coast, by putting you in touch with a tour company or the *papaasi*, according to your price budget.

Taxi

The saloon car taxis which are available around Zanzibar Town can be hired to take you further afield, but some drivers do not like to go off the tar roads as the rocky dirt roads are liable to damage the undersides of their beloved vehicles (the minibuses have higher clearance, or at least the drivers seem not to worry).

A taxi to Jozani Forest is US$20–25 one-way, or around US$30–35 return, possibly more if you plan to spend all day in the forest. To Nungwi or Bwejuu is around US$30 one way.

Public bus, public minibus and *dala-dala*

It is possible to reach many parts of Zanzibar Island by public bus, although few visitors use their services, especially on routes covered by tourist minibuses. The buses are converted lorries with seats and sides made from wood. All buses leave from the market area, or from Darajani Bus Station, both on Creek Road in Zanzibar Town. Fares are very cheap: for example, it costs about only US$1 to travel half the length of the island between Zanzibar Town and Bwejuu. Note, however, that prices can rise suddenly if there is a fuel shortage.

On most routes, especially the longer ones, there is only one bus each day. They usually leave Zanzibar Town around midday to take people back to their villages after visiting the market. They reach their destinations in the evening, and 'sleep' there before returning to Zanzibar very early in the morning (between 02.00 and 04.00) in time for the start of that day's market. Some of the longer journeys can be very slow. For example, Zanzibar Town to Nungwi takes three to five hours, Zanzibar Town to Makunduchi between four and eight hours.

The bus route numbers and destinations are:

Route No 1, to Mkokotoni, on the west coast, north of Zanzibar Town, occasionally continuing to Nungwi, on the north coast

Route No 2, to Bumbwini and Makoba, on the west coast, north of Zanzibar Town, via Mangapwani

Route No 3, to Kidichi and Kizimbani, an area of plantations to the northeast of Zanzibar Town, via Welezo

Route No 4, to Mchangani, in the centre of the island, northeast of Zanzibar Town, via Dunga, Bambi and Uzini (some buses also go to Umbuji)

Route No 5, to Ndagaa, in the centre of the island, northeast of Zanzibar Town, via Kiboje

Route No 6, to Chwaka, about halfway down the east coast (some buses continue to Uroa)

Route No 7, to Fumba, at the end of a peninsula south of Zanzibar Town, via Kombeni

Route No 8, to Unguja Ukuu, about halfway down the southwest coast, opposite Uzi Island

Route No 9, to Paje, on the east coast, and sometimes to Bwejuu and Jambiani

Route No 10, to Makunduchi, at the southern end of the east coast, via Tunguu, Pete and Munyuni

Route No 11, to Fuoni, about 7km east of Zanzibar Town, via Tungu and Binguni
Route No 13, to Dunga (on the east coast road) then north to Bambi
Route No 14, to Uroa on the east coast, north of Chwaka
Route No 16, to Nungwi, via Mahonda, Kiniasini and Chaani
Route No 17, to Kiwengwa, on the east coast, north of Uroa
Route No 18, to Matemwe, on the northern part of the east coast.

Buses do not always go to their final destination. For example, bus No 1 (the route for Nungwi) may only go as far as Mkokotoni. Therefore, always check that the bus *is* going to the destination you think it should be.

Some of the bus routes listed above are also covered by public minibuses or *daladalas*, which fill the gaps in the bus service 'timetables'. These are usually slightly more expensive than the buses, but also tend to be quicker.

Hitchhiking
Hitching around Zanzibar Island is possible, but there are few private cars on the island and traffic is very light, so you will need a lot of patience. However, a combination of public transport, walking and hitching is sometimes the only way to travel, unless you hire a bike or car. In the northern part of the island, there are occasional vehicles on main roads between Zanzibar Town and Nungwi (via Mahonda and Kiniasini), and between Zanzibar Town and the junction near Dunga, where the roads to Bambi New Town and Chwaka divide. In the southern parts of the island, the main road between Zanzibar Town and Kitogani (where the roads to Kizimkasi and the beaches on the southern part of the east coast divide) is slightly busier, so you may be able to hitch a lift here, or get picked up by one of the tourist minibuses that travel up and down this route.

NUNGWI
Nungwi is a large fishing village at the far northern end of Zanzibar Island. It is traditionally the centre of Zanzibar's dhow-building industry, and until about ten years ago was rarely reached by tourists. When we came here in 1992 to write the first edition of this book there was quite simply nowhere to stay. In the second edition we listed a couple of fledgling guesthouses. Today, you can choose between about 20 hotels and lodges, ranging from basic to total luxury, plus an equally diverse range of restaurants and bars. Without a doubt, with clean white sand, turquoise sea and stage-set palm trees, it's a beautiful setting, and very relaxed, but Nungwi is probably one of the busiest tourist beach areas on the whole of Zanzibar Island.

WATER, WATER ALL AROUND...
There's ocean on both sides, but Nungwi often suffers shortages of freshwater. Nearby wells are shallow, and as an increasing number of tourist developments tap into the natural water table, the local people fear their supply will run dry. For many existing guesthouses, the flow is already erratic, and at some larger hotels the water has to be trucked in for bathroom and kitchen use. It's not clear where the water will come from for the several major new hotels and resorts that are proposed or under construction.

For drinking, you can buy bottled water. Nevertheless, Nungwi is a place to watch your water consumption – that is, go easy on the showers, not the rehydration!

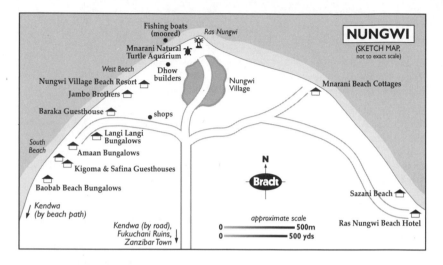

Walking along the beach, there's always something to see: dhows being built or moored out at sea waiting to go out fishing; local men in dug-out canoes, or cycling along the beach with a recent catch of fish hanging from poles, women tending to the seaweed harvest (more on this below); kids swimming and playing; and an interesting selection of tourists – stranded hippies, cool dudes, mature types, families, backpackers on a world tour and bright young things escaping busy jobs in Europe for a week or two.

The main beach (just west of the village) is busiest as the reef does not extend immediately from the shore so the water is deep enough for swimming, whatever the state of the tide. As the beach faces west it is also good for watching the sun go down. Most of the cheaper places to stay are on this west side of Nungwi, and this is the liveliest area.

Things are quieter to the east of Nungwi village and the peninsula of Ras Nungwi (which marks the northernmost point on the island); on this side there are only a few small beaches, in coves between low cliffs of coral rock, and just three hotels – two middle-range and one top-quality place.

Nungwi is also a popular place for diving and fishing, and a number of dive and game-fishing operators have set up bases here.

Despite the influx of tourists, Nungwi is a traditional, conservative place. It was one of the last coastal settlements of any size on Zanzibar to have a hotel, or any tourist facilities. As recently as the mid-1990s proposals for large developments in the area were fiercely opposed by local people. Today, although local people are not unfriendly, they are proud and independent. You rather get the impression tourists

NUNGWI HOTEL FIRE WARNING

Just as this book was going to press, we received important news from Nungwi: a major fire had damaged several hotels in the South Beach area. Despite the destruction, it's likely that most hotels will be rebuilt fairly quickly and will be operating as normal again by the time you read this. Be warned, however, that some hotels may differ in shape or size from the descriptions in this section.

are here on sufferance. If you're trying to make friendly contact, a little bit of respect and politeness goes a long way – especially if you know a few words of Swahili.

Some visitors, particularly backpackers, find themselves torn between coming either to Nungwi and the north coast, or going to Paje, Bwejuu and Jambiani on the east coast. For some more thoughts on the differences between these two areas see the Paje section later in this chapter.

Getting there and away
Nungwi can be reached by bus, tourist minibus or by hired vehicle. From Zanzibar Town the main road to Nungwi goes via Mahonda, Kiniasini and Chaani New Town. The road directly north from Mahonda to Mkokotoni is in poor condition – although it does go through better scenery.

Getting around
Most places in and around Nungwi are walkable, but if you're staying on the more upmarket east side of the peninsula, and fancy letting your hair down on the lively west side, the local taxi service charges US$3 each way. Ask your hotel to put you in touch with a driver.

If you want to tour this part of Zanzibar Island (for example to visit Fukuchani and Mveleni Ruins – see below) Amaan Bungalows offers car and motorbike hire: a four-seater Suzuki 'jeep' costs US$50 per day, and 250cc and 500cc motorbikes (Suzuki or Honda) cost US$25 per day. Bicycles are also available for around US$10 per day.

Where to stay
The following hotels and guesthouses are listed roughly in a clockwise manner, from the southwest side of the peninsula, round the tip, then down the east side. As elsewhere in this book, all the hotel prices quoted here are for the high season. At quieter times most places offer discounts and are open to negotiation, especially if you plan to stay a few nights.

South Beach
The road into Nungwi from Zanzibar Town reaches a fork on the village outskirts. To reach places at the southern end of the west side of the peninsula, go left here, along a dusty track, towards the sea. This area has become unofficially known as South Beach, but it's a handy name, and might stick.

Amaan Bungalows (PO Box 4769, Zanzibar; tel: 024 2240026, 0741 327747; email: amaanbungalow@yahoo.com; web: www.amaanbungalow.com) is easily the largest and most organised of the budget places, although constant growth and improvements mean this place is now a notch or two above the normal 'budget' rating. There's a massive choice of rooms, from small double rooms with shared facilities for US$25, double rooms with en-suite bathroom for US$40, slightly bigger en-suite doubles for US$55 and luxury bungalows with sea-views for US$75. A single costs about 60% of the double rate. Amaan has a very well-stocked and popular bar, with seating under shade, a fine sundowner deck overlooking the beach, and comes complete with music and satellite TV, bringing sports coverage from around the world. Attached to the bar, a food counter serves highly rated pizzas, burgers and other 'pub grub' in the US$3–5 range. The same kind of food, plus grills, chicken and seafood meals are also served in the quieter Blue Sea Restaurant, overlooking the sea, complete with director's chairs and checked tablecloths. Prices are the same or similar. Other services include Sensation Divers and Sail Zanzibar (see *Chapter 4 – Practical Information*), plus car and motorbike hire, shop, internet bureau and a handy travel information service (free to internet customers).

Kigoma Beach Guesthouse, in Amaan's back yard (tel: 0747 415421), is a clean and straightforward locally run place, with simple doubles for US$30, and en-suite doubles for US$40 (US$60 with hot water). Next door is **Safina Bungalows** (tel: 0747 415726), not spacious but light, airy and clean, with en-suite doubles for US$25 (US$50 with hot water). Some people stay here, and use the bar and restaurant facilities of Amaan Bungalows.

South of Amaan and its satellites is South Beach proper, with several bars and cafés (see *Where to eat*, following).

At the south end of South Beach is **Baobab Beach Bungalows** (tel: 0747 416964, 0742 740106; web: www.baobabbeachbungalows.com), with two rows of bungalows perpendicular to the beach. The rooms are clean and nicely furnished, with en-suite bathrooms, but are quite small for the price: US$60 a double, US$40 a single. There are also some older, cheaper rooms (US$44 a double), which have a nicer view, and more space, making them the better choice. The restaurant enjoys the best position of all – right on the beach.

West Beach

Northwards from Amaan Bungalows, still on the west side of the peninsula, is another stretch of beach, which for the purposes of this book we'll call West Beach. The places to stay here are described south to north.

Langi Langi (tel: 024 2240470; fax: 2240471; email: langi_langi@hotmail.com) is a new place – which may explain the spartan décor – although everything is neat and comfortable. The rooms are all en suite, and cost US$55 a single, US$70 a double. A disadvantage of this hotel is the view overlooking the dirt road and the back of the dive centre, but it does have its own tiny strip of beach, complete with sun-loungers. An advantage is the lovely rooftop restaurant, with tasty toasted sandwiches (US$2.50) and meals like garlic prawns or lobster thermador for US$4–7.

Paradise Beach Club (tel: 0741 326574) used to be just a row of straightforward double rooms with shared bathrooms, but when we visited in mid-2002 renovations were under way, and the local guys who run the place promise major improvements – all for US$25 a double. Dive Zanzibar is based here – see *Chapter 4 – Practical Information* for more details.

Baraka Guesthouse (tel: 024 2240412) is owned and managed by the friendly Mr Baraka himself, where simple en-suite bungalows with verandas, and some with hot showers, cost US$15 a single or US$35 a double. There are also some triples and a few older bungalows for US$10 per person. The restaurant has a huge menu, and offers snacks like pizzas and toasted sandwiches at US$3. Meals include chicken and chips, octopus in coconut, grilled kingfish steak in garlic butter, all for US$3 to US$4, or you can splash out on garlic tiger prawns for US$8, but not all the items are available, and ideally you need to order at least an hour before you plan to eat.

Continuing north along the beach from Baraka are some more budget places, including:

Jambo Brothers Guesthouse (tel: 0747 422906), a group of little bungalows on the sand, with singles at US$20, doubles US$35 and triples US$45.

Almost next door is **Union Bungalows** (tel: 024 2240002) another small and friendly place with doubles for US$30. Bathrooms are shared – some have hot water, and some don't! Next along is **Nungwi Village Beach Resort** (tel: 024 2240476, 0747 415975; fax: 024 2240491; email: nungwi@nungwivillage.com; web: www.nungwivillage.com), a large and spacious mid-range place which caters for up to 80 guests. There's a sense of being apart from the other hotels here, and this place gets good reports, making it good value in the middle range. Double rooms with sea views in two-storey houses rising between the palm trees costs US$100–110. Smaller rooms at the back of the hotel cost US$60 per double. The food is good,

although the choice can sometimes be limited, and the air conditioning can sometimes be erratic at night. Further planned improvements include a swimming pool and conference facilities.
Smiles Beach Hotel Tel: 0747 418293; web: www. smileszanzibar.com. A smart new mid-to upper-range place towards the far northern end of the beach, with rooms in an arc around colourful central gardens dominated by two giant giraffe woodcarvings. The rooms are comfortable, with air conditioning, tiled floors, pristine bathrooms, hot showers, phone and TV. The only slight disadvantage is this place feels slightly cramped, but otherwise it's worth seeking out if this is your budget. Singles are US$65, doubles US$85. The restaurant serves unfussy, good-quality food, and sometimes tables are moved on to the beach in the evening so you can eat under the stars, but service is on the slow side.

East side
At the tip of the Nungwi peninsula is the lighthouse and then the coast curves back sharply to the south. This eastern side of the peninsula is much quieter than South Beach and West Beach, with a smaller (but good) choice of places to stay.

Mnarani Beach Cottages Tel: 024 2240494; email: info@mnaranibeach.com; web: www.mnaranibeach.com. Near the lighthouse, and one of the few places on Zanzibar where you can see sunrise *and* sunset, is a good choice in the middle range. The staff are friendly, and there are just 12 rooms in six comfortable bungalows, each with its own private veranda, pleasantly built in local style, set in a shady colourful garden overlooking the sea. Rates are US$60 per single, and US$84 per double, which is good value although the doubles are a bit small. Triples and family cottages start from around US$100, and there's also a 'honeymoon suite'. In any of these rooms, half board costs an extra US$12 per person.
Ras Nungwi Beach Hotel PO Box 1784; tel: 024 2232512, 2233767; fax: 024 2233098; email: info@rasnungwi.com; web: www.rasnungwi.com. One of the smartest establishments on this part of the island, the hotel is a few kilometres down the east coast from Nungwi village. The spacious hotel gardens open out on to a beautiful sandy beach, with great ocean views, and facilities include bar, restaurant, freshwater swimming pool, shop, fully equipped scuba diving and deep-sea fishing centres, and equipment for other sports, like windsurfing and snorkelling. There are 20 large and well-appointed chalets, 12 very comfortable lodge rooms, and a highly luxurious 'Ocean Suite' with its own private living space and plunge pool. Although there are other similar resort-style set-ups on Zanzibar, Ras Nungwi Beach Hotel has resisted the urge to be giant and offers guests a relatively intimate experience. Additionally, efforts are made to attract visitors from several overseas countries, to avoid the domination of any one nationality. High-season rates for lodge rooms are US$105 per person, and chalets are US$135–185 per person. Exclusive use of the Ocean Suite costs US$550–580 per night. All these rates are half-board, so include breakfast and dinner in the hotel's good-quality restaurant, where lunches are also available. Low-season rates are about 15% less, and transfers from Zanzibar Town or airport are US$25 per person (less for groups of more than five).
   The hotel has its own fully equipped dive centre, offering single, double or multiple dives, plus PADI courses, and also operates top-quality deep-sea game fishing in association with the Pemba Channel Fishing Club. Although diving and fishing are big attractions here (the hotel makes full use of its position at the tip of the island, and boats can reach a good range of diving and fishing sites), other watersports such as kayaking and windsurfing are also popular. But the management never forgets that many guests come to Ras Nungwi simply to relax on the sand or take an occasional cooling dip in the shallows, so only non-motorised watersports are allowed near the beach (ie: no waterskiing), to ensure that lazers are not disturbed. All in all, this hotel is a very good choice in this range. You can make enquiries or reservations through agents overseas or in Zanzibar, or direct to Ras Nungwi Beach Hotel's office in Zanzibar Town.

Sazani Beach PO Box 4200, Zanzibar; tel: 024 2240014, 0741 324744; email: sazanibeach@ aol.com; web: www.sazanibeach.com. A collection of ten white bungalows with thatched roofs on a rise overlooking a small sandy beach, surprisingly close to the neighbouring Ras Nungwi Beach Hotel. It's quiet, with a pretty garden, and rooms (all with bathroom and veranda) cost US$60. A cheaper option is one of the basic *bandas* with shared bathroom for US$40. Meals (all around US$4.50) are served in the airy open-sided dining area, which also has sea views. The attached Divemaxx dive centre (email: divemaxx@zanlink.com; web: www.divemax.com) offers snorkel trips to Mnemba, as well as diving and PADI courses. For more details see the *Diving* section in *Chapter 4 – Practical Information*.

Nungwi village
Away from the beaches, in Nungwi village itself, are a couple of budget options. **Morning Star Guesthouse** (tel: 024 2240045) has simple rooms for US$20, and even deeper in the village, **Ruma Guesthouse** is another quiet and basic (verging on the dilapidated) local-style place with rooms at US$10 per person.

Where to eat
Nearly all the hotels and guesthouses in Nungwi have attached restaurants, open to guests and non-guests alike. See the *Where to stay* section for more details.

Near Amaan Bungalows is **South Beach** with lots of little local-style cafés, bars and curio shops. The cafés all serve seafood dishes for around US$3, and snacks and burgers for around US$2. We didn't actually see any, but it can't be long before banana pancakes grace the menu. The cafés and bars also serve soft drinks, milk-shakes, and of course beer. Many do happy hours, backpacker meal-and-beer specials, etc. There's no regulation here, it seems, and places often close and spring up again overnight – when you're using bits of wood and palm leaves, it doesn't take long. A few chairs and tables, or logs, on the sand, and you're in business. Only the names change. When we were researching here, names included Cool Running Café, Gossip Bar, Funny Bunny Restaurant and Mango Bar. When the sun goes down, people wake up, and the whole place is particularly fun and lively at night.

North of here, a favourite when we visited seemed to be **Cholo's Bar & Restaurant**, a funky establishment right on the beach under shady palms. There's rustic furniture, pumping music, a cool crowd – it's especially popular in the evenings – and some nice little shacks for backpackers at US$10 per person. Or you can stroll along the beach to nearby **Jambo Brothers**, a simple shack with a motley collection of tables but a good-value no-frills menu; sandwiches or chips from US$1, meals around US$2.50.

A new place in Nungwi, already getting good reports, is **Waves Bar & Restaurant** (tel: 0474 415488; email: olivercheetham@yahoo.com) on the south beach, between Baobab and Safina. The food is delicious yet no more expensive (mains US$4–8) than the hotel beach restaurants nearby. Run by a friendly British couple, Oliver and Elaine, it has a pleasant atmosphere, and accommodation is also available at the attached Spice Lodge, with one large room at US$60/night and a 'cottage' at US$15 per person (sleeping up to three); both rates include breakfast.

For a more grassroots flavour, deep in the village, the **Ikibal Guesthouse** has been recommended for good cheap local fare in the pilau-rice-with-chapatis line from around US$1 (they don't seem to do rooms any more). **Jelo's Restaurant** is another good one in the same league.

Shopping
In Nungwi village are several shops selling souvenirs, such as carvings, paintings and jewellery. **Tabasam Shop** and **Maradadi Shop** seem to have a good stock,

but there are several others to try – the number seems to increase every year. **Admwanga** has lots of watercolours of dhows, Stone Town and other local scenes, while **Mwafaka** specialises in T-shits and *kangas* (local-style sarongs).

If you're looking for imported luxuries, head for **Nungwi Supermarket**. In among the potatoes, tinned goods, soft drinks and biscuits you'll find toothpaste, chocolate bars, Pringles (why do they get everywhere?), postcards, and a wide range of other goods and toiletries.

Communication
Amaan Bungalows has a phone and internet service. International calls cost US$4 per minute, and checking your email on the web costs US$1.50 per 15 minutes.

Next to the supermarket, **Suliman Family Shop** is a small telephone bureau, offering local calls, fax and photocopying. To make an international call, they'll sell you a US$10 phonecard, which you can use in the public booth outside. In the back room is an enormous freezer filled with kingfish, octopus, prawns and several unidentifiable forms of marine life – a perfect spot to browse while you're waiting for a connection...

What to do and see
Of course, in this wonderful position, **water activities** are a big thing. On the west side of the peninsula, especially at South Beach, local guys offer various boat rides and snorkelling trips. Prices are all very similar, and to decide who offers the best trip try and get a recommendation from other visitors. All day to Mnemba is US$20 per person, including lunch, and a sunset cruise is US$10. If you want to go out for a day's fishing it's US$250 for the boat. If you're alone it's easy enough to find other people to make up a group and reduce prices.

Diving is especially popular here, and many of the hotels offer dives and dive courses: you can go on the local reef, or go further afield to reefs such as Leven Bank and Mnemba. (Full details of all the operators are listed in the *Diving and sailing* section in *Chapter 4 – Practical Information*.)

If you're into **windsurfing** or **fishing**, Ras Nungwi Beach Hotel has all you need – as well as top-notch diving gear – see the *Where to stay* section above. You don't have to be a resident to take advantage of some of their services.

If **sailing** appeals, contact **Zanzibar Sail** (tel: 0747 418378; email: zanzibarsail@yahoo.de; web: www.zanzibarsail.com), a German-skippered 43-foot yacht normally based at Nungwi, and available for charter by up to eight passengers for sheer sailing or for diving, or a mix of sailing, diving, snorkelling, fishing, visiting local villages or stretches of tropical rainforest. Dive courses are also available. Anything is possible: four-day to two-week trips to Pemba or Mafia, or one-day trips to Mnemba Atoll, or shorter sunset cruises. The cost is US$125 per person per full day (24 hours), full board. Day trips (10.00 to 18.00) are US$60 per person. A popular destination is Pemba Island, and the boat is often used by groups of divers to reach reefs in the Nungwi area. The yacht is fully kitted out with diving gear, safety equipment and so on. More details are available at the Zanzibar Sail booking office at Amaan Bungalows in Nungwi.

Despite the range of watersports on offer, the most popular activity at Nungwi seems to be having henna 'tattoos' painted on your skin by the friendly local ladies (who also offer a hair-braiding service). As you'll see elsewhere on Zanzibar, the place is full of people with vaguely Arabic or Celtic-style rings round their biceps. It looks cool, but be warned, these things can badly stain your bed sheets, which naturally annoys the hotel owners.

As well as being a tourist destination, Nungwi is also the centre of Zanzibar's traditional **dhow-building** industry. Various hardwood trees, particularly good for boats, grow in this area. The teams of craftsmen work on the beach outside the village, under the shade of the palm trees. With great skill, and using only the simplest of tools, they turn planks of wood into strong ocean-going vessels. Another important material is rope made from coconut husks (coir); little in the way of iron or steel is used. It is a fascinating place to see the dhows at their various stages of construction. However, you should show respect for the builders, who are generally indifferent towards visitors, and keep out of the way. Most do not like having their photos taken (so ask before you use your camera), although a few have realised their photogenicity has value and very reasonably ask for payment.

Fishing employs many local men, and it's great to watch the local **fishing boats** go out – usually in the evening, although it depends sometimes on the state of the tide. Sometimes there's as many as 40 going out at once, with their distinctive lateen sails silhouetted against the sun – it's a perfect sight, and unchanged for centuries. The catch is brought ashore early in the morning and around 06.00 there's a fish market on the beach. If you can't make it this early (although you should try, as it's a lovely time of day) there's a smaller session of buying and selling around 15.00.

Nungwi's other industry is **seaweed**. Local women tend this newly introduced crop on the flat beach area just beyond the low tide mark. The seaweed is harvested, then dried in the sun and sent to Zanzibar Town for export. (For more details, see the box on *Zanzibar seaweed*, on page 71.)

Another attraction for visitors to Nungwi is **Mnarani Natural Turtle Aquarium**, at the north end of the west beach, very near the lighthouse which marks the actual headland of Ras Nungwi and the northernmost tip of Zanzibar Island. (In Swahili, *ras* means head, *mnara* means tower or lighthouse, and Mnarani is 'place of the lighthouse'.) With encouragement from various conservation bodies, the local people have created what is essentially a very large rock pool, where the water level goes up and down with the tide, which is home to a large 'family' of turtles. There are a few adults and several young which are released into the sea when they reach a certain size. Turtles are an endangered species, and are captured elsewhere on Zanzibar for food, while their shells are made into souvenirs (see the box on page 71 for more details). Tourists are charged US$2 to enter the aquarium. It's interesting to see the turtles at close quarters, and money raised goes to various local community schemes. It may sound a bit zoo-like, but only if animals have a tangible value are local people likely to protect them.

The **lighthouse** at Ras Nungwi is still in operation, and not open to visitors, and officially photographing the lighthouse is not allowed, as marines on guard may point out.

Places to visit
Fukuchani and Mveleni Ruins
About 12km south of Nungwi, on the main road to/from Zanzibar Town, are the ruins at Fukuchani and Mveleni, the remains of large houses dating from the 16th century; worth a stop if you're driving this way, and a possible excursion from Nungwi if the beach just gets all too much.

Fukuchani Ruins are on the edge of the village of the same name. There's a small signpost, and you reach the ruins by walking across the school football field. The ruin is known locally as the 'Portuguese House' but this structure is considered by archaeologists to be of Swahili origin, although some Portuguese settlers may have built houses on Zanzibar during this period. It is built of coral bricks, with arched doorways and rectangular niches in the walls of the main room,

NUNGWI NEW DEVELOPMENTS

About 3km south of Nungwi, at Kendwa, there are more places to stay (see the next section for details), and between Nungwi and Kendwa a major new hotel resort complex is under development. When we were researching here, massive earth-moving equipment was levelling the ground, although to comply with new Zanzibari government regulations this was happening some distance back from the beach. We understand the new complex will be aimed at the Italian package-tour market, and it was rumoured that the hotel developers may build a jetty across the beach and out into the ocean to make access to the reef easier for guests. This may not be true, but obviously, if it does happen, it would damage the visual appeal of the beach, as well as the natural environment. Large developments of this sort are also worrying because elsewhere on Zanzibar hotel owners seek to prevent local people from walking across 'their' stretch of the beach. This obviously affects fishermen, seaweed farmers and anyone else who uses the beach as part of their livelihood, and a reader contacted us to say that: 'If part of the beach is closed off to locals, school kids who walk along the beach everyday could be deprived of their shortest route to classes.' Apparently, some local businesses are petitioning the government to force the developers to shelve some of these plans, but at the time of research it was unclear if any action would be taken.

and surrounded by a stone wall in which small holes have been inserted. It has been suggested that these are for the purposes of defence, but a more recent theory suggests they were to hold projecting beams which supported a raised walkway, so that anyone inside the enclosure could see over the wall. The ruins are in good condition, compared to many others on Zanzibar of a similar age, and quite impressive. Buildings of a similar style have been found at other sites along the East African coast.

Behind the ruin, a path leads to a small beach. Across the channel you can see Tumbatu Island, with the lighthouse at its northern tip clearly visible. At the southern end of the island are the remains of a large town, dating from around the 12th century (for more details see the Tumbatu Island box on page 203).

Mveleni Ruins lie just to the south of Fukuchani, on the other side of the road (east). There's a small signpost. From the roadside, next to a few huts and a small shop, a path leads through banana and palm plantations to reach the site. Like Fukuchani, this structure was also a house, and is sometimes described as Portuguese, but it's more likely to be of Swahili origin. The house was once larger than the one at Fukuchani, with thicker walls, but the ruins are in poor condition, and overgrown with vegetation. The most interesting feature of this house is the large natural cavern just outside the main wall with a pool at the bottom – it was probably a source of water when the house was occupied.

KENDWA

About 3km south of Nungwi, on the beach on the west coast, is the tiny village of Kendwa. What a relief after Nungwi! It's a serene place (most of the time) – so laid back it's almost horizontal, with just a few nice places to stay, some small bars, a dive school and not much else – apart from the glorious, wide, white sandy beach. Kendwa caters mostly for backpackers and other tourists who prefer a relaxed (let's say mellow) atmosphere. Night-times are sometimes more lively, and Kendwa is particularly noted for its beach parties at full moon, but apart from that it's an absolute haven. Let's hope it stays this way.

Getting there and away

You can get to Kendwa by boat from Nungwi. Most of the places to stay at Kendwa run a free transfer service, or the places in Nungwi can put you in touch with a local boatman who will take you for a few dollars. Alternatively, you can simply walk along the beach at low tide (although ask around in Nungwi before doing this as there have been a few incidents of people being robbed on the remote stretch of beach between Nungwi and Kendwa).

If you've got a car, coming from Zanzibar, you turn off the main road about 5km before Nungwi, then follow some very rough tracks for about another 5km. High clearance is essential.

Where to stay

The first place you reach coming down the beach from Nungwi is **Palm Leaf Hotel**. This is Kendwa's latest arrival, a small and absolutely delightful place, with neat white bungalows on a small cliff overlooking the beach. You can choose between *bandas* (simple cabins) made of palm leaves (naturally) at US$10 per person, or bungalows at US$25 per person. Meals and drinks are served in the lovely wood-decked bar-restaurant.

Whitesands (tel: 0747 415720) is the next place along the beach. You can choose to stay in a *banda* built from palm leaves, which are cool and clean with a sand floor and local-style beds for US$7–10 per person. More comfortable en-suite bungalows cost US$20–35, and meals and beers are available in the beach restaurant.

Sunset Bungalows (tel: 0747 413818, 0747 414647; email: kendwasunset@allaboutzanzibar.com) in the last few years has moved up a gear or two and

---

EASY TRAVEL BY BOAT

We received this email from an adventurous and quick-thinking reader, James Gillies, with ideas about travel between Kendwa or Nungwi and other parts of the Zanzibar coast:

I was working on Zanzibar, but allowed myself a week to relax on the beach. My sister, cousin and a friend arrived at the airport to join me on the beach for my last week on the island. I had decided to take us all up to Kendwa Rocks for three nights, and then go over to Matemwe for a further two nights. We planned to go across the island by taxi, but why? We travel far too often by road around our own country, so after a little negotiation with a local fisherman (a man that runs snorkelling trips) he strapped a 40hp outboard to his boat and we set off around Ras Nungwi and down past Mnemba to Matemwe. What a great way to travel, to watch dolphins playing around the boat, and to look upon a tropical island that is yet to undergo heavy development. Hardly a building was seen for over an hour until we passed the Bungalows at Kigomani and travelled inside the reef down towards Matemwe. We pulled up on the beach outside the hotel to the amazement of guests, staff and the locals. Crazy English people arriving by boat, why could we not just come by taxi like everyone else? It was a novel and extremely relaxing way to travel from Kendwa to Matemwe. Well, that's what you get for staying on the island for three months.

TUMBATU ISLAND

Tumbatu is one of the largest of Zanzibar's offshore islands, measuring about 8km long by 2km to 3km across. The people of the island, the Watumbatu, speak their own dialect of Swahili. They have a reputation for pride and aloofness, and are reputed not to welcome visitors on their island. The Watumbatu men are traditionally known as the best sailors on Zanzibar, or even on the whole East African coast.

On the southern end of Tumbatu Island are a group of Shirazi ruins, thought to date from the 12th century. An Arab geographer writing in the 13th century recorded that the Muslim people of Zanzibar Island were attacked (by whom is not clear) and retreated to Tumbatu Island where they were welcomed by the local inhabitants, who were also Muslim, and it is assumed that these people were responsible for the Shirazi ruins.

The ruins were probably abandoned in the early 16th century, but the Watumbatu still claim to be descended from Shirazi immigrants.

is now more mid-range than backpacker. In the lovely quiet setting, the rooms are in coconut log bungalows with thatched roofs, simple but clean, and nicely decorated with coloured mats and Zanzibar beds. The shared bathrooms are all clean, double bungalows cost US$30, or US$45 for a triple. There are also some double rooms at US$55 but it's not worth paying the extra. Other facilities include a bar (which can get lively at night) and restaurant on the beach. This is also the base of Scuba Do dive centre (see *Diving* in *Chapter 4 – Practical Information*).

Kendwa Rocks (tel 0747 415475, 415527; email: kendwarocks@ allaboutzanzibar.com) is just along the beach. Originally established as a low-key campsite in the mid-1990s, over the years some rustic *bandas* and bungalows have been built, and the whole place smartened up a bit. Simple palm-leaf *bandas* are US$9 per person. Nicely decorated bungalows, with Zanzibar beds, pictures on the wall and en-suite bathroom, are US$40–45 a double. Meals, snacks and drinks are sold in the beachfront bar-restaurant. A final option is **Amaan Annex**, with a nice garden and straightforward en-suite bungalows with electricity at US$25 a double.

What to do

Diving and snorkelling are the main activities at Kendwa (you can rent snorkel gear at some of the hotels), and all the places arrange boat rides to Tumbatu Island, and some rent out kayaks too. For details of the operators, see the *Diving and sailing* section in *Chapter 4 – Practical Information*.

Look out too for *Salama Sailing*, a big dhow under the charge of a jolly group of Rastafarians. Get a group together, and a full day out is US$25 per person. A shorter trip to Kendwa Reef is US$10.

MKOKOTONI

Mkokotoni is a busy fishing village on the west coast of Zanzibar Island, about 15km south of Nungwi, with a market, a few shops, and a police station, on the main road between Zanzibar Town and Nungwi. In 1984, Chinese coins were discovered on the beach north of the village indicating that trade between China, India, Arabia and Zanzibar existed long before the arrival of the Europeans. Today, this village is an interesting place to wander around, if only because very few tourists ever stop here. There is no official accommodation.

MATEMWE

Matemwe is a small village on the northeast coast of Zanzibar, about 15km south of Nungwi. It's a pretty place, with little houses on the beach among masses of coconut palms. The sand is so white and smooth here, the wind blows it into mounds that look like snow drifts. The villagers seem very friendly to tourists, and the kids go bonkers whenever they see a foreign face. For some reason, Matemwe has a great collection of incredibly fat ducks and turkeys, which delight in sitting on the sandy track through the village. Take care if you're driving!

Despite the jollity, Matemwe is very much a working beach, especially the end near the village (down by the Matemwe Bungalows it's quieter), and this is part of its attraction for visitors looking for just a bit more than palms and sunshine. The main employment here is fishing, and the dhows go out most evenings, then deliver their catch on to the beach each morning and everyone goes down to the beach to help with the catch or other tasks. There's also a bit of seaweed farming going on – you can't miss the racks of purple fronds drying in the sun.

Locals don't seem to mind tourists watching the scene, but this isn't a spot for in-your-face photography.

Getting there and away

If you're staying at either of Matemwe's hotels, transfers to/from Zanzibar Town can be arranged by them, or by a tour company in town. Alternatively, a private taxi or minibus from Zanzibar Town is about US$30–35.

If you are driving, you can approach Matemwe direct from Mkwanjuni (east of Mkokotoni), or via Kiniasini and Pwani Mchangani, then go up the small coastal track to Matemwe village. The bungalows are 4km north of the village. To get through soft sand, 4WD is highly recommended.

By public transport, the nearest regular bus goes to Pwani Mchangani village, and there's a daily *dala-dala* (No 18) from Zanzibar Town to Matemwe village which then continues up the coast to within about 2km of Matemwe Bungalows.

Where to stay

At the northern end of the village is **Matemwe Bungalows** (PO Box 3275, Zanzibar; tel: 024 2236535; fax: 2236536; email: info@matemwe.com; web: www.matemwe.com), a small, friendly and very comfortable hotel, built on a low coral cliff overlooking the ocean. The 16 individual bungalows are widely spaced and surrounded by beautiful gardens. They all have whitewashed walls, thatched roofs and private verandas, complete with hammocks and deckchairs. The newer rooms are larger (they're called suites), with high airy ceilings, big beds with all-embracing mosquito nets, huge bathrooms, lots of windows with louvre shutters and wide doors onto the veranda which open to give a view of the sea.

Chairs, tables, door frames and shutters are made from coconut wood, which traditionally has not been used by carpenters because it's very hard and difficult to work with, but it's worth the effort – the furniture is well made and beautiful. The hotel has a generator, but a lot of the lighting is solar powered. The rooms and restaurant are also lit by lamps. Accommodation in a suite is US$150 per person. The hotel also has a few bungalows which are not en suite and have separate shared bathrooms; these cost US$85 per person. All rates are full board. Credit cards are accepted, and the usual surcharge is *not* made if you pay in one go. (If you pay a deposit and the balance later, they add 10%.) Alternatively, any tour company in Zanzibar Town will make a reservation for you.

The hotel has been here at least 12 years, and become well known around the world for its genuine 'eco-tourism' philosophy, long before this became a trendy, and all too easily applied, buzzword. The management are taking great steps to reduce their impact on the local people and surroundings. New grass has been planted to prevent soil erosion, and

THE FUTURE FOR ZANZIBAR'S EAST COAST

The east coast of Zanzibar is idyllic, but no-one can stop the march of progress. The days of just a few little bungalows and guesthouses are long gone, as an increasing number of hotels are planned for the future on this stretch of coast, from Nungwi in the north, through Matemwe, and all the way down to Jambiani. Some of these will be fairly big resorts and holiday complexes. Rumour has it that even the corporation which brought Sun City to South Africa has a plot earmarked for development here. Tourism development isn't necessarily bad. It can be very positive. For the people of Zanzibar, tourists can bring much needed jobs and money – as long as local needs and wants are taken into account, rather than steamrollered. We can only hope that these new places are built with the same sensitivity that Matemwe Bungalows brought to the area.

visitors are encouraged not to damage the nearby reef, nor buy coral and shells from villagers. The hotel buys as much fresh produce locally as possible, and has provided finance to support local artists and a women's cooperative which makes money from selling local handicrafts. The hotel also runs a small sea-turtle nest protection project. Local people are paid a fee to report finding a turtle nest, and a bonus for every hatchling which makes it to the sea. Several biologists, zoologists and other scientists have based themselves at Matemwe over the years, and the hotel now has a good library of booklets, manuals, field guides and reports on marine and terrestrial wildlife.

It's easy enough to pass the time at Matemwe. From the hotel it's a very short walk down to the beach, or you can go further and visit the village (see the notes in the introduction to this section). Speed boat trips are *not* offered, but you can go sailing in a traditional outrigger for US$10 per hour. Snorkelling trips are also available (US$5 for equipment, US$15 for a boat ride to the reef), or you can go out on a boat with the local fishermen. If you strike lucky the chef will prepare your catch for dinner. For more aquatic activity, based at the hotel is Dhow Dive Centre. See the *Diving* section in *Chapter 4 – Practical Information* for more information.

Matemwe Beach Village (tel: 0747 417250; email: matemwebeachvillage@ zitec.org; web: www.matemwebeach.com) is a small hotel about 1km south of Matemwe Bungalows and is a good choice in the middle range. The hotel consists of a neat row of bungalows overlooking a truly beautiful stretch of beach, and a small but charming central lounge-dining area. Rooms are spacious, and there's an all-round relaxed but efficient atmosphere. Beach wraps and sunhats are provided for guests, which is a nice touch. Single/double rooms cost US$50/80 including breakfast, and for an extra US$10 lunch or dinner is included as well.

Zanzibar Dive Centre One Ocean has a base here. You can get more information on the hotel from the dive company's office in Zanzibar Town (tel/fax: 024 2238374, 0742 750161; email: oneocean@zanlink.com; web: www.zanzibaroneocean.com) or from the Diving section in Chapter 4.

MNEMBA ISLAND

Mnemba Island lies about 3km off the coast, to the northeast of Matemwe. It is a small island, about 1km around, surrounded by a large circular coral reef. The island and reef together are sometimes rather fancifully known as Mnemba Atoll, lending this place an extra feel of style and exotica.

On the island is **Mnemba Club**, a refined and very exclusive 'barefoot luxury' hotel run by a South African company called Conservation Corporation Africa.

The ten bungalows are made from palm and other local materials, and rooms are very spacious with massive beds and lots of nice furniture. The en-suite bathrooms are super-stylish with wooden floors and glass-beaded showers, with shampoo and designer soap provided. Each room is very private, spaced far from the others, among the luxuriant undergrowth. They're back from the beach, but overlook it, and each room has its own private area of sand with sunbeds (rustic, of course) and a palm-leaf parasol. The main beach shelves fairly steeply so you can swim whatever the tide.

The food in the restaurant is quite good, with buffet-style breakfast and lunch and a three-course dinner, with wine served. There's also a library and a beach bar, with seats which are low and stylish but oh so impractical!

Activities include strolling on your private beach. You're unlikely to bump into fellow guests, but you'll certainly meet crabs, wading birds and (at the right time of year) turtles. The hotel marks the spot where eggs are laid with a 'due date' so guests have a chance of seeing the babies hatch and run for the sea.

If you want more action, a large game-fishing boat, complete with crew and tackle, is available for hire. With effectively its own reef on the doorstep, Mnemba naturally offers scuba diving as well. Mnemba is one of the best scuba sites around Zanzibar, but only the island is private – anyone can come to the reef, and sometimes a whole clutch of dive boats is moored nearby, within clear view of the island – which rather dilutes the 'exclusive' nature of it all.

Nevertheless, Mnemba is a popular place, often frequented by the rich and famous. Some people, wanting complete exclusivity, hire the whole island. Thus, advance reservations are essential, through major travel agents in Zanzibar Town and through specialist agents overseas. High season rates start at US$625 per person per day (sharing a double), which includes everything except transfers from Zanzibar airport and champagne. For more information see www.ccafrica.com.

PWANI MCHANGANI

About 6km south of Matemwe village is the larger settlement of Pwani Mchangani, which (along with Chwaka) is one of the island's main fish markets. In and around this area are several good places to stay.

Uzioni Beach Bungalows (tel: 0747 417701; email: uzioni@hotmail.com) is about 2km north of Pwani Mchangani, or 4km south of Matemwe village. This is a new and very pleasant place, with ten straightforward but perfectly adequate en-suite rooms, and a nice restaurant. Singles are US$40, doubles US$50, and for an extra US$10–15 half-board and full-board deals are available.

Tufikiniwe Guesthouse, in Pwani Mchangani village itself, is owned and run by a local women's cooperative group, offering simple good-value accommodation for US$2.50 per person. This is a basic place offering a chance to stay in a village setting, and maybe learn a little about the local community. This is *not* a place to sunbathe on the beach. All meals are extra and could be arranged long in advance, while just a short distance away a local eating house sells tea, bread and chapatis and maybe simple meals.

Mapenzi Beach Club A new road along the coast links Pwani Mchangani and Kiwengwa, and if you follow this road, less than 2km south of Pwani Mchangani village is Mapenzi Beach Club, a large and luxurious resort with many facilities (and with some of the largest palm-thatch *makuti* roofs anywhere in Africa) catering mainly for large groups of Italian fly-in package tourists, although smaller parties and individuals are also welcomed. The rates here are totally all-inclusive (as are some of the other big hotels catering for package tourists on Zanzibar) and for US$94 per person per day in a double room, you get accommodation, meals,

Above Colourful Zanzibari painting (AZ)
Below left Tingatinga artist, Zanzibar Stone Town (AZ)
Below right Basket weaver (AZ)
Next page Beach at Matemwe (HT)

drinks and activities, but there's a three-day minimum stay. Each room has air conditioning, safety deposit box, telephone and hairdryer, and other facilities include swimming pool, jacuzzi, two boutiques, a disco and nightly entertainment. A travel agent in Zanzibar or overseas will make bookings for you. Next along is the similar **Coral Reef Village**.

Shooting Star Inn (PO Box 3076, Zanzibar; tel: 024 2232926, 0747 414166; email: star@ zanzibar.org; web: www.zanzibar.org/star) is just south of Coral Reef, on cliffs overlooking the northern end of Kiwengwa Beach. This place is run by Elly Mlanga, a warm and gentle guy from near Arusha, and originally started as a restaurant to cater for guests from the nearby large hotels. An increasing number of visitors came from Zanzibar Town on day trips and wanted to stay longer, so the guesthouse was born, and its popularity keeps growing. Double en-suite rooms in cottages cost US$130. Each cottage has two rooms and adjoining doors mean families can hire the whole cottage (sleeping up to six people) if required. Singles and triples are also available. Smaller en-suite 'lodge' rooms cost US$110 per double. These prices may be a touch on the high side for what you get, but this place gets good reports from most guests, and it's popular, so they must be doing something right. For those on tighter budgets, some simple thatched *bandas* with shared bathroom facilities cost US$15 per person. At peak times a US$10 per person supplement is charged. Half board costs an extra US$20, and full board an extra US$30. There are also very good discounts for children. There's nowhere else to eat nearby, but the hotel's restaurant serves lunches from around US$5 and three-course evening meals from US$9 to US$17. Steps lead down to the beach, but it's good for swimming only when the tide is in. An alternative is to walk down the beach to Bluebay Beach Resort (see below) which has a swimming pool, as well as a dive centre which is open to guests from other hotels in the area.

Bluebay Beach Resort (PO Box 3276, Zanzibar; tel: 024 2241240; email: mail@bluebayzanzibar.com; web: www.bluebayzanzibar.com, or www.bluebayhotelzanzibar.com) is about 2km south of the Shooting Star and is a sharply contrasting establishment. This large hotel has about 90 rooms, catering for tourist groups (small and large) from various European countries. All rooms are en suite, with two double beds (which makes the rooms a little cramped), veranda, sea view, air conditioning, TV, phone and minibar. Compared to most of the other large resort-type hotels along this bit of coast, Bluebay seems relatively quiet and relaxed. There are activities and entertainment provided, but it's fairly low key, and guests can easily snooze on the beach, rather than be constantly encouraged to try beach volleyball or water aerobics. The hotel seems to be taking genuine steps to reduce its environmental impact, with several energy-saving, water-collecting and rubbish-disposal schemes. Rates are US$120 per person in a double (US$160 per person in a deluxe double) and US$145 in a single (US$200 deluxe), half board. For an extra US$18 you get full board. If you book through a travel agent (in Zanzibar Town or in your home county) you'll probably be able to get rates somewhat lower. One Ocean has a dive centre at the hotel (for more details see *Diving* in *Chapter 4*), which is open to guests from other hotels in the area.

Protea Beach Resort (tel: 0747 417782; email: enquiries@zanzibarbeachresort.com; web: www.proteahotels.com) is the latest arrival on this stretch of coast, dealing mainly with groups and individuals on package tours from Europe and South Africa. Surrounded by high walls, topped by razor wire, there are 40 rooms inside. The hotel fronts on to a lovely beach, and offers all sorts of water activities, such as canoeing, waterskiing, windsurfing, diving and fishing. When we were researching here, local seaweed farmers were being cleared from the area, presumably to make room for the tourists.

KIWENGWA

Kiwengwa is a small coastal village, with several large hotels nearby all catering exclusively for Italian package tourists. Just south of the village is **Sea Club Kiwengwa**, and north of the village hotels include **Karibu Beach Resort** (part of the VentaClub chain), **Zanzibar VeraClub** and **Bravo Beach**. The last of these club-resorts is very near Kiwengwa village and, although there is a wall between the two, there's an open gateway. The sudden contrast between the traditional Zanzibari fishing village and the crowded hotel grounds complete with sun-loungers, parasols and beach volleyball is remarkable to the point of being almost surreal.

Getting there
The easiest way to reach Kiwengwa from Zanzibar Town is along the new tar road via Mahonda and Kiniasini. You can come by taxi, rented car or motorbike, or arrange a minibus through a tour company. By public transport, *dala-dalas* (No 17) run several times a day between Zanzibar Town and Kiwengwa – the fare is US$0.75.

Where to stay
Although the large hotels are aimed at (mainly Italian) tour groups, individuals can arrange to stay. The best way of doing this is through a tour agent in Zanzibar Town.

If you want more of a Zanzibari experience, in the village itself, **Paradise Guesthouse** provides local-style accommodation, with a couple of small bungalows right on the beach for US$15 per person. Bookings are not possible. It's a turn-up-and-try-your-luck situation.

Reef View (tel: 0747 413294, 414030; email: reefviewinzanzibar@hotmail.com; web: www.reefview.com) is about 1km south of Kiwengwa village, and a long-standing popular place at the budget end of the scale. It's very low-key, quiet and relaxed, run by Haroub and Helen, a friendly English-Zanzibari couple. Simple *bandas* are US$10 per person, and bungalows are planned. The palm-thatch bathrooms are clean but basic with bucket showers and long-drop loos, although flush models are also planned. There's a bar and restaurant, with meals around US$5–6, and a bookshop with an impressively large selection of paperbacks for sale or exchange. The management have good links with local fisherman and can set you up with boat rides, or arrange diving, fishing and even horse-riding at some of the nearby big hotels. For more information email: reefviewinzanzibar@hotmail.com or asko@zanzinet.com (subject: Reef View).

Nature Safari Lodge (tel: 0747 414704) is another budget place, about 4km south of Kiwengwa, with just five little bungalows with basic en-suite bathroom, all overlooking a quiet stretch of beach, There's a simple thatched dining area, with chickens wandering around to provide eggs for breakfast (and maybe something more substantial for an evening meal), and that's about it. A place for total relaxation. Rooms cost US$15 per person, and meals are around US$4.

Pongwe Beach Hotel (tel: 0747 414134) is another 1km south (5km from Kiwengwa) – a quiet, almost sleepy, place where bungalows with a small ocean-facing veranda and two to four beds in each cost US$30 per person. There's a private beach, and the swimming is good at high tide. It's possible this place may be sold and turned into a large resort, so make enquiries before just turning up here.

UROA
The small village of Uroa is on the coast about halfway between Kiwengwa and Chwaka. It can be reached from Kiwengwa along the coast track, but most easily (if you're coming from Zanzibar Town) via Chwaka. One part of the village is dominated by the large **Uroa Bay Village Resort,** which was completely closed (in fact, abandoned) when we were researching here, but it might re-open in the future.

Where to stay

White Villa (PO Box 2424, Zanzibar; tel: 0741 326874), in the centre of the village, is a small good-quality guesthouse, run by a friendly German-Zanzibari team, where en-suite double rooms cost US$70–80, and some rooms with shared bathroom US$60. Single rooms cost US$20 less.

Tamarind Beach Hotel (tel: 0747 413709; email: tamarind@zanzinet.com; web: www.tamarind.nu) is a group of villas set in slightly scruffy gardens next to the beach. The villas have en-suite rooms and upstairs balconies overlooking the palm-lined seashore. Some bathrooms are a tad dilapidated, so choose your room carefully. Singles are US$30, doubles US$40, and triples US$56, with discounts for children. Half board is an extra US$12, full board US$24. You can get more information from Fisherman Tours in Zanzibar Town.

Zanzibar Safari Resort (tel: 0741 330345; tel/fax: 024 2238553; email: zanzibar.safari.club@africaonline.co.tz; web: www.zanzibarsafariclub.co.tz) is at the southern end of Uroa, a relaxed hotel with 40 air-conditioned en-suite rooms in bungalows around a swimming pool, a pleasant restaurant and a bar on the beach. It's used by some groups from Europe, but it doesn't have a 'packagey' feel, and the management is very friendly. Based at the hotel, Mwawimbi Watersports offers diving and boat rides. Rooms with sea view are US$95 a single, US$180 a double. Without a sea view this drops to US$85 and US$150. Half-board and full-board rates are also available.

CHWAKA

Chwaka is a large fishing village halfway down the east coast, directly due east of Zanzibar Town. In the early 19th century, Chwaka was a slave port, and later, during colonial times, its sea breezes and lack of mosquitoes made it a popular holiday resort for wealthy Zanzibaris and British officials. Today, Chwaka has one of the island's largest fish markets, and has a lively atmosphere in the mornings when the fishing boats land.

Getting there

Chwaka can be reached by public bus, or by hired car or bike. There are no tourist minibuses coming here, although you could hire one through a tour company in Zanzibar Town.

Where to stay

The former **ZTC bungalow** now seems to be permanently closed; in fact it's half fallen down, although if you really wanted to stay you could make enquires at the ZTC office in Zanzibar Town (details in the *Zanzibar Town* chapter).

Chwaka Bay Hotel (tel: 024 2233005) at the north end of the village is your other option, with bungalows at US$55 for singles, US$75 for doubles. Half board is an extra US$15–20. The bungalows all have private bathroom, hot water, fans and nets, but when we were researching this edition major renovations and improvements were under way (including a pool under construction), and prices here may rise in the future. You can get more information from a travel agent in Zanzibar Town.

Onwards from Chwaka

If you come to Chwaka by bus and want to continue travelling down the east coast without going all the way back to Zanzibar Town, you can get a ride on a boat across Chwaka Bay to Michamvi on the peninsula north of Dongwe and Bwejuu. Local people travel this way, but only the occasional adventurous tourist is seen here. Boats from Michamvi come across to Chwaka fish market most mornings, then go back around noon, but there are no set schedules; you need to ask around on the beach. A ride will cost about US$1. The new hotel being built at Michamvi may start a ferry service for guests, so ask about this if you miss the fishing boats.

UFUFUMA FOREST HABITAT

Near Chwaka, this project was set up by the people of Jidele Village. Its aims are to protect the habitat of nearby Ufufuma Forest and to help the village use it in a sustainable way; to make it a place for locals and foreigners to visit; and to conserve the local traditional activities performed here connected with the worship of *shetani,* or spirits (see box, *The Shetani of Zanzibar,* on page 42).

The forest area is at present only 1km², but the villagers are leaving the surrounding 4km² area uncultivated to allow the forest to regrow and the habitat to expand in size. Tiny paths wind through thick vegetation, while underfoot is coral, with lots of roots.

A visit here is not a massive wildlife experience, nor is it meant to be, although animals you might see include red colobus, black colobus, lots of birds, snakes, lizards and so on. (Morning is the best time for seeing birds and monkeys.) A few villagers act as guides, but they are not really wildlife specialists and don't know a lot of the bird names. But they are trying to learn, and meanwhile, they are very enthusiastic about the Ufufuma's cultural importance – which is the primary reason for a visit here.

Reader Alex Liambey echoes this enthusiasm: 'It's owned by the local village, unlike Jozhani Forest, which is government owned. The villagers are trying to get returns from it in order to support the community, so when you visit you really feel you are helping people locally. The monkeys are not used to humans (unlike in the Jozhani Forest) so they don't come close; in fact, the ones we saw sat at a respectful distance and observed us closely. There are also interesting caves of local spiritual importance, with rudimentary altars where offerings are made to spirits. It was almost the highlight of our stay.'

There are three *shetani* caves in the forest that tourists can visit. When local people are sick they come with the local witch doctor to these sites and perform rituals to cure themselves. The caves themselves are nice and spooky, with the smell of smoke from recent fires, and red bits of cloth hanging from the ceilings. It's a fascinating insight into a rarely seen aspect of Zanzibari culture.

It costs about US$4 per person to walk through the forest for an hour or two, after which you are welcome to go back to Jidele, see the village and ask questions. The cost includes the services of a guide, a visit to the caves, and snacks of fruit. As the forest floor can be damp, you need to take good shoes, and in the hot season take water to drink.

If you want to see a full *shetani* ceremony, consisting of about seven hours of singing, dancing and various rituals, this costs U$50 (for one or two people).

Getting there

To reach Ufufuma, take the road to Chwaka and the forest is on the left, about 5km before Chwaka. There is no sign or specific parking spot, and only tiny paths leading into the forest. You're better off continuing to Jidele Village, where you can ask in the central market area for a guide of the forest. Recent visitors have suggested to the locals that they should put up a sign saying 'Jidele Village & Forest Reserve', so one may appear.

DUNGA RUINS

About halfway between Chwaka and Zanzibar Town (about 13km from each), in the centre of the island, very near the modern village of Dunga, lie Dunga Ruins.

SEAWEED ON THE EAST COAST

During December and January, some of the beaches on the east coast are covered in dark brown seaweed which is washed ashore from the ocean by the wind. This can be quite a shock if you expect pristine picture-postcard tropical beach conditions. The seaweed normally stays on the beaches until mid-February, or the start of the rainy season, then gets carried back out to sea. After March, and up until November, the beaches are mostly clear.

These are the remains of the palace built for King Mohammed, the Mwinyi Mkuu (Swahili ruler) of Zanzibar, some time between 1846 and 1856. It may have been built on the site of an earlier house. Before that, the residence of the Mwinyi Mkuu had been at Kizimkazi or Unguja Ukuu (described on page 225).

A Swahili royal line is believed to have already existed on Zanzibar when the first Shirazi immigrants arrived here from Persia in the 10th century AD. Leading figures among the Shirazis are thought to have married into the family of the Swahili ruler, as the Mwinyi Mkuu (literally the 'Great Chief') later claimed to be descended from a Shirazi prince. In the following centuries, while the island was controlled by the Portuguese, and later by the Arabs and British, a Mwinyi Mkuu continued to be regarded as traditional leader by the people of Zanzibar.

Local legend holds that when Dunga Palace was built, slaves were buried alive in the foundations, while others were killed so that their blood could be mixed with the mortar, to bring strength and good fortune to the house. (There may be some truth in this story as, in the 1920s, a nearby well was found to be half full of human bones.)

Part of the Mwinyi Mkuu's regalia was a set of sacred drums and horns, and these were kept at Dunga during King Mohammed's rule. The drums were carved from mango wood, and inscribed in Arabic. They were said to beat on their own to warn the king of impending trouble. The horns were always kept hidden in a secret place, known only to the Mwinyi Mkuu. When the Mwinyi Mkuu was near death, the hiding place would be revealed to the next in line. Another story holds that when King Mohammed left the palace at Dunga, anyone gathering coconuts or cloves up a tree would have to come down, as nobody was allowed to be higher than him.

Mohammed died in 1865 and was succeeded by his son Ahmed, but he died of smallpox in 1873, leaving no male heir. His two sisters married into prominent families of Arab landowners, but the ruling dynasty came to an end.

Today, only the main walls of the palace at Dunga remain, but it is still an imposing ruin, retaining something of its original grandeur. A few old passages, pillars and staircases can also be seen. The windows are empty and their decorative frames are now in the Peace Memorial Museum, along with the Mwinyi Mkuu's sacred drums and horns.

PAJE

Paje is a small fishing village, where the main road from Zanzibar Town meets the coast, and from where minor roads go north to Bwejuu and south to Jambiani. The area around the three villages of Paje, Bwejuu and Jambiani used to be the busiest part of the east coast, especially for backpackers, as there was a good choice of cheap places to stay, although over the last few years some middle range and upmarket places have been added as well.

Some travellers now give this area a miss, preferring the livelier environs of the west side of Nungwi and Kendwa on the north coast. The end result is that the Paje, Bwejuu and Jambiani area is probably a bit quieter than it used to be. That may not be an altogether bad thing. Another difference is there are more palm trees along the Bwejuu–Paje–Jambiani stretch than on the north coast, and so a bit more shade behind the beach. The disadvantage is that when the tide goes out on the east coast it's harder to swim, whereas at Nungwi you can swim from the beach at any time of the day, or night. Deciding whether to visit the north coast or the east coast comes down to a matter of taste. If you can't decide, you could always try both!

Getting there and away

To reach Paje, the main road from Zanzibar Town leads though Tunguu, Pete and Kitogani, then heads east to the coast. From Paje a road leads north to Bwejuu, Domwe and Michamvi, while another road south leads to Jambiani, from where a very bad and rarely used dirt track leads to Makunduchi, in the far southeast corner of the island.

Paje, Bwejuu and Jambiani can be reached by public transport, and by tourist minibus. You can also arrange for a taxi or privately hired minibus to bring you here, or come by self-drive rental car, motorbike or bicycle. If you want to go north beyond Bwejuu or south past Jambiani, there's no public transport, so you'll need to have your own wheels or enjoy a good walk.

If you come to the Bwejuu-Paje-Jambiani area by tourist minibus, the drivers get commission from some of the hotels and will try to take you to these, unless you have a reservation or specifically say you want to go to one of the other places.

Where to stay

There are several places to stay in Paje.

The first one you might reach as you come in from Zanzibar Town is the **Ufukwe Guesthouse,** a very simple place with double rooms for US$10 per person.

Next along is **Kitete Guesthouse** (tel: 024 2240226; email: kitete@hotmail.com; web: www.kitete.com), locally owned and under friendly Swedish management. Simple, but comfy, this place feels more like a home than a hotel. All sea activities, and tours around the island, can be arranged. It costs US$30 per en-suite double room, with a couple of rooms attached to the restaurant for US$20. Also available are family rooms at US$30 for the first two people, then US$5 per person extra (up to six people). The restaurant is in a separate building, overlooking the beach, and is also open to non-guests. Snacks are US$1.50 to US$2 and meals US$3 to US$5.

Paje by Night (tel: 0741 211981; email: hotelpbn@yahoo.com or borisve@hotmail.com; web: www.pajebynight.com) has been here for years, and keeps getting better. Also known as **PBN Bizzare Hotel**, it's managed by a friendly German team, and the accommodation comprises single, double or triple rooms (all en suite, some with hot water) from around US$15 per person, all spaced around a big sandy courtyard. Comfortable en-suite double bungalows are US$50 (single US$25). The restaurant is deservedly famous for its pizzas (from US$2.50 to US$5) and other snacks are US$2–3, lunches US$2–5, and a big three-course dinner US$5. You can make international calls, fishing or snorkelling trips can be arranged, and tours to places like Jozani and Kizimkazi (to see monkeys or dolphins) are available.

Paradise Beach Bungalows (PO Box 2346, Zanzibar; tel: 024 2231387; fax: 230891; email: Lsaori@cats-net.com) is about 1km nort of Paje village, and marked by a large sign, which also rather unexpectedly advertises Japanese home cooking. But all is revealed when you meet Mrs Saori Miura from Japan who has run this place for many years, and it is regularly recommended by travellers. Rooms are a bit dark, but you'll be on the beach most of the day, and fair value with singles for US$25, doubles for US$35, triples for US$45. On the beach is a nice bar and restaurant, where lunches start at US$2.50 and very good fixed-menu three-course evening meals (European, Swahili or Japanese) are US$5.

Wherever you stay, if you don't want to eat at your hotel, a small **café** has been opened by the junction where the road to Zanzibar Town leaves the coast.

What to do and see
Number one activity here is lounging on the beach, closely followed by swimming. If you want more activity visit Paje East Coast Diving Centre (more details in the *Diving* section in *Chapter 4*), next door to Kitete Guesthouse.

Next to Paje East Coast Diving, you can't fail to miss the huge grandiose mansion built in Arabic and Oriental styles. It looks like a theme hotel but it is in fact a private house. Also nearby, but from a different era, is the old mausoleum, a low rectangular edifice with a castellated wall, inset with antique plates and dishes. This design is thought to have originated in Persia, and may indicate that this part of the island was settled by Shirazi immigrants before the western side of the island near present-day Zanzibar Town.

BWEJUU
Bwejuu village is about 5km north of Paje, a spread-out settlement sitting just back from the beach, with huts and houses in between the palm trees. It's a quiet area, excellent for sheer relaxation, and the only sound you'll hear when you're out of the village is the wind in the palm leaves. The sea goes out for miles, and there's a great feeling of space. The local people do some fishing, and the women make rope from coconut husks, but seaweed farming seems to be the major industry here. Unlike at some other places, in Bwejuu the hotels seem comfortable *inside* the village, and don't dominate it, so there's a still a nice traditional atmosphere.

Getting there and away
You get here via Paje, and transport details are given in that section.

Where to stay
Roughly halfway between Paje and Bwejuu is **Sun & Sea View Hotel**, (tel: 0747 420774; email: ssvresort@zenjcom.com), a nice medium-budget place with five neat white bungalows, each with two rooms, set in a spacious garden. The floors are beautifully tiled, and the en-suite bathrooms have large Persian-style baths. The dining-room is an open-sided *banda*, on a raised platform on the beach, with superb views. At US$50 a single and US$75 a double, this is good value.

In the same area, **Seven Seas Guesthouse** is a good budget option overlooking the sea with neat little thatched bungalows, each with en-suite bathroom. There's a small beach bar, which also serves food (look out for the whalebone tablepieces!). Singles are US$15, double US$25 and triple US$30.

In Bwejuu itself, the **ZTC bungalow** has three rooms, which are clean, but plain and dreary. Officially, it costs US$20 to rent the whole bungalow (reservations should be made at the ZTC office in Zanzibar Town) but it might be possible to make an arrangement with the caretaker if you want only one room.

Palm Beach Inn (tel: 024 2240221; email: mahfudh28@hotmail.com; web: www.palmbeachzanzibar.com) is in the heart of Bwejuu village – a long-time and ever-popular choice in the lower to middle range, which always gets good reports. Set in a green and shady garden, this place has a quiet atmosphere and wide range of nicely decorated rooms overlooking the beach – all with fridge, fan, air conditioning and good bathroom – for US$60 a double, US$40 a single. There's also a family room for US$100. The Palm Beach has an airy restaurant with a good selection of local meals, including lobster, for between US$4 and US$8 (advance orders are appreciated), and a beach bar.

This hotel is owned by the famous and wonderfully formidable Niala, a local girl made good, who now wields considerable influence in some parts of Zanzibar. She makes a point of buying all her supplies locally, and employs as many Bwejuu residents as possible – especially those who might not get a job elsewhere (such as single mothers, which means there's sometimes a few more babies around the place than you might expect!). Some evenings, groups of locals come to the hotel to sing and dance with guests, and local kids may put on an acrobatic display (but Niala only lets those who go to school do the show). All in all, this is a good, enjoyable place with a definite non-sophisticated, local feel.

Dere Guesthouse (tel: 024 231017) is just a short distance north of Palm Beach. A former backpacker favourite, it seems to have lost some of its former charm, and has the feel of a place going downhill. At US$10 per person, though, it's cheap, and the manager is friendly. It may be worth checking in case things pick up again.

Where to eat

The hotels do food, but if you want to eat elsewhere, Bwejuu village has a few local-style eating houses. Several travellers have recommended **Jamal's Restaurant**, near the Palm Beach Inn. There are also a few small shops in the village.

What to do

You can explore the offshore reef with snorkelling gear, hired from the Dere Guesthouse or Palm Beach Inn (around US$3 per day for mask, snorkel and flippers), although this means walking out at low tide. You can also hire bikes (US$4) or scooters (US$40) from local villagers (arranged through either of these hotels) and ride a few kilometres north up the beach to the 'lagoon' at Dongwe, near the big Club Vacanza resort, where there's a break in the reef and you can snorkel off the beach at low tide.

NORTH OF BWEJUU

North of Bwejuu village, towards Dongwe and Michamvi, there are a still a few huts and houses dotted among the palms, but generally speaking the local population thins out here. In their place, you'll find a wide choice of places to stay, spaced along the coast for several kilometres, with something to cater for every taste and budget. The beach is beautiful here, and the water its customary deep turquoise – making this area an ideal place to relax for a day or a week...

Where to stay

The hotels and guesthouse are described in this section from south to north.

Kilimani Bungalows (tel: 024 2240235; email: drabien@kilimani.de) is the first place you reach as you head north from Bwejuu, set back from the beach. With the help of energetic Dirk Rabien, the local villagers have built this place as a community project, with a proportion of each guest's payment going back into local facilities. So far the villagers have used the income to build a library and self-help education centre. Accommodation is in four white bungalows, all spotlessly clean and well-kept, with en-suite bathrooms, all for US$15 per person. Good local-style meals and seafood dishes are served in the restaurant. In sharp contrast to some other places to stay on Zanzibar, there are deliberately no fences here – locals are free to walk through the grounds.

Belleview Restaurant & Bungalows (tel: 0744 328361; email: bellevue01@hotmail.com) is nearby, set back from the beach, up on a cliff (to catch the breeze) with just three en-suite rooms at US$15 for a single, US$25 a double. Half board costs an extra US$5 per person and full board an extra US$10. The simple little restaurant does meals for US$4–5 (which need to be discussed with the chef long in advance), plus an interesting selection of spiced coffees.

Evergreen Bungalows (tel: 0747 416932) is about 1km out of Bwejuu, run by a friendly local called Edmond. There's no electricity but lamps are provided. Rooms are small but clean, and good value in this range at US$15 a single, US$25 a double. Bathrooms are en suite (although mostly involve bucket showers). The food is good, with snacks from US$1.50, and meals US$3–4. A dive centre is planned for the future.

Next along is **Twisted Palm** (tel: 024 2240060), known as 'New Twisted Palm', with three bungalows up on a small hill away from the beach, and four bungalows nearer the sea under palms. The location is good, although the rooms are a tad dreary, and the mozzie nets have seen better days. The upstairs restaurant has fine views, with local and seafood meals around US$2–3.50.

Nearby is another place called **Twisted Palm** (now called 'Old Twisted Palm') consisting of two open-plan houses with five rooms each. The upstairs lounge is cool and airy but the rooms are small and falling into disrepair. It's undeniably quiet and peaceful, but it could be because nobody stays these days. Even at US$10 per person, it's only just fair for this price-range, although it might be worth checking in case things pick up. **Shell's Bungalow**, nearby, is similar in most respects.

Robinson's Place (tel: 0747 413479 between 19.00 and 22.00 only; email: robinsonsplace@hotmail.com) is fairly new on the scene, a small and delightful place run by a welcoming Swiss-Zanzibari couple. *Robinson Crusoe* is the inspiration here (not *Swiss Family Robinson*) and there are only four rooms, each in a separate cottage and each individually designed, with brightly painted floors and walls, colourful mats and bedspreads, and many little touches like carvings, pictures, wall hangings, lamps and candles (which are handy as there's no electricity). The thatch on each cottage doesn't quite meet the top of the wall so a natural cooling breeze blows through. Pride of place goes to the Robinson Room, which is open-sided with a view of the sea, and worth booking if you can. None of the rooms is en suite; there is a simple but spotless bathroom, with bucket showers. In the garden there are hammocks and swings and the whole place is very pretty. At US$20 per person (single or double) it's a bargain. Lunches are not available, but excellent Zanzibari evening meals are available for around US$5, and eaten local style on a mat on the floor. Drinks may only be available if you book in advance.

Sunrise Hotel (PO Box 3967, Zanzibar; tel/fax: 024 2240170; email: sunrise@zanlink.com; web: www.sunrise-zanzibar.com) is about 3km from Bwejuu village. It's small but smart, with urbane management and a slightly genteel old-fashioned atmosphere which is frequently recommended by visitors. The hotel is set in lush gardens, and there's a great view of the ocean from your bar stool. The beach is just a few steps away, but as with anywhere on the east coast reaching the sea takes a while at low tide. To this end, a nice little swimming pool has been built. En-suite double bungalows cost US$75–90 (singles US$65–80). Meals in the restaurant are very highly recommended and start at US$5. Lunches and snacks are equally tasty and start from about US$2. Credit cards are accepted.

Andy's Karibuni Bungalows (tel: 0742 740037; email: nakupenda@ bluemail.ch) is about 1km beyond the Sunrise. Run by the well-travelled Andrea, with help from a friendly team of locals and several equally friendly dogs, this is a calm and spacious place. Rooms are in bungalows, all nicely decorated, and the gardens are lovely. The menu and restaurant hours are very relaxed; basically you tell Andrea what you fancy eating, and when, and she'll sort it out. Hungarian, Italian and Swahili specialities are all available. Singles are US$35, doubles US$40 and triples US$45 – excellent value in this range.

Breezes Beach Club (PO Box 1361 Zanzibar; tel 0741 326595; tel 0741 333151; email: breezes@africaonline.co.tz; website: www.breezes-zanzibar.com) is about 8km from Bwejuu. It's a fairly large hotel with 70 rooms in bungalows and cottages widely spaced in a well-maintained garden, so it feels like a place half its size. Some visitors comment that despite its name it isn't really that 'clubby' – a definite plus in our view. It's also not part of a chain, and managed personally by the owners who deliberately reject the constant organised-activity-and-entertainment style of some of the other big hotels and resorts along the Zanzibar coast. There is nightly entertainment but it's low key; there is a disco but it's separate from the main hotel – and soundproofed. Other facilities include a fitness centre and the Rising Sun Dive Centre– for more details see the *Diving* section in *Chapter 4 Practical Information*. This hotel also encourages small groups from several different countries, which makes for a calmer atmosphere, whereas some other big hotels are dominated by very large parties all from one place. In summary, this is probably one of the best hotels of its type in Zanzibar, and well worth a visit if this is your price range. Standard rooms cost US$90–100, while deluxe rooms with a sea view are US$110–120, half board. If you want full board it's an extra US$12 per day. Drinks for the bar are extra, and some guests find these quite expensive. You can book direct, or through an agent in Zanzibar Town. In Europe the hotel is represented by specialist travel agents and also features in many mainstream tour brochures.

The Palms (tel: 0748 203092; email: info@palms-zanzibar.com; web: www.palms-zanzibar.com) is a new and highly exclusive choice on the east coast; six cool and stylish luxury villas with top-quality facilities set in spacious grounds. You can see the ocean from your bed, and each villa even has its own private terrace and thatched parasol on the beach. All inclusive rates (transfers, full board, bar) are US$295–365 per person.

Sultan Palace (tel: 024 2240173; fax: 2240188; email: info@sultanzanzibar.com; web: www.sultanzanzibar.com), about 10km north of Bwejuu, is a small hotel consisting of 15 huge semi-circular cottages, each with veranda, sea-views, private garden and a bathroom you could get lost in. The main central building is also huge, with a bar, lounge and restaurant upstairs. Reports on the décor here range from 'stylish and imaginative' to 'brash and tasteless' – it probably depends on your own preferences. The food and service in the restaurant, however, is high quality, and the hotel is a member of the international Relais & Chateaux marketing chain. Full board costs US$180 per person. A single is US$300. Steps lead down to a beautiful beach, which is also used by guests from nearby **Club Vacanza**, a much larger resort-hotel.

Last in the line, almost at the village of Michamvi, is the **Hotel Karafuu**, which caters for both individuals and large package groups.

Onwards from Bwejuu

From Bwejuu, and the beaches north of there, independent and adventurous travellers who want to keep heading north up the coast, and avoid back-tracking around Chwaka Bay, can take a local boat from Michamvi across to Chwaka. See the *Onwards from Chwaka* section earlier in this chapter for details. You'll probably also need to ask around at the hotels in Bwejuu for more information.

JAMBIANI

Jambiani is south of Paje. The village's name comes from *jambiya*, meaning an Arab-style dagger. Local legend holds that some early settlers found a dagger here: proof that even earlier visitors had been here before them.

This is a very long settlement, spread for several kilometres down the coast, with a wide choice of places to stay, mostly low-budget with a couple of mid-range places as well. In between those mentioned below, other new places are constantly popping up, so expect a few more names by the time you arrive. The village also has a school (which invites visitors to donate money to improve facilities), several basic food stores, a local craft shop (which also sells delicious natural honey) and a bakery.

Where to stay
Places to stay are described from north to south.

Horizontal Inn, at the northern end of the village, reached first as you come in from Paje, is a small family-run place with clean rooms from US$7 per person. Lunch and dinner are also available, for around US$3, but you must order several hours in advance. Nearby is **Molly's Restaurant**, serving local food, snacks and drinks.

The **ZTC bungalow** is next in line, offering the standard ZTC service for the standard ZTC price of US$20 for five people. In the 1980s this was the only place to stay in Jambiani. Little has changed, apart from a coat of paint in 1990 and the installation of electricity in 1994, but if you're spending most of your time on the beach this is a fair deal. Officially you need to book in advance at the ZTC office at Livingstone House in Zanzibar Town.

Blue Oyster Hotel (tel: 0741 33312; email: blueoysterhotel@gmx.de; web: www.zanzibar.de) is one of the first 'proper' hotels you come to in Jambiani. It's a two-storey place with rooms downstairs around an inner courtyard and a breezy restaurant with beautiful veranda overlooking the beach and ocean. With friendly staff, clean rooms, good beds and furniture, running water and electricity, this is a fine deal in the low-to-middle range. Double rooms are US$30, or US$40 with en-suite bathroom. The single rate is US$25 and US$30 en suite. Triple rooms are also available for US$60, and have a balcony with sea view; for the triple rate you can have it as an extra-spacious double. In the restaurant, snacks and sandwiches are US$2–3, pizzas up to US$5, and good evening meals like octopus in coconut with rice are US$4.

Oasis Beach Inn (tel: 024 2240259) is just along the beach from the Blue Oyster, with simple rooms at US$8 per person, and good clean en-suite doubles for US$25 the room. There's a bar and restaurant (with meals from US$2–5 and an elaborate-looking menu, which boasts crab claw masala and banana flambee). Snorkel trips can be arranged from US$4 per person.

Sau Inn Hotel (tel: 024 2240169, 2240205; email: sauinn@zanlink.com) was once the best hotel in Jambiani, with cool and comfortable en-suite rooms and cottages set in pleasant gardens, often recommended by readers, but in recent times it's gone downhill a bit, with dirty bathrooms, peeling paint and sun-loungers in dire need of repair. The swimming pool is a definite plus though (although watch out for the surrounding wall – just low enough to trip over), and there's a good restaurant overlooking the beach, and a bar with a TV. The hotel is used by some tour groups and often has a lively, friendly atmosphere. Singles are US$60, doubles US$70, triples US$80. Half-board and full-board rates are US$10 and US$20 extra. Other facilities include an email service (send and receive only, open to non-guests).

East Coast Visitors Inn (tel: 024 2240150; email: visitorsinn@zitec.org) is about 1km past the Sau Inn along the village main street, past the health centre and the school. It's quite large for a budget place, clean and pleasant with friendly staff, and often gets good reports – although there's nothing exactly special about it either. Rooms with shared bathrooms in the 'guesthouse' are US$13 per person, and double en-suite bungalows, with fridge and sea-view are US$40 a double. Meals in the restaurant start at around US$3.

Jambiani Beach Hotel, (tel: 024 2240155) is small and peaceful, with en-suite rooms facing the ocean, but not right on the beach like some of the other places. As one of the first guesthouses in Jambiani, though, this place is feeling its age, and can only honestly be described as only adequate, although with rooms costs US$15 per person, you can't complain too much. The hotel's restaurant serves local dishes for between US$4 and US$7, and has a quiet bar.

Shehe Guesthouse (tel: 024 2240149; email: shehebungalows@hotmail.com) is another kilometre or so along the beach from Jambiani. This is a very friendly place, which has been popular on the backpacker trail for many years, although some travellers report that it's lost some of its once-legendary laid-back atmosphere. Older en-suite rooms, set round a sandy courtyard, cost US$10 per person. In the newer annex, slightly more comfortable en-suite bungalows cost US$25 per double. The guesthouse also has a small shop selling biscuits, soft drinks, and a few items of tinned food, and an upstairs bar-restaurant (with TV) serving snacks and a cheap fixed-menu lunch and dinner (from US$3), plus other meals around US$5, but everything must be ordered several hours in advance.

About 1km beyond the Shehe, at the quieter southern end of the village, are some more places:

Shiaba Guesthouse and Restaurant, is small, local and friendly but not right on the beach, charging US$8 per person in en-suite rooms.

Kimte Guesthouse (tel: 024 2241212; email: mzale2002@yahoo.com) offers a warm welcome and big, cool, airy en-suite rooms for US$10 per person, and a double without bathroom for US$8 per person. There's also a good restaurant (see *Where to eat*).

Another 1km or so, and you reach the southern end of the beach:

Gomani Guesthouse (tel: 024 2240153) is a clean and friendly place perched on low coral cliffs, with excellent views over the ocean, and rooms with fan, net and bathroom for US$30 per double.

Red Monkey Bungalows (tel: 024 2240207; email: standard@zitec.org) is last in line, also on the low coral cliffs. This place gets its name because it's on the edge of the village, near the forest, and monkeys are often seen. There are seven rooms in four bungalows, not very roomy, with odd narrow bathrooms. However, everything is clean and tidy, there's a nice view of the beach (which is reached by a short flight of steps), and the management and staff are very friendly. Double rooms are US$25 to US$30. The skilful chef prepares fresh fish and other good meals for about US$2.50 to US$4.

Where to eat

All the places to stay listed above have restaurants. Notable is the **Sea Breeze Restaurant**, attached to the **Kimte Guesthouse**, where friendly helpful staff serve good-value food (around US$3 for chicken, up to US$5 for prawns) in a shady garden courtyard, and the sign promises 'free transport back to your hotel after your heavy dinner'! Ordering long in advance (meal and lift) might be advisable here. If you want supplies, the main village shop (which also sells stamps) is near Jambiani Beach Hotel. Also nearby is a cluster of local eating-houses. Worth seeking out is the **Women's Restaurant** (close to the village football field), which serves good local fare.

In the same part of the village, but right on the beach, is **Coco Beach Café** (tel: 0741 324994), a European-style place run by Rachid who used to be at the French-owned Fisherman Restaurant in Zanzibar Town. Good quality meals, naturally with a seafood emphasis, cost US$4–9, and drinks, snacks and lunches are also available, and if your taste-buds get the better of your wallet, you can pay with a credit card. There's also a couple of attached bungalows, in true *avec chambres* tradition, for US$15 per person.

Services

If you need money, there's a **change bureau** at the East Coast Visitors Inn, and Coco Beach Café might be able to give you cash on a card if you get short (although you'll need to have a meal there). A basic **email** service is available at the Sau Inn.

THE MWAKA KOGWA FESTIVAL AT MAKUNDUCHI

If you happen to be visiting Zanzibar during the last week of July, try to reach Makunduchi. Every year there's a large festival here called the *Mwaka Kogwa* when local people come from all over the island for a great get-together of singing, dancing, drumming, making new friends and meeting old ones. It's no problem for tourists to see the festival, and when it's running several of the tour companies listed in the *Zanzibar Town* chapter run day trips to Makunduchi.

The festival is also called *Mwaka Nairuz* and it originates from Persia, marking the start of the New Year in the Shirazi calendar (for more details on the Shirazis in Zanzibar see the *History* chapter) and involves several rituals, including a mock fight where men from different parts of the village beat each other with banana stems. It is believed that this fight gives each combatant a chance to vent his feelings, and in this way the disagreements and arguments of the past year are exorcised so that the new year can be started peacefully. (Although this is a mock fight, it can still get pretty serious. Fortunately the men are only fighting with banana steams – they used to do it with real clubs and cudgels!)

While the men are beating each other, the women have a far more pleasant way of celebrating: dressed in their finest clothes, they parade around the village singing. The songs contain comments about love, families and village life.

The next stage of the festival is the ritual burning of a traditional hut, which has been built especially for the purpose. A local healer goes inside before the fire is lit and runs out again when the hut is burning strongly. It is thought that the burning of the hut symbolises the passing of the old year and also ensures that during the coming year should any house in the village catch fire its inhabitants will escape unharmed.

After the fighting and the hut-burning, a large feast is held with all the villagers bringing food and eating together. People from other parts of Zanzibar are welcomed, as a local tradition holds that any villager without a guest must be unhappy.

After the eating, the music starts – traditional *ngomas* and *taarab* (see the section on *Music and dance* in *Chapter 4*), but these days may include some more modern amplified sounds as well. The locals dance into the night and die-hard partiers move onto the beach to continue singing and dancing until dawn.

What to do and see

As with most coastal villages, the main items on the tourist agenda are swimming and sunbathing. Diving can also be arranged with the East Coast Dive Centre in Paje – see *Chapter 4 – Practical Information* for details.

If you want a change from the beach and the village, an interesting place to visit, about two hours' walk outside Jambiani, is a large underground cavern called Kumbi, which contains a natural spring. According to local legend, it was lived in at one time. Today it is a traditional shrine: local people go there to pray and make offerings. You'll need a local guide to show you the way. Even if the cave doesn't awe you, the walk is nice. Around the village, you can also see several old tombs decorated with plates and dishes, similar to the one at Paje.

Onwards from Jambiani

At the end of Jambiani village, the beach fizzles out and low coral cliffs, covered in vegetation, come right down to the sea. The dirt road heads inland and cuts through the scrub for 10km to Makunduchi. There are no hotels along this stretch of road, and no public transport. If you want to keep heading south to Makunduchi, you may be lucky and find a lift on one of the occasional vehicles passing this way. Otherwise, if you decide to walk, it takes about three to four hours.

MAKUNDUCHI

The village (or town – just) of Makunduchi lies at the southeastern end of Zanzibar Island, and is divided into two distinct parts: on the coast is the small village of 'old' Makunduchi, which has some local huts and houses, a few holiday cottages, and a small beach from where you can sometimes spot dolphins. About 2km inland is Makunduchi New Town. Despite its grand title, this settlement has one main road, some dusty side-streets, a bank, post and telephone office, police station, small shop and a few incongruous blocks of flats, similar to the ones in the new part of Zanzibar Town, built as part of a 1970s East German aid scheme.

Very few visitors come to Makunduchi (except to see the *Mwaka Kogwa* festival – see the box on page 219 for details) and it is much quieter than Bwejuu or Jambiani – not that they are particularly noisy. For a place to stay, your only option is the **ZTC bungalows** in 'old' Makunduchi village, but it seems to be permanently closed, although if you wanted to stay here you could make enquires at the ZTC office in Zanzibar Town (details in the *Zanzibar Town* chapter). There used to be another guesthouse called Kigaeni Reef Lodge near the beach, but this is also closed, although it or something similar might reopen in the future.

Makunduchi can be reached by public bus, or by rented car, scooter or bike, but there are no tourist minibuses working regularly on this route, although you could hire one specially through a tour company in Zanzibar Town. You can also reach Makunduchi from Jambiani; see the *Onwards from Jambiani* section above.

KIZIMKAZI

The village of Kizimkazi lies at the southwestern end of Zanzibar island about 12km to the west of Makunduchi. At one time, the Mwinyi Mkuu (the traditional king of Zanzibar) had a residence at Kizimkazi, but there's no evidence of royalty today – although the village does have many houses, a school, a dispensary, some places to stay, and a burgeoning tourist industry based on dolphin-watching.

Dolphins are regularly seen off the coast here, and Kizimkazi has become a launch point for boats taking visitors out on viewing trips. Most visitors come on all-inclusive 'dolphin tours' arranged in Zanzibar Town which includes road transport, the boat, snorkelling gear and lunch. If you don't take an all-in tour from town, or want to spend the night at Kizimkazi, you can make your own way here, then hire a boat on the spot or arrange to join a group. Near Jichane Restaurant are a couple of stalls selling souvenirs and renting out masks and flippers.

Technically, Kizimkazi consists of two villages: Kizimkazi Mkunguni and Kizimkazi Dimbani. Most boats go out to see the dolphins from Kizimkazi Mkunguni, and this is generally just called Kizimkazi. As an increasing number of tourists have arrived over the last few years, so an increasing number of 'guides', touts and hustlers have arrived as well, and they're all over the village now – some of them can be quite unpleasant. If you're driving, watch out for the squad of touts that sit in the road at the entrance to the village, waiting for custom.

Kizimkazi Dimbani is 2km north along the coast from 'main' Kizimkazi (3km by road); it's smaller, and much quieter, but a few boats go out from here as well. There are no touts, probably because it's mainly groups who come here; the whole scene is sewn up by two large restaurant-and-boat operations.

All the guesthouses and restaurants in Kizimkazi Mkunguni and Kizimkazi Dimbani can set you up with a boat to go and see the dolphins, although because Dimbani is more group orientated, it might be harder finding spare seats here. To reduce costs you can ask around and find some other people to team up with, or wait until groups arrive from Zanzibar Town and ask to join one of them. For a more intimate experience you can charter your own boat. For an idea of prices and more details see the *Kizimkazi dolphins* on page 222.

Getting there

Most people come to Kizimkazi by tourist minibus, or as part of a tour. Your other alternative is to come by hired car, scooter or bike. To reach Kizimkazi Dimbani, turn off the main road between Zanzibar Town and Makunduchi at Kufile junction, and follow this small road to a fork: right goes to Kizimkazi Dimbani and the ancient Shirazi mosque; left goes to the main part of Kizimkazi (Kizimkazi Mkunguni), from where most of the boats are launched.

You can also can get here independently by public bus or minibus: some buses running between Zanzibar Town and Makunduchi divert down to Kizimkazi Mkunguni. Otherwise you'll have to get off the bus at Kufile junction and walk to Kizimkazi Dimbani (4km) or Kizimkazi Mkunguni (6km).

Where to stay

Kizimkazi Beach Villa (tel: 0741 352685) is at the end of the tar road, the first place you reach as you come into Kizimkazi village from the north. It's a fairly basic bungalow overlooking the beach, charging US$10 per person. Meals (all in the US$2 to US$5 range) can be prepared to order.

Dolphin Shadow Guesthouse is a little further along the coast, although it may be closed, and construction nearby when we were researching here indicates something larger may rise in its place.

Dolphin View Village (tel: 024 2236577; email: rukiandame@yahoo.com) is about 1.5km from Kizimkazi Beach Villa, southwards along the sandy track that runs parallel to the coast. This place has friendly staff and large comfortable double or triple bungalows with private bathrooms and lounge, but its finest feature is the small secluded beach, in a cove between two coral-rock outcrops, where swimming and sunbathing are possible out of sight from the locals. Rooms are US$30–40.

In Kizimkazi Dimbani are a few more choices:

Just past the ancient mosque (described in the *What to see and do* section following) and overlooking the beach is a so-far nameless **guesthouse**. This is a new place and may have a proper name in the future, but it's a little gem and worth seeking out. There are only two rooms, each with straightforward but decent furniture, fresh paint and simple but clean bathroom. A double room costs US$30. There's no sign, so if you can't find it, or it looks closed, go to Cabs Restaurant (see below), and ask for Yussuf.

As this book was going to press, we heard about a new place under construction in Kizimkazi called **Funky Shamba** (tel: 0747 419008, email: funkyshamba@hotmail.com; web: www.funkyshamba.com). Under the command of a guy called Andrew Stannard, there are three bungalows, all built from local materials. It sounds great so will probably be worth checking when you're there.

Kizidi Restaurant and Bungalows (tel: 0747 417053; email: kizidi@hotmail.com) is

KIZIMKAZI DOLPHINS

The shallow coastal waters around Kizimkazi have been favoured by dolphins for many years (quite possibly for millennia) because the area offers a reliable food supply and is a good place to nurse calves or simply to rest and socialise. Two species of dolphin occur here: several pods (groups) of Indo-Pacific **bottlenose dolphin** (*Tursiops aduncus*) are resident all year round; and there are also pods of Indo-Pacific **humpback dolphin** (*Sousa chinensis*), which seem to have a more sporadic presence. The bottlenose dolphin is more sociable, and more readily observed, whereas the humpback dolphin is a shyer creature.

Various studies have so far revealed that there are about 150 bottlenose and 50 humpback dolphins inhabiting the area. A catalogue of all the individual dolphins has also been compiled based on the shape, nicks and marks of their dorsal fins and most of the animals have been given names. (Look closely when you see the dolphins and you'll notice that they all look different.)

Tourists first started coming to see dolphins at Kizimkazi in the early 1990s. The continued presence of these popular creatures has attracted growing numbers of visitors, so that tourism has now become an economic mainstay of the village. Contrary to the practices of other fishing communities in the Indian Ocean, the fishermen of Kizimkazi are very protective of the dolphins and no longer hunt them. In 1997 men from Kizimkazi helped arrest fishermen from Dar es Salaam who were using dynamite, which poses a deadly threat to dolphins.

For tourists who want to see the dolphins, boat excursions can be arranged with local fishermen through the guesthouses and restaurants in Kizimkazi. Traditional wooden fishing boats are most commonly used, although several fishermen have converted to modern fibreglass boats. Chartering a boat at Kizimkazi costs about US$30–35 for the whole boat. If you're in a small group, you can of course share these costs, although you'll probably find that for groups of five or six the price for a boat may go up to about US$40, or you'll be charged US$10–12 per person. You can also hire snorkels, masks and flippers (around US$2–5 per person), essential if you want to get in the water and observe the dolphins below the surface – which is highly recommended. As competition between the boatmen is stiff, some include free snorkel gear in the price of the boat, so it's always worth asking about this.

Generally, dolphin-viewing trips last for about two to three hours – usually enough time to locate the dolphins – although some captains trim the time down to about 90 minutes. Sometimes tourists get bored if they don't get quick and easy sightings, and decide to go back even sooner.

Most people who visit Kizimkazi come on a fully organised tour arranged in Zanzibar Town, or at hotels on the east coast. On these tours, costs vary between US$25 and US$100 per person, depending on the season, the quality of the vehicle, the standard of driver and guide, the number of passengers, and whether you want a private tour or are happy to share with others. The price normally includes transport to/from Kizimkazi, the boat, all snorkelling gear and lunch.

The most favourable time of year to see the dolphins is between October and February. From June to September, the southerly winds can make the seas

primarily a large restaurant aimed almost exclusively at tour groups of dolphin-viewers from town and the coast hotels, but also has three small bungalows with double rooms for US$35 en suite (or 'self-container' as it says in the brochure). Built in 2001, it's simple but

rough, while during the rainy season (March to May) conditions in the boat can be unpleasant. However, out at sea you're likely to get wet anyway. You should also protect yourself against the sun.

Dolphin tours are often promoted in a misleading light. It is important to realise that sightings cannot be guaranteed, and swimming with the dolphins is a rare occurrence. This is not a Florida-style dolphinarium. These animals are wild and their whereabouts cannot be predicted. It is they who choose to interact with people, not the other way around.

Observing dolphins in the wild, as with any other animals, requires time and patience. Shouting and excessive movement will not encourage them to approach your boat. Be satisfied with passive observation – do not force the boat-driver to chase the dolphins, cross their path, or approach too close, especially when they are resting. If you decide to swim, slip quietly into the water and avoid splashing. Never jump in. Stay close to the boat and let the dolphins come to you instead of you trying to catch up with them. You could try attempting to excite their curiosity by diving frequently and swimming below the surface, maintaining your arms alongside your body to imitate their own streamlined shape.

In reality, unless you charter your own boat and go out early in the morning so as not to be disturbed, you're unlikely to be able to put any of these theories into practice. On some days it's not unusual to see 20 or more boats, with at least ten people in each, all chasing the dolphins and desperate for a sighting. When the dolphins are seen, big groups of people jumping in does little to attract the animals any closer. One visitor told us: 'It's billed as "swimming with dolphins" but it's actually "jumping into the water a long way from the dolphins".' Another called it a 'shambolic turkey-hunt'. In fact, it's a wonder the dolphins haven't cleared off for somewhere more peaceful. (Which they may well do in the future, as soon as, for them, the costs – ie: disturbances from too many boats – outweigh the benefits of food and shelter). In recent years, the number of sightings has definitely gone down. They used to be almost guaranteed, but it's not unusual now for groups to return without having seen a single dolphin.

Over the years there have been a number of studies carried out at Kizimkazi, to check the interaction between dolphins and tourists. It's thought that the overall effect is detrimental, but there is still no management plan or strategy in place to restrict the number of boats going out or the actions of captains and tourists, and every day it's a free-for-all. It seems like the dolphins have made the first move, and simply decided to visit the area less frequently. This is a shame, because with proper management, this could be a totally sustainable way for the local villagers to earn money from tourists. It would be pretty good for the dolphins too.

This section is based on material provided by Angelique Todesco of the original Kizimkazi Dolphin Project, and Dr Per Berggren, Department of Zoology, Stockholm University, Sweden. In 2002 the section was updated by David Else (not a dolphin expert!), who accepts all responsibility for subsequent errors which might have been introduced.

perfectly adequate, and has nice sea views. Once the tour groups have gone, it's very quiet and peaceful. Kizidi also runs a fleet of six ten-seater wooden boats for dolphin trips. If you want to book a place here, the agent in Zanzibar Town is Sama Tours.

DOLPHIN-WATCHING GUIDELINES

Kizimkazi is one of very few places where wild dolphins can be admired in their natural habitat.

The following guidelines minimise the disturbance to dolphins while allowing tourists to make the most of the experience. By following these guidelines and encouraging your boat-driver to do likewise, it is possible that tourists may continue to enjoy dolphin-watching for the foreseeable future.

Guidelines for boats

1 Drive the boat slowly with a steady speed. Do not rev the engine and avoid going in and out of gear.
2 Approach the dolphin group from the side or from behind. Never head-on.
3 Do not chase the dolphins around. Let them come to the boat.
4 Always make sure the dolphins have an escape route.
5 Never be more than two boats on one group of dolphins.
6 Never approach a mother and calf.
7 Never stay longer than 30 minutes with the same group of dolphins.
8 Dolphins slapping their tails at the surface, making coughing sounds, leaping or turning away from the boat, indicate that they are disturbed. Leave them alone and look for other animals.

Guidelines for swimmers

1 Enter the water as quietly as possible. Do not jump or dive in.
2 Stay close to the boat and hold on to the rail or to lines alongside.
3 Do not swim after or chase the dolphins. Let them come to you.

Where to eat

In the main part of Kizimkazi, near where the boats are launched, is the **Jichane Restaurant**, serving mainly lunches for the tour groups from Zanzibar Town.

In Kizimkazi Dimbani, there are two places – both geared mainly around feeding large groups. **Kizidi Restaurant and Bungalows** is mentioned above, and serves mainly seafood from around US$4–5. **Cabs Restaurant** (tel: 0747 415554) has meals like chicken and chips or grilled seafood for around US$3–4. This place also has a fleet of six boats for dolphin viewing, which again caters mainly for the big groups, but it's reckoned by local operators to be one of the safest and best organised outfits based here.

What to see and do

The main reason people visit Kizimkazi is to see the dolphins, but if you're keen on history you might also want to stop off at the ancient **Shirazi mosque** in Kizimkazi Dimbani. The oldest part of the mosque is the niche which faces Mecca, and some of the inscriptions inside this date from AD1107, which makes it the oldest known Islamic building on the East African coast, although the rest of the mosque has been rebuilt on several occasions, most recently around 1800. From the outside, it does not appear very old at all, as a corrugated iron roof has been built to protect it.

Archaeological evidence suggests that when the mosque was built Kizimkazi was a large walled city. Tradition holds that it was founded and ruled by a king called Kizi, and that the architect of the mosque itself was called Kazi. Legend has it that when the city was once attacked by invaders, Kizi prayed for divine intervention and the enemies were driven away by a swarm of bees. Later the enemies returned, but this time Kizi evaded them by disappearing into a cave on the shore. The cave entrance closed behind him and the enemies were thwarted once again.

Today, very little of the old city remains, but it is possible to visit the mosque. Non-Muslims (men and women) can go inside, but it's normally locked, and you'll probably have to find the caretaker with the key (he lives nearby, but is usually found under the trees near the beach a few hundred metres further down the road). Show respect by taking off your shoes and covering bare arms and legs (this part of the island is very traditional so, out of politeness, your arms and legs should be covered anyway – see the *Clothing* section in *Chapter 3*). On leaving you'll be shown the collection box; a donation of around US$1 per person is fair enough.

The most interesting aspect of the mosque's old inscriptions are around the niche at the eastern end of the mosque (facing Mecca). These are Kufic, carved in a decorative style called 'floriate'. Similar inscriptions have been found in old buildings in Persia. The silver pillars on either side of the niche are decorated with pounded mullet shells from the island of Mafia. The two decorative clocks, which show Swahili time (six hours different to European time), were presented by local dignitaries. The more recent additions of electrical sockets and flex have not been installed with a comparable degree of style or decoration.

Outside the mosque are some old tombs, some decorated with pillars and one covered by a small thatched roof. The pieces of cloth tied to the edge of the tomb are prayer flags. The raised aqueduct which carried water from the well to the basin where hands and feet were washed is no longer used: running water is piped straight into a more recently built ablution area at the back of the mosque.

UNGUJA UKUU AND BI KHOLE RUINS

For keen fans of history and archaeology, there are two places of interest in the part of Zanzibar Island to the southeast of Zanzibar Town. They are both just off the main road between Zanzibar Town and Jozani Forest, Paje and Kizimkazi, so could easy be tied in with visits here if you've arranged your own private tour or you're in your own vehicle.

Unguja Ukuu

This is the site of the oldest settlement known on Zanzibar, dating from the end of the 8th century AD. It was believed to have been founded by early Shirazi immigrants from Persia, but recent archaeological evidence from here and other sites on the east coast of Africa suggests that it was Swahili in origin. Research at Unguja Ukuu is still taking place and more evidence may yet come to light.

Unguja is the local name for Zanzibar Island today, and *Ukuu* means 'great'. It is believed that the settlement may have been quite large, but it was abandoned in the 10th century, possibly because the population, who were probably Muslim, came under attack. An Arab geographer, writing in the 13th century, recorded that the people of 'Lenguja' had taken refuge from their enemies on the island of Tumbatu, off the northwest shore of Zanzibar Island (see the *Tumbutu Island* box on page 203).

Despite this site's fascinating history, today there is very little remaining that would be of any interest to anyone except the keen archaeologist: just some shallow earth pits and the remnants of a few crumbling walls.

To reach this site, you need to pass through the modern village of Unguja Ukuu, reached by turning south off the main road between Zanzibar Town and the southern part of the east coast, at a junction about halfway between the villages of Tunguu and Pete. South of the village, a small track branches off the dirt road that leads to Uzi Island (reached by tidal causeway). Follow this to reach the remains of old Unguja Ukuu.

Bi Khole Ruins

The Bi Khole Ruins are the remains of a large house dating from the 19th century, situated about 20km to the southeast of Zanzibar Town. Khole was a daughter of Sultan Said (*Bi* is a title meaning 'Lady') who came to Zanzibar in the 1840s, after Said moved his court and capital from Oman. With her sister Salme she helped their brother Barghash escape after his plans to seize the throne from Majid were discovered (as described in the box on page 24 of the *History* chapter).

Khole had this house built for her to use as a private residence away from the town; she is recorded as being a keen hunter and lover of beautiful things. The house had a Persian-style bath-house where she could relax after travelling or hunting, and was surrounded by a garden decorated with flowering trees and fountains. The house was used until the 1920s, and is now ruined, with only the main walls standing, and overgrown in some places.

The main front door has collapsed, but this is still the way into the ruin, over a pile of rubble. Directly in front of the door is a wide pillar, designed so that any visitor coming to the door would not be able to see into the inner courtyard, in case Khole or other ladies of the court were unveiled. In this room are alcoves and niches with Arabesque arches, although the windows are rectangular.

The Bi Khole Ruins lie a few kilometres to the west of the main road from Zanzibar Town to the southern part of the east coast, about 6km south of the village of Tunguu. The road passes down a splendid boulevard of gnarled old mango trees, supposed to have been planted for Khole (although they may date from before this period), and the track off to the ruins is about halfway down this.

ZANZIBAR'S WILDLIFE AREAS

You can see dolphins at Kizimkazi and turtles at Nungwi, and fish on reefs all over the place, but the best area to see Zanzibar's terrestrial wildlife is in the south-central part of the island, where there are three contrasting conservation projects. More details on the mammals and other inhabitants of these areas are given in the *Wildlife* section of *Chapter 3*.

Zanzibar Heritage Conservation Park

This rather grand-sounding place is actually a fairly low-key project run by some local people, to the north of the main road from Zanzibar Town to the east coast, west of the village of Tunguu. They have some game birds on display (which are not that interesting), and a vast garden (which is more interesting) full of spices, herbs, fruit trees and medicinal plants. Everything is labelled, and sometimes a guide is available to show you round and explain the uses of the different plants. There's a small entry charge and it might be worth visiting this place on the way to Jozani Forest.

Zala Park

The Zanzibar Land Animals Park (Zala Park for short) is in the village of Muungoni, just south of Kitogani, where the main road from Zanzibar Town divides into roads to Paje and to Makunduchi.

At first glance it's just a zoo, with various pens and compounds to hold the animals – mostly reptiles – but this private project run by the tireless and enthusiastic Mohammed Ayoub has a more important purpose. It's primarily an education centre for groups of schoolchildren to come and learn about their island's natural heritage. For tourists too this is one of the few places in Zanzibar where you can observe snakes and lizards at close quarters. The chameleons are particularly endearing. Also look out for the geometric tortoises which are not native but brought to the park by customs officials who confiscated them at the airport from an exotic pet smuggler. There are a few other species on display, most notably the small group of tree hyrax who spend some time in their pen and some time in the nearby forest. These part-time zoo animals come back mostly at feeding time, then seem quite content to rest or play in their pen before returning to the trees at nightfall.

Zala Park is only about 3km down the road from Jozani Forest Reserve (see below), and can be combined with a visit there. If you have a genuine interest in wildlife, conservation or education you could consider staying in the small one-roomed guesthouse – although this is sometimes used by visiting volunteers. Mohammed plans a nature trail in the nearby forest and mangrove stands, and can organise guided walks if you are interested in seeing more of this area. Ideally, this should be arranged in advance: Mohammed can usually be reached on tel: 0741 329357 or email: mohdayoub@hotmail.com. Entrance is US$3, and free for children.

Jozani Forest Reserve

Jozani is the largest area of mature indigenous forest remaining on Zanzibar Island, although today it is a tiny remnant of the forest that once covered much of the central part of the island. It stands on the isthmus of low-lying land which links the northern and southern parts of the island, to the south of Chwaka Bay. The water table is very high and the area is prone to flooding in the rainy season, giving rise to this unique 'swamp-forest' environment. The large moisture-loving trees, the stands of palm and fern, along with the high water table and humid air, give the forest a very 'tropical' feel.

Historically, local people have cut trees and harvested other forest products for many centuries, but commercial use started in the 1930s when the forest was bought by an Arab landowner and a sawmill was built here. In the late 1940s the forest came under the control of the colonial government and some replanting took place. Jozani has been protected since 1952 (see the *Vegetation* section in *Chapter 3*) and, as the forest in other parts of the island was cleared, much of the island's wildlife congregated here. The forest was declared a nature reserve in the 1960s, but despite this the trees and animals were inadequately protected. Local people cut wood for building and fuel, and some animals were hunted for food or because they could damage crops in nearby fields.

Nevertheless, Jozani Forest retained much of its original natural character, and now forms the core of the Jozani-Chwaka Conservation Area, a partnership between the Zanzibar government's Commission for Natural Resources and the charity CARE-International, with funding from various sources including the government of Austria, the Ford Foundation and the Global Environment Facility, to protect natural resources which in turn should improve conditions for local people and wildlife in the area.

Trees include moisture-loving palms (five species, of which three are true palms), figs (two species) and red mahogany (*mtondoo* in Swahili), plus some introduced species such as Sydney blue gum. Red mahogany was formerly regarded as an introduced exotic, but the weight of evidence is that it is native or anciently naturalised; this tree is found on other Indian Ocean islands and, like the mangrove, its seeds can float and survive in sea water. Although the size of the trees

RULES FOR RESPONSIBLE MONKEY WATCHING

Jozani Forest asks all visitors to observe the following rules. They apply to watching primates anywhere in Zanzibar, or elsewhere in Africa:

- You must be accompanied by an official guide.
- Do not approach monkeys closer than three metres, and preferably remain at a distance of five metres. This is for your own safety – the monkeys are wild animals and can bite or pass diseases to you.
- Do not invite any interaction with the monkeys or try to feed them. If they come close, avoid eye contact and move away. Do not make noises to attract their attention.
- You are one of the major threats to the monkeys, as primates are susceptible to human diseases. Do not visit the monkeys if you are suffering from any illness, particularly cold or flu.
- Observe the speed limits if driving through Jozani, and ask your driver to slow down if you're in a minibus. Even though speed-humps have been introduced, monkeys are regularly killed by cars.

in Jozani is impressive, few trees become truly huge as the soils are too shallow to allow deep roots to penetrate, and they get blown over by strong monsoon winds. With areas of mangrove and saltmarsh, the Jozani-Chwaka area contains several diverse habitat types, each with its associated, and equally varied, wildlife.

Several rare and endemic animal species occur in Jozani, making it a major attraction for **wildlife** fans. Even if you've only got a passing interest, a visit can be fascinating. The main reason most visitors come here to is to see some of the famous red colobus monkey (full name: Zanzibar red colobus or Kirk's red colobus) which are unique to Zanzibar and only found in and around Jozani Forest. Many wildlife fans rate the red colobus of Jozani as one of the best monkey viewing experiences in East Africa. Nowhere else can you get so close to a monkey in the wild that is not aggressive or likely to bite, as well as being attractive, endearing and very rare.

Brochures produced in the mid-1990s said there were 1,500 individual colobus monkeys in Zanzibar, but this was an estimate, and more accurate surveys in 1997 put the figure at around 2,300. The red colobus population of Jozani is growing, which is partly due to conservation efforts. However, recent research shows that this is most likely the result of monkeys from elsewhere fleeing ongoing destruction of the small patches of forest elsewhere on the island into the safety of the Jozani area, giving the impression of an increase. Researchers think that Zanzibar's overall red colobus population levels are probably stable, but emphasise that habitiat destruction is still a major threat.

Other residents of Jozani include a population of blue or Sykes monkey, which you are also quite likely to see. The forest is also home to Aders' duiker, a species of small antelope found only on Zanzibar and some parts of the Kenyan coast, and suni, another antelope which is even smaller than the duiker, but both of these are extremely shy and unlikely to be seen. The Ader's duiker is virtually extinct in Kenya now and is one of the two rarest antelopes in the world. Its only chance of survival is on Unguja. Its population is between 400 and 1000 and efforts have been underway over recent years to ensure its survival, including protecting Jozani, working with local communities to establish sanctuaries and the proposed translocation of some individuals to Chumbe Island Coral Park.

There are even reported to be leopards in Jozani. Again, they are a local sub-species, smaller than the mainland version, and also very unlikely to be sighted. (For more details on leopards, and the other wildlife in Jozani and Zanzibar, see the *Wildlife* section in *Chapter 3*.)

Jozani has a fairly good **bird** population, with over 40 species recorded, although many of the forest birds are shy, and therefore hard to spot. Species occurring here include Kenya crested guinea fowl, emerald spotted wood dove, little greenbul, sombre greenbul, wood hoopoe, cardinal woodpecker, red capped robin chat, east coast batis, dark-backed weaver, golden weaver, olive sunbird and crowned hornbill. An interesting speciality is the Zanzibar Fischer's turaco (slightly larger than its mainland namesake, with blue-purple on the wings instead of green). In the mangroves you'll see various kingfishers, sunbirds and coucals.

If you're especially keen on birds, it is well worth engaging the services of a bird guide. Jozani has two bird specialists on the staff: Ali Addurahim is an ecologist and chief bird guide; Ali Khamis Mohammed was trained by the other Ali, and also knows his stuff. They have a bird checklist and a copy of the big fat Zimmerman *Birds of Kenya and Northern Tanzania* book, which includes most species which occur on Zanzibar.

A network of **nature trails** has been established. The main one takes about an hour to follow at a leisurely pace, with numbered points of interest which relate to a well-written information sheet which you can buy for a nominal cost at the reception desk. There are also several shorter loops. Some other information leaflets and species lists are also available, and there are some very good display boards and other exhibits.

As you walk around the nature trails, you'll see lots of birds and probably a few colobus and Sykes monkeys, but these animals are shy, and will leap through the trees as soon as they hear your approach. On the south side of the main road live two groups of monkeys who are more used to humans, and with a guide you can come and watch these at close quarters. This is ideal animal viewing – the monkeys are aware of your presence but not disturbed. They are not tame at all, and don't come close, but just get on with their usual feeding, playing, grooming or resting. Because the colobus monkeys look so cute, some visitors have been tempted to try and stroke or give sweets to them. This is bad for the monkeys, but can be bad for tourists too – several people have been given a nasty nip or scratch. Read the rules in the box opposite, and look but don't touch.

South of the forest, a long thin creek juts in from the sea, and is lined with mangrove trees. A fascinating boardwalk has been constructed, the only one of its type in Africa, so you can easily and harmlessly go deep into the mangrove to experience this unique ecosystem. This is also a community project and revenue from visitors coming to the boardwalk helps fund local development projects.

The entrance to Jozani Forest Reserve is on the main road between Zanzibar Town and the southern part of the east coast, north of the village of Pete. You can visit at most times of the year, but in the rainy season the water table rises considerably and the forest paths can be under more than a metre of water. The reserve is clearly signposted, and entrance costs US$8.

Since 1998, the Forest Reserve administrators have shared revenue from tourists visiting the forest and the mangroves with village communities in the surrounding area. So far, funds have been contributed to projects such as building nursery schools, health facilities and mosques, and improving local electricity supply. Only if forests and wildlife are seen as resources in this way, which directly benefit local people, can their survival be assured. A large carved wooden chest in the information centre holds the Jozani Community Fund – please donate at least US$1.

Many tour companies include Jozani on their East Coast Tours or Dolphin Tours, but you can easily get here by bus, hired bike or car. Alternatively, take a tourist minibus heading for the east coast, and alight here. This road is well used by tourist minibuses and other traffic throughout the day, so after your visit to the forest you could flag something down and continue to the coast or return to Zanzibar Town.

If you are a keen naturalist, and prefer to watch wildlife undisturbed (or just like a bit of peace and quiet) you may find it better to visit the reserve either very early or in the middle of the day, as most groups come here between about 09.00 and 10.00 on their way to the coast, or between 15.00 and 16.00 on their way back. Between 12.00 and 14.00 the heat means the monkeys and birds are mostly quiet, so about 14.00 to 15.00 seems to be the perfect time.

Pemba Island

Pemba Island lies about 80km to the northeast of Zanzibar Island (Unguja), and about the same distance from the Tanzanian mainland, directly east of the port of Tanga. Pemba Island is smaller than Zanzibar Island, but it has a more undulating landscape, even though its highest point is only about 95m above sea level. Pemba is also more densely vegetated than Zanzibar (with both natural forest and plantation) and has always been seen as a more fertile place. The early Arab sailors called it *El Huthera*, meaning 'The Green'. Today, more cloves are grown here than on Zanzibar Island.

For today's visitor, attractions include vast empty beaches, fantastic diving and snorkelling, and a small number of historical sites, but Pemba is also a place where travel for its own sake (by car, bus, bike or foot) should be the main reason for visiting.

The largest town on Pemba is Chake Chake, the island's capital and administrative centre, about halfway down the western side of the island. Other towns are Wete, in the northern part of the island, and Mkoani, in the south – a smaller town although with a more important port. Few visitors come to Pemba, so compared to Unguja there is little in the way of tourist facilities. Of course, for many people, this is one of the island's main attractions. However, things are changing gradually, and although options are still limited, you now have more choices than ever before.

GETTING THERE AND AWAY
To/from Zanzibar Island
By air
The most reliable flights between Zanzibar (Unguja) and Pemba are run by **ZanAir** and **Coastal**, both with daily services. At the time of research, ZanAir flights depart Zanzibar around 08.00 and depart Pemba around 09.00, while Coastal's flights are in the early afternoon, although these schedules could be revised. On all flights, the one-way fare for non-residents is US$70.

Your other option for reaching Pemba is to fly with one of the local air-charter companies based in Zanzibar Town. If you can get a group together and charter a whole plane, it can sometimes be cheaper per person than buying a ticket on a regular flight. Details are given under *Air charter companies* in the *Zanzibar Town* chapter (see page 141). Alternatively, these companies often have spare seats on charter flights to Pemba and sell these to individuals for between US$50 and US$100. In the high season there are flights most days (or at least every other day) so it's worth contacting the charter companies, or getting a travel agency to do it for you, to see if there's anything going.

If you're in Pemba and want to fly to the mainland, contact Partnership Travel (the ZanAir agent) or Pemba Aviation & Airport Services (the Coastal agent) in Chake Chake for details on scheduled or charter flights. Alternatively you can

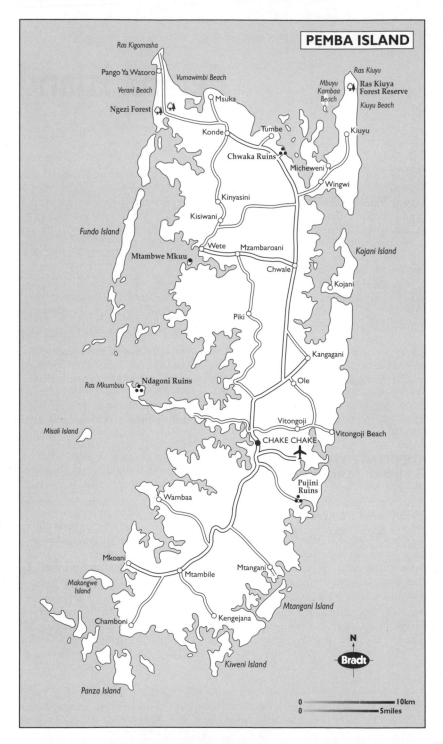

PEMBA ISLAND

Ras Kigomasha

Pango Ya Watoro
Verani Beach
Vumawimbi Beach

Ras Kiuyu
Mbuyu Kambaa Beach
Ras Kiuya Forest Reserve
Kiuyu Beach

Msuka

Ngezi Forest

Konde
Tumbe
Kiuyu

Chwaka Ruins
Micheweni

Wingwi

Kinyasini

Kisiwani

Fundo Island

Kojani Island

Wete
Mzambaroani

Mtambwe Mkuu
Chwale

Kojani

Piki

Kangagani

Ras Mkumbuu
Ndagoni Ruins
Ole

Misali Island

Vitongoji
CHAKE CHAKE
Vitongoji Beach

Pujini Ruins

Wambaa

Mkoani
Mtangani

Makongwe Island
Mtambile

Mtangani Island

Chamboni
Kengejana

N

Bradt

Kiweni Island

Panza Island

0 ————————— 10km
0 ————————— 5miles

phone the airport control tower (tel: 024 2452238) and enquire yourself. This is a fairly standard procedure – the charter companies often tell the tower if they're looking for passengers to fill spare seats.

Air Tanzania (ATC) suspended flights between Zanzibar Town and Chake Chake in 1997. In 2002 there were vague plans to recommence services, but nothing else. If flights do start again in the future, local travel agents in Zanzibar Town will have details.

Airport tax At Pemba airport, the tax for flights to Zanzibar Town is US$2.50 per person (payable in TSh).

By sea
Ships
Nearly all passenger ships, and some cargo ships, coming into Pemba arrive at the town of Mkoani (at the southern end of Pemba Island), while it's mostly cargo ships and dhows that go to/from Wete (at the northern end of Pemba Island). Very few ships or dhows, other than local fishing boats, go to/from Chake Chake. (In fact the old harbour of Chake Chake is silted up and only canoes can get here; the town's port is now at Wesha, about 10km west along the coast.)

Going to Pemba from Zanzibar Island, full details on buying tickets and on all the ships listed below are given under *Shipping companies* in the *Zanzibar Town* chapter on page 143.

Going from Pemba to Zanzibar Island you can buy tickets in Chake Chake, Mkoani or Wete – full details are given under *Travel and tour agencies* in the relevant town section.

Mapinduzi Between Zanzibar Island and Pemba, the old government-run Zanzibar Shipping Corporation ship *Mapinduzi* goes about once a week between Zanzibar Town and Mkoani. Currently it departs Zanzibar on Friday evening, arrives Pemba Saturday morning, then returns from Pemba to Zanzibar Town on Sunday. Services are cheap, around US$5 for a place on the deck, or US$9 for a bed in a cabin, but the timetable is flexible and constantly liable to change.

Aziza Another bargain option is the *Aziza 1*, which runs a leisurely service between Zanzibar and Pemba, twice a week. The fare between Pemba and Zanzibar is US$6.50. The timetable is hard to pin down but seems to be as follows: Monday, Wete to Zanzibar to Dar; Tuesday, Dar to Zanzibar to Mkoani; Wednesday, Mkoani to Zanzibar to Dar; Saturday, Dar to Zanzibar to Wete.

Serengeti Much more reliable than the old ZSC vessel is the passenger ship *Serengeti*, operated by Azam Marine Ltd. This runs between Zanzibar Town and Mkoani three times a week in each direction (currently Tuesday, Thursday and Saturday). The journey takes six to eight hours and costs US$25 plus US$5 port tax.

Sepideh Operated by Mega Speed Liners, the *Sepideh* runs between Dar es Salaam and Zanzibar once a day, with a service to Pemba three times a week in each direction (currently Monday, Wednesday and Friday). Between Zanzibar and Pemba is US$35, plus US$5 port tax, and the journey takes just under three hours.

For several years reports have circulated that the ships *Flying Horse* and *Sea Express*, which normally run between Zanzibar and Dar es Salaam, are due to extend their services to Pemba some time in the future. If this does ever happen, fares are likely to be around the same as the Dar to Zanzibar trip.

Dhows
Most of Pemba's dhow traffic goes to/from Tanga on the mainland, and only occasionally do dhows go between Zanzibar Town and Pemba. Of those that do,

most land at Mkoani. It is illegal for tourists to travel by dhow, and not especially safe, but some intrepid travellers have reported finding captains willing to take them on board. There are no set sailing days or times, and you have to barter hard over the 'fare', but Zanzibar to Mkoani should cost about US$5–10. More details on travel by dhow are given under *Getting to Zanzibar* in *Chapter 3*, and in the *Zanzibar Town* chapter.

To/from the mainland
By air
Daily services between Dar es Salaam and Pemba are run by **ZanAir** and **Coastal**, although all flights go via Zanzibar, and may involve a change of plane. At the time of research, ZanAir flights depart Zanzibar in the morning, while Coastal's flights are in the early afternoon, although these schedules could be revised. On all flights, the one-way fare for non-residents is US$85.

Coastal also has a daily flight between Tanga (on the Tanzania mainland) and Pemba for US$55, and also has plans to launch a direct service between Pemba and Mombasa in Kenya.

If you're coming from any other part of Tanzania or Kenya and want a direct flight, your only option is to charter a plane. In Dar, Nairobi or Mombasa, a travel agent will be able to help you. Spare seats on charter flights are sometimes sold to individuals – once again, the best thing to do is contact a travel agent – they will probably phone the airport or one of the local charter companies to see if anything is going your way.

By sea
Passenger ships
Although there have been direct services to Pemba from Tanga (in Tanzania) and Mombasa (in Kenya) in the past, at the time of research the only way to get from the mainland to Pemba by ship is on the *Sepideh* service, which goes via Zanzibar Island (Unguja). Services between Dar and Zanzibar are daily, but the *Sepideh* only goes on to Pemba three times a week. The fare between Dar and Pemba is US$55, plus US$5 port tax.

More details on ships from the mainland are also given under *Getting to Zanzibar* in *Chapter 3*.

Cargo ships
Some travellers have reported that a small cargo ship called the *Baracuda* (which is also called the *Maschukuru*) runs once a week between Tanga and Mkoani, then goes on to Zanzibar and Dar. The fare for passengers is US$30, the voyage takes eight hours, and on Pemba the place to get information is the tyre shop near the Old Mission Lodge in Chake Chake.

Dhows
You can reach Pemba by dhow from Tanga (for about US$5 to US$10, payable in Tanzanian shillings) or from Mombasa, in Kenya (for about US$10 to US$15, payable in Kenyan shillings), although this is often tricky as the police at the port are unwilling to let tourists board. Most dhows from Tanga or Mombasa go to Wete, but a few go to Mkoani. It's also worth remembering that services are irregular and far from idyllic. For more details see *Getting There* in *Chapter 3*.

Immigration formalities
Whichever type of boat you use to reach Pemba from the mainland (Kenya or Tanzania), you need to show your passport to the immigration officials at the port. This is a very relaxed and low-key affair. So low key in fact that sometimes the office is empty, and you have to go to the police station in town to present your credentials, or get redirected to wherever the immigration staff might be.

GETTING AROUND PEMBA ISLAND
Options for getting around on Pemba are limited compared to Zanzibar Island, although public transport allows independent travellers to see at least some parts of the island. To get further afield independently you'll have to hire a bike, motorbike, car or boat. It is also possible to arrange a car with driver, or an organised excursion, through a local tour company (see *Travel and tour companies* in the relevant town sections).

Car hire
There is no dedicated car hire company on Pemba, but most of the tour companies listed in the town sections will rent you a car with driver for about US$60 a day, depending on the distance you want to travel, including petrol. If you want to self drive, rates start at US$50 a day for a small saloon car, plus petrol. As well as the tour companies, North Lodge in Wete also rents cars – see the *Wete* section for details.

Alternatively, you can hire a car and driver privately. In Chake Chake, vehicles and drivers wait for business outside the ZTC Hotel. In Mkoani and Wete they can be found near the market. Rates vary according to the vehicle: pick-ups, saloon cars, minibuses, Land-Rovers and small Suzuki 'jeeps' are often available. Rates are also negotiable and should be discussed fully (and agreed) in advance. To give you an idea, a trip from Chake Chake to Wete or Mkoani costs about US$15 return. If you're planning a tour, from Chake to Wete, Ngezi Forest and Manta Reef Hotel, and back, costs about US$40 in a newish pick-up with 4WD. All rates include petrol. Whatever you hire, part payment in advance is usually required, and the first stop is always the petrol station.

When planning your route around Pemba, note that the main road from Chake Chake to Mkoani is tarred but has many potholes. From Chake Chake to Wete, the direct main road (the 'old' road) direct via Mzambaraoni is in fair condition (and goes through beautiful scenery), and it is also possible to take the newer road via Chwale, which rejoins the other road at Mzambaraoni. From Wete northwards, the road direct to Konde (for Ngezi Forest) is in a bad condition for cars (although OK on a bike in dry weather). The best route for cars is via Mzambaraoni, Chwale and Tumbe. It seems a long way round, but it's quicker, easier and more comfortable.

Motorbike and bicycle hire
There is no official establishment in Pemba for hiring bikes, although Partnership Travel in Chake Chake can set you up with something. The system seems to involve simply finding somebody who is not using their bike and doesn't mind making some extra shillings lending it out to tourists. Rates start at about US$2 a day for a bicycle, and US$20 for a motorbike.

Alternatively, you can normally arrange to hire a bike or motorbike through your hotel. Tell the reception clerk what you want to do, and they'll inevitably know someone who can help you out – prices will be the same as mentioned above. If you're staying at Swahili Divers in Chake Chake, single-gear mountain bikes are available – free for guests. North Lodge in *Wete* also rent bikes – see the Wete section for details.

Bus, minibus and *dala-dala*

Pemba used to be served by quaint old buses (actually converted trucks with wooden benches and canopies on the back), but these days they've been replaced by more modern minibuses or *dala-dalas* (converted pick-ups). Routes and numbers are listed below. On the main routes (No 3, No 6, No 34 and No 35) there are several services each day (at least once an hour after 06.00, or after 04.00 in Ramadan), but on the minor routes it might only be a few times – or just once – per day, and that'll be in the morning. The No 34 seems the most frequent service (several times an hour in the mornings) and is also very useful for getting between Chake Chake town centre and Venus Lodge (see *Where to stay*). Services to/from Mkoani are tied in closely with ship (especially *Sepideh*) arrival and departure times. In fact, it seems that Pemba Island's entire public transport system revolves around ship timetables. The fare on the longer routes (eg Chake Chake to Mkoani) is about US$0.50. For shorter trips it's half that.

Route No 3	Chake Chake to Mkoani
Route No 4	Chake Chake to Ukutini
Route No 5	Chake Chake to Wesha (Chake's port)
Route No 6	Chake Chake to Wete (on the old road, direct via Mzambaraoni)
Route No 10	Wete to Wingwi, near Micheweni, on the northeastern side of the island
Route No 16	Chake Chake to Vitongoji, a village about 5km east of Chake Chake
Route No 17	Chake Chake to Tundaua
Route No 24	Wete to Konde
Route No 33	Wete to Micheweni
Route No 34	Chake Chake to Wete (on the new road via Chwale, rejoining the old road at Mzambaraoni)
Route No 35	Chake Chake to Konde (on the new road via Chwale and Tumbe).

ACCOMMODATION

Pemba has a small number of places to stay compared to Unguja (Zanzibar Island), but there's a wide range, from small and cheap local guesthouses through to some mid-range places, and up to a couple of more upmarket hotels.

As on Zanzibar Island, all accommodation on Pemba must officially be paid for with hard currency: cash US dollars are preferred, and anything else (pounds, francs, marks) may not be accepted. If you only have TSh, these are usually accepted at the current rate of exchange. Breakfast is normally included in the room price unless stated otherwise. Other meals are payable in TSh.

And as on Zanzibar Island, during quiet times many of the lodges and guesthouses on Pemba lower their rates. Even if reductions aren't advertised, it's often worth asking about this. At the smaller cheaper places, rates are often negotiable at any time of year.

ELECTRICITY ON PEMBA

Power cuts are more frequent on Pemba than they are on Zanzibar Island, and last much longer.

Although the power is more reliable at night, when choosing a room remember that having an electric fan is not nearly as important as having some sort of natural breeze.

FOOD

All the hotels described in this chapter also serve food, although at the cheaper places it has to be ordered in advance – sometimes long in advance. Additionally, the three main towns have local restaurants where you can get simple meals, and Chake Chake has a couple of places with more elaborate options.

For lunches or picnics, you can buy fresh fruit at the markets and roadside stalls in Chake Chake, Mkoani or Wete. You can also buy fresh bread – look for men on bikes with baskets of fresh loaves on the back. Shops in all three main towns sell a reasonable range of food in tins and packets, imported from the mainland or elsewhere in the Indian Ocean, but in the smaller villages this kind of stuff is more difficult to find.

LOCAL SERVICES
Tourist information

The Pemba office of the Zanzibar Tourist Corporation (ZTC), the state travel service, is in Chake Chake (tel: 0747 4218364), and open 07.00 to 15.30 Monday to Friday. The manager and members of staff are helpful, and happy to give advice and information about the area, but services they can provide are limited.

Banks and change bureaux

There is a branch of the People's Bank of Zanzibar in each of the three main towns – although the one in Wete is open only on Wednesday morning. The banks will change money – US dollars are best – but only the bank in Chake Chake will deal happily with travellers' cheques, and even then it takes an hour. US dollar bills are quicker (30 minutes if you're lucky), and much more useful if you are arriving in Wete or Mkoani.

For any kind of money exchange though, you're slightly better off dealing with a change bureau. There is one in Chake Chake opposite the ZTC Hotel; it only takes US dollars cash, and often runs out of shillings anyway. Your best bet in Chake, and especially in Wete and Mkoani, is to ask at your hotel – staff will normally be able to direct you to any local traders who might help. Again, you'll need cash dollars for this.

The easiest thing of all, of course, is to change your money before you get here!

Communications

Yellow public phone booths have sprung up in Chake Chake; these take phonecards which cost US$15 and are available from the Tanzanian Telecommunications office, and some other outlets, and often from a local entrepreneur who loiters in the street nearby. From phone booths, calls to Zanzibar or the Tanzanian mainland are about US$1 a minute. International calls are US$3 a minute. The cheapest place for international or local phone calls is at the Zantel office near Partnership Travel. International calls here are US$2 per minute.

In Mkoani, there's an international phone bureau in the line of shops and travel agencies down by the port, charging US$2.50 a minute for international, and US$4 for ten minutes for local calls.

In Wete you can make international calls (US$4 per minute) from the impressively titled Global Telecommunications Centre opposite the Wete Hotel.

More general information on telephone services into and out of Zanzibar is given in *Chapter 4 – Practical Information*.

Chake Chake, Wete and Mkoani all have post offices, and to check your email the Adult Training Centre in Chake Chake has a computer and charges US$1 for initial connection, plus US$3 per additional ten minutes. Also in Chake, Old Mission Lodge has an email service for guests. There are no public email services in Mkoani or Wete.

Hospital

The island's main hospital is in Mkoani. This is a modern place, built with overseas aid, and staffed by Chinese and Tanzanian doctors. The staff are dedicated, but the hospital suffers from shortages of drugs and other essential supplies. There's also a smaller hospital in Chake Chake.

Cinema

Chake Chake's cinema offers a nightly diet a Hindi melodrama and cheap action movies, with Hollywood films once a week or so. There's more of the same at Wete's inappropriately named Novelty Cinema.

CHAKE CHAKE

Chake Chake is the largest town on Pemba, about halfway down the western side of the island. This is the island's capital and administrative centre, and the hub of the bus and *dala-dala* network. Although Chake Chake has been settled for as long as Zanzibar Town, it has never achieved the same degree of importance, and thus has little in the way of grand palaces or the winding narrow streets of the old Stone Town. (Historical remains are pretty much limited to the tumbledown tower of an Omani fort, near the hospital.)

When we came here in the early 1990s to research the first edition of this book, Chake Chake – and Pemba itself – was a real sleepy backwater. (Later, we met a volunteer who'd been here in the 1980s, who spent all the free time of his two-year stint writing letters, as there was nothing else to do, and waiting for friends who never arrived because transport links were so bad. His Swahili was pretty good though.) Today, Chake Chake is definitely on the up and gets more modern by the day. There are two video rental shops, and many of the tin-roofed houses have sprouted satellite dishes.

In other ways, it's still very quiet and traditional: there are still ox-carts on the high street (although there are even more scooters), and down the back streets are shops selling everything from fresh bread and tins of jam to car parts and plastic mops. In tiny booths tailors will knock you up a suit or skirt on an ancient treadle sewing machine. The whole place is much more peaceful than Zanzibar Town, with a very laid-back atmosphere, and tourists get no hassle at all, so it's great to just stroll around. The market is sometimes lively, and the old port, down the hill from the town centre, is also worth a walk. There are even a couple of tiny spice and souvenir shops, all set to cash in on the tourist rush – as soon as it happens!

Where to stay

Chake Chake Hotel, in the centre of town, is run by the Zanzibar Tourist Corporation (ZTC). This angular concrete construction has become very dilapidated over the years, with none-too-clean and rather threadbare rooms. Some rooms have electric fans, and all have bathrooms, but the water supply hardly works so buckets are provided. The hotel has a restaurant, where meals must be ordered long in advance, and a bar – where at least the beer is cold. Rooms cost US$10 per person. Reservations are not normally necessary but, if you are coming from Zanzibar Island, the ZTC office or any private tour company in Zanzibar Town can make advance bookings for you.
GT Hotel (tel: 0747 417542) was just being finished when we were researching here, and may be worth checking if you're looking for a budget option. It's on the edge of town as

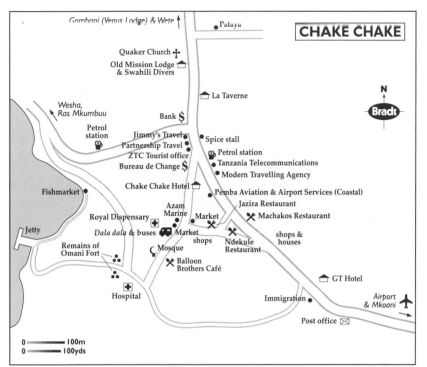

you come in from the airport, opposite the big grey Immigration office. It's unappealing on the outside, but inside the rooms are nicely furnished, with clean en-suite bathrooms. At US$12 per double, it's a fair deal.

Hotel le Taverne (tel 024 2452660) is on the main street, between the Chake Chake Hotel and the Old Mission Lodge, above a small row of shops. The clean rooms cost US$15 per person. (If you're asking for directions, forget French; it's pronounced Lee Tavern.)

Old Mission Lodge (tel: 024 2452786; email: swahilidivers@intafrica.com; web: www.swahilidivers.com) is a popular, friendly and laid back place on the northern side of the centre, just a few hundred metres from the Chake Chake Hotel. Although originally set up as the base for Swahili Divers to cater for people coming here to go scuba diving, plenty of travellers stay who have no intention of going under water (they are often persuaded to try though, by taking a beginner's introductory dive, and the boat and snorkelling trips which Swahili Divers organise are also very popular). There's also a dormitory where a bed costs US$10 (or US$7 in the older dorm). Upstairs is a breezy veranda with easy chairs, magazines, board games and a view of the harbour. Downstairs is a terrace cafe and restaurant (see *Where to eat* for details). Historical tours and forest walks can be arranged, and mountain bikes are available. You can make international calls and send or receive email. For more details on Swahili Divers' diving options see the *Diving* section in *Chapter 4* – Practical Information or contact them direct. Double rooms cost US$50, and triples US$60; some have en-suite bathrooms, other have shared facilities.

Venus Lodge (tel: 0744 312484, 0744 422231) is about 4km north of the town centre, on the main road out of Chake Chake towards Wete (reached easily on a No 34 *dala-dala* from the centre. It's simple but spotlessly clean, with very friendly management. Double rooms (some en suite) cost US$25 per person. Food is also available, with meals like chicken and chips for US$4. If you phone in advance, airport transfers can be arranged.

Pataya Lodge (tel: 024 2452827) is a new placer even further out of town, but great if you want a feel of leafy suburban living, Pemba-style. This simple local guesthouse has six rooms (only one is en suite), basic but clean, for US$20 per person. To get here, go out of town, past Venus Lodge, and then first right (it's the first major right turn you come to – look out for the big white wall with railings on the top). Pataya Lodge is signposted, and is on your left about 20m down from the junction.

Where to eat and drink

Chake Chake Hotel has a dreary restaurant, serving lunches and evening meals for around US$6. The food is generally reasonable (especially given that the kitchen staff have to contend with frequent power cuts and cook on charcoal stoves) but has to be ordered long in advance. The ZTC hotel also has a bar serving beer (usually cold) which doubles as the town 'pub' – one of the very few places in this predominantly Muslim community which sells alcohol.

Old Mission Lodge has a very nice café and restaurant on the terrace. A big breakfast is US$4, sandwiches US$2, a cooked lunch US$3 and a three-course evening meal US$6.50. The management are serious coffee fans (having spent many years in Istanbul) and their copious flasks of strong black brew never seem to run dry. A big cup is US$0.50, with a jug of fresh creamy milk to top it off if you prefer.

The other guesthouses listed in *Where to stay* above also have restaurants which are open to non-residents, although normally food has to be ordered several hours in advance.

Jazirah Restaurant, in the town centre, is a good local-style place, clean and tidy with plastic tables. There's usually only a few choices on the menu, such as chicken and chips or fish and rice (or vice versa) for about US$3. If you stroll in at lunchtime you should find something ready, but if you want to eat here in the evening it's best to arrange things in advance. On the same street, **Ndekule Restaurant** is similar.

Machakos Restaurant is more basic than the Jazirah, but the food is good, and there's reggae music on the beatbox. It's on the main street downhill from the back of the Chake Chake Hotel. You can get chicken and chips for US$3, or rice and sauce for US$1.25. Almost opposite is a small nameless **food stall** selling hot food in the evening: meat and chips US$1, egg and chips even less, and chips only for US$0.50.

There are a few other smaller places around the market and bus station area although food (if they have any) is usually only served in the morning and maybe up to lunchtime; the **Bismilahi** seems best, and is especially good for a no-frills lunch.

Near the Chake Chake Hotel are a couple of **shacks** serving simple meals such as chicken or fish with chips or rice for around US$2.50. Local-style meals such as beans and rice are also available for around US$1. In the same area around the road junction, more small **booths** open up in the evening, selling cold drinks, while on the pavement outside there are stalls where you can buy bread, grilled meat, fish or octopus. To wash it all down, a couple of local coffee sellers sell Zanzibar coffee in dainty little cups. You can eat and drink here for less than US$1.

Travel and tour companies

Details for the **Zanzibar Tourism Corporation**, the state travel service, are given under *Tourist information* above. This office can arrange tours of the island by car or minibus for around US$90 per vehicle, or trips to Ngezi Forest for US$65. Boat trips to Misali cost US$90. **Partnership Travel** (PO Box 192; tel: 452278, 0747 420345) is a fairly switched-on agency, especially when the owner (a friendly man named Tahir) is around. The office is on the main street in between the Chake Chake Hotel and the bank. This place is an agency for the Mega Speed Liners' ship *Sepideh*, and also sells tickets for the *Serengeti* ship. For getting around Pemba Island, Partnership Travel offer a range of tours by car, although there are no fixed itineraries – trips are based on what clients want to do. An all-day trip cost US$50 for one person, US$30 each for two, US$20 each for three and US$15 each for four (including lunch). If you don't have lunch, the tour costs US$50 for the vehicle, carrying one to four people. Partnership can also assist with boat hire. To visit the ruins at Ras Mkumbuu (details below) from Chake Chake, you can hire a small motorboat for about US$60 (including petrol and captain). Much more popular is a boat trip to Misali Island, which costs about the same.

Jimmy Travel & Tours (tel: 2454193) is a new company which has opened right next door to Partnership. The eponymous owner is friendly and enthusiastic, although his intriguingly named partner (Mr Cheaper Price) seems to work behind the scenes. This company offers car hire, or car with driver for trips to Ngezi Forest, to various ruins, and a choice of village visits or spice tours. Dhow trips to Misali are also available. Prices seem vague and eminently negotiable.

Modern Travelling Agency, on the other side of the main street behind the Chake Chake Hotel, is the main agent for the *Sepideh* ship to/from Zanzibar and Dar. Down the hill from the Chake Chake Hotel towards the market is the **Azam Marine** office, the main agent for *Serengeti* enquiries. For the *Azizah* ship, the agent is in a general trading shop opposite the Chake Chake Hotel.

Swahili Divers, naturally, offer a very wide range of diving and snorkelling trips – for more details see the Dive Companies section in *Chapter 4* – Practical Information. This company also runs boat trips to Misali for swimming, snorkelling and 'feed-your-face' picnics. The staff here can also set you up with tours around the island. They have good links with local historians and archaeologists who are happy to work as guides for a small fee, although quality varies, so make sure they find you someone reliable.

What to see

Around Chake Chake are some sites of archaeological interest – although it has to be said they're more likely to appeal to history buffs than casual observers. However, the sites give a glimpse into Pemba's past and also provide a great reason for a day out in the country. For example, the route to Pujini Ruins goes through scenic fields and farmland and a few small villages, while a visit to Ras Mkumbuu involves a beautiful boat ride down the bay, and a walk through a grove of massive palms.

Pujini Ruins

The Pujini Ruins lie about 10km to the southeast of Chake Chake, near the village of Pujini. These are the remains of a fortified palace built around the 15th century by Swahili people. Its local name is Mkame Ndume, meaning 'milker of men', derived from the name of a reputedly despotic king who ordered the palace walls to be built by local inhabitants who were then forced to carry large stones while shuffling on their buttocks.

Today, the ruins of the palace cover an area of about 1.5 hectares, and the remains of the defensive ramparts and surrounding ditches can still be seen, although much of the area is overgrown. The ditch was once connected to the sea by a 1km-long channel. Inside the walls, a team of archaeologists working here since the mid-1990s have found remnants of three large buildings, and an underground shrine with plaster bas reliefs on the walls, and several other features. It is also possible to see some wide stairways that presumably allowed access to the defensive ramparts, the remains of a walkway that joined the town to the shore, and the site of the well.

Another legend about Pujini tells of a ruler with two wives who lived in separate parts of the palace and never knew each other. A wall was built across the well so that they could not meet if they came to get water at the same time.

The ramparts are the most interesting feature of the Pujini Ruins, in that they can be seen and appreciated by any visitor, and also because there is nothing else like them at any other Swahili site on the whole coast of East Africa. They were built when the Swahili civilisation was at its zenith (for more details see the *History* chapter), and when the presence of Portuguese ships in the area posed a very real threat.

It seems, however, that the walls may not have been strong enough to withstand the invaders. Some Portuguese records dating from the 1520s mention the sacking of a fortified 'treasury' on the east coast of Pemba. Archaeological evidence suggests that although the palace may have fallen on hard times after this invasion, it remained occupied (or was possibly re-occupied) and only finally abandoned in the 19th century. Remains of other buildings, including a mosque, have been found in the area around the palace, suggesting that it did not stand alone, and that a town or larger settlement also existed here – possibly for many centuries.

You can walk from Chake Chake to Pujini and back in a day, but it is easier to travel by hired bike or car. To get there, leave Chake Chake on the road south, and turn left on to a dirt road just after the tar road turns off to the airport. Follow the dirt road to a fork near a small dispensary, where you go left. At the next junction, go right to reach a flat grassy area which is usually wet. The ruins are amongst the trees and bushes on the far side of the grassy area. (If you get lost, ask for directions to Mkame Ndume.)

Ras Mkumbuu Ruins

Ras Mkumbuu is a headland at the end of a long peninsula about 14km to the west of Chake Chake. The ruins are at the tip of the peninsula and also seem to be called Ndagoni (although Mkumbuu and Ndagoni may have been different places). This is the site of a Swahili settlement, thought to have been one of the largest towns on the coast (and in East Africa) during the 11th century.

Today, the remains of a large mosque can still be seen here, although this is becoming very overgrown, and also several pillar-tombs, graves with a tall 'chimney' at one end, used to mark the burial place of prominent Muslims. Pillar-tombs are found in other parts of East Africa and held to be one of the most distinctive forms of monument built by the Swahili people. The tombs here are in poor condition, although an inscription on one states that they were repaired in 1916.

A road from Chake Chake leads westwards along the peninsula towards Ras Mkumbuu, but it becomes impassable and turns into a track for the final 5km which is negotiable only by motorbike (it might be more comfortable to walk). The easiest and most enjoyable way to reach the ruins is by hired boat (see the *Boat hire* and *Travel and tour companies* sections), or on an organised tour – which may also visit Misali Island on the same day. Near the ruins is a small fishing village, and to reach the mosque and tombs you walk through maize fields and a plantation of tall palms with smooth white trunks.

MISALI ISLAND

This small island (also spelt Mesali) lies to the west of Chake Chake town, and is surrounded by a coral reef. Due to its remoteness, the notorious pirate Captain Kidd is reputed to have had a hideout here in the 17th century, and even to have buried treasure here. Today, local fishermen (and some from Unguja) use the island as a temporary base, and set up simple camps. Misali is also a popular destination for tourists, as it's quite easy to reach by boat from Chake Chake or Mkoani. There are some idyllic beaches and the island is a good place for a swim (it's one of the few places in Pemba where you can swim at high or low tide), and even better for snorkelling, with clear shallow water, and a good display of corals. It's also a favourite spot for divers.

Misali Island is covered in forest, with a mix of evergreen and deciduous species, and most notably many large baobabs. Birds to be spotted here include red-eyed dove, mangrove kingfisher, paradise flycatcher, Pemba white-eye and Pemba sunbird. Fischer's turaco has also been recorded. An increasing number of green turtles are successfully nesting on the beach on the western side of the island.

In recent years, the island and the surrounding reef have received some official recognition and protection, and together they are now called Misali Island Marine Conservation Area. The area is run by Misali Island Management Committee, a partnership of the Zanzibar Government's Department of Crops, Fruits & Forestry, the local fishermen's association and Misali Island Conservation Association (MICA), with support from CARE International. Fisherman are a majority on the Misali Island Management Committee, and the rangers are employed by MICA.

The Misali fishermen welcome visitors to the island and ask visitors to respect both local culture and the natural beauty of the island. Tourism is encouraged – entry for tourists is US$5. Of this, 60% of revenue goes towards managing the island and 40% is for community development. Conservation measures involve the input of local fishermen, who can continue working here in a managed environment. As just one example of how the scheme is working, local fishermen are prevented from camping on the beach itself (they camp among the trees), so as not to disturb turtles nesting. Additionally, the nests are monitored and protected, along with the rest of the island, by a dedicated team of conservation rangers – who are all former fishermen. The rangers are trained by the environmental education organisation Green Ocean, under the auspices of CARE-International.

Locally, Misali has 'holy island' status, as people believe the prophet Hadhara used it as his prayer mat. The strong Islamic environmental stewardship ethic is being used to support management and environmental education, and the island was a 'Sacred Gift' to the earth from the Islamic faith as part of an ecumenical Millennium celebration organised by WWF in Nepal in November 2000.

A series of beautiful walking trails have been established through the forest, and some inter-tidal and underwater trails set up along the beach, across the reef and to a nearby stand of mangrove forest. There is a small information centre on the island, which shows you where to go and what you will see when you get there.

Misali Island can be reached by hired boat from Chake Chake or Mkoani (see the *Boat hire* and *Travel and tour companies* sections). Swahili Divers also organise popular day trips here. Alternatively, several of the dive centres based in the northern part of Zanzibar Island, and the boat-based operators such as Cat-Diving, run trips here. More details can be found in the *Zanzibar Town* and *Zanzibar Island* chapters. The island is also visited by groups from passing cruise ships.

MKOANI

Mkoani is the smallest of Pemba's three main towns, but the passenger boat services linking it to Zanzibar Town and other places in the outside world make the port the busiest and most important on the island. Any time a boat is docking or leaving there's a buzz in the air, but for the rest of the time Mkoani is very quiet and sleepy.

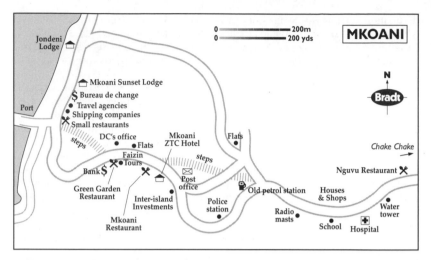

For most visitors, Mkoani is the main gateway to Pemba, and several new guesthouses have been built in recent years to cater for this. Around the town some more hotels have been built recently or are under construction.

Where to stay

The ZTC-run **Mkoani Hotel** is exactly the same as the ZTC hotel described in the Chake Chake section above, and equally uninspiring (right down to the water problems), with the same prices.

Mkoani Sunset Guesthouse (tel: 024 2456102), down near the port, has basic but clean rooms, US$10 per person, and US$30 for the en-suite double.

Jondeni Guesthouse (tel: 024 2456042, email: pembablue@hotmail.com) is by far the best place to stay in Mkoani, on a small hill to the north of town, about 15 minutes' walk from the port. The clean white-painted bungalow is set in lush gardens, and the friendly staff make staying here a pleasure. Single rooms are US$15, double US$20, and their are dorm beds for US$8. If you want en-suite facilities singles are US$20, doubles US$30. Drinks and meals (around US$5) are available, taken on the shady terrace overlooking the sea – a perfect place for whiling away a hot afternoon. If you're feeling more active, the hotel can also arrange snorkelling, sailing and fishing trips.

Where to eat

Apart from the hotels which serve food, places to eat include the **Mkoani Restaurant**, on the main street just down from the ZTC Hotel, with local-style meals for around US$1 or less. Next door, the nameless white **restaurant** also does meals, and opposite the Mkoani Hotel, next to the post office is a very nice little **coffee stall**. A bit further down the main street, **Green Garden Restaurant**, just below Faizin Tours, is a good choice, with meals (local style or chicken and chips) in the same price-band. You can eat inside or in the garden. The basic **Nguvu Restaurant** is on the main road on the edge of town, beyond the water tower, and also similarly priced. All the local places seem to close around 16.00.

Down by the port, the **Salsad Café** serves simple local-style meals for around US$1 and fruit drinks made with bottled water. Nearby, on the steps which lead up to the main part of town, is another local-style **eating-house**, also with meals around US$1. A couple of **stalls** sell fruit, sweets and biscuits for the passing boat-passenger trade.

Travel and tour companies

At the port are several travel agents, all selling tickets for the *Sepideh, Serengeti* and other boats serving Pemba. The only tour operator in town is **Faizin Tours and Travel Agency**, also trading as **Inter-Islands Investments** (PO Box 70, Mkoani; tel: 024 2456106), with an office on the main street just before it drops down to the port. Faizin/Inter-Islands was established to encourage small-scale environmentally sensitive tourism on Pemba, but in reality they are not at all set up for walk-in visitors. If you want to arrange a tour or anything else they need at least a day's notice, and possibly more. You might have more luck arranging things with them through Partnership Travel in Chake Chake or through a tour company in Zanzibar Town. Faizin/Inter-Islands organise tours around the island, to smaller fishing villages, and to Ngezi Forest, or to any other place you want to go. Prices start at US$50 per vehicle, but are not fixed. This company also run boat trips to Makongwe Island, Misali Island or the beach at Wambaa. Prices are around US$30-45 for the boat. They also claim to organise bull-fighting and traditional devil-dance shows. Traditionally, bull-fighting takes place on Pemba mostly between August and November after the harvest and before the short rains (for more details see the *Bullfighting on Pemba* box at the end of this chapter) but Faizin/Inter-Islands can arrange a show at any time, with food and transport if required. As the whole package costs US$600 this is likely to be of interest only to tour groups.

WAMBAA

Wambaa is the name of a small village to the north of Mkoani. Nearby is the long and idyllic Wambaa Beach, facing southwest overlooking Mkoani Bay and out towards the Pemba Channel.

This is the site of a luxurious and fairly exclusive hotel called **Fundu Lagoon** (tel: 024 2232926, 0741 326551; fax: 024 2232937; email: fundu@africaonline.co.za; web: www.fundulagoon.com). The team of owners come from the heady worlds of fashion, architecture and property development and – not surprisingly – their hotel exudes imagination, style and comfort. In a word – it's cool. Although only opened in early 2000, major spreads in glossy mags like *Harpers & Queen* mean this place is already in demand. It's certainly a place to be seen in trendy designer gear.

There are 20 rooms in large East African-style safari tents, covered with palm-thatch shades, with raised wooden floors, verandas, sea views and en-suite bathrooms, spread out along a rise behind the beach, each separated from the others by trees and bushes, and linked to the rest of the hotel by sandy walkways. The hotel has a top-class restaurant, and two bars (one in the main building with big wicker armchairs, white cushions and muslin drapes, and the other on a jetty which is perfect for watching the sunset).

When it comes to activities, you're spoilt for choice, with snorkelling, waterskiing, wakeboarding and canoeing on offer, as well as a fully equipped dive centre (more details in the *Diving* section of *Chapter 4*, see page 108). If you prefer to avoid effort, boat rides to Misali Island and sunset dhow cruises (with champagne, naturally) are also available. If shopping counts as activity, you can even stock up on the hotel's own range of Fundu Lagoon handmade aromatherapy toiletries in the gift shop.

Full board in the high season is US$300 per person. Low season is US$275, and there are no half-board rates. Rates include all meals, drinks (excluding champagne), Misali Island snorkelling trips, mangrove canoe trips, the dhow sunset cruise, laundry, and boat transfer to/from Mkoani. Road transfers between Mkoani and Chake Chake Airport are US$50 per vehicle each way (maximum five passengers). Rates do not include diving and other motorised watersports, but the hotel sometimes offers a combined room and dive package. You can make arrangements through a travel agent in Zanzibar Town or your home country, or direct to the hotel.

SHAMIANI ISLAND

Shamiani Island, also called Kiweni Island, is a remote and beautiful spot east of Mkoani, off the far southeastern tip of Pemba Island. A hotel has been planned, and even been under construction here for several years, but when we were researching in 2002 the situation was unclear.

To reach Kiweni you'll probably have to arrange private transport from Chake Chake to the village of Kengeja, reached by branching off the main Mkoani to Chake Chake road at Mtambeli. The vehicle will cost a minimum of US$10 return. South of Kengeja is a small beach, and from here you have to sail across to Shamiani Island. This will cost about US$7 to US$10. It is well worth establishing the current status of accommodation on Kiweni before coming here. Partnership Travel or the staff at Swahili Divers in Chake Chake should be able to keep you up to date.

WETE

Wete is the second largest town on Pemba, at the head of a large inlet on the west coast, in the northern part of the island. It's a nice town, quieter than Chake, with more ox carts and fewer mopeds. For most travellers Wete is a good base for exploring northern Pemba: from here Tumbe, Chwaka, Konde and Ngezi Forest can all be easily reached.

Wete has a large harbour, mainly used by cargo ships and dhows. It can sometime be busy here, with vessels from Tanga off-loading cement or timber,

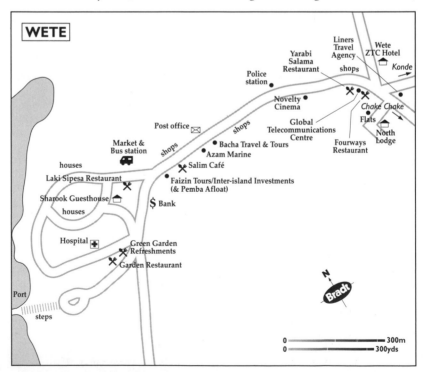

and loading up with cloves, coconuts or other Pemban commodities. Local ferries also sail across the inlet to Mtambwe Island, where you can get to the ruins of Mtambwe Mkuu, and to Fundo Island.

Where to stay

The ZTC-run **Wete Hotel** (contact as for Chake Chake Hotel, page 238) is exactly the same design as the ZTC hotel described in the *Chake Chake* and *Mkoani* sections above, but compared with the ZTC hotels in those towns the Wete version is by far the nicest. It's had a clean-up on the outside, and a total repaint on the inside (all in bright turquoise!). The big en-suite rooms are dilapidated but clean, with fans, nets and running water, and seem airier than those in the comparable Chake Chake and Mkoani hotels. The staff make a bit of an effort, and the hotel itself is in a nice setting, with the bar terrace overlooking a small garden and the busy main street. With singles at US$10, and doubles at US$15, it's not a bad deal.

North Lodge (office tel: 024 2454193, 0748 342956) is not far from the ZTC hotel, behind a block of flats on the other side of the road. This converted house has four rooms, which are basic but clean, with singles at US$10 and doubles (only one en suite) at US$25. Tours can be arranged and cars or bikes are available for rent. To make reservations, or before reaching the lodge if you're turning up on spec, call in at the 'office' opposite the Wete Hotel, next to the Zantel shop, and ask for Amar – the manager of the lodge.

Sharook Guesthouse (tel: 024 2454386) is in the lower part of town, on a quiet side-street near the market and bus station. It's a small family-run place, peaceful and friendly, with rooms at US$10 per person (US$25 for the en-suite double room). Dinner, with local dishes, is US$4, but must be ordered well in advance. This place has a generator which means constant running water and functioning TV. The friendly staff can arrange bike hire (US$4 per day), and also offer a range of tours around the island (see *Travel and tour companies* for more details). A new place called **Sharook II** is planned for the area down by the port.

Where to eat

All the hotels and guesthouses serve food, and Wete also has a choice of local eating houses. Near the ZTC Hotel is the **New Pop Inn**, open lunchtime and evenings, with local meals like soup, beans and rice around US$1. Nearby is another little restaurant made out of red corrugated iron, with simple meals and even cheaper prices. Farther down the hill, near the market, are some other small local eating-houses, including our favourite, **Laki Sipesa** (which means '100,000 has no value'), serving pilau rice for US$0.50, meat for the same price, plus bread, chapatis and tea. This place shuts at 16.00 after all the buses have left.

Garden Restaurant is a pleasant open-air café near the end of the main street where it drops down to the port. Omelette and chips or beans and rice are less than US$1, and other meals are also available. It's open all day, but not always at weekends. Next door is **Green Garden Refreshments**, a shop and take-away snack bar, also selling drinks, postcards and stamps.

Travel and tour companies

On the main street, **Raha Travel Agency** sells tickets for the *Sepideh* (although this ship goes to/from Mkoani). Opposite the post office is **Azam Marine**, which sells tickets for the *Serengeti*, and opposite Green Garden Refreshments, the **ZSC office** sells tickets for the ship *Mapinduzi* (although these ships also go to/from Mkoani only).

Bachaa Travel and Tours (tel: 0747 422639) opposite the post office, offers boat tickets, and can also make air ticket reservations. This company has an outrageously optimistic list of tours, but can set you up with visits to Ngezi Forest and Vumawimbi

Beach (US$60 for one person, US$30 per person for two to four) and also offers cultural tours which includes a village visit and a display of traditional dancing.

Inter-Islands Tours (tel: 024 2454352) is a branch of Faizin Tours and Inter-Islands Investments in Mkoani (see that section for details) with a small office on the main street near the market in Wete. The helpful manager can help you with tours, including dhow trips to Misali or Fundo islands, or car trips to Ngezi Forest and Vumawimbi Beach (US$60 per day for the car). Through this company you can also contact the **Pemba Afloat** live-aboard diving outfit (for more details see the *Diving* section of *Chapter 4 – Practical Information*).

Sharook Guesthouse (tel: 2454386) offers a good range of tours: a boat ride to Mtambwe Mkuu ruins costs US$5 per person; a minibus to Ngezi Forest costs US$35. Highly recommended all-day trips to Fundo Island cost US$30 for the whole motorboat (seating up to ten) or US$27 for a dhow; or you can go to Misali Island for US$70.

Car and bike rental
If you want to reach the places of interest around Wete independently, North Lodge (see *Where to stay*) can arrange small Suzuki 'jeeps' for US$50 per day, motorbikes for US$20 per day, and bikes for US$5 per day.

Shopping
Highly recommended by local foreign residents is the small craft shop called Asmini run by a local lady named Asha, selling clothes, bags and souvenirs all made by women of Pemba. It's in the area called Jadida, on the left side of the main street as you come in from Chake Chake, before you reach the turn-off to North Lodge.

What to see
Mtambwe Mkuu
The ruins of Mtambwe Mkuu are on the small island of Mtambwe, which is joined to the mainland at low tide, directly south of Wete. Silver coins have been found here, one of very few examples of pre-colonial minted silver currency anywhere in East Africa. Despite its rich past, there's little to see at Mtambwe Mkuu these days, although a trip there from Wete is a very pleasant way to pass the day. From Wete harbour you go by small dhow or canoe to Mtambwe village, then walk south, west and north around a creek and through mangrove swamps to reach the ruins. Apparently, when the water is high, you can get cut off at the ruins, or be forced to wade back to Mtambwe village through the mangroves, so careful checking of the tides is recommended. Sharook Guesthouse in Wete can arrange tours or give you advice.

Ras Kiuyu Forest Reserve
Located at the northern tip of the Kiuyu Peninsula (almost an island, joined to the main part of Pemba by a narrow strip of land), this forest is smaller than Ngezi (see page 250), with a less impressive range of vegetation and wildlife. We heard from two travellers who visited this area, and highly recommended it as a day trip from Wete, as much for the interesting journey through the fields and villages than the forest itself. The nearby Mbuyuni Beach, on the east side of the forest, was another attraction.

By public transport, you can catch an early *dala-dala* from Wete to the village of Micheweni, which has a school, a hospital, a few shops but no place to stay, about 5km from the main tar road that runs between Konde and Wete. (Micheweni is also sometimes called Wingwi, which seems to be the name of the surrounding area, as well as another village a few kilometres from Michaweni.) From Micheweni, it's a 5km walk to the village of Kiuyu and another 5km into the forest

WITCHCRAFT ON PEMBA

For the people of East Africa, the island of Pemba is particularly known as a centre for traditional medicine and witchcraft. The British writer Evelyn Waugh, in his classic travel book Remote People (1931), described Pemba as a centre of 'black art' learning, and went on to record how '...novices would come from as far as the great lakes [of Central Africa] to graduate there. Even from Haiti, it is said, witch-doctors will come to probe the deepest mysteries of voodoo. Nowadays everything is kept hidden from the Europeans, and even those who have spent most of their lives in the country have only now and then discovered hints of the wide, infinitely ramified cult which still flourishes below the surface.'

Sixty years later, little had changed. A 1995 travel story in a British newspaper reported that the village of Vitongoji, in the centre of the island, was 'the capital of Pemban sorcery...a place of dark secrets. Some years ago a witch-doctor was arrested for eating children in the course of his duties.' This report may have been tongue-in-cheek, but it's an inescapable fact that local people seeking cures for spiritual or physical afflictions still come to the local doctors of Pemba from Zanzibar Island, mainland Tanzania, Kenya, and even from as far as Uganda and Congo.

More details on traditional religion and witchcraft are given in the section on the *People and Culture of Zanzibar* on page 41, but as a visitor to Pemba from the West, you shouldn't expect to be taken to see any cures or ceremonies. This type of thing is strictly for the locals. Even the most innocent of questions about witchcraft from tourists here will be met with nothing more than embarrassed smiles or polite denials.

itself. About 3km beyond Kiuyu village a narrow track branches right (east) to Mbuyuni Beach. Nearby, another track branches left to another small beach on the west side of the peninsula called Mbuyu Kambaa.

Tumbe

Tumbe is a large village in the northern part of the island, just off the main tar road about 5km east of Konde. It is the largest fish market on Pemba and people come from all over the island to buy fish here. The mornings are especially busy. Tumbe can be reached by bus or bike from Wete.

Chwaka Ruins

Southeast of Tumbe, near the coast, are the ruins of the town of Chwaka, dating from the 16th century and associated with a local king called Harouni, son of Mkama Ndume, builder of Pujini (also now ruined and described above). The ruins themselves are sometimes referred to as Harouni. The most easily recognised buildings are two small mosques, and there are also remains of houses and tombs, but very little can be seen, and (to be honest) this site is only likely to excite real history buffs. It can be reached from the main road just north of where it crosses a swampy area on an embankment with metal crash-barriers on either side. There's a small signpost on the east side of the road. The 20-minute walk through the fields and palms is enjoyable, and the view over the bay across to Michiweni is splendid.

Nearby is another group of tombs and an 18th-century fort built by the Mazrui group of Omanis (also signposted), and on the other side of the road are some more remains called Old Tumbe.

NGEZI

The Ngezi Peninsula is the northernmost point on Pemba, jutting out from the north-western corner of the island. Much of the area is taken up by Ngezi Forest, the last remains of a huge tract of indigenous forest which used to cover much of Pemba.

On the east side of the peninsula is Vumawimbi Beach, one of the most beautiful on Pemba, with endless miles of dazzling white sand, flanked by pristine forest, with a couple of dhows waiting for the tide and a few fisherman wandering around. There are rumours of a planned hotel here, but for now it's totally untouched.

On the west side is Verani Beach, with a place called Pango ya Watoro ('the cave of the fugitives') at its northern end. At the far northern end of the Ngezi Peninsula, near Ras Kigomasha, is a lighthouse built by the British in the 1800s; officially, permission is required to visit.

Getting there and away

You can get from Wete as far as Konde by public transport, but from there you'll have to walk (5km) along the road to the Ngezi Forest entrance gate. If you make an early start this walk is a nice part of the day out. Alternatively, and especially if you want to reach Verani or Vumawimbi Beach, you'll need to hire a car from Wete or Chake. (Details are given in the Chake section.) Beyond Ngezi Forest entrance gate the road is rough, and to get to the beach it's very sandy, so high-clearance 4WD is recommended.

Where to stay

You can visit the forest and beaches around Ngezi for the day, and stay overnight in Wete, which has several accommodation options. Alternatively, there is one place to stay nearby:

Manta Reef Lodge (PO Box 82234, Mombasa, Kenya; tel: 0741 320025; fax: 00254 11 473462; email: onearth@africaonline.co.ke; web: www.africa-direct.com) overlooks the northern end of Verani Beach, in a truly stunning location. Linked to other Reef hotels in Kenya, this is a dedicated diving place, pleasant but not at all fancy, aimed at people who want to dive all day, so without a lot of the usual hotel trimmings and facilities. It's open August to March (the best time for diving), with most guests coming directly from Kenya (90 minutes away by speedboat), although this place doesn't seem to get as many guests as they'd like. There are 15 double cottages, all with a deck and one side open to the sea, and a spacious en-suite bathroom. There's also a central bar and restaurant overlooking the sea. If you want to dive off Pemba, it might be worth considering this place. Rates are US$130 per person half board, but if you arrange things on the spot while in Zanzibar this can be lower – sometimes almost half price if there are rooms free. You can get more information from their Kenya office. More details on their diving arrangements are given in the *Diving* section in *Chapter 4 – Practical Information*.

Ngezi Forest Reserve

Ngezi Forest Reserve is a protected area of forest on the Ngezi Peninsula, in the northwest corner of Pemba Island. The reserve is virtually all that remains of a vast area of indigenous forest that used to cover much of the island, and is a beautiful place to visit – especially if you've got an interest in wildlife. The reserve is easily visited from Wete (which has several places to stay), and even a day trip from Chake Chake is quite feasible.

Getting there

Ngezi is rarely visited by individual tourists, although you may see groups from the nearby Manta Reef Lodge or other hotels on Pemba. To get here by public

BULL-FIGHTING ON PEMBA

Somewhat surprisingly, the island of Pemba is a place where you might see bull-fighting in Iberian style. The origins of this sport are uncertain although it is thought to have been introduced here by the Portuguese during the 16th century. Bull-fights take place, during holiday times, mostly between August and November, after the harvest and before the short rains, but also between December and February after the short rains. Local 'matadors' put on a brave display, posing in front of the bull, goading him into a charge and then standing aside at the last moment, much to the appreciation of watching villagers. At the end of the fight, the bull is not killed but praised by the fighter, and sometimes decorated with flowers and leaves, then paraded around the village.

If you happen to be in Pemba when a bull-fight is planned, it's worth going to see, but although sometimes it can be a lively and fascinating spectacle, a few visitors have reported that in reality some bull-fights can be fairly uneventful, and seem to involve a group of local wide-boys annoying an apathetic cow by beating her with sticks, while the local girls shriek loudly.

Exactly when a bull-fight is about to take place is hard to find out. Ask at your hotel or a reliable tour company for more details.

transport, you can get a *dala-dala* as far as Konde, but then you have to walk the last 5km to the forest entrance. Alternatively you can hire a car in Wete or Chake Chake to take you to the forest (and maybe on to one of the nearby beaches). From Konde, follow the tar road (which becomes a dirt road) north and west for about 5km, through farmland, until you reach the entrance to the forest, marked by a small barrier and an office.

History and ecology

Historically, the forest was used by local people, as it provided timber, fuelwood, edible plants, medicinal plants, and material for baskets and ropes, but at the same time areas of forest were being cleared for small-scale agriculture, and since the early 19th century for large plantations – especially for cloves. The reserve was established in the 1950s, but even after this time a commercial sawmill extracted timber until the mid-1960s. Through the 1970s and 1980s Ngezi was virtually ignored by the government, while encroachment and over-use by local people endangered the forest and its wildlife. In 1995 funds were received from the Forest and Park Service of Finland, and a management plan was drawn up to strengthen conservation efforts and improve management, so the remaining forest could be preserved. In this way the local people could still utilise the forest, but at a sustainable rate, while local wildlife could also benefit. It is also hoped that the forest can be developed to attract tourists as a way of raising revenue – which would in turn ensure its future protection.

The reserve covers a relatively small area but contains an interesting range of vegetation, the most dominant type being tropical moist forest, found mainly in the central and eastern parts of the reserve (the part most easy reached by visitors) with some trees reaching over 40m in height – most notably the *Odyeana zimmmermanii*. Other vegetation types include swamp forest, coastal thicket, heathland, mangroves and palms. The mix is unique in East Africa, with several species more usually found in lowland mountain regions, as well as the species more often found in coastal areas, plus eastern Indian and Madagascan species, and even a Southeast Asian wild banana. There are also several introduced tree species.

The forest is home to several animal species, most notably the Pemba flying fox, a large fruit bat which is the only fully endemic mammal (ie: it is found nowhere else) on Pemba, and classified as a globally endangered species. Its name comes from its red fur and dog-like snout and ears. This animal prefers moist conditions and needs a ready supply of fruit and tree blossoms. Pemba flying foxes roost throughout Pemba, particularly along the west coast and on islands off the west coast, but are most readily seen at Ngezi Forest where the forest rangers monitor their whereabouts.

Other animals found in Ngezi include vervet monkey, Zanzibar tree hyrax, blue duiker and marsh mongoose. Bird species include hornbills, kingfishers, flycatchers, turacos and starlings. There are also four endemics: russet scops owl (also called Pemba scops owl), Pemba white-eye, Pemba green pigeon and Pemba violet-breasted sunbird. (For more details, see the *Flora* and *Wildlife* sections in *Chapter 3 – Background Information.*)

A band of wild European pigs, descended from domestic animals introduced by the Portuguese centuries ago also live in the forest. As most people on Pemba are Muslims and abstain from pork, these animals are not hunted.

Practicalities

The reserve office is open 07.30 to 15.30 every day. Entrance for tourists costs US$4. (If you're just transiting the forest on your way to Manta Reef you pay US$2.) You can drive through the forest but it's much better to walk. A short nature trail has been established, through sections of moist forest, and past several large ponds. It's 2km long and takes about one hour. You get much more from your visit if you take a forest ranger to act as guide; the fee is negotiable and should be agreed beforehand, but around US$5 for a small group is reasonable. The rangers can also guide you at night, or late evening, when you have a much better chance of seeing the flying fox and owl, but this needs to be arranged in advance, while the office is open.

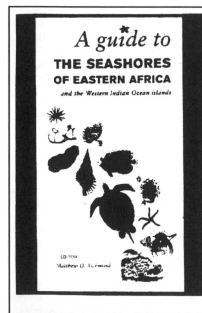

A Guide to the Seashores of Eastern Africa and the Western Indian Ocean Islands. Matthew D. Richmond (ed.) Published by Sida/SAREC (1997). This book contains 448 pages, including 154 pages of colour illustrations. Over 1,600 species of marine plants and animals illustrated, plus notes on geology, climate, ecology and human activities. This book is an essential tool for all visitors to the region. Proceeds from sales are used for marine education purposes in the region through the SEA Trust (www.seatrust.org).

Available from good bookshops in Zanzibar, & specialist bookshops worldwide.

Southern Tanzania Safaris

Philip Briggs

In recent years, there has been a great increase in the number of tourists from Zanzibar visiting the national parks and reserves of southern Tanzania – especially the Selous and Ruaha, and to a lesser extent Sadaani. For many decades these areas were overshadowed by their more famous northern counterparts (Lake Manyara, Ngorongoro Crater and the Serengeti), but today the secret is out, and southern Tanzania is a definite 'must' for all safari aficionados.

Zanzibar is a mere 200km away from the Selous, the largest of all Tanzania's (and indeed Africa's) game reserves, and easily reached by air. Ruaha is further – about 400km from Zanzibar – while Sadaani is just a 25km hop away, directly across the channel separating Unguja (Zanzibar Island) from the mainland.

For tour groups, a 'southern circuit' has developed, linking Dar es Salaam to Zanzibar and Selous or Ruaha, and with regular straightforward flights this option is open to independent visitors as well. Whether you go out and back from Zanzibar, or tie in Zanzibar and the parks of southern Tanzania with wider travels, this chapter will help you plan your trip, and the information should certainly help you enjoy it to the full.

SELOUS GAME RESERVE

Covering more than 45,000km², the Selous (pronounced 'Seloo') is Africa's single largest game reserve, three times larger than the Serengeti, more than twice the size of South Africa's Kruger National Park, and roughly 50% bigger than either Belgium or Swaziland. It is, furthermore, the core sanctuary within the greater Selous-Niassa ecosystem, which extends over 155,000km² of practically uninhabited wilderness in southern Tanzania and northern Mozambique – the largest chunk of comparably untrammelled bush left in Africa.

The claim that the Selous lies at the core of the greatest surviving African wilderness is supported by the prodigiously large mammal populations protected within the reserve and the greater ecosystem. The elephant herd of 65,000 represents more than half of the Tanzanian population, and 5–10% of the African total. The buffalo population, estimated at 120–150,000, and the reserve's 40,000 hippo and 4,000 lion are probably the largest on the continent. The Selous also harbours an estimated 100,000 wildebeest, 35,000 zebra, 25,000 impala and significant herds of greater kudu, hartebeest and eland. It is also one of the most important sanctuaries in Africa for the endangered black rhinoceros, African wild dog, and sable and puku antelope.

Background information

That the Selous ranks as one of East Africa's most alluring and satisfying safari destinations is not in dispute. However, given that much of the publicity surrounding the Selous bangs on and on about its vast area, prospective visitors should be aware that the extent of the reserve is in practice something of a red

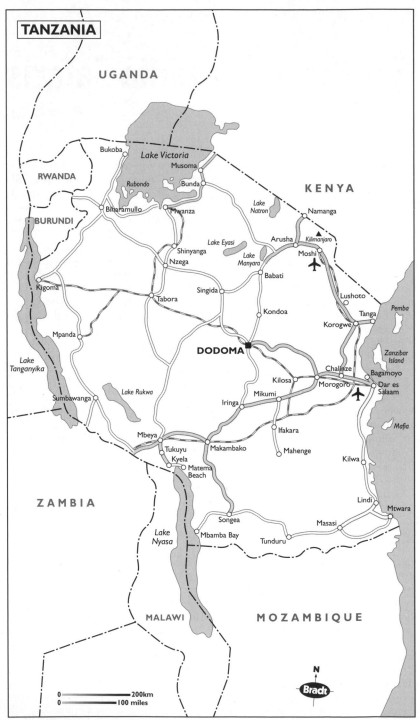

TANZANIA

UGANDA

Bukoba

Lake Victoria

Musoma

RWANDA

Rubondo

Bunda

KENYA

BURUNDI

Biharamullo

Mwanza

Lake Natron

Namanga

Lake Eyasi

Arusha

▲ *Kilimanjaro*

Shinyanga

Lake Manyara

Moshi

Kigoma

Nzega

Babati

Lushoto

Pemba

Tabora

Singida

Kondoa

Tanga

Korogwe

Mpanda

Zanzibar Island

Lake Tanganyika

DODOMA ■

Chalinze

Bagamoyo

Kilosa

Morogoro

Dar es Salaam

Lake Rukwa

Mikumi

Sumbawanga

Iringa

Ifakara

Mafia

Mbeya

Tukuyu

Makambako

Mahenge

Kyela

Matema Beach

Kilwa

ZAMBIA

Lindi

Mtwara

Songea

Masasi

Lake Nyasa

Mbamba Bay

Tunduru

MALAWI

MOZAMBIQUE

N

Bradt

0 ——— 200km
0 ——— 100 miles

herring. The Selous is divided into two disproportionate parts by the Rufiji, Tanzania's largest river, which together with the Great Ruaha, a major tributary, runs through the reserve from west to east. The roughly 90% of the Selous that lies to the south of the river has been divided into a number of privately leased hunting concessions, all of which are off-limits to casual tourism. A proportion of the northern sector has also been set aside for hunting concessions, with the remainder – no more than 5% of the reserve's total area – forming what to all intents and purposes is the Selous Tourist Reserve. The five main lodges (and most tourist activities) are actually concentrated within an area of 1,000km² immediately north of the Rufiji.

Fortunately, the public part of the Selous is wonderfully atmospheric, a dense tract of wild miombo woodland abutting the meandering Rufiji River, and an associated labyrinth of five pretty lakes connected to each other and the river by numerous narrow streams. Arriving by light aircraft, as most visitors do, it is exhilarating to sweep above the palm-fringed channels teeming with hippos and waterfowl, the swampy islets where immense herds of elephant and giraffe graze alongside each other, and exposed sandbanks where antelope drink and all manner of shorebirds scurry about. No less exciting are the boat excursions along the Rufiji, which generally culminate with a brilliant red sun setting behind the tall borassus palms and baobabs that line the wide sandy watercourse. Gulp-inducing dentist-eye views of the Selous's trademark gigantic crocs can pretty much be guaranteed from the boat, as can conferences of grunting, harrumphing hippos – and you'd be unlucky not to be entertained by herds of elephant, buffalo or giraffe shuffling down to drink.

The most memorable aspect of the boat trips, however, is the profuse birdlife. Characteristic waterbirds along this stretch of the Rufiji include yellow-billed stork, white-crowned and spur-winged plovers, various small waders, pied and malachite kingfishers, and African skimmer. Pairs of fish eagle and palmnut vulture perch high on the borassus palms, seasonal breeding colonies of carmine and white-throated bee-eater swirl around the mud cliffs that hem in some stretches of the river, and pairs of trumpeter hornbill and purple-crested turaco flap between the riparian trees. Worth looking out for among a catalogue of egrets and herons is the Malagasy squacco heron, a regular winter visitor, while the elusive Pel's fishing owl often emerges at dusk to hawk above the water.

Game drives along the network of rough roads to the north of the Rufiji are reliably rewarding, especially towards the end of the dry season, when large mammals concentrate around the five lakes. More frequently seen ungulates include impala, common waterbuck, bushbuck, white-bearded wildebeest, eland, greater kudu, buffalo and common zebra. The northern sector of the park has been dubbed Giraffic Park, with some justification, as herds exceeding 50 individuals come down to drink in the heat of the afternoon. Oddly, the giraffes are entirely absent south of the Rufiji, which also forms a natural barrier between the ranges of the distinctive white-bearded and Niassa races of wildebeest. The endangered African wild dog is commonly observed, as is the spotted hyena, while leopards are common but elusive, but cheetah have not been recorded in this part of the reserve for about 20 years.

Much in evidence are Selous's lions, with two or three different prides' territories converging on each of the five large lakes. The lions typically have darker coats and less hirsute manes than their counterparts elsewhere in East Africa. During the dry season, the lions of Selous evidently rely on an unusual opportunistic diurnal hunting strategy, rarely straying far from the lakes, where they rest up in the shade to wait for whatever ungulate happens to venture within pouncing distance on its way to drink. On our most recent visit to Selous, we witnessed or came across the aftermath of half a dozen diurnal hunts, but – despite seeing lions in most morning drives – we saw no evidence of a single nocturnal lion kill. Based on our experience, the Selous probably offers a better chance of seeing a lion kill than almost any reserve in Africa.

While the marketing line of 'only five small camps in a 50,000km² wilderness' does rather overstate the exclusivity of the Selous experience, it is true that a mere 5,000 foreigners annually – about 1% of tourist arrivals to Tanzania – ever make it to this excellent reserve. Particularly if you are based at one of the western lodges – Beho Beho, Sand Rivers and Sable Mountain – it is still possible to undertake a game drive in the Selous without coming across another vehicle. Whereas the national parks of northern Tanzania are dominated by large impersonal hotels that evidently aim to shut out the bush the moment you enter them, the Selous boasts a select handful of low-key, eco-friendly, thatch and canvas lodges whose combined bed capacity amounts to little more than 100 clients. Furthermore, because the Selous is a game reserve and not subject to the regulations that govern Tanzania's national parks, visitors are offered a more primal and integrated bush experience than the usual repetitive regime of one game drive after another. In addition to boat trips, all lodges offer guided game walks, which come with a real likelihood of encountering elephant or buffalo – even lion – on foot. Better still are the overnight fly-camping excursions offered by most camps, which entail sleeping beneath a glorified mosquito net on the shore of a lake teeming with hippos and crocs – thrilling stuff!

Roads within the Selous become impassable after heavy rain. As a consequence the camps close towards the end of the wet season, in April, and re-open in July.

Entrance fees
An entrance fee of US$25 per person per day is charged, and payable in hard currency. On most organised tours this will be included in your overall price, but it's worth checking this when booking.

Further information
Two useful booklets are *Selous Game Reserve: A Guide to the Northern Section* and the glossier *Selous: Africa's Largest & Wildest Game Reserve*. Most lodges stock both and they are similar textually. For details on the man behind the park's name, read *The Life of Frederick Courtney Selous* by J G Millais, published by the Gallery Publications and available in Zanzibar.

Getting there and away
Several tour companies in Zanzibar offer a variety of packages to the Selous, which usually include flights to/from the reserve and all accommodation, and typically running from two to seven nights in duration. Some packages are combined with Ruaha National Park (see the next section).

Many tour agents offering fly-in packages use the scheduled daily flights from Zanzibar to Dar es Salaam operated by Coastal Travel, which connect with flights to Selous and Ruaha, and can stop at any of the camp airstrips by prior arrangement. Another main operator of flights is ZanAir, and their associated tour company ZanTours offers a range of Selous visits. For example, a two-day, one-night tour costs US$450–500 per person, all-inclusive of transfers, flights, top-class accommodation, meals, park fees, game-viewing by car or boat and the services of a guide. Three days and two nights costs US$500–600, depending on season.

If you are travelling in mainland Tanzania it's perfectly possible to reach the Selous by air from Dar es Salaam, without going to Zanzibar, and it's also possible

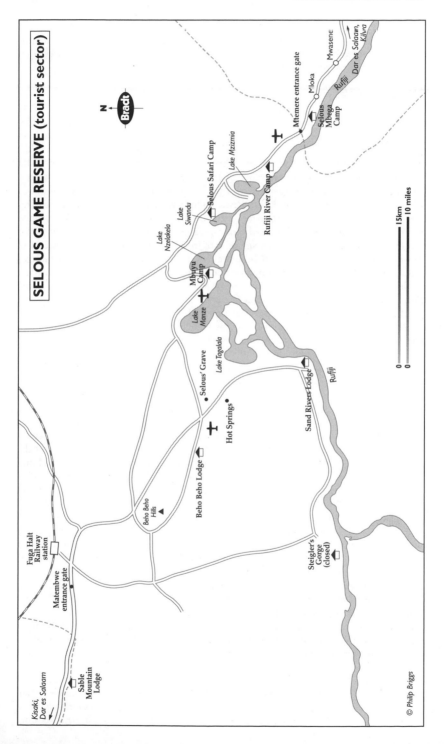

SELOUS GAME RESERVE (tourist sector)

N

Bradt

Kisaki,
Dar es Salaam

Sable
Mountain
Lodge

Fuga Halt
Railway
station

Matembwe
entrance gate

Beho Beho
Hills

Beho Beho Lodge

Hot Springs

Selous' Grave

Steigler's
Gorge
(closed)

Lake Tagalala

Rufiji

Sand Rivers Lodge

Lake
Manze

Mbuyu
Camp

Lake
Nzelakela

Lake
Siwandu

Selous Safari Camp

Rufiji River Camp

Lake Mzizmia

Mtemere entrance gate

Selous
Mbega
Camp

Rufiji

Mloka

Mwasene

Dar es Salaam,
Kilwa

0 ———— 15km
0 ———— 10 miles

© Philip Briggs

to get there by road (although that won't necessarily save any money). These methods are beyond the remit of this *Zanzibar* book. For more detail on the Selous, and getting there by other means, *Tanzania, The Bradt Travel Guide* by Philip Briggs is of course highly recommended.

Where to stay

Sand Rivers Selous Tel: 022 286 5156; fax: 022 286 5731; email: sand-rivers@twiga.com; web: www.sandrivers.com. Set above a wide, sandy bend in the Rufiji River, this is probably the most luxurious lodge in the Selous, and the most isolated, situated in the wild southwest of the public part of the reserve, an area that is infrequently visited by vehicles from the other lodges. The lodge consists of 16 airy and elegant stone and *makuti* units, each with a large double bed, en-suite shower and toilet, and private balcony overlooking the river. There is a swimming pool. The emphasis at Sand Rivers is very much on walking safaris, and the standard of guiding is exceptionally high. Game drives are also offered, with nearby Lake Tagalala being one obvious goal, and it is the only lodge that offers boat trips through the stunning Stiegler's Gorge, the most reliable place in the reserve for sightings of leopard and black-and-white colobus monkey. Plenty of animals come down to the river to drink, and black rhino are resident in the surrounding dense bush, though seldom seen by tourists. Full board rates inclusive of all activities are US$730 double.

Beho Beho Camp Tel: 022 260 0352/3/4; fax: 022 260 0347; email: oysterbay-hotel@twiga.com. This recently renovated and refurbished lodge, which formally re-opened in October 2002, consists of 12 large and attractively decorated en-suite stone cottages set on the footslopes of the Beho Beho Hills in the west of the public part of the reserve. A particularly attractive feature of this lodge is the tall *makuti*-roofed lounge and dining area, which offers a fabulous view over the plains to Lake Tagalala. Although Beho Beho is the only lodge within Selous set away from the river, a permanent pool below supports a resident pod of hippos and attracts a surprising amount of game and birdlife. As with Sand Rivers, the relatively remote location means that far fewer tourist vehicles are found in the vicinity, and excellent game viewing can be had at nearby Lakes Tagalala and Manze. Game walks are offered, as are boat trips on Lake Tagalala, which reputedly – and credibly – has one of the highest crocodile populations in Africa. Nearby sites of interest include Selous's Grave and a group of hot springs set in a patch of riparian woodland. Full-board rates inclusive of all activities are US$250 per person.

Selous Safari Camp Tel: 022 213 4802; fax: 022 211 2794; email: info@selous.com; web: www.selous.com. Almost entirely rebuilt after the El Niño floods a few years back, this plush camp on the shores of Lake Siwando consists of 12 spacious double standing tents, set far apart from each other, and with fans, attached open-air showers, and a good view. The common lounge and dining area is a fabulous stilted treehouse lit at night by dozens of gas lamps. Game drives, boat trips, guided walks and fly-camping are all offered. Full-board rates inclusive of all activities are US$470/640 single/double.

Rufiji River Camp Tel: 022 22 277 5164; fax: 022 277 5165; email: info@hippotours.com; web: www.hippotours.com. The first lodge to be established in the Selous, the ever popular and reasonably priced Rufiji River Camp is situated at the eastern extremity of the tourist sector overlooking an atmospheric stretch of the Rufiji River alive with hippos and crocs and regularly visited by elephants. The camp consists of 20 standing tents with en-suite facilities and fans, spaced along the river in a lush stretch of woodland populated by monkeys and numerous birds – and occasionally visited by more exciting large mammals. The lodge has a refreshingly informal and unpretentious atmosphere and delicious home-cooked food reflecting the nationality of the laidback Italian owner-manager. Rufiji River Camp offers an excellent range of boat and foot activities, as well as half-day game drives encompassing the three nearby lakes, full-day excursions further afield and overnight fly camping. Full-board accommodation exclusive of activities but inclusive of park fees costs US$175 per person, with any activities charged at US$30 per person, while full-board accommodation inclusive of activities and park fees costs US$235 per person.

Mbuyu Tented Camp Tel: 0742 781971; fax: 022 211 1139; email: stgs@twiga.com; web: tanzania-safari.com. This attractively located camp lies on the shore of Lake Nzerakera, and its lounge and dining area are built around a large baobab tree. Accommodation is in 20 self-contained tents with en-suite toilet and shower, and attractive ethnic décor, but no fan. The tents are arranged in two rows, one set in front of the lake, the other directly behind it, which makes it feel a bit more cramped than the other Selous lodges. An attractive feature is the stilted hide at the far end of the camp, overlooking the lake, visited by numerous animals. The usual range of activities – game drives, guided walks, boat trips, fly camping – is offered. Accommodation costs US$205/290 full board exclusive of activities or US$250/500 full board inclusive of activities.

Sable Mountain Lodge Tel: 022 270 1497; mobile: 0741 323318; email: safariscene@intafrica.com. This relatively new lodge is situated 1km outside of the western park boundary near the Matembwe Gate, in a patch of small hills offering views into the surrounding dense *brachystegia* forest. It consists of eight double cottages with en-suite hot shower and toilet and 24-hour electricity set spaciously across the hillside. A treehouse on one of the slopes offers a grandstand view over a waterhole regularly visited by buffalo and elephant. The surrounding woodland is very thick, and guided walks offer the opportunity to see forest-associated species such as blue monkey, black-and-white colobus and the amazing chequered elephant shrew, as well as a host of forest birds including the exquisite Livingstone's turaco, a variety of hornbills and the vociferous forest weaver. Between December and May, sable antelope move into the area. Game drives concentrate on the plains north of the main cluster of lodges, which can be very worthwhile seasonally, with very few other vehicles around. Fly-camping is also available, as are river trips during the wet season on the lushly forested Mbega River. The base rate of US$95 per person makes this the most affordable established lodge in the Selous, especially if you arrange to go there by train rather than to fly.

Selous Mbega Camp Tel: 022 265 0250; fax: 022 265 0251; email: zapoco@afsat.com. This small and spanking new German-owned camp lies on the banks of the Rufiji immediately east of the park boundary close to the Mtemere Gate. Accommodation is in self-contained tents set in the riparian woodland fringing the river, and a treehouse offers views over a small waterhole. Game drives, guided walks, and boat trips can be arranged. Standard non-resident rates are US$95 per person sharing but, by prior, arrangement substantial discounts are offered to backpackers who are prepared to bus from Dar es Salaam to the village of Mloka, about 4km from the camp (a free transfer is provided).

RUAHA NATIONAL PARK

Tanzania's second largest national park extends over 10,300km² of wooded hills and open plains to the west of Iringa, and it lies at the core of a greater ecosystem that is five times larger, embracing six other protected areas including the contiguous Rungwa and Kizigo game reserves. Ruaha is widely regarded by Tanzania's safari cognoscenti to be the country's best-kept game-viewing secret, and it has unquestionably retained a compelling wilderness character that is increasingly savoury when compared to the package safaris and 100-room game lodges common in the parks of northern Tanzania.

Background information

The dominant geographical feature of the park is the Great Ruaha River, which follows the southeast boundary for 160km, and is known to the local Hehe people as the Lyambangori (Ruaha being a corruption of the Hehe word *luhava*, which

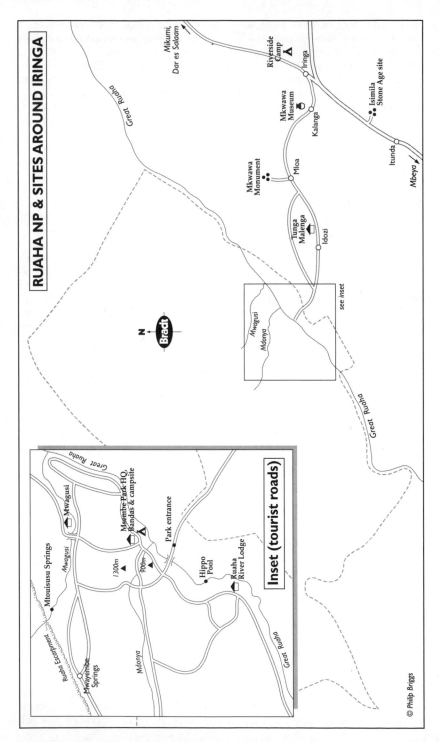

RUAHA NP & SITES AROUND IRINGA

Mikumi, Dar es Salaam

Riverside Camp

Iringa

Isimila Stone Age site

Mkwawa Museum

Kalanga

Itunda

Mbeya

Great Ruaha

Mkwawa Monument

Mloa

Tunga Malenga

Idozi

see inset

Mwagusi

Mdonya

Great Ruaha

N

Bradt

Great Ruaha

Inset (tourist roads)

Great Ruaha

Mwagusi

Msembe Park HQ, Bandas & campsite

Park entrance

Mtouisusu Springs

Mwagusi

Mwagusi

1300m

900m

Hippo Pool

Ruaha River Lodge

Ruaha Escarpment

Mwayembe Springs

Mdonya

Great Ruaha

© Philip Briggs

simply means 'river'). Only the small part of the park around the river is developed for tourism, but with just two small lodges currently operating – though more are likely to open over the next couple of years – even this limited 400km road circuit sees relatively few visitors, and has a reassuringly untrammelled mood.

Ruaha has a hot and rather dry climate, with an average annual rainfall of around 500mm falling almost exclusively between October and May, and peaking in February and March. Daytime temperatures in excess of 40°C are regularly recorded, particularly over October and November before the rains break, but a very low humidity level makes this less noticeable than might be expected, and it cools down reliably at night. The best game viewing is generally from May to November, but the bush is greener and prettier from January to June, and birding peaks during the European winter months of December to April. The vegetation of Ruaha is transitional to southern miombo and eastern savannah biomes, and a wide variety of habitats are protected within the park, including riparian forest along the watercourses, swamps, grassland, and acacia woodland. The dominant vegetation type is *brachystegia* woodland and several areas of the park support an impressive number of large baobab trees.

The floral variety of Ruaha is mirrored by the variety of wildlife likely to be seen over the course of a few days on safari. The most common ungulates, not unusually, are the widespread impala, waterbuck, bushbuck, buffalo, zebra and giraffe, all of which are likely to be encountered several times on any given game drive. The park lies at the most southerly extent of the range of several East African ungulate species, including lesser kudu and Grant's gazelle. Yet it also harbours a number of antelope that are rare or absent in northern Tanzania, most visibly the splendid greater kudu – some of the most handsomely horned males you'll come across anywhere in Africa – but also the more elusive roan and sable antelope. The elephant population is the largest of any Tanzanian national park, despite heavy losses due to poaching in the 1980s, with some 12,000 elephants migrating through the greater Ruaha ecosystem. The most impressive pair of tusks weighed in the 20th century – combined weight 201kg – were from an individual shot in Ruaha in the 1970s, but the poaching of the recent past means you're unlikely to see anything comparable these days.

Ruaha is an excellent park for predators. Lions are not only numerous and very habituated to vehicles, but the prides tend to be unusually large, often numbering more than 20 individuals. The park also boasts a justified reputation for good leopard sightings, and while it's not as reliable as the Seronera Valley in the Serengeti, leopard are usually seen every few days and they are less skittish than in many game reserves. Cheetah, resident on the open plains, are quite often encountered in the Lundu area – known locally as the mini Serengeti – northeast of the Mwagusi River. More than 100 African wild dogs are thought to be resident in the greater Ruaha ecosystem. Wild dogs are known to have very wide ranges, and their movements are often difficult to predict, but one pack of about 40 individuals regularly moves into the Mwagusi area, generally hanging around for a few days before wandering elsewhere for a couple of weeks. Visitors who particularly want to see wild dogs should try to visit in June or July, when they are normally denning, and are thus more easy to locate than at other times of year. Black-backed jackal and spotted hyena are both very common and easily seen, and the rarer striped hyena, though seldom observed, is found here at the southern limit of its range.

With 450 species recorded, Ruaha also offers some excellent birding, once again with an interesting mix of southern and northern species. Of particular note are substantial and visible populations of black-collared lovebird and ashy starlings, Tanzanian endemics associated with the Maasai Steppes found here at the southern extreme of their distribution. By contrast, this is perhaps the only savannah reserve in East Africa where the crested barbet – a colourful yellow and black bird whose loud sustained trilling is a characteristic sound of the southern African bush – replaces the red-and-yellow barbet. Raptors are well represented, with bateleur and fish eagle probably the most visible large birds of prey, and the localised Eleanora's falcon quite common in December and January. The watercourses support the usual water birds.

Ruaha is best visited between July and November, when animals concentrate around the river. Internal roads may be impassable during the rainy season (December to May).

National park fees
An entrance fee of US$20 per 24 hours must be paid in hard currency. On most organised tours this will be included, but it's worth checking this when booking.

Further information
The *Ruaha* booklet published in 2000 by the African Publishing Group is normally available at the lodges, and contains useful maps, animal descriptions and checklists, and details of where to look for localised species. The older 64-page booklet *Ruaha National Park* is just as useful, and cheaper, assuming that you can locate a copy!

Getting there and away
The most straightforward way to reach Ruaha from Zanzibar is by Coastal Travel's daily scheduled flights via Dar es Salaam, which also serve the Selous Game Reserve. Fly-in packages, most often combined with a visit to Selous, can be arranged with some travel agents and tour operators in Zanzibar. More details are given in the Selous section above. As a sample, a three-day two-night all-inclusive Ruaha tour is about US$800 per person. A five-day tour of Selous and Ruaha is about US$1,300.

As with the Selous, if you are travelling in mainland Tanzania you can reach Ruaha by air from Dar es Salaam, without going to Zanzibar, and it's also possible to get there by road. For more details see *Tanzania: The Bradt Travel Guide* by Philip Briggs.

Where to stay
For fly-in tourists, Ruaha has two choices:

Mwagusi Safari Camp Tel/fax: (UK) + 44 (0)20 8846 9363; email: tropicafrica.uk@virgin.net. This small and exclusive tented camp, situated on the north bank of the seasonal Mwagusi River, is to my taste one of the most alluring lodges anywhere in East Africa, immensely comfortable, yet with a real bush atmosphere. The accommodation, strung along the riparian woodland fringing the river, consists of about a dozen spacious walk-in tents, enclosed in a wood, thatch and reed shelter, each of which has a vast shower and toilet area, and a private balcony. Because the lodge is owner-managed, the service is top-notch, and includes some great touches – most memorably, starlit bush dinners around a campfire in a clearing above the camp or in the riverbed. Game viewing from the camp is superb, with elephant and greater kudu regularly putting in an appearance, and plenty of birds hopping around the trees. Wild dogs are regularly sighted in the area, several lion prides are resident, and the closest game-viewing circuits are situated far enough from the larger Ruaha River Lodge and park headquarters that you feel you have the whole park to yourself. Game walks with an armed ranger are also offered, with a good chance of encountering elephants and other large animals on foot. All-inclusive fly-in rates are slightly higher than at Ruaha River Lodge (see below).
Ruaha River Lodge Tel/fax: (UK) +44 1452 862288; tel: 0744 237422, 0741 237422; fax 0741 327706; email: fox@tanzaniasafaris.info or fox@bushlink.co.tz; web:

www.ruahariverlodge.com. This highly regarded and comfortable private lodge is situated on a rocky hillside above a set of rapids on the Ruaha River, 10km from the entrance gate. Game viewing is excellent from the camp, with rock hyrax scuttling around everywhere, hippos resident on the river and many other animals coming down to drink. Accommodation is in unpretentious stone cottages or fixed tents. There is a restaurant and bar. Full-board accommodation for drive-in customers costs US$140/200 single/double for non-residents or US$55 per person for residents, in addition to which must be paid US$35 per person per game drive. A full fly-in package costs US$240/400 single/double, inclusive of all meals, game drives, park fees and airport transfer, but exclusive of the cost of the flight.

SAADANI NATIONAL PARK

Protected as a game reserve since 1969 and due to be gazetted as a national park before the end of 2002, Sadaani is the only wildlife sanctuary in East Africa with an Indian Ocean beachfront. The original 200km² game reserve, centred on the small but ancient fishing village of Saadani, was expanded to cover 500km² in 1996, and it is likely to redouble in area with the proposed incorporation of a tract of former ranchland when the national park is gazetted.

As recently as ten years ago, despite its proximity to Dar es Salaam, Saadani was among the most obscure and inaccessible conservation areas in East Africa, lacking tourist facilities in any form. Inadequate protection and resultant poaching also meant that wildlife had been severely depleted, to the extent that Saadani's status as a game reserve seemed all but nominal. In recent years, however, Saadani has received renewed attention from conservationists and tourists alike. A top-notch private tented camp has been established, access has improved, there's been a concerted clampdown on poaching and an attempt to integrate adjacent villages into the conservation effort that was initiated by the Department of Wildlife with assistance from Germany's GTZ agency in 1998.

Viewed purely as a wildlife destination, Saadani cannot yet bear comparison to Tanzania's finest – though if present trends continue, it may well be up with them ten years hence. But even as things stand, Saadani is a thoroughly worthwhile and enjoyable retreat, allowing visitors to combine the hedonistic pleasures of a perfect sandy beach with guided bush walks, game drives, and boat trips up the Wami River. It is also the closest national park to Zanzibar – 15 minutes away by air, with scheduled flights likely to be introduced in the near future.

Background information

Inland of its 20km coastline, Saadani supports a park-like cover of open grassland interspersed with stands of acacia trees and knotted coastal thicket. Along the coast, palm-lined beaches are separated by extensive mangrove stands, while the major watercourses are fringed by lush riparian woodland. The park supports a wide range of ungulates, with game densities generally highest in January and February, and from June to August, when the plains near the lodge hold more water. At all times of year, however, you can be reasonably confident of encountering giraffe, buffalo, warthog, common waterbuck, reedbuck, hartebeest and wildebeest, along with troops of yellow baboon and vervet monkey. Something of a Saadani special, likely to be seen a few times on any game drive, is the red duiker, a diminutive, beautiful and normally very shy antelope of coastal scrub and forest. Quite common, but less easily seen, are greater kudu and eland. Saadani also harbours a small population of Roosevelt's sable, an endangered race elsewhere found in the Selous Game Reserve.

The elephant population, though small, is on the increase, and herds of up to 30 are sighted with increasing frequency. Lion are also making something of a comeback, with at least three different prides observed during 2001, one of which actually came to drink at the lodge waterhole! Leopard, spotted hyena and black-backed jackal are also around, along with the usual small nocturnal predators. In addition to game drives, guided walks offer a good chance of seeing various antelope and representatives of Saadani's rich variety of woodland birds. Hippos and crocodiles are normally encountered on river trips, along with a good selection of marine and riverine birds. The beaches in and around Saadani form one of the last major breeding sites for green turtles on mainland Tanzania.

The lodge – and effectively the park – is often forced to close over April and May when the black cotton soil roads tend to become waterlogged.

Entrance fees
Entrance to the game reserve costs US$20 per person per 24 hours. Whether this will increase once the national park is gazetted remains to be seen.

Getting there and away
No scheduled flight currently lands at Saadani airstrip, though negotiations are underway for a scheduled service to be introduced from Zanzibar. Otherwise, air charters can be arranged in Zanzibar through reliable tour operators or agents, or through the Original Saadani Experience, the company that runs Saadani Safari Lodge. The lodge also operates a thrice-weekly road shuttle to/from Dar es Salaam, so you could fly between Zanzibar and Dar and go the rest of the way to Sadaani by road. The shuttle leaves Dar at 09.00 on Wednesday, Friday and Sunday, arriving Saadani at around 13.00. The shuttle starts the return trip to Dar es Salaam on the same days at 14.00, arriving there about four hours later. The shuttle is for the exclusive use of lodge clients.

Where to stay
Saadani Safari Camp Tel/fax: 022 2151106; email: tentview@intafrica.com; web: www.saadani.com. This small and intimate tented camp runs attractively along a palm-fringed beach about 1km north of Saadani village. Accommodation is in comfortable framed canvas tents with a *makuti* roof, en-suite facilities, solar electricity and twin or double bed. The open, wooden bar and dining area is very peaceful, while a treehouse overlooks a waterhole regularly visited by waterbuck, bushbuck, buffalo and various waterbirds – and very occasionally by lion and elephant. Activities include game drives at US$30 per person, guided walks with a ranger at US$15 per person, and boat trips on the river for US$35 per person. Full-board rates are US$75 per person (residents) or US$95 per person (non-residents).

Appendix 1

SWAHILI – THE LANGUAGE OF ZANZIBAR

Thanks to Said el-Gheithy for help in compiling this section

The indigenous language spoken throughout Zanzibar is Swahili (*Kiswahili* when you're actually speaking the language). This language is also spoken as a first language by Swahili people along the East African coast, particularly in Kenya and mainland Tanzania, and as a second or third language by many other people throughout East Africa (including Kenya, Tanzania and Uganda, and in parts of several other countries such as Rwanda, Mozambique and Congo), making Swahili the common tongue of the region.

Swahili is an African language, and includes many words and phrases of Arabic origin, plus words from other languages such as Persian, English and Portuguese. Over the centuries Swahili has developed into a rich language, lending itself especially to poetry. Zanzibar is regarded as the home of Swahili – it is spoken in its purest form here and in pockets on the coast of Tanzania and Kenya. In fact in these areas, tradition dictates that ordinary conversation should approximate the elegance of poetry. Generally, as you travel further inland on the East African mainland, the Swahili gets increasingly more basic and simplified.

For visitors, English and several other European languages, such as French and Italian, are spoken in Zanzibar Town and most tourist areas. However, if you get off the beaten track a few words of Swahili may be useful to ask directions, to greet people or even to begin a simple conversation. Even in the tourist areas, using a few Swahili words (for example, to ask the price of a souvenir, or order a meal in a restaurant) can add to the enjoyment of your visit.

Pronunciation of Swahili is generally straightforward: every syllable is sounded and there are no 'silent endings'. In longer words the stress is on the penultimate syllable. The most confusing feature for learners is that many words have a prefix and suffix which change according to subject and tense. However, when speaking, beginners can ignore these additions, and still be understood.

Of course, the best way to learn is to listen to the people around you. For more detailed information, use a phrasebook (see the *Further Information* appendix), or visit the Kiswahili Institute (details in the *Zanzibar Town* chapter).

Useful Swahili words and phrases

The following basics are necessarily very simplified, and may not be grammatically correct, but by using them you will be understood in most situations. Many Zanzibaris will be delighted to hear a visitor using a few Swahili words – even if they are mispronounced or put in the wrong order!

Introductions

Introductions and salutations are very important in Swahili culture, particularly when speaking to adults or people older than yourself, even if the age difference is slight. (Children are not usually greeted by adults outside their family.)

The most common forms of address are the traditional Muslim greetings (in Arabic), regardless of the religion of the people being greeted:

Salama aleikum	Peace be with you
Aleikum salam	And peace be with you (the response)

You can also use the following greetings when addressing older people:

Sblakheri	Good morning
Msalkheri	Good afternoon / good evening
Shkamoo	(a general greeting which can be used at any time of day)
Marahaba	(response to '*shkamoo*')
Habari zako or *hujambo*	How are you?
Al humdul allah	Everything is well (response: literally 'Thanks be to Allah')

For people of the same age, and especially for friends, you can use: *Habari*, which means 'Hello' (also meaning 'How are you?', literally 'what news?'). The reply might be *Al humdul allah*, or the more casual *Nzuri* ('good'), *Nzuri sana* ('very good') or *Safi* ('fine'). In areas where Swahili is not spoken as a first language the reply is often *Mzuri*, with an 'M', rather than 'Nzuri'. *Mambo* is an even more casual way of greeting friends, meaning 'how's it going?'. The response is *Poa* (something along the lines of 'neat', 'cool' or 'dandy'). *Habari* can also be used for 'Excuse me' (when attracting somebody's attention), but it is still considered impolite to simply say '*Habari*' ('hello') to someone older than you.

Children in Zanzibar greet adults with *Chechei*, usually followed by the title of the adult. The response is the same.

Other useful words in this context are *Asante* (*sana*) meaning 'Thank you very much' and *Kwaheri* meaning 'goodbye'.

Even when speaking in English a Swahili acquaintance will ask 'How are you?', 'How are things today?', 'How is your husband/wife/friend?'. You should do the same. Launching straight into any subject without the opening questions is rude. Traditional Zanzibaris expect women to be less forward than men, although in areas used to tourists this does not apply.

Jambo also means 'hello', but Zanzibaris never use this word speaking to each other, and it only tends to be used by Zanzibaris talking to tourists. In the same way, the oft-quoted '*Hakuna matata*' ('No problem') is mock-Swahili-for-tourists imported from Kenya, and not used by Zanzibaris. If you want to express this idea, a more correct alternative would be '*Hamna neno*' or '*Haidhuru*'.

Hodi means 'Hello, anyone at home, can I come in?' used when knocking on somebody's door. *Karibu* is the response, meaning 'welcome' (literally 'come near').

Conversation starters and enders

What is your name?	*Jina lako nani?*
My name is David	*Jina langu David*
Where are you from?	*Unatoka wapi?*
I am from...	*Mimi ninatoka...*
	(the *mimi* is often dropped)
Where do you live?	*Unakaa wapi?*
Where are you staying? (ie: locally)	*Umefikia wapi?*
I am sorry, I don't understand	*Samahani sifahamu*
I don't speak Swahili	*Sijui Kiswahili*
I speak a very little Swahili	*Nazungumza Kiswahili kidogo tu*

Useful words and phrases

yes	*ndiyo*
no	*hapana*
OK (agreement)	*sawa*
sorry (condolences)	*pole* (not used for apologies)
where?	*wapi?*
what	*nini*
here	*hapa*
there	*hapo*
please	*tafadali*
there is	*ipo*
is there...?	*iko...?*
there isn't...	*hakuna...*
how much?	*bei gani?* (literally 'what price?')
how many shillings?	*shillingi ngapi?*
I want to go to Bububu	*Nataka kwenda Bububu*
Where is the bus for Makunduchi?	*Liko wapi basi la Makunduchi?*
Where is the ruin?	*Liko wapi gofu?*
I am ill	*Mimi mgonjwa*
Where is the hospital?	*Iko wapi hospitali?*
Where is the doctor?	*Yuko wapi daktari?*
I am lost	*Nimepotea*
shop	*duka*
market	*soko*
cafe, local eating-house	*hoteli ya chakula*
food	*chakula*
beef	*nyama ya ngombe*
chicken	*kuku*
fish	*samaki*
water	*maji*
tea	*chai*
coffee	*kahawa*
milk	*maziwa*
sugar	*sukari*
left	*kushoto*
right	*kulia*
straight on	*moja kwa moja*
near	*karibu*
far	*mbali*
today	*leo*
tomorrow	*kesho*
yesterday	*jana*

The word *soda* means any fizzy drink in a bottle. In the smarter hotels in Zanzibar Town, if you want soda water try asking for a Club Soda.

You may hear the word *mzungu* directed to you, particularly by children. This means 'white person', but is not disrespectful.

Numbers

1	*moja*	21	*ishirini na moja*
2	*mbili*	30	*thelathini*
3	*tatu*	40	*arobaini*
4	*nne*	50	*hamsini*
5	*tano*	60	*sitini*
6	*sita*	70	*sabini*
7	*saba*	80	*themanini*
8	*nane*	90	*tisini*
9	*tisa*	100	*mia*
10	*kumi*	101	*mia na moja*
11	*kumi na moja*	102	*mia na mbili*
12	*kumi na mbili*	200	*mia mbili*
20	*ishirini*	300	*mia tatu*

Time

Swahili time starts at 06.00, the hour of sunrise, and is therefore six hours apart from Western time.

What time is it?	*Saa ngapi?*	08.00	*saa mbili*
07.00	*saa moja* (literally one o'clock)	noon	*saa sita*
		13.00 (1.00pm)	*saa saba*

When finding out about bus or boat departures, check if the time you've been told is Swahili time or Western time. This can be complicated further by some buses leaving outlying villages very early in the morning.

Appendix 2

FURTHER INFORMATION
Books
History and background
General histories of Africa

Coupland, R, *The Exploitation of East Africa 1856-1890: The Slave Trade and the Scramble* (Faber, London, 1939).

Davidson, B, *The Story of Africa* (London, 1984).

Freeman-Grenville, G S P, *The East African Coast: Select Documents* (Oxford University Press, 2nd ed, 1975).

Oliver, R, and Mathew, G, *A History of East Africa* (Oxford University Press, London, 1963).

Pakenham, T, *The Scramble for Africa* (Weidenfeld and Nicolson, London, 1991).

Prestage, E, *Portuguese Pioneers* (A & C Black, London, 1933).

Taylor S, *Livingstone's Tribe* (HarperCollins, London 1999).

The above books are general histories of Africa or the East African region, which include sections on Zanzibar. Some are old and now long out of print, but make interesting reading if you can find them – try a specialist historical bookshop. Pakenham's classic history of Africa from the 1870s onwards is particularly compulsive, and often reprinted in paperback. Taylor's book about the European settlers who 'stayed on' in East Africa after the countries gained independence, looks at the colonial past in the present context, and neatly combines history with contemporary travel writing.

Early histories of Zanzibar

Brode, H, Tippu Tip *His Career in Zanzibar and Central Africa* (Gallery Publications, Zanzibar, 2002). This is a reprint of the original 1903 study of the career of Tippu Tip, Zanzibar's most famous (or infamous) trader. A fascinating and highly readable account of life on Zanzibar and the East African mainland over a century ago.

Gray, J, *History of Zanzibar from the Middle Ages to 1856* (Oxford University Press, London, 1962).

Ingrams, W H, *Zanzibar: Its History and People* (Witherby, London, 1931).

Lyne, R N, *Zanzibar in Contemporary Times* (Darf, London, 1905). Reprinted 1987.

Ommanney, F D, *Isle of Cloves* (Longmans, London, 1957)

Pearce, Mjr F B, *Zanzibar: The Island Metropolis of Eastern Africa* (Fisher Unwin, London, 1920).

The above five books cover Zanzibar specifically, but they are old guidebooks and histories from British colonial days, and all long out of print. Lyne's book was reprinted in 1987 and 2000 by Gallery Publications – a local Zanzibar publisher. Likewise Pearce's *Island Metropolis* and Ommanney's *Isle of Cloves* have also been reprinted or are due for reprint in 2003, by the same publisher.

General histories of Zanzibar and the Indian Ocean

Hall, R, *Empires of the Monsoon* (HarperCollins, London 1999). A fascinating history of the lands around the Indian Ocean, including good sections on Zanzibar.

Hamilton, G, *In the Wake of da Gama* (Abacus, London, 1951).

Hamilton, G, *Princes of Zinj* (Hutchinson, London, 1957). Comprehensive and accessible historical accounts, with an emphasis on readability, sometimes at the expense of accuracy.

Modern histories of Zanzibar

Nurse, D and Spear, T, *The Swahili: Reconstructing the History and Language of an African Society* (The Ethnohistory Series. University of Pennsylvania Press, Philadelphia, 1985). This is an excellent, short, readable book which argues convincingly that the Swahili culture is more of an African (and less an Arab) phenomenon than previously thought. Highly recommended.

Horton, M C, *The Swahili Corridor*. This article was published in *Scientific American* 255(9) 86–93 (1987). Horton has been one of the most influential archaeologists to work on the East African coast, and has done excavations and surveys on Pemba and Unguja (Zanzibar Island). This is an excellent short piece that touches on some of the Mediterranean connections with East Africa.

Mapuri, O, *The 1964 Revolution* (published in 1996). This short, locally published book is a concise history of Zanzibari politics, covering the period from 1964 up to the 1995 elections.

Martin, E B, *Zanzibar: Tradition and Revolution* (Hamish Hamilton, London, 1978)

Sheriff, A, *Slaves, Spices and Ivory in Zanzibar* (James Currey, London, 1987)

Sheriff, A, and Ferguson E D, *Zanzibar under Colonial Rule* (James Currey, London, 1991).

The above three books are modern, post-revolution, textbook-style histories.

Zanzibar and Oman

Al-Maamiry, A H, *Oman and East Africa* (Lancers Books, New Delhi, 1979).

Al-Maamiry, A H, *Omani Sultans in Zanzibar* (Lancers Books, New Delhi, 1988).

Bennett, N R, *A History of the Arab State of Zanzibar* (Methuen, London, 1978).

Bhacker, M R, *Trade and Empire in Muscat and Zanzibar* (Routledge, London, 1992).

The above four books are modern and very detailed, with specific reference to the Oman-Zanzibar link.

Railways and ships

Hill, M H, *The Permanent Way* (East African Literature Bureau, Nairobi, 1949) and Miller, C, *The Lunatic Express* (Macmillan, Ballantine Books, Random House, 1971). These two books are histories of the East African railways, both with good sections on Zanzibar.

Patience K, *Zanzibar and the Bububu Railway* (published by the author, 1995). A fascinating little booklet about the only railway on Zanzibar, which existed at the beginning of the 20th century.

Patience K, *Zanzibar and the Loss of HMS Pegasus* (published by the author, 1995) and Patience K, *Zanzibar and the Shortest War in History* (published by the author, 1994). Two excellent booklets written and published by Zanzibar historian Kevin Patience. Well researched, they describe in full events which might otherwise be confined to the footnotes of history. The gunship *Pegasus* was sunk during World War I and this book also contains background information on British naval ships in East Africa, while *Shortest War* describes the 1896 bombardment of the sultan's palace, with several fascinating archive photos.

Patience K, *Königsberg - A German East African Raider* (published by the author, 1997). The *Königsberg* was the German gunboat which sunk the British *Pegasus,* fully described in an earlier book by the same author. I his painstakingly researched book covers historical events before and after the *Pegasus* incident, including the *Königsberg*'s final sinking by another British ship in the Rufiji Delta, southwest of Zanzibar. The chapter describing the present-day position of the *Königsberg's* relics scattered all over East Africa is particularly interesting.

Architecture and history

Mwalim, M A, *Doors of Zanzibar* (Gallery Publications, Zanzibar, 2002). Using hundreds of photographs by Uwe Rau, this fascinating book catalogues the unique doors which have become an icon of Zanzibar Stone Town, and covers the various Indian, Arabic and Swahili influences.

Pitcher, G and Jafferji, J, *Zanzibar Style* (Gallery Publications, Zanzibar, 2001). This celebration of Zanzibari architecture is listed under *Large-format photo books*.

Siravo, F, and Bianca, S, *A Plan for the Historic Stone Town* (Gallery Publications in association with the Aga Khan Trust for Culture, Zanzibar 1997). A large and detailed discussion document, full of fascinating photos, plans and drawings, which analyses the current situation then proposes a major and systematic plan for the repair, preservation and conservation of the many old buildings in Stone Town. This is a vital reference for anyone interested in the history and architecture of Zanzibar.

Sheriff, Prof A, *Zanzibar Stone Town, An Architectural Exploration* (Gallery Publications, Zanzibar, 1998). With skilful photographs by Javed Jafferji and illuminating text by a leading Zanzibar historian, this handy little pocket-sized book is an ideal guide and companion for your strolls around the narrow streets of Stone Town. Highly recommended.

Sheriff, Prof A, *The History and Conservation of Zanzibar Stone Town* (published by James Currey). This book is part of Currey's Eastern African Studies series, and although quite academic in tone, it has a lot of useful information for anyone keen on the history of Zanzibari architecture.

Princess Salme

Ruete, E (born Salme binte Said Al-Busaidi), *Memoirs of an Arabian Princess from Zanzibar* (Gallery Publications, Zanzibar, 1998). This book is a translation of *Memoiren einer Arabischen Prinzessin*, which was first published in 1888. It was also reprinted by Markus Wiener Publishing (New York, 1989), but the latest translation is now easily available in Zanzibar bookshops. It is a very readable first-hand account by a unique figure in the history of Zanzibar, providing a good overview of the period and several fascinating personal insights. Highly recommended.

Ruete, E (born Salme binte Said Al-Busaidi), *An Arabian Princess Between Two Worlds: Memoirs, Letters, Sequels to the Memoirs*, editor E Van Donzel, (E J Brill Publishing, Leiden, Netherlands, 1993). Volume 3 in a series on Arab History and Culture. This is a very detailed and comprehensive account of Salme's life in Zanzibar, Germany and Syria. Includes a biography of her son, Said-Rudolph Ruete. Expensive and hard to obtain.

Travel and exploration

Batchelor, J and J, *In Stanley's Footsteps* (Blandford Press, London, 1990) and Wilson, C, and Irwin, A, *In Quest of Livingstone* (House of Lochar, Scotland, 1999). Two books in which British couples follow the routes of the great explorers in Africa. Livingstone started many of his travels in Zanzibar. The Batchelors mount a full expedition, while Colum Wilson and Aisling Irwin trace Livingstone's final journey through Tanzania and Zambia at a more grassroots level.

Burton, Richard Francis, *Zanzibar: City, Island and Coast* (London, 1872). Many early European explorers in Africa mentioned Zanzibar in their journals, but Burton, perhaps the most 'colourful' of them all, is the only one to write a specific book on Zanzibar. Although published first over a century ago, reprints are sometimes available.

Hugon, A, *The Exploration of Africa* (New Horizons, Thames and Hudson, 1999) This is a fascinating and beautifully illustrated little book, with good coverage on the journeys of Livingstone, Stanley and others in East Africa.

Moorehead, A, *The White Nile* (Hamish Hamilton, London, 1960). A classic book on the history of European exploration in the East African region. Often reprinted. Readable and recommended.

Mountfield, D, *A History of African Exploration* (Domus Books/Hamlyn, London, 1976) and Richards, C, and Place, J, *East African Explorers* (Oxford University Press, London, 1960). Two books on exploration in Africa, although both out of print and hard to find, including some mentions of Zanzibar where many journeys began and ended.

Royal Geographical Society (Editor John Keay), *History of World Exploration* (Paul Hamlyn, Reed International, London, 1991). Includes sections on exploration of East Africa

Teal, J, *Livingstone* (Putnam, New York, 1973). A fine biography of the great explorer.

Waugh, E, *Remote People* (Duckworth, 1931), republished 1985 by Penguin Books, UK, as part of their 20th Century Classics series. Waugh travelled to many parts of Africa, including Zanzibar, as a newspaper correspondent, and his dry observations are as engaging today as they were when first written.

Large-format photo books

Jafferji, J, and Rees Jones B, *Images of Zanzibar* (HSP Publications, London, 1996). Much of East Africa has been covered by publishers of lavishly illustrated 'coffee-table' books, but until recently Zanzibar seems to have escaped their notice. Local photographer Javed Jafferji has made up for this with *Images of Zanzibar* – a portfolio of his finest work, showing rich colours and an eye for detail perfectly capturing the spirit of the islands.

Jafferji, J, Jafferji, Z and Waterman, P, *A Taste of Zanzibar: Chakula Kizuri* (Gallery Publications, Zanzibar, 2001). Not hungry? You will be if you read this bountiful cookbook which celebrates (and helps you create) Zanzibar's delicious cuisine, enhanced with 250 mouthwatering colour photos.

Pitcher, G and Jafferji, J, *Zanzibar Style* (Gallery Publications, Zanzibar, 2001). This sumptuous and stimulating book combines evocative photos by Javed Jafferji and text by Gemma Pitcher to explore the themes that have inspired Zanzibar's unique architecture and interior design – from Europe, Oman and India, as well as of course the natural forms of Africa – and also covers related aspects such as crafts, textiles and furniture. Listed by *The Times* newspaper as one of the 'Top 20 travel books for Christmas' 2001.

Sheriff, A, *Zanzibar – Romance of the Ages* (HSP Publications, London, 1996). Accomplished photographer Javed Jafferji compiled this fascinating collection of archive photos from the late 19th and early 20th centuries – while the text and captions were provided by Abdul Sheriff, Professor of History at the University of Dar es Salaam and Principle Curator of the Zanzibar Museums.

Fiction and autobiography

Bateman, G, *Zanzibar Tales* (Gallery Publications, Zanzibar, 2002). Another reprint from the industrious Gallery house; a collection of amusing (and sometimes confusing) Zanzibari folktales originally recorded and translated into English by George Bateman almost a century ago, and enhanced by lively illustrations by Walter Bobbett.

Haji, M M, *Sowing The Wind* (Gallery Publications, Zanzibar, 2002). This autobiographical novel explores life and politics on the islands of Zanzibar during the turbulent years which led to independence in 1963, and the revolution which followed.

Kaye, M M, *Death in Zanzibar* (Penguin, London, 1984 – first published as *The House of Shadows*, Longmans 1959) and Kaye, M M, *Trade Wind* (Longmans 1963, Penguin 1982). Two historical romantic novels set in Zanzibar. *Death in Zanzibar* is also published with two other M M Kaye *Death in…* stories in a larger book called the *House of Shade*.

Field guides
Mammals and birds

Kingdon, J, *The Kingdon Fieldguide to African Mammals* (Academic Press, USA and UK, 1997). For animals on Zanzibar, a field guide to the more common species of East Africa is of limited use. However, Kingdon's book is by far the best, as it covers every species in Africa in detail, including those on Zanzibar, with excellent illustrations and background notes.

van Perlo, B, *Illustrated Checklist of the Birds of Eastern Africa* (Harper Collins, London, 1996) and Williams, J, and Arlott, N, *A Field Guide to the Birds of East Africa* (Collins, London). For birds, the fieldguide you choose is determined by your level of interest. Of the books listed above, the van Perlo *Illustrated Checklist* is complete, with illustrations of every bird occurring in Africa, including those on Zanzibar, while the classic Williams & Arlott also has fairly good coverage. The large and comprehensive *Birds of Kenya & Northern Tanzania* by Zimmerman is used by keen birders, and it includes most species which occur on Zanzibar, but it's quite heavy to carry around.

Marine wildlife

Richmond, M, (ed), *A Guide to the Seashores of Eastern Africa and the Western Indian Ocean Islands* (Sida/SAREC, 1997). This excellent book contains around 450 pages, including over 150 of colour illustrations. More than 1,600 species of marine plants and animals are illustrated, plus notes on geology, climate, ecology and human activities. This is an essential tool for scientists, and a useful handbook for all visitors to the region. Proceeds from the sales of this book are put towards marine education purposes in the region, administered by the SEA Trust. Although hard to find overseas (only specialist stores stock it), this book is readily available in Zanzibar from all good bookshops.

Forstle, A, and Vierkotter, R, *Marine Green Book* (Green Ocean, Zanzibar, 1997). This handy little pocket encyclopaedia covers everything you need to know about marine life (from algae to zooxanthellae) and marine activities (from anchor damage to the Zanzibar Sea Turtle Project) in and around the Zanzibar archipelago. It also covers snorkelling, diving, coral reefs, fish and marine habitats. It is available in Zanzibar bookshops at a very reasonable price, and all proceeds go to fund environmental education projects.

Manuals, guidebooks and phrasebooks

Bogaert, P, *The Krazy Kanga Book* (Gallery Publications, Zanzibar, 2002). An offbeat 'adult' study of the *kanga* or 'wrap', the ubiquitous and vital garment for the women of East Africa.

Dawood, R, *How to Stay Healthy Abroad* (Oxford University Press)

Leonard, R, *Swahili Phrasebook* (Lonely Planet)

Hatt, J, *The Tropical Traveller* (Pan)

Koornhof, A, *Dive Sites of Kenya & Tanzania, including Zanzibar, Pemba & Mafia* (New Holland)

Wilson-Howarth, Jane, and Ellis, Dr Matthew *Your Child's Health Abroad: a Manual for Travelling Parents* (Bradt, UK, 1998, with updates on www.bradt-travelguides.com).

Bookshops

The Travel Bookshop 13 Blenheim Crescent, London W11 2EE, UK; tel: 020 7229 5260; fax: 020 7243 1552. Stocks guidebooks, phrasebooks, history, fiction, maps, and anything else to do with travel publications. They can source old and out-of-print books, and operate a worldwide mail-order service.

Risborough Books 81 Manor Park Av, Princes Risborough, Bucks HP27 9AR, UK; tel: 01844 343165. Specialises in secondhand books on East Africa, and offers mail order only. Contact them by post (no fax or email) for a list.

Websites

If you've got access to the internet, as part of your preparation you can get further information on Zanzibar from the following websites. Most have links to other useful relevant sites.

Africa Confidential (www.africa-confidential.com) gives the inside story on political events across Africa, including Tanzania and Zanzibar.

Africa News (www.africanews.com) covers events across the whole continent, including Tanzania and Zanzibar.

Africa Travel Association (www.africa-ata.org) has close links with *Africa Travel* magazine and is a great source of information on the whole African continent, including coverage of mainland Tanzania and Zanzibar.

African Travel and Tourism Association (www.atta.co.uk) represents many tour agencies and operators covering Africa, and the website is full of information to help you plan an organised trip.

Internet Living Swahili Dictionary (www.yale.edu/swahili) is a very handy on-line Swahili-English dictionary, with links to other Swahili-related sites.

Planet Earth (www.tidusa.com) covers many areas, and has a useful section on Tanzania, including Zanzibar, with very good links to the Tanzania Tourist Board, Tanzanian newspapers and other local sites.

The Hunger Site (www.thehungersite.com) is not directly related to Zanzibar, but if you visit this site (no more than once per day) and click on a 'donate' button, the site's sponsors will give two *free* cups of food to a developing country.

The SEA Trust (www.seatrust.org) is a conservation and education programme, doing a lot of work in and around Zanzibar.

The Swahili Coast (www.swahilicoast.com) is the web version of the colour magazine which 'promotes coastal eco-tourism in Tanzania', with historical and general articles, pictures and information about local events.

Travel Notes (www.travelnotes.org) is a travel information site, which includes sections on Zanzibar and mainland Tanzania.

Zanzibar Travel Network, also called **Zanzibar Net** (www.zanzibar.net) has sections on history, diving, touring, beaches, history, travel tips and so on. It also has a good selection of links to other sites which cover Zanzibar.

Zanzibar.org (www.zanzibar.org) is a gateway site with pages on several hotels in Zanzibar Town and around Zanzibar Island, plus coverage of various aspects of Zanzibar such as culture, history and wildlife.

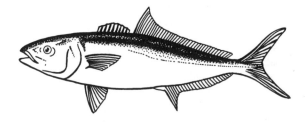

MEASUREMENTS AND CONVERSIONS

To convert	Multiply by
Inches to centimetres	2.54
Centimetres to inches	0.3937
Feet to metres	0.3048
Metres to feet	3.281
Yards to metres	0.9144
Metres to yards	1.094
Miles to kilometres	1.609
Kilometres to miles	0.6214
Acres to hectares	0.4047
Hectares to acres	2.471
Imperial gallons to litres	4.546
Litres to imperial gallons	0.22
US gallons to litres	3.785
Litres to US gallons	0.264
Ounces to grams	28.35
Grams to ounces	0.03527
Pounds to grams	453.6
Grams to pounds	0.002205
Pounds to kilograms	0.4536
Kilograms to pounds	2.205
British tons to kilograms	1016.0
Kilograms to British tons	0.0009812
US tons to kilograms	907.0
Kilograms to US tons	0.000907

5 imperial gallons are equal to 6 US gallons
A British ton is 2,240 lbs. A US ton is 2,000 lbs.

Temperature conversion table
The bold figures in the central columns can be read as either centigrade or fahrenheit.

°C		°F	°C		°F
−18	**0**	32	10	**50**	122
−15	**5**	41	13	**55**	131
−12	**10**	50	16	**60**	140
−9	**15**	59	18	**65**	149
−7	**20**	68	21	**70**	158
−4	**25**	77	24	**75**	167
−1	**30**	86	27	**80**	176
2	**35**	95	32	**90**	194
4	**40**	104	38	**100**	212
7	**45**	113	40	**104**	219

NOTES

NOTES

NOTES

NOTES

NOTES

Bradt Travel Guides

Africa by Road Charlie Shackell/Illya Bracht
Amazon, The Roger Harris/
  Peter Hutchison
America, Eccentric Jan Friedman
Antarctica: A Guide to the Wildlife
  Tony Soper/Dafila Scott
Arctic: A Guide to Coastal Wildlife
  Tony Soper/Dan Powell
Azores David Sayers
Baltic Capitals: Tallinn, Riga, Vilnius,
  Kaliningrad Neil Taylor et al
Belize Alex Bradbury
Botswana: Okavango, Chobe, Northern
  Kalahari Chris McIntyre
Britain, Eccentric Benedict le Vay
British Isles: Wildlife of Coastal Waters
  Tony Soper/Dan Powell
Cambodia Anita Sach
Canada: North – Yukon, Northwest Territories,
  Nunavut Geoffrey Roy
Cape Verde Islands Aisling Irwin/
  Colum Wilson
Cayman Islands Tricia Hayne
Chile and Argentina: Trekking Guide
  Tim Burford
China: Yunnan Province Stephen Mansfield
Croatia Piers Letcher
Cuba Stephen Fallon
Cyprus see *North Cyprus*
East and Southern Africa: The Backpacker's
  Manual Philip Briggs
Eccentric America see *America, Eccentric*
Eccentric Britain see *Britain, Eccentric*
Eccentric France see *France, Eccentric*
Eccentric London see *London, Eccentric*
Eclipse see *Africa & Madagascar*
Ecuador, Climbing and Hiking in
  Rob Rachowiecki/Mark Thurber
Ecuador, Peru and Bolivia: The Backpacker's
  Manual Kathy Jarvis
Eritrea Edward Denison/Edward Paice
Estonia Neil Taylor
Ethiopia Philip Briggs
Falkland Islands Will Wagstaff
France, Eccentric Piers Letcher
Gabon, São Tome &Principe Sophie Warne
Galápagos Wildlife David Horwell/
  Pete Oxford
Gambia, The Craig Emms/Linda Barnett
Georgia Tim Burford
Ghana Philip Briggs
Haiti and the Dominican Republic Ross Velton
Iran Patricia L Baker

Iraq Karen Dabrowska
Latvia Stephen Baister/Chris Patrick
Lithuania Gordon McLachlan
London, Eccentric Benedict le Vay
London, In the Footsteps of the Famous
  Nicholas Best
Madagascar Hilary Bradt
Madagascar Wildlife Nick Garbutt/
  Hilary Bradt/Derek Schuurman
Malawi Philip Briggs
Maldives Royston Ellis
Mali Ross Velton
Mauritius, Rodrigues and Réunion
  Royston Ellis/Alex Richards/
  Derek Schuurman
Mongolia Jane Blunden
Montenegro Annalisa Rellie
Mozambique Philip Briggs/Ross Velton
Namibia Chris McIntyre
North Cyprus Diana Darke
Palestine, with Jerusalem Henry Stedman
Paris, Lille & Brussels: Eurostar Cities
  Laurence Phillips
Peru and Bolivia: Backpacking and Trekking
  Hilary Bradt/Kathy Jarvis
River Thames, In the Footsteps of the Famous
  Paul Goldsack
Russia and Central Asia by Road
  Hazel Barker
Rwanda Janice Booth/Philip Briggs
St Helena, Ascension, Tristan da Cunha
  Sue Steiner
Seychelles Lyn Mair/Lynnath Beckley
Singapore John Nichol/Adrian Phillips/
  Isobel Dorling
South Africa: Budget Travel Guide Paul Ash
Southern Africa by Rail Paul Ash
Southern African Wildlife Mike Unwin
Spitsbergen Andreas Umbreit
Sri Lanka Royston Ellis
Switzerland: Rail, Road, Lake
  Anthony Lambert
Tanzania Philip Briggs
Tasmania Matthew Brace
Tibet Michael Buckley
Uganda Philip Briggs
USA by Rail John Pitt
Venezuela Hilary Dunsterville Branch
Your Child's Health Abroad Dr Jane Wilson-
  Howarth/Dr Matthew Ellis
Yunnan see *China*
Zambia Chris McIntyre
Zanzibar David Else

Bradt guides are available from bookshops or by mail order from:
Bradt Travel Guides, 19 High Street, Chalfont St Peter, Bucks SL9 9QE, England
Tel: 01753 893444   Fax: 01753 892333
Email: info@bradt-travelguides.com   Web: www.bradt-travelguides.com

Index

Page references in italics indicate maps.

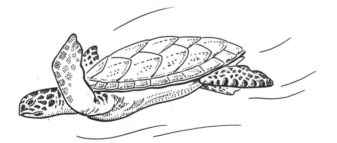

Hawksbill turtles